DATE DUE

MAY 1 0 1999	
DEC 2 6 2001	
OCT 1 9 2003	

GAYLORD   PRINTED IN U.S.A.

HUMANKIND
EMERGING

This volume has been adapted in
part from materials published by
TIME-LIFE BOOKS in two series:
The Emergence of Man and
The LIFE Nature Library.

HUMANKIND EMERGING

BERNARD G. CAMPBELL, Editor
University of California, Los Angeles

Little, Brown and Company
Boston   Toronto

Library of Congress Catalog Card No. 75-20736

First printing

Published simultaneously in Canada by Little, Brown & Company (Canada) Limited

Printed in the United States of America

Art editing and cover design: Tonia Noell-Roberts
Artists: Charles Joslin, David Lindroth, Susan Phelps, Richard H. Sanderson
Interior design: Judy Arisman
Cover: background photo: Jacques Jangoux; fossils: Musée de l'Homme and the National Museums of Kenya

Edited portions of the following volumes are included in this text:

Cro-Magnon Man by Tom Prideaux and the Editors of TIME-LIFE Books. © 1973 Time Inc. Consultants: Philip E. L. Smith, Richard Klein.
Early Man by F. Clark Howell and the Editors of TIME-LIFE Books. © 1965, 1973 Time Inc.
Evolution by Ruth Moore and the Editors of TIME-LIFE Books. © 1962, 1964 Time Inc.
Life Before Man by the Editors of TIME-LIFE Books and Peter Wood, Louis Vaczek, Dora Jane Hamblin, and Jonathan Norton Leonard. © 1972 Time Inc. Consultants: A. W. Crompton, Farish A. Jenkins, Jr., Robert T. Bakker, Theodore Delevoryas, John H. Ostrom, Elwyn L. Simons.
The First Men by the Editors of TIME-LIFE Books and Edmund White and Dale Brown. © 1973 Time Inc. Consultants: Bernard G. Campbell, F. Clark Howell.
The Missing Link by Maitland A. Edey and the Editors of TIME-LIFE Books. © 1972 Time Inc. Consultants: Sherwood L. Washburn, Bernard G. Campbell.
The Neanderthals by George Constable and the Editors of TIME-LIFE Books. © 1973 Time Inc. Consultant: Ralph S. Solecki.

Acknowledgments

The author acknowledges permission to use material from the following sources:

Pages xiii and 363 From *The Collected Poems of A. E. Housman.* Copyright 1922 by Holt, Rinehart and Winston, Inc. Copyright 1950 by Barclays Bank Limited. Reprinted by permission of Holt, Rinehart and Winston, Publishers; The Society of Authors as the literary representative of the Estate of A. E. Housman; and Jonathan Cape Limited, publishers of A. E. Housman's *Collected Poems.*

Introduction *Page xiv* photograph by Frank Siteman; painting of primitive man by Burt Silberman.

Chapter 1 *Page 6* photograph by Frank Siteman; painting by Burt Silberman. *Figure 1-1* Culver Pictures. *Figure 1-2* Bettmann Archive. *Figure 1-3* courtesy Lennart Nilsson.

(continued on page 453)

PREFACE

It is more than a century since a few remarkable men began searching for the elusive remnants of our ancestors. Today this search has grown into the developing science of human evolution, or paleoanthropology —the science that fits together evidence for mankind's past into a coherent statement. First there were the fossils and stone tools—some of them unearthed long before their finders had any idea of their significance. To this basic evidence have been added insights gained from technological developments of more recent years and from recent studies of our nearest animal relatives, the monkeys and apes. Although we are still far from any final statement, we now have a good idea of how, when, and where we came to exist—and where to look next. The mystery is a particularly exciting one in that it involves all of us. *Humankind Emerging* is an attempt to convey this excitement to students who are investigating physical anthropology for the first time.

In its emphasis on the historical side of physical anthropology, this book is intended to be easy to read as well as informative. Chapters have been kept short, and each one tells a story at the same time that it expounds an important topic. Further, the book is designed to show as well as to describe the evidence. It is heavily illustrated with photographs, drawings, charts, and tables of what we know about our ancestors, how we know it, where the evidence comes from, when it was uncovered, and who found it. In addition, *Humankind Emerging* includes color illustrations of various aspects of paleoanthropology, which should give the book a real advantage as a teaching tool. The word *man* (e.g., "Neandertal man") and its pronouns *he, him,* and *his* are used in this book, as is customary, to refer to the human race as a whole, and are not intended to imply any emphasis on the male sex. The biological roles of the two sexes are to a great extent complementary, and they have played an equal part in the evolution of the human race.

Much of *Humankind Emerging* grew out of material in Time Inc.'s *Emergence of Man* series and the *Life* Nature Library. For this, I give my thanks to the editors and authors of those series. Anthropologists Leslie Aiello, Margaret Bond, Nicholas Fintzelberg, F. Clark Howell, Clifford Jolly, Frank Poirier, and Dennis Shaw helped by reviewing the manuscript. I also wish to thank my wife, Wendy Campbell, and my colleague at U.C.L.A., Bob Byles, both of whom have helped me with different parts.

Finally I wish to thank the publishers, Little, Brown and Company, and especially Carol Verburg and Kathy Field, whose cooperation, diligence, and good taste have made a great contribution to the successful completion of this book.

CONTENTS

Introduction   **1**

PART ONE / BEFORE HUMANITY   4

Chapter 1   The Study of Mankind   **6**

The Scientific Study of Human Nature   8

Classification of *Homo sapiens* / The theory of evolution
The modern perspective: Evolutionary biology / The study of human origins

Human Characteristics   15

Locomotion / Vision / Hands / The brain / Language / Cultural adaptation
Summary

Chapter 2   The Riddle of Heredity   **28**

The Work of Gregor Mendel   30

The first experiments / Experiments using many characteristics
Laws of segregation and independent assortment / Multiple independent
characteristics

Mendel's Work Rediscovered   36

De Vries' work on *Oenothera*

Chapter 3   Genes and Populations   **40**

Mutation and Natural Selection   41

The case of mimicry / Mathematical evidence / The role of mutations

The Units of Heredity   44

The chromosomes / Morgan's work on *Drosophila* / Muller's work with X rays
The raw material of heredity: DNA / Structure of DNA / The universal code of
inheritance

Populations and the Species   51

Genotype and the gene pool / Gene flow, speciation, and genetic drift / Sexual
selection / Polymorphism and genetic load

Chapter 4   Pioneers of Prehistory   **56**

Theories of Human Origins   57

Early Naturalists   58

John Ray / J. F. Esper, John Frere / Boucher de Perthes / Problems of early

investigators / Georges Cuvier / William Smith
Charles Lyell / Charles Darwin

Unearthing the Human Chronicle 63
From Neandertal and Spy / From the Dordogne: Cro-Magnon / Dubois in Java:
Homo erectus / Dart in South Africa: *Australopithecus*
Other fossils from Africa and India

Paleontology in Progress 71
The scarcity of human fossils / Fossil sites / Dating methods: Earth and fossils
Dating methods: From physics and biochemistry / Modern excavations
Overview

Chapter 5   Back beyond the Apes 82

The Earliest Primates 84
Natural selection and speciation / The prosimian adaptation / The prosimians'
competitors

The First Higher Primates 89
Apidium and *Parapithecus* / Evaluating the morphological pattern

The Early Apes 91
Characteristics of apes / *Propliopithecus* / *Aegyptopithecus* / *Dryopithecus*

A Human Ancestor? 97
Ramapithecus / Reassessing the fossil picture
Overview

PART TWO / AUSTRALOPITHECUS 104

Chapter 6   African Ancestors 106

Dart's Discovery of the Taung Skull (1924) 107
Evidence for the "missing link" / Dart's claims dismissed / The dentition of Taung

The Discoveries of Robert Broom 112
A skull from Sterkfontein (1936) / *Australopithecus robustus* at Kromdraai
The age of *Australopithecus africanus* / New discoveries at Sterkfontein (1947)
Assessing *Australopithecus*

Fossils and Artifacts 119
Overview

Chapter 7 The Great Savanna **122**

Discoveries at Olduvai 123

Discovery of *Australopithecus boisei* (1959) / The age of *Australopithecus*
Discovery of *habilis* (1960–1964) / Classifying *habilis*
Relating gracile and robust *Australopithecus*

From Omo and East Rudolf 134

The Omo hominids (1967–1974) / Robust hominids at East Rudolf (1969–1974)
Gracile hominids at East Rudolf (1969–1974) / Discoveries at Hadar (1973–1974)
Origins of gracile and robust hominids / Evidence of early stone tools

***Australopithecus* Revealed 141**

Daily life / From *Ramapithecus* to *Homo*: One theory
Overview

Chapter 8 Walking and Toolmaking **148**

Locomotion of Nonhuman Primates 149

Early work with primates / Goodall and the Gombe Stream Reserve / The first
primates / Quadrupedalism versus brachiation / Asiatic apes: Gibbon and
orangutan / African apes: Gorilla and chimpanzee / Chimpanzees as tool users

Hominid Locomotion 157

From the trees to the ground / Tool use and bipedalism / Physical adaptations
Knuckle walking / Tool use, bipedalism, and brain development / The problem of
causation / The seed-eating hypothesis

Early Technology 165

The earliest stone industry: The Oldowan / Occupation floors / The first shelters
The first stone tools: East Rudolf
Overview

Chapter 9 Social Organization and Hunting **172**

The Basis of Social Organization 173

Learning in childhood / Dominance / Friendship

Evolution of the Family 177

The estrous cycle / Role of the environment / One-male groups: Hominids

Evolution of Male and Female Roles 181

Physical differences / Prolonged youth and the female's role / Providing food:
Hunting and gathering / Behavior of *Australopithecus*

Hunting 186

Hunting among chimpanzees / Social carnivores: Cooperation / Social carnivores:
Food sharing / *Australopithecus* as hunter and scavenger / Hunting and language
Schaller and Lowther's experiment / A reconstruction
Overview

PART THREE / HOMO ERECTUS 198

Chapter 10 Discoveries of the First Humans 200

The Work of Eugene Dubois 202
Nineteenth-century background / Dubois' search for the missing link / Discovery of Java man (1891) / The Java man controversy

Twentieth-Century Discoveries 209
Heidelberg man: The Mauer jaw (1907) / Search for Peking man / Peking man discovered (1927) / Intensive work at Choukoutien / Assessment of Peking man Culture at Choukoutien / Relationship of Java man and Peking man / Fate of the Java man fossils / Fate of the Peking man fossils

The Meaning of the Fossils 217
Piltdown man: The great hoax / The pattern of human evolution
Overview

Chapter 11 Bones and Stones 224

Terra Amata 225
Site and excavation / Huts and living floors / The dune campsites / Other clues

Characteristics and Achievements 230
Anatomical development / The brain / Territorial expansion / Use of fire Evidence from Choukoutien

Stone Tools 238
The Oldowan industry / Materials and techniques / Core and flake tools The Acheulian industry / Cultural adaptation
Overview

Chapter 12 Hunting and the Evolution of Society 250

***Homo erectus*, the Hunter 251**
Olorgesailie: A scenario / The hunter's diet / Skin adaptation / Hunting and intelligence

Hunting Methods 255
Persistence hunting / Spheroids / The ambush / Torralba and Ambrona: A scenario / History of Torralba / Elephant butchery / Hunting and life style

New Social Developments 263
Interdependence and the family / The incest taboo / Exogamy / The home base

Intraspecies Aggression 269
Theories of aggression / Aggression among *Homo erectus*
Overview

Chapter 13   The Evolution of Language   274

Ways to Communicate   275

Early theories of the origins of speech / Communication among animals / Limbic and nonlimbic communication / The nature of language

The Ability to Speak   280

Talking apes? / The pharynx / Language centers of the brain / The limbic system

The Evolution of Speech   285

Lieberman and Crelin: The vocal apparatus / Krantz: The brain / Speech among the first humans
Overview

PART FOUR / EARLY HOMO SAPIENS   290

Chapter 14   Discovery of Neandertal   292

First Views of Neandertal   293

The discovery of Neandertal (1856) / Missing links in the Chain of Being / *Homo neanderthalensis?* / Discoveries at Spy (1886) / La Chapelle-aux-Saints and other finds (1908) / Boule's reconstruction (1911–1913) / Other views of the "grisly folk"

Discovery of non-European Neandertals   301

Rhodesian man / The Asian fossils / Discoveries from Israel

Search for the Origins of Modern Humans   303

The Swanscombe and Steinheim skulls (1933–1936) / The evaluation of Swanscombe (1964) / The Arago discovery (1971)

Reassessment of Neandertal   306

Species and speciation / Characteristics of western Neandertal / Nonwestern Neandertal / Neandertal and the species model / Neandertal's present status
Overview

Chapter 15   Conquest of the North   316

The Great Interglacial Period   317

Range of early *Homo sapiens* / Evidence of adaptations / The stone industries
The prepared core: Levallois technique

The Riss Glaciation   321

Changes around the world / A stimulus to intelligence and ingenuity / The Riss-Würm interglacial period / Cranial capacity of Neandertal / Evidence of intelligence

The Würm Glacial Period   326

Sunlight and skin color / Disk-core technique: The Mousterian industry
The Fauresmith and Sangoan industries / Expansion and adaptations
Unexplored territories
Overview

Chapter 16   Rituals of Life and Death   336

Life during the Early Würm   337

Neandertal scenario: Winter / Neandertal scenario: Spring and summer
Tundra adaptations / Evidence for handedness and language

Neandertal Rituals and Art   346

Hunting rites and magic / The bear cult / Beginnings of art / Symbolic notation?

Death and Burial   349

Evidence of burial customs / La Ferrassie (1912–1934) / Traditions of the Mousterian
industry / Non-European burials / The old and the handicapped / Evidence of
violence / Cannibalism and ritual / A cult of skulls?
Overview

PART FIVE / MODERN HUMANITY   360

Chapter 17   Enter Cro-Magnon   362

The First Modern People   363

Discovery in the Dordogne / Characteristics of Cro-Magnon

The Fate of Neandertal   365

The sequence of tools / Flakes and blades / The Perigordian industry / The fossil
record / Anatomical comparison: Neandertal and Cro-Magnon / Regional survey
The problem of western Europe

From Neandertal to Cro-Magnon   374

Brace's hypothesis / Pilbeam's hypothesis / Completion of the transition
Overview

Chapter 18   Adaptation and Survival   378

A New Breed   379

Variability of Cro-Magnon / Advantages of the large gene pool

New Lands and Adaptations   381

New territories occupied / Diet and hunting / The Siberians / The Nelson Bay
people / The Kôm Ombo people

An End to Wandering   389

A new life style / Mastery of fire / Solutrean laurel leaves / Tool specialization
Overview

Chapter 19   Hunting, Magic, and Art   396

Cro-Magnon: Hunter par Excellence   397

Spear throwers and points / Bow and arrow? / Fishing gear / Sedentary life and
sewn clothing

xi

Art and Ritual of Cro-Magnon 401

Cave art / Painting and hunting magic / Art and fertility / The craft of the painter
Sculpture and ceramics / Female figurines / Burial customs and rites / Conclusions
Overview

Chapter 20   The Human Condition   **418**

The Story of Mankind   419

Environmental history and adaptations / Cultural history

Human Variability   422

Africans / Amerindians / Australians / Asiatics / Caucasians / Oceanics / Racial
differences / Racism and IQ

Modern Man: A Relic of Early Man   427

Stress / The Bushman and stress / Cholesterol and life style / Adaptations to
modern life

Success or Failure?   432

Population and evolutionary success / Limits to growth / Survival
Prospect of failure

Bibliography   **439**
Glossary   **443**
Index   **457**

I, a stranger and afraid
In a world I never made.

A. E. HOUSMAN, 1859–1936
LAST POEMS, xii

Introduction

Know then thyself, presume not God to scan;
The proper study of mankind is man,
Placed on this isthmus in a middle state,
A being darkly wise, and rudely great:
With too much knowledge for the sceptic side,
With too much weakness for the Stoic's pride,
He hangs between, in doubt to act or rest;
In doubt to deem himself a God or beast;
In doubt his mind or body to prefer;
Born but to die, and reasoning but to err;
Alike in ignorance, his reason such,
Whether he thinks too little or too much;
Chaos of Thought and Passion, all confused;
Still by himself abused or disabused;
Created half to rise and half to fall;
Great Lord of all things, yet a prey to all;
Sole judge of truth, in endless error hurled:
The glory, jest, and riddle of the world!

Perhaps the most brilliant description of human nature to come from the prescientific age were these lines by the eighteenth-century poet Alexander Pope (1699–1744). Throughout history, man has been puzzled and exasperated by the strange duality of his nature—half animal, half angel—and much religious and philosophic teaching has been an attempt to understand and integrate these two sides of human nature. Neither priest nor philosopher has offered us any explanation that has really proved either intellectually satisfactory or (to use modern jargon) operationally effective. Whatever our most revered ancestors have written through the ages has not enabled the majority of the human race who have thought on these things or faced the usual moral dilemmas that are our inheritance to come to terms finally with humanity's dual nature. On the one hand, we carry the marks and nature of an animal, while on the other hand, we find ourselves alienated and unsure in the natural world and in the face of our own biology. In our imaginations, we travel far beyond the bounds of our own environment and our biological nature, and yet we still feel rooted to that nature which seems to constrict the highest reaches of our humanity. The forces of our nature tend to be ranged opposite each other like the poles and we find ourselves torn between them, caught in a conflict that has been cruelly sharpened by the demands of every culture in every age.

1

Humanity has, quite logically, looked to the past to explain the present and in so doing has developed mythological accounts of human origins. In the Judaeo-Christian religions the duality of human nature is explained by a story about disobedience to a stern God, who placed man and woman in paradise and then expelled them from it. This story of mankind's fall from perfection has been used to account for the darker side of human nature.

Today, we have a new story to explain our duality. It began in the work of the English geologist James Hutton, who demonstrated in 1795 that the world was vastly older than anyone had ever supposed. As this remarkable scientific deduction became generally known, humanity's short past was stretched a thousandfold, and to the future, present, and immediate past was added prehistory. This fourth dimension of human history has become a major consideration in understanding our present.

This book is about this fourth dimension. It recounts the extraordinary story of the discovery of, and the evidence for, humanity's long past. It begins to reveal to us the nature of our distant ancestors who began the long journey from the African forests to Cape Canaveral. It brings this dimension to bear upon present-day human nature and thus gives us an entirely new way to approach and understand ourselves. The evolutionary perspective, which we owe to the genius of Charles Darwin and Alfred Russel Wallace, throws light not only on our humanity but on that darker side of our nature which derives from our animal past. But this is not all: it also shows us the integrated and dynamic evolution of both, and their essential interlocking relationship. The evolutionary perspective gives us profound insights into human nature and shows us that its duality arises not from two warring halves but from two interdependent aspects of an integrated whole—or what should and could be an integrated whole if we saw ourselves as we truly are instead of as we have mistakenly believed ourselves to be.

This is just one small part of the revolution in knowledge and understanding brought about by the work of Charles Darwin and his successors. Our past has to a great extent determined and influenced every part of our lives, for it is not just the lifespan of each individual that determines his condition, important though it may be, but the whole history of the human species. We are, in this sense, a product both of our childhood and of our prehistory.

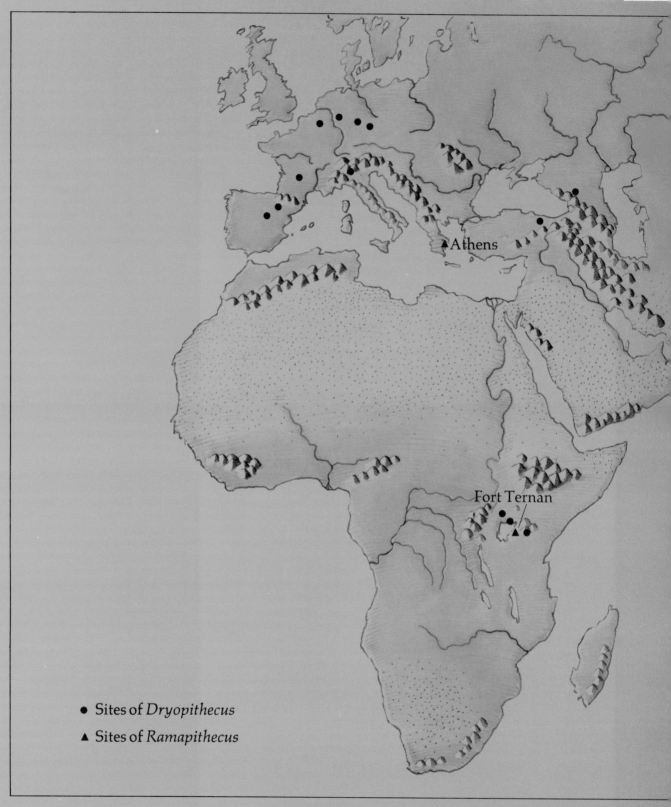

PART ONE

▲Athens

Fort Ternan

● Sites of *Dryopithecus*

▲ Sites of *Ramapithecus*

BEFORE HUMANITY

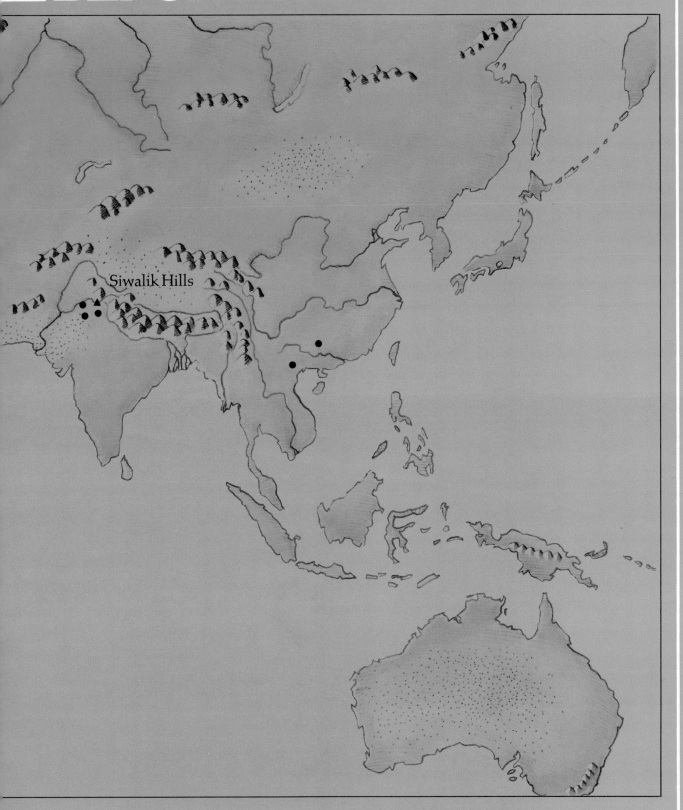

Siwalik Hills

Chapter 1

The Study of Mankind

What a piece of work is man! How noble in reason! How infinite in faculty! In form, in moving, how express and admirable! In action how like an angel! In apprehension how like a God! The beauty of the world! The paragon of animals!

WILLIAM SHAKESPEARE, 1564 – 1616.
HAMLET, II, ii.

"Who am I?" Every thinking person asks himself that question at one time or another: it is the most profound and interesting question there is. The answer he gets will depend on whom he asks. For example, you have a name that identifies you to strangers. But your name is less useful to your mailman than the number of the street you live on. You may be known to a bank teller by your account number, or to your employer by a Social Security number.

But what about *you?* Your driver's license gives a few clues. It tells whether you are a male or a female, are 5 feet 3 inches or 6 feet tall, have brown, blue, or green eyes.

But what do those facts mean? If you are a male, six feet tall, you are tall, but not exceptionally so. About four inches taller than the average American male, several inches taller than the average human. How did you get that way, if both your parents were short and three of your grandparents very short? Perhaps your fourth grandparent or one of his grandparents was responsible for your height. And the color of your eyes: if it is different from your parents', whom did you inherit it from? What else was handed down to you by a relative you never knew—a certain attitude toward life, a peculiar response to pleasure or to pain?

It is impossible to say for sure. All you know is that you are a product of your parents, grandparents, and grandparents' grandparents: a new combination of inherited bits and pieces contributed by all of these people and shaped by the environment in which you live. When you ask yourself who you are, you are forced to look back past a mother and father, whom you probably know very well, through eight great-grandparents who are little more than names, to sixteen great-great-grandparents whose very names you probably do not know. A thousand years ago about a million different people, all living at the same time, were your ancestors. You may feel little kinship with them, but in a very real sense you *are* them. You carry their genes in your body: your looks, your shape, your desires, your predisposition toward certain ailments, your ways of feeling and thinking—something from every one of them.

Going back two thousand years, your ancestors may well have been tribesmen, living in forests and along rivers, perhaps primitive agriculturists. Some of them may never have had their hands on a piece of metal. Still, they were your ancestors.

A hundred thousand, five hundred thousand, a million years before that, our ancestors no longer looked like ourselves: their brains were smaller, their minds without much imagination, their thought processes narrow. If they could talk at all, they did so in a most primitive way. If they wore anything, they wore skins. Some of them may not even have known about the use of fire and may have lived off berries, roots, and small animals like frogs and rabbits caught and eaten raw.

Who are you? You are all these people. For a proper answer to the question must be a genetic one, an evolutionary one that relates each of us to the whole of mankind, in fact, to all living creatures. Through an evolutionary approach you can truly find out who you are, how it is that you have a large brain that enables you to write, to read, and, for that matter, to build cities, to invent and drive automobiles, to fly to the moon. More basically, perhaps, you can learn how it is that you can walk upright, speak, and speculate about yourself as you are doing now.

There was a time when your ancestors could do none of these things. They were not human beings but apelike creatures living in trees. Somehow they became human. There are links somewhere in your ancestral line, on the very edge of humanness, that connect creatures that clearly were humans to creatures that clearly were not. The purpose of this book is to answer the question "what is man?" In order to find an answer, we must identify the connecting links, examine them, and see if their ancestors and descendants can provide a satisfactory explanation of the process by which an ancestral arboreal ape became a human—in short, how you came to be what you are.

THE SCIENTIFIC STUDY OF HUMAN NATURE

Mankind is biologically classified under the Latin name *Homo sapiens*; *sapiens* means wise. Man has also been labeled a political animal, a tool-using animal, a social animal, a speaking animal, and a creature that is aware of itself. We are all these things, and more. And because of our unique qualities and abilities we are, for the moment at least, in control of this planet Earth.

The answer to the question of how we became what we are is a long, complex story that begins at the moment when life first appeared on earth more than three billion years before man himself existed. This last quarter of the twentieth century is an especially good moment to trace the story, for this era is seeing a new phase in the study of mankind. In the past the most meaningful descriptions of the human state were made by prophets, artists, philosophers, and poets. Theirs were personal views colored by personal, subjective biases. We do not lack for such descriptions today, but at the same time we are gaining another perspective on ourselves, a more objective view through the lens of modern science. The lens does not present a fixed image; instead it builds an expanding mosaic of fascinating details.

Humans as a species are closely similar in anatomical structure to monkeys and apes. In 1758, Linnaeus, the great classifier of the organic realm, placed man with monkeys and apes together in the *order* called *Primates.* The primates were in turn grouped with other furry, warm-blooded creatures that suckled their young in the *class Mammalia.* We mammals have backbones and share an even more general structure with such animals as fish and birds, with whom we constitute the *phylum Vertebrata.* We can summarize our position in this type of hierarchical classification, known as a *taxonomy,* as shown in Table 1–1. In the pages that follow, we shall hear much of our genus, *Homo,* of its two species, *sapiens* and *erectus,* and of our zoological family, the *Hominidae,* in which are included all hominid ancestors since their divergence from the lineage leading to the living African apes. Our species *Homo sapiens* may also be subdivided into smaller units—into modern and ancient subspecies such as *Homo sapiens neanderthalensis* and the variety of living races that constitutes *Homo sapiens* today. (See Chapter 20.)

Such a taxonomy shows our structural position in the animal kingdom and gives some indication of our relationship to other animals, but our true physical and genealogical relationship to other animal species was not understood until the time of Charles Darwin (1809–1882).

In 1859 Charles Darwin published his revolutionary book *On the Origin of Species.* It presented a theory that was the product of many years of observation and recording by two naturalists, Darwin and Alfred Russel Wallace (1823–1913) (see Figures 1–1 and 1–2). Both men travelled widely and observed in great detail the variation that exists within animal and plant species. Members of species, they noted, are not identical but show variation in size, strength, health, fertility, longevity, behavior, and many other characteristics. Darwin in particular realized that humans use this natural variation when they selec-

Classification of *Homo sapiens*

The Theory of Evolution

TABLE 1-1 CLASSIFICATION OF MANKIND

Taxonomic Category	Group Including Humans	Members
Species	*sapiens*	Modern humans, including early subspecies and all living races
Genus	*Homo*	Early man (*Homo erectus*) and modern man (*Homo sapiens*)
Family	Hominidae	Man (*Homo*), ape-man (*Australopithecus*), and early ape-man (*Ramapithecus*)
Super-family	Hominoidea	Hominidae, Pongidae (orangutan, chimpanzee, gorilla), and Hylobatidae (gibbon, siamang)
Suborder	Anthropoidea	Hominoidea, Old World monkeys, and New World monkeys
Order	Primates	Anthropoidea and Prosimii (the lower primates: tarsiers, lorises, lemurs, etc.)
Class	Mammalia	Primates and all other warm-blooded furry animals that suckle their young
Phylum	Vertebrata	Mammals and all other animals with backbones
Kingdom	Animalia	Vertebrates and all other animals

Figure 1–1 Charles Darwin in his sixty-sixth year. In his *Autobiography* he wrote: "In September 1858 I set to work by the strong advice of Lyell and Hooker to prepare a volume on the transmutation of species, but was often interrupted by ill-health. . . . [The book] cost me thirteen months and ten days hard labour." Darwin was an intermittent invalid for 40 years, but invalidism had some advantages. He wrote: "Even ill-health, though it annihilated several years of my life, has saved me from the distractions of society and amusement." He lived to the age of 73.

tively breed plants and animals, in that a breeder allows only particular individuals possessing desired qualities to interbreed.

In due course, an understanding of the means by which a selection similar to that practiced by human breeders operates in nature came to both Darwin and Wallace from the same source. The first edition of *An Essay on the Principle of Population* by an English clergyman, T. R. Malthus, appeared in 1798. In his book, Malthus showed that the reproductive potential of mankind far exceeds the natural resources available to nourish an expanding population. He argued that, in practice, the size of human populations is limited by disease, famine, and war and that, in the absence of "moral restraint," such factors alone appear to check what would otherwise be a rapid growth in population.

Both Darwin and Wallace read Malthus' essay independently and, remarkably enough, both men recorded in their diaries how they realized that in the book lay the key to understanding the evolutionary process. It was clear that what Malthus had discovered for human populations was true for populations of plants and animals: the reproductive potential vastly exceeds that necessary to maintain a constant population size. They realized that the individuals that do survive must be in some way better equipped to live in their environment than those that do not survive. It follows that in a natural interbreeding population any variation would most likely be preserved that increased the organism's ability to produce fertile offspring, while the variations that decreased that ability would most likely be eliminated.

Around these ideas Darwin and Wallace formulated a theory of evolution. It is not difficult to understand and may be stated as follows:

1. Organisms produce far more offspring than required to maintain their population size, and yet their population size generally remains more or less constant over long periods of time. From this, as well as from observation, it seems clear that there is a high rate of mortality among immature individuals.
2. Individuals in any population show much variation, and those that survive probably do so to some extent because of their particular characteristics. That is, individuals with certain characteristics can be considered better *adapted* to their particular environment.
3. Since offspring resemble their parents closely, though not exactly, successive generations will maintain and improve on the degree of adaptation by gradual changes in every generation.

This process of variation and selection by the environment for better-adapted individuals is called *natural selection,* and the change in the nature of the population which follows upon selection is the process of *organic evolution.* Substantially the same processes occur among both plants and animals.

Darwin and Wallace had thus provided a rational and convincing explanation of the diversity and changing nature of species. If humans, too, were seen as products of this process, mankind had to develop a completely new attitude toward the natural world and face an entirely novel view of human origins. This agonizing reappraisal was possible only for those who were capable of rational thought, free from earlier ideas and prejudices. It would not be unreasonable to claim that Darwin's book is the most important book ever published and the changes that it has brought about in our view of ourselves are only a part of its revolutionary impact. From it derives our modern and extraordinarily fruitful perspective on mankind—*evolutionary biology.*

Evolution is a creative process and, as the eminent geneticist Theodosius Dobzhansky pointed out, "Any creative process involves a risk of failure, which in biological evolution means extinction. On the other hand, creativity makes possible striking successes and discoveries." In the billions of years of the grand procession of life on earth, there have been both successes and failures. Thousands of forms have arisen to swim, wriggle, crawl, walk, or fly past some immutable reviewing

Figure 1–2 Alfred Russel Wallace was a complete contrast to Darwin in both background and character. Whereas Darwin did not need to work for a living, Wallace earned his way by collecting rare tropical plants and animals for private collectors and museums. As a result he travelled far more widely than Darwin in both South America and Southeast Asia. Later in his life he wrote a number of books on evolution. Although of considerable interest, they do not have the originality and intellectual integrity of Darwin's writings.

The Modern Perspective: Evolutionary Biology

stand and then collapse. There were creatures that seemed merely bizarre experiments, and there were others that were temporarily successful: the dinosaurs ruled the earth for 130 million years before they vanished, leaving no descendants. Some dropouts were crucial to the development of human beings, and the human line can be traced to early vertebrates that first possessed a rudimentary backbone and the beginnings of a brain. The human body is full of traces of ancestors that were very different from us and led wholly different lives: for instance, we have a coccyx, the vestige of a tail, at the end of our spines, and as an embryo (as shown in Figure 1–3) we carry ephemeral gill slits, which remind us that our ancestors were once marine creatures. This book is about one experiment in the creation of animal life that, although starting from the same ancestral sources as the dinosaurs, did not end in an evolutionary blind alley. In time it led to modern *Homo sapiens,* a product of variation and selection that began more than three billion years ago.

The search for the origin of human beings begins with the very first life on earth, in the primitive sea where living cells first reproduced themselves. There was no hint then, of course, that more than three billion years later closely similar cells multiplied a billion-billionfold would manifest themselves in the complex cellular structure of our bodies. Yet it happened. We are here to prove it. And if we are to gain any real understanding about ourselves, we must learn to recognize the age-old elements from which we have emerged, and how and why they go together as they do.

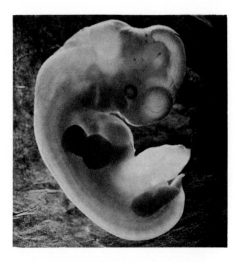

Figure 1–3   The human embryo grows in a salty solution called amniotic fluid, which is not greatly different in composition from the ocean. The embryo shows certain characteristics of ancestral forms, some of which are remnants of marine fishlike adaptations of 500 million years ago. At about four weeks gill slits and a tail can be seen, which rapidly develop into other structures.

The Study of Human Origins

Paleoanthropology is the branch of science dealing with the study of early men. It involves connecting human and nonhuman on a chain so long lost that the few links that have come to light almost defy assembly. For those engaged in this science, today is a time of extraordinary interest. Recent discoveries and analysis now begin to make it possible to lay out some of those links next to one another and to look at them closely in relation to one another.

In 1859, when Darwin propounded the theory of evolution, scientists knew of only two fossils that were relevant to the search for our origins: one of an extinct ape and another of the early type of *Homo sapiens* called Neandertal man. Just a little more than a hundred years later, expeditions in the Lake Rudolf area of East Africa unearthed more than 150 near-human bones in a single five-year period. One of these bones, the so-called Lothagam jaw, is about 5.5 million years old; it is evidence that creatures not unlike us existed more than three million years earlier than any fossil-find previously had indicated. The discovery and interpretation of such evidence of our ancestors today involves many specialists (see Table 1–2).

The knowledge and insights of other modern sciences also contribute to attempts to understand our ancestors. Atomic physicists, for example, have determined that certain radioactive elements discharge energy at a constant rate and, in the process, turn into certain other materials. This knowledge provides paleontologists with new

TABLE 1–2   SPECIAL SKILLS TO STUDY FOSSIL SITES

Specialist	Skills
In the Field	
Paleoanthropologist	In charge of investigations from start to finish, he must pick the site, obtain financial support, hire the labor, and organize, plan, and supervise the work in progress. Finally, he must integrate the data collected by each of the specialists and then publish his conclusions.
Geologist	Often assists in selecting the site. His knowledge of the geologic history of the region is indispensable in determining the relative ages of fossil finds. His study of the strata at the site will also determine the natural processes—erosion, volcanic action, mountain-building—that laid them down.
Surveyor	Maps the general region of the site and the site itself, plotting it in relation to natural landmarks and making a detailed record of its contours before they are obliterated by digging.
Draftsman	Records the exact position of all fossils, tools, and other artifacts as they are excavated, marking their relationships to each other in both the horizontal and vertical planes.
Photographer	Documents fossil remains and artifacts and their associations as they are uncovered, records work in progress and the use of special equipment, and provides over-all views of the site as well as of personnel at work.
In the Laboratory	
Petrologist	Identifies and classifies the rocks and minerals found around the site. He can determine the nature of rocks from which tools were made and identify stones that do not occur naturally in the area—indicating that the stones were imported by early humans.
Palynologist	Specializes in fossil plant pollen, which may shed light on early man's environment and diet.
Pedologist	An expert on soils and their chemical composition, his findings round out the picture of the environment as it once was.

Continued

TABLE 1–2   (continued)

Specialist	Skills
In the Laboratory	
Geochemist	With the geophysicist, conducts chemical and physical tests in the laboratory to determine the absolute age of material found at the site. He may also study the chemical composition of bones and artifacts.
In the Field and Laboratory	
Preparator	Preserves and protects fossils and artifacts with various hardening agents and makes plaster casts for particularly fragile bones and other organic remains. Later in the laboratory, the preparator will clean and restore the specimens, making them ready for study by various specialists.
Paleontologist	Studies the fossil animal remains found throughout strata at the site. From the finds, he can learn much about the ecology of the environment and the eating habits of early humans.
Physical anthropologist	A specialist in the comparative anatomy of apes and humans, he evaluates the human remains found at the site and the evolutionary status of the fossil hominid who lived there.

methods to establish the age of fossils and interpret the stages in the evolution of life.

Equally valuable have been the contributions of modern biochemistry. In the past decade biochemists have deciphered the code found in the substance DNA (see Chapter 3) by which instructions for building new cells and new organisms are passed along. Knowledge of this code provides insights into how members of a species reproduce themselves, generation after generation, virtually unchanged; how, on the other hand, minute variations do occur in offspring; and how these variations may accumulate over time. Knowledge of how these variations create differences in the structures of proteins can be used to determine the affinity between different types of organisms. Some scientists believe that these differences accumulate at a steady rate over time, so that this biochemical knowledge can provide yet another method of dating to determine when existing species of animals first emerged.

Other clues to the past are coming from studies of a very different kind involving living animals—the science of animal behavior. It is a

Figure 1–4 The more closely chimpanzees are studied, the more like them we appear to be, especially in the realm of individual relationships and nonverbal communication. Here, an adult chimpanzee stretches out its hand to reassure a young individual, and to receive a kiss of submission.

relatively new discipline, but a flourishing one. Studies of the behavior of living animals (for example, the chimpanzees shown in Figure 1–4) have been used to help explain the basis for some human behaviors and to suggest how ancestral humans may have acted and why. In particular, we will see the usefulness of animal behavior studies when we discuss the social organization of our ancestors (Chapter 9).

HUMAN CHARACTERISTICS

From studies like these, a new view of ourselves and of our ancestry has been emerging. It places mankind in perspective in a vast span of millions of years amid a vast crowd of creatures, and it shows something of why he is, as Shakespeare said, the "paragon of animals." But before we turn to distant places and distant times, let us look at the finished product, the hero of the story. We cannot completely answer our question, "What is man?" until we can answer a simpler question, "What makes humans different from other creatures?"

His mind, to be sure. But what our new knowledge makes clear is that the mind is not enough. Without a remarkable combination of organic hardware that supports and abets it, the mind would be useless. Man dominates the animal kingdom not only because he possesses a relatively big, complex brain but also because of a special combination of physical characteristics that is often taken for granted. When compared with the sleek grace of a jungle cat, the streamlined strength of a 1,800-pound tuna, or the regal bearing of a horse, what is man's puny body? The answer to that rhetorical question, as a careful examination of our physical adaptations will illustrate, is: everything.

Among the physical traits that, added together, separate all humans from all other animals, there are three of overwhelming significance: a skeleton built for walking upright; eyes capable of sharp, three-dimensional vision in color; and hands that provide both a powerful grip and nimble manipulations. These features are found in some

degree in many primates; it is the elaboration of them in special combination with one another which characterizes us. Controlling and making use of this equipment is the brain—a physical organ itself, but one that introduces the capacity for rational thought and, with the body, makes possible that other most human of all our distinctive abilities, speech.

These attributes, uniquely combined in humans, interact with one another. It is impossible to say that one led to the next, or that one is necessarily more important than the others. Each one reinforces the others and makes improvements in them possible. Nevertheless, one attribute stands out simply because it is so conspicuous: upright walking. It is a remarkably effective method of locomotion, and no animal can use it as consistently as man does.

Locomotion

For all its apparent simplicity, walking is an adaptation as specialized as flying is to a bat or swimming to a seal. True, man is not the only animal to stand on its hind legs alone; birds, bears, and a number of man's primate cousins are bipedal on occasion. But with the exception of a few flightless birds such as the ostrich, man is the only animal that depends exclusively on two legs for locomotion. Using his two legs, a human has the endurance to outrun a deer. He can carry heavier loads, pound for pound of body weight, than a donkey. (The French-Canadian *voyageurs* who transported Indian trade goods through the North Woods routinely back-packed 180 pounds over nine-mile portages, and a legendary hero among them named La Bonga is said to have portaged 450 pounds.) No terrain is totally impassable to a man. He can reach an eagle's nest or a pearl oyster's bed. Only a human, the British scientist J. B. S. Haldane noted, can swim a mile, walk twenty miles, and then climb a tree.

Like horses, human beings have a variety of gaits; they amble, stride, jog, and sprint. The simple stride, though, is at once the most useful and the most peculiarly human way of getting from one place to another. Probably evolved on the African grassland, or *savanna,* where our early ancestors often covered many miles in the course of a day's food-gathering or hunting, the stride has taken us to every corner of the earth. It is no minor accomplishment. When compared with the way four-legged animals get about, human walking turns out to be a sur-

prisingly complex feat. "Without split-second timing," says John Napier, a British authority on primates, "man would fall flat on his face; in fact with each step he takes, he teeters on the edge of catastrophe." Human walking is actually a balancing act in which the muscles of the feet, legs, hips, and back are alternately contracted and relaxed according to synchronized orders from the brain and spinal cord.

Balanced bipedalism is uniquely human, and to those who can see it with fresh eyes, it is strangely beautiful in its sheer efficiency and its superb adaptation of bone and muscle, brain and nerve, to the tricky problem of moving about on two legs rather than four. The adaptation was achieved at considerable cost. Back trouble, foot ailments, and difficulty in giving birth are common among humans and result partly from upright posture.

Why is it so important to human evolution that we stand erect and walk on two legs? Part of the answer has to do with the human head. The head is where the eyes are, and the taller a person stands the more he sees. A dog running through tall grass is forced to leap into the air time and again to get his bearings, but even on a smooth surface where no obstacles obstruct vision the advantage of height is enormous. Eyes that are two feet above level ground can detect low objects about six miles away; eyes five feet above the ground can theoretically see nine miles farther.

The advantage of height is especially important because in our evolution vision has been one of the most important of our five major senses. Scientists estimate that some 90 percent of all the information stored in the brain arrived there through the agency of the eyes. Not surprisingly, human eyes are attuned precisely to human needs. For general seeing they are unsurpassed by any other eyes in the world. A hawk may see more sharply but cannot move its eyes easily and generally moves its head instead to follow its prey. A dragonfly can follow faster movement than a person but cannot focus a sharp image. A horse can see almost completely behind its head but has difficulty seeing objects straight ahead at close range. Most important, among higher animals only human beings and their nearest primate relatives have the special combination of full *stereoscopic* vision and

Figure 1–5 Bipedalism involves split-second balancing feats with precise muscular control. When a person takes a stride, his right foot pushes off from the toe; the left foot bears the full body weight while the right leg moves ahead to land on the heel; then the left foot thrusts off. To run fast, a human being stays on his toes.

Vision

Figure 1–6 More distant information about its environment is available to an animal with eyes three or four feet above ground level than to one of low height. These photographs taken from different heights are sharp at all distances; animals other than primates, however, can usually focus only at certain ranges of distance.

color vision: human eyes, placed at the front of the head rather than at the sides, can focus together on an object so that it is perceived as a single three-dimensional image in the brain. Within this image, color vision enables us to pick out details by hue as well as by form, relationship, and brightness.

Taken together, color and depth perception bring us enormous advantages over most other animals, the majority of which are color-blind and have a relatively poor capacity to judge visual distances or to focus in fine detail upon particular objects. What a hunting dog sees when it looks out over an open field is little more than what a black-and-white movie might show, and the dog's distance focus is limited. If there is a rabbit in the field, the dog is unlikely to spot it unless it moves—that is one reason why rabbits and similar prey freeze to conceal themselves from their enemies. A human hunter, on the other hand, can scan a scene from his feet to the horizon in a few seconds by focusing sharply and selectively upon a succession of different images. And he sees more images than any dog does because his eyes are raised at least three feet higher above the ground.

Hands

Man stands up partly in order to see, and stays up partly because he sees so well. But the freedom that his posture gives to his arms and particularly his hands has proved even more decisive. Chimpanzees, among our closest competitors in upright posture and bipedal movement, have never really mastered the art of walking on their hind legs, and so they lack free use of the arms. For a brief while they can get around in their forest homes with a bunch of bananas or a baby chimp in their arms, but they must always be ready to lend their balance the help of a knuckle on the ground. We humans have far less need for caution. Babies may crawl on all fours; old people may rely on canes; but most human beings go about with never a thought of support from anything but two legs. Their hands are free to grab and use things.

Not needing our hands for support, we have been able to use them for more complicated and more creative tasks. With 25 joints and 58 distinctly different motions, the human hand represents one of the most advanced mechanisms ever produced by nature. Imagine a single tool that can meet the demands of tasks as varied as gripping a tool, playing a concerto, wringing out a towel, holding a pencil, gesturing, and—something we tend to forget—simply feeling. For, in addition to its ability to perform tasks, the hand is our prime organ of touch. In the dark or around corners, it substitutes for sight. In a way, the hand has an advantage over the eye, because it is a sensory and a manipulative organ combined. It can explore the environment by means of touch, and then it can immediately do something about what it detects. It can, for instance, feel around on a forest floor for nuts and roots, seize them on contact, and pop them into the mouth; at the same time that your eyes are reading these words, your hand can finger the corner of the page in preparation for turning it.

The hand itself may be a marvelous tool, but it is used to full value only when it is employed to manipulate still other tools. This capacity is a second-stage benefit of upright walking. With our erect posture, our hands are free; with hands free, we can use tools; with tools we can get food more easily and exploit the environment in other ways to ensure our survival. Humans are not the only animals that employ tools, but they are the only ones that do so to any great extent and consistently.

There are two distinct ways of holding and using tools: the *power grip* and the *precision grip*, as John Napier termed them. Human infants and children begin with the power grip and progress to the precision grip. Think of how a child holds a spoon: first in the power grip, in its fist or between its fingers and palm, and later between the tips of the thumb and first two fingers, in the precision grip. Many primates share the power grip with humans. It is the way to get firm hold of a tree

Figure 1–7   The power grip (top left) and precision grip are illustrated in these photographs together with the uniquely human independent control of five fingers.

branch. But neither a monkey nor an ape has a thumb long enough or flexible enough to be completely *opposable*, able to reach comfortably to the tips of all the other fingers, as is required for our delicate yet strong precision grip. It is the human thumb and independent control of the fingers that makes possible nearly all the movements necessary to handle tools, to make clothing, to write with a pencil, to play a flute.

If the precision grip required to play a flute can be related to upright walking, then the mind required to make such music may be related to the grip. Tools and brain seem to have developed together. It is the hand that carries out some of the most critical and complex orders of the brain, and as the hand grew more skillful so did the brain.

The human brain is not much to look at (see Figure 1–8). On the dissecting table, with the skull removed, it is a "pinkish-gray mass, moist and rubbery to the touch . . . perched like a flower on top of a slender stalk." (The stalk is the spinal cord, which may be considered an extension of the brain.) An ape's brain does not look very different. But there is a difference, and it is crucial. It is in the gray layer called the *cortex*, which constitutes the outer layer of the largest part of the brain. The cortex, scientists now know, plays the major role in reasoned behavior, memory, and abstract thought—and also supervises the delicate and accurate muscular movements that control the precision grip. The cortex is quite thin, but it represents 80 percent of the volume of the human brain. If spread out flat, it would be about the size of a newspaper page. It fits inside the head only by being compressed like a crumpled rag (the famous "convolutions" of the brain are mainly the folds and overlaps of the cerebral cortex). This compression demonstrates the fact that the cortex has all but outgrown its allotted space. Somehow, the increase in the size of the cortex has made the human brain the uniquely human thing it is.

Although there are many mysteries about the brain that remain to be solved, some of the secrets and the importance of the huge cortex are now well understood. The cortex is not only the seat of intelligence; it is also, and perhaps more significantly, the part of the brain where sense impressions and memories are stored to be called forth and acted upon as circumstances suggest. There is in the working of the human cortex no fixed pattern in which associations between experience and memory need to be made, as there is in some animal brains, and few predetermined responses are generated in the cortex. Among animals, many patterns of action are effectively automatic, performed by inborn programs or through previous conditioning. In man, these patterns are, to a considerable extent, performed consciously, or refrained from consciously, or replaced by completely new patterns, again consciously. This use of the brain results in what is known as reasoned behavior, a phenomenon typically human and only rarely seen in other animals.

The great brain gap between man and lower animals can be visualized by looking at what happens when a human hand pokes the outspread tentacles of a sea anemone. The anemone will instantly retract its tentacles into its body. The reaction is automatic, since what

The Brain

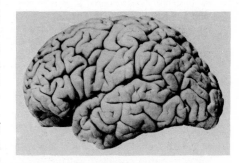

Figure 1–8 The surface of the human brain is deeply folded, as can be seen from this photograph of the brain's left side.

passes for a brain in the anemone is programmed for only one pattern of action: in response to touch the tentacles retract. No reasoned behavior is involved. In response to the same contact, the human may pull his hand back, or he may not. His brain considers options, and his action will depend on many things—whether he thinks anemones are dangerous or harmless, whether the contact is pleasing or discomforting, whether he touched the anemone on purpose or accidentally. Most higher animals can react to a given stimulus in a variety of ways, but not a single other animal has anything like the number or diversity of potential responses available to a human being. And humans are completely alone in their capacity to examine all options in advance, to look inward upon themselves, and to observe the processes of their own minds. Perhaps even more important, when humans think, they know they are thinking.

Conscious thinking is one of our most striking characteristics, yet it remains one of the most puzzling. We cannot yet explain the operation of brain cells in the way we can analyze the movement of bones and muscles in walking and grasping. But a start has been made. Thinking depends on memory and association in the cortex. Ideas and thought are registered in the nerve cells, or *neurons,* somewhat as they are in a man-made computer, in the form of electrical patterns, and they are retrieved and shuffled about by electrical actions. This much is quite clearly established, since thinking produces measurable electric currents in the brain and many experiments demonstrate the effect of electric stimulation in such processes as memory. Electroshock therapy of a schizophrenic patient, for example, can erase some of the patient's recent memories while leaving unchanged memories that date from the more distant past. Like a computer, the brain evidently has two memories: one for storing considerable information more or less permanently, another for temporarily recording current data.

The brain's similarities to a computer are remarkable, but they are only coarse similarities. Comparing a brain with a computer is much like comparing an aircraft carrier with a bark canoe. The human brain contains an estimated 10 billion nerve cells, each of which may be thought of as a switching point for the electrochemical signals of mental activity. The largest modern computer, by contrast, contains 1.5 million switching points. The system of circuits within the brain is obviously many thousands of times larger and more complex than that of the most complicated computer yet devised. As Warren McCulloch, an American student of the brain, has put it, "The brain is like a computing machine, but there is no computing machine like the brain."

If the brain is more than a computing machine, it is also more than a thinking machine. Reasoned behavior itself did not make us the paragon of animals. We rose to dominance through the crucial physical achievements made possible as our extraordinary brain evolved with our body. Both the senses and the skills of humans (as of any animal) must be attributed to the joint evolution of a highly complex body and brain structures that function in total dependence upon each other.

The ceiling of the Sistine Chapel was painted by a precision grip and color-sensitive eyes controlled by Michelangelo's brain. Neither bodily machinery nor creativity alone could have produced this masterpiece; both were needed, working together.

The great significance of this combination of human brain and human body is perhaps best shown by man's most important innovation: language. Only humans can talk, although all animals communicate with their fellows. Bees dance to direct the swarm to food; wolves warn off intruders by marking their territories with scent; one bird call announces danger, another invites love-making. Besides employing these primitive methods of communication, these bodily movements and simple sounds, humans also use language, a repertory of sounds that can be combined in an almost infinite number of ways as units to express very complex facts and ideas. The prairie dog's quick, high-pitched barks can send up a vague alarm; they cannot specify: "Five men armed with shotguns are approaching from the west and will be upon us in half an hour."

Such communications obviously depend on the human brain, for some animals equal humans in vocal performance without mastering language. Myna birds and parrots can mimic a human's voice perfectly; they can even be taught to repeat sentences of several words or more; but they cannot really talk, because their brains are incapable of abstract thought. They cannot, therefore, combine elements from two different sentences learned by rote and use these elements to construct a third sentence.

Language is so clearly dependent on brainpower that its equal dependence on the body is often overlooked. The role of the body is most clearly demonstrated in the case of chimpanzees. Chimpanzees have brains that appear to be adequate for some degree of abstract thought. For example, they can stack several boxes on top of one another to reach a bunch of bananas, a simple act requiring the imaginative combination of superficially unrelated elements. They also can produce a wide range of sounds. It seems that they ought, then, to be able to talk. Since the turn of the century scientists have been trying to teach chimpanzees to speak. The best anyone has been able to do, after years of patient tutelage, is to get a chimpanzee to say "mama," "papa," and one or two other infant words. Only recently has the reason for this failure been traced. It involves not simply brain size but another aspect of the anatomy. Chimpanzees are indeed able to construct very simple sentences—but not spoken sentences. A close examination of chimpanzees shows that they lack, among other things, the kind of pharynx that enables humans to articulate vowels. They can "speak" not with auditory symbols but with visual ones—specifically, with the symbols of the American Sign Language, originally designed for the deaf. Man remains the only creature that has developed both the physical structures and the powerful, specialized brain needed to produce speech.

Language

Cultural Adaptation

Language was perhaps the last of our major biological characteristics to evolve. With the gift of speech, we acquired an immensely powerful tool for *cultural evolution.* Until about a million years ago, the evolution of all animals was a response to the challenge of the environment, and nature alone influenced the developments that eventually provided the human body with its internal skeletal support, its constantly warm temperature, its legs for walking upright, its hands for deft manipulation. If the climate was cold, natural selection favored the development of special adaptations such as fur and fat. When supplies of leaves and grass increased and spread, so did mutations favoring crunching and grinding teeth. Every animal was at the mercy of its surroundings. If a species suited its environment, it prospered; if it did not, it evolved to meet the conditions of the environment in which it found itself, moved somewhere more suitable, or became extinct.

This dominance of natural environment over species evolution became profoundly modified in the evolution of mankind. If humans had to find food by preying on other creatures, they did not need to develop fangs and claws; they made weapons of wood and stone. When the climate turned cold, they wrapped themselves in the skins of other animals instead of growing a furry coat. This acquisition of a material culture and the resulting capacity to adapt culturally was something completely new on earth, enabling humans to insulate themselves from the environment and to exploit that environment.

The ability to speak facilitated and speeded up cultural adaptation. From the beginning, the members of human hunting and gathering bands used their ability to communicate verbally in planning a hunt, passing on information, or agreeing on a rendezvous. But the greatest benefit mankind gained through language came later, through the ability to learn from the accumulated experience of other people and other groups. Before the birth of language, human experience was pitifully brief and transitory; when a human being died, much of his knowledge died with him. By the gift of language the shared experience of mankind could more readily be preserved and kept accessible over many generations—first through recited lore and legends and later through the written word.

Physically, modern humans are hardly distinguishable from humans who lived 30,000 years ago. But socially, human life has been transformed by the accumulation of the experience of millions of human lives over thousands upon thousands of years. This new social world is based entirely on words. Once a species surviving in a tropical savanna, mankind has come to occupy the entire globe. From an estimated population of 10 million as recently as 10,000 years ago, we have multiplied to 3.6 billion today, and threaten by our very success to exhaust the resources of the earth before the next century is well advanced.

Summary

This is man as he stands today, unique among the animals and alone in command of his planet. There is nothing like the human body in

Figure 1–9   Manipulation of the environment is not unique to human beings. Nest-building is a common example of it among birds and many other animals. But humans have taken manipulation further. They are not only builders, but toolmakers as well, and this makes possible much more complex structures.

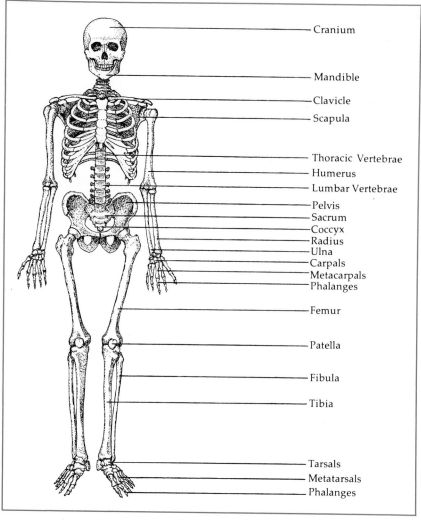

Cranium

Mandible

Clavicle

Scapula

Thoracic Vertebrae

Humerus

Lumbar Vertebrae

Pelvis

Sacrum

Coccyx

Radius

Ulna

Carpals

Metacarpals

Phalanges

Femur

Patella

Fibula

Tibia

Tarsals

Metatarsals

Phalanges

Figure 1–10   The human skeleton has the same set of 200 distinct bones as found in other primates; here the most important are labeled.

all the world. It is the only organism that combines the abilities to think about itself, talk, habitually walk on its hind legs, make things with its hands, and enjoy stereoscopic color vision. No other creature depends both on its cultural adaptations and its physical adaptations to enable it to survive. The foot that evolved from a branch-gripping prehensile organ to an organ capable of carrying a human being steadily over a rolling grassland may now be found encased in a boot, slogging with its human owner through freezing city slush. The hand that first wielded a stick as a weapon and later chipped flint into a cutting edge today may fashion tools that make tools that make more tools that make rocketships that reach other planets. The eye that used to spot a wounded giraffe hiding in a grove of trees may now scan this page. And the mind that learned to analyze the migrations of game, to recognize dozens of different animal spoors, to distinguish among hundreds of varieties of plants, may now dictate the playing of a game of chess, the writing of a book, the waging of a war.

Chapter 2

The Riddle of Heredity

Variety's the very spice of life,
That gives it all its flavour.

WILLIAM COWPER, 1730 – 1800.
THE TASK, BOOK 2.

It may well be difficult to accept that our unique and miraculous qualities are a product of natural selection. Is it possible that Bach's Mass in D minor is merely the result of a lengthy process of chance and change? Organic evolution is in fact more complex than chance alone, and more efficient. Natural selection operates on accumulated variations: selection is not the only creative factor in the evolutionary process.

For decades after the principles of evolution had been formulated, a knotty problem remained: why do living things vary, and how do variations occur? It was at last clear that evolution functions through the selective preservation and elimination of inherited differences between individuals, yet no one could say how such differences come about in the first place. To complicate the problem, there was no certain knowledge of the way a given trait is handed down from parent to offspring. Black-haired parents could produce a child with red hair inherited from a grandparent or an even more remote ancestor. Baffled, people fell back on the idea that heredity is somehow transmitted with the blood, and that a child bears a blend of the bloods of his parents. So deeply rooted was this idea that it became a part of the language— a prince "of royal blood"; a "blooded" mare; "blood will tell."

In Darwin's day, this idea of *blending inheritance* held sway, and yet it introduced a seemingly insurmountable problem. For if each child is a blend of its parents' characteristics, the succession of generations must result in a loss of variation. The long-term effect of sexual reproduction within a population would have to be decreasing variability, until all individuals were almost exactly the same. And yet the opposite is true: in nature, variability is maintained and often increases.

Darwin was plagued for years by this problem. In an attempt to discover how traits are inherited, he experimented with the garden pea and other plants. For all the care he took, he could never figure out the pattern or order of inheritance that he felt certain must exist. Nor, apparently, could anyone else. Darwin read many scientific journals; none of them enlightened him. And yet, by an ironic coincidence, the basic laws of evolution and the fundamentals of heredity were discovered at about the same time.

THE WORK OF GREGOR MENDEL

Just as Darwin was turning at last to the final formulation of the theory of evolution, the obscure Austrian monk shown in Figure 2–1, Gregor Johann Mendel (1822–1884), in 1856 launched the first of a series of experiments that were to demonstrate that inheritance, like evolution, is not chaos, chance, or miracle but a matter of law. Darwin never heard of Mendel's work, and the monk's reports lay ignored by the scientific world for over thirty years.

Mendel was born on July 22, 1822, in a little village in what is now Czechoslovakia. His father, Anton, was known for his fine fruit trees, and he taught young Johann how to improve them with grafts from the orchards of the local manor house. Johann did so well in his academic classes that he was recommended for higher schooling, but there was little money to pay for it. By the time he had gone on to a two-year philosophical course at the Olmütz Institute, he knew that he would have to look for a profession in which he would be "spared perpetual anxiety about a means of livelihood." A teacher suggested that he enter the Augustinian monastery at Brünn. When he was accepted in 1843, he gratefully began his studies there, assuming the name Gregor.

From his youth, as he once said, he had been "addicted to the study of Nature." In the atmosphere of the monastery he was free, as he continued his religious studies, to work on botanical experiments. In a small strip of garden Mendel began experimenting with crossbreeding flowers. He soon discovered that when he crossed certain flower varieties the same characteristics kept appearing with surprising regularity. The books he consulted helped very little. Many studies of *hybridization*, the crossing of two varieties or species, had been made. The varieties that resulted seemed to follow no rule, occurring in all sizes, colors, and forms.

Figure 2–1 Gregor Mendel's country childhood gave him a deep knowledge and a sympathetic understanding of the plant world. As a monk with some leisure, he took up gardening with remarkable and brilliant results.

The First Experiments

It struck Mendel, a student remarkably free of preconceptions, that the studies themselves had been chaotic. No one had bred hybrids systematically for generation after generation and recorded exactly what individual characteristics appeared in each plant or even worked out the kinds of experiments that would make this possible. Mendel decided to develop a workable procedure, realizing as he started that the experiments would have to be done on a large enough scale to rule out small accidents of chance.

To begin with, he needed *true-breeding* plants, plants that showed little variation from generation to generation. He also needed a plant easily protected from all foreign pollen, for if a single insect or vagrant breeze should introduce outside pollen, an experiment on the inheritance of some selected character would be ruined. The legumes most nearly fulfilled his needs, and after some testing Mendel chose the common garden pea for his experimental plant. The pea ordinarily fertilizes itself and is easily protected from outside pollen. Mendel ordered 34 varieties from seedsmen and subjected them to a two-year trial, eventually selecting 22 as suitable for his experiments.

One of Mendel's greatest assets was that he worked step by step in patient, well-disciplined ways. Instead of trying to compare plant with plant in all possible respects, a procedure that soon would have led him into a morass of difficulties, he decided to study a few easily compared pairs of characteristics of the pea. He selected seven, as illustrated in Figure 2–2:

1. The form of the ripe seeds—round or wrinkled
2. The color of the peas—yellow or intense green
3. The color of the seed coats—gray or white
4. The form of the ripe pods—inflated or constricted between the seeds
5. The color of the unripe pods—green or vivid yellow
6. The position of the flowers—axial (distributed along the stem) or terminal (bunched at the top of the stem)
7. The length of the stem—long (6 or 7 feet) or short (9 to 18 inches)

Mendel was now ready to produce hybrids, and he decided to start by crossing wrinkled-seed plants with round-seed. As soon as the buds formed on the vines, Mendel opened those of each wrinkled plant and pinched off the stamens to prevent the pea from producing pollen for its own fertilization. To keep any chance pollen from being carried in, he tied a little paper or calico bag around each bud. Then he collected pollen from the round-seed plants. This pollen he dusted on the stigmas of the wrinkled buds, removing their protective bags to do so. To settle any doubt that his results might be influenced by the choice of plants to serve as the seed parents, he also reversed the fertilizing process, dusting some of the wrinkled pollen on round buds. Mendel then repeated the interchange with each of the other pairs of characteristics he was testing. Altogether he made 287 fertilizations on 70 plants.

Then he could only wait until time, sun, and rain performed their work, but finally he was able to open the pods of his round–wrinkled hybrids. In them nestled only round peas. The wrinkling, a trait of half of the parents, had disappeared as completely as though it had never existed. So it was with the other six characteristics of his test plants: although he crossed tall plants with short ones, all the offspring were tall; although he mated yellow peas with green, all the offspring were yellow. In each of the test plots one characteristic and only one prevailed in this first hybrid generation (Figure 2–3).

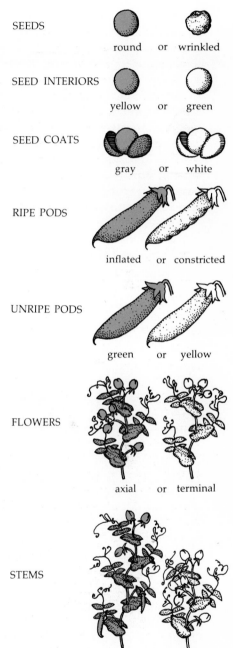

Figure 2–2 Mendel's pioneering observations of the pea plant were based on a comparison of these seven, easily identifiable characteristics.

During the winter, as Mendel worked with his jars of labeled pea seeds, he decided to call the characteristic that prevailed (like round-ness or yellowness) _dominant,_ and the one that seemingly disappeared (like wrinkledness or greenness) _recessive._ Thanks to his methodical approach, he knew what had gone into his hybrids. The next step was to see what characteristics these hybrids might be hiding. To find that out he planned to let the hybrids fertilize themselves in the normal manner of peas. In the spring he planted his hybrid seeds and waited.

Once again the critical time came when the pods could be opened. Mendel broke open the first. Inside lay both round and wrinkled peas, side by side in the same pod! The lost wrinkling of the wrinkled grand-parent had reappeared. Mendel harvested 7,324 peas: 5,474 were round and 1,850 wrinkled; the ratio was nearly 3 round to 1 wrinkled.

It was the same with the other test plantings in the second generation of hybrids. In the experiment on pea color there were three yellow peas to each green. Overall, and ruling out a few small deviations introduced by chance, the ratio was always 3 to 1. Here was no haphazard recur-rence of the traits of the grandparents but an exact recurrence.

What would happen in the third generation? The next year Mendel planted his 3-to-1 group and again permitted each plant to fertilize itself. Now the wrinkled seeds, that is, those showing the recessive characteristic, produced only wrinkled peas, and as long as Mendel continued to plant their descendants, through as many as seven genera-tions, they produced only wrinkled peas.

The story was remarkably different with the round seeds. In appear-ance they were all indistinguishable, but internally some were different from others. When Mendel planted them these differences appeared (see Figure 2–5). Two out of three of the plants produced both round and wrinkled peas, in the ratio of 3 to 1. One out of three plants bore only round peas. Why did seemingly identical peas produce such varied descendants? With this question, Mendel began to solve the age-old riddle of heredity. The true hereditary nature of the round peas was hidden in their genetic apparatus. Some were truly round and produced only round descendants. Others merely looked round, and produced both wrinkled and round descendants. Which was which could be revealed only by planting them to see what kind of seeds they would produce. This test disclosed that two out of three plants that showed the round-seed characteristic were actually hybrids containing both the round and the wrinkled trait; only one in three was a true round. Today, we call the true genetic qualities of a plant or animal its _geno-type,_ and their outward manifestation the _phenotype._ Thus a pea whose phenotype was round-seeded might have either a round or a round-and-wrinkled genotype.

Mendel labeled the dominant characteristic _A_ and the recessive one _a._ When _A_ and _A_ came together it meant two dominants and the possibility of nothing but round peas: these are described as _homozy-gous._ When _a_ and _a_ came together it meant two recessives—and the possibility of nothing but wrinkled peas. It was only when _A_ was com-bined with _a_ to form the _heterozygous_ type _Aa_ that hybrids occurred.

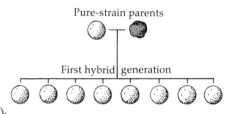

Figure 2–3 This diagram shows the results obtained when Mendel crossed a plant produced by round seeds with one produced by wrinkled seeds. The hybrid seeds show the character of only one parent (round); this character Mendel termed dominant.

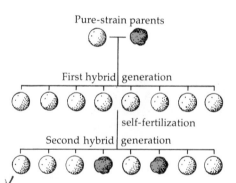

Figure 2–4 The production of a second hybrid generation by self-fertilization of the plants produced by the seeds in Figure 2–3 showed that the first-generation hybrids had carried the characteristics of both their parents, but with the wrinkled character hidden. The new generation of seeds were of both kinds (like the pure-strain parents) but in the proportion of three round ones to one wrinkled.

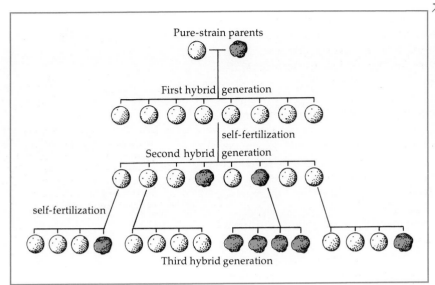

Pure-strain parents

First hybrid generation

self-fertilization

Second hybrid generation

self-fertilization

Third hybrid generation

Figure 2–5 Mendel found the explanation of the 3:1 proportion shown in Figure 2–4 when he allowed the plants produced by the second-generation seeds to self-pollinate. In the third hybrid generation he found new combinations of characteristics. The small proportion of wrinkled seeds had bred true (and would always do so); some of the round peas also bred true, while others repeated the 3:1 ratio.

Mendel had concentrated up to this point on single contrasting characteristics. What would happen, he eventually asked, if two or more diverse characteristics were united? To see, he crossed round yellow peas (peas showing two dominant characteristics) with wrinkled green peas (two recessive). As he anticipated, all the first-generation offspring were round and yellow. But in the next plantings, the round yellows revealed their inner nature—their genotype. As Mendel broke open the dry pods, he found in some of them four different kinds of peas: round yellow, wrinkled yellow, round green, and wrinkled green peas.

Mendel sorted the 556 peas borne by his fifteen double-hybrid plants: 315 were round yellow, 101 wrinkled yellow, 108 round green, and 32 wrinkled green. The ratio was almost exactly 9:3:3:1. Then he went on to the extremely difficult experiment of crossing plants that differed in three characteristics. He crossed round yellow peas having grayish seed coats (*ABC*) with wrinkled green peas having white seed coats (*abc*). It took "time and trouble," Mendel noted, but he obtained all the different varieties his calculations had predicted.

Charles Darwin in his experiments also had obtained the 3-to-1 division in the hybrids. Being no mathematician, he failed to understand the significance of what he was seeing. Mendel grasped it easily. If each trait marked a separate hereditary factor, then he was obtaining every combination that could be formed. Combine *A* and *a* and only one unit could be formed: *Aa*. But if *Aa* and *Aa* came together, three different combinations could be made: *AA, Aa,* and *aa*. Thus from a cross of a pair of hybrids (*Aa* × *Aa*) three kinds of offspring would be produced; from a cross of a pair of double hybrids in which two kinds of character are studied (*AaBb* × *AaBb*), nine kinds (as shown in Figure 2–7); from a triple-hybrid cross, twenty-seven. The combinations would pile up three times three times three, in cubic power. In short order the possible variations could reach an astronomical number.

Experiments Using Many Characteristics

Hybrid parents

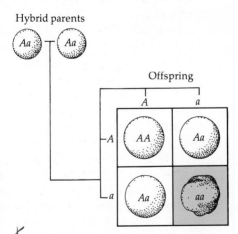

Offspring

Figure 2–6 The experiment described in Figure 2–4 was explained by Mendel in this way. Using the letters *A* and *a* for the characters smooth and wrinkled, he accounted for the 3:1 proportion by proposing that *A* is always dominant to *a* in every hybrid.

Mendel lacked the microscopic techniques to peer into the inner structure of his peas and search out the physical units of heredity that his experiments told him must exist. His results, however, were explainable in no other way. Mendel proceeded to formulate the biological laws that he saw must underlie his findings:

1. Heredity is transmitted by a large number of independent, inheritable units.
2. When each parent contributes the same kind of factor, a constant characteristic is produced in the progeny. If each furnishes a different kind, a hybrid results, and when the hybrid forms its own reproductive cells the two different units "liberate" themselves again.
3. The hereditary units are unaffected by their long association in an individual. They emerge from any union as distinct as when they entered.

Mendel himself at first regarded his findings only as hypotheses that required further testing. If he was correct, though, and each hybrid pea was made up of independent hereditary units, it should be possible to prove the point by a different shuffling of the units. Two experiments would suffice.

If the heterozygous hybrid *AaBb,* a pea round and yellow in appearance, was backcrossed with the homozygous parent plant *AABB,* also round and yellow-seeded, and if Mendel's theory was correct, then only four combinations could be formed—*AABb, AaBB, AaBb,* and *AABB.* Since each combination would contain two dominants, all the peas would be round and yellow in appearance. Their true nature would emerge on later plantings.

Mendel made this test cross-fertilization. When the pods finally matured they contained 98 peas, every one of them round and yellow.

The same experiment in reverse backcrossed the hybrid *AaBb* with the recessive *aabb,* the green wrinkled one. It went with equal precision. Mendel's calculations showed that four combinations should be formed —*AaBb* (round yellow), *Aabb* (round green), *aaBb* (wrinkled yellow), and *aabb* (wrinkled green)—and that all of them should appear in equal numbers. When he harvested his peas he had 31 round yellow, 26 round green, 27 wrinkled yellow, and 26 wrinkled green. As he had predicted, the ratio, allowing for small chance variations, was 1:1:1:1.

"In all the experiments," said Mendel with modest understatement, "there appeared all the forms which the proposed theory demands." All the necessary tests had been made. The results had been predicted, and nature had responded with astonishing exactness. The time had come for Mendel to publish a report on his eight years of work. During the fall and winter of 1864 he wrote the paper that would demonstrate for the first time how individual traits are transmitted from parent to offspring.

On a frosty night in February 1865 Mendel read his paper before the Brünn Society for the Study of Natural Science. The members listened

Laws of Segregation and Independent Assortment

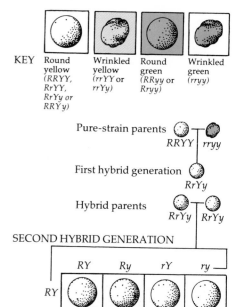

Figure 2–7 **A way of showing Mendel's law of independent assortment is the Punnett square. Here, a pea with two dominant characteristics (roundness and yellowness, *RR* and *YY*) is crossed with a pea having two recessive characteristics (wrinkledness and greenness, *rr* and *yy*). The hybrid that results will combine all four genes of its parents (*RrYy*). If hybrids are then crossed, their genes will produce the combinations shown in the square, which will result in four different-appearing kinds of peas in a ratio of 9:3:3:1.**

in unbroken silence to his discussion of the unvarying ratios in pea hybrids. At the next meeting Mendel went on to explain what the ratios meant. The combination of mathematics and botany was an unheard-of one, and the idea that lay behind it, a vast shuffling of unseeable, unknown units, ran completely contrary to the belief that heredity was a whole or overall matter of "blood." The minutes recorded no questions and no discussion. But Mendel was invited to prepare his paper for publication in the Society's proceedings. The monk's monograph, "Experiments in Plant Hybridization," appeared in 1866. Copies of the Brünn publication were sent as usual to more than 120 other scientific organizations and universities in Europe and America. Once more there was silence. No one praised or disputed Mendel's work, or gave it any attention at all.

Soon after this, Mendel undertook considerable work with hawkweed, a plant that soon proved unsuitable for his work. He also tried beans. Some upsetting results began to appear. Only in certain characteristics did the flowers follow the same laws as the peas. When Mendel crossed a white-flowered, white-seeded bean with a bean having reddish-purple flowers and red seeds flecked with black, all of the first generation bore pale red flowers unlike either parent. In the next hybrid generation Mendel was greeted with a burst of color, from the pure white of one flower through a wide spectrum ending in reddish-purple. He looked upon some colors that had not previously appeared in any of his test plants.

Could he have been wrong? Could an error have been made in his first results, which had shown that the first hybrid generation resembled the dominant parent? As Mendel puzzled over the in-betweenness of the pale red flowers of the first generation and the many colors of the second, it occurred to him that if the trait of color is determined in some species not by a single hereditary unit but by two such units acting together, then all of the nonconforming results could be explained. The two could produce nine variations of color, as shown in Figure 2–8. Only one-ninth of the plants would bear white flowers, and eight-ninths would produce almost exactly the range of color he had observed.

Mendel's eventual explanation for the in-between appearance of many offspring suggested that more than one hereditary unit entered into the production of certain traits. Though Mendel knew nothing of how the hereditary units might be arranged in the cell, he had come upon another of the basic laws of heredity.

The modest monk did not dare to recognize how far he had gone. In his report to the Brünn Society, he said only that anyone studying color in plants "could hardly escape the conviction" that color, too, follows a definite law, but one that finds "expression in the combination of several independent color characters." He stopped with this statement. He did not admit that he had rounded out his formulation of the laws of heredity—that the whole basic pattern, the understanding the world had sought for centuries, was now laid out.

Multiple Independent Characteristics

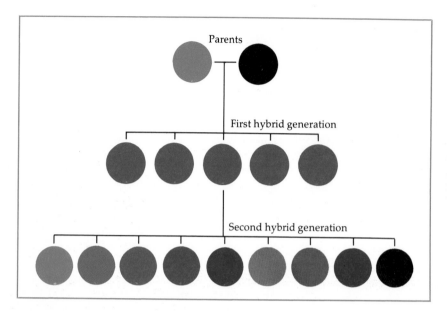

Parents

First hybrid generation

Second hybrid generation

Figure 2–8 The question of flower color in beans proved complex. When red- and white-flowered strains were crossed, the first generation bore flowers of a single intermediate color, whereas the second bore flowers of many intermediate shades. By a brilliant insight, Mendel realized that this could be explained by postulating that two hereditary characters are responsible for flower color in this species. This meant that one in nine of the second-generation plants would bear flowers similar to each parent stock and the remainder would be intermediate.

In 1868 Mendel was elected abbot of the monastery. At first he thought that the new post would afford wider opportunities for his work. But this proved a futile hope. Other duties pressed on him, and soon his experiments with hybridization had to be dropped entirely. Death came to the abbot on January 6, 1884. The townspeople and civil and religious authorities gathered for the funeral of a man held in the highest esteem. But in all the gathering and indeed in the world at large, it was doubtful that anyone realized that a great scientist had gone or that his fame would be everlasting. Mendel's experimental notes and records were burned by the monks.

MENDEL'S WORK REDISCOVERED

Darwin had died two years earlier without finding the answer to the ever-present problem of the evolutionary base—the variations on which natural selection acts. With the passing of the years, the problem became increasingly critical. In the 1880s one of those asking how the variations and modifications of life come about was Hugo De Vries (1848–1935), a botanist at the University of Amsterdam. De Vries (Figure 2–9) accepted Darwin's thesis that descent with modification is the main law of nature in the organic world. But if natural selection has only small, individual variations to act upon, how can wide differences between species be produced?

De Vries knew that breeders could produce only limited changes when they had only small individual differences with which to work. By selecting the redder tulips in their gardens they could breed a more intensely red flower. But for a completely different shade of red they had to wait upon nature to produce what De Vries called a *mutation*, a distinct change from previously existing qualities. Darwin had used the word "sport" for such suddenly appearing new characteristics and had emphasized their importance. Some of his followers, in their all-out insistence on natural selection, tended to dismiss the effect of these sudden changes.

De Vries decided to watch for the occurrence of mutations. He thought that they would most likely be found in some place where a plant was adapting itself to new living conditions. One afternoon in 1886 as he walked through the countryside near Hilversum, Holland, a yellow mass of the evening primrose, *Oenothera lamarckiana*, caught his admiring eye. The tall plants with the golden flowers had recently escaped from a nearby park and were multiplying rapidly in a former potato field. De Vries noticed that they varied widely. There were differences in the shape of the leaves, in the mode of branching, and in the height of the plants.

De Vries found ten specimens of a new type growing by themselves in a corner of the field that had not been invaded by any of the other primroses. Their petals were smaller and more oval than the heart-shaped petals typical of *O. lamarckiana* plants. Were they truly a new species, and would they produce others of their kind? De Vries could not know until he planted their seeds. When he did they produced new plants with small, oval petals like those of the parent plant and quite unlike the petals of *O. lamarckiana*. He felt certain that he had a new species and named it *Oenothera laevifolia*.

During the next decade De Vries raised or observed 53,509 primrose plants. Among them he discovered what he believed to be several new species. The new plants always appeared full-blown: no intermediates between *O. lamarckiana* and the newcomers were found. And once the new plant had appeared it went on repeating itself; it did not revert to its ancestral form.

De Vries also noticed that the new plants did not change in all their aspects, as he and most naturalists would have expected. On the contrary, they changed in only one or a few characteristics. In *O. rubrinervis* the color of the veins turned to red, but there was little other change; the flowers and the general size of the plant were unaffected. Yet it was a different plant.

If plants and other living things changed only at one or a few points, this suggested that the characteristics must be produced by separate hereditary units. If this were so, then each part could vary separately. Though what he was working with were segregated characteristics, not mutations, De Vries struck out boldly—and correctly: "Attributes of organisms consist of distinct, separate and independent units. These units can be associated in groups and we find, in allied species, the same units and groups of units. Transitions, such as we so frequently meet with in the external form both of animals and of plants, are as completely absent between these units as they are between the molecules of the chemist."

This was venturing onto new ground and introducing concepts completely at variance with most of the beliefs that had always been

De Vries' Work on *Oenothera*

Figure 2–9   Hugo De Vries was a Dutch botanist of great distinction. From his observations of the evening primrose, *Oenothera lamarckiana*, De Vries developed a theory of mutation that was to prove very important in the development of genetics. He was also the first to recognize the importance of Mendel's observations—35 years after Mendel announced them.

accepted. De Vries wanted to find whatever support might be available for so radical a theory. He searched the literature to see if any other naturalist had suggested that heredity is not a whole but a compound of separate units. Turning through a work on plant hybridization by a German scientist, W. O. Focke, De Vries came upon a reference to a hybridization experiment by an Austrian monk, Gregor Mendel. "Mendel believed," said Focke, "he had found constant numerical ratios among the types produced by hybridization."

Constant numerical ratios! This implied separate units. De Vries tracked down the reference and thus in the year 1900 discovered the work Mendel had published in 1866. On the basis of his own work, De Vries knew at once the import of what he was reading. Time and progress had at last caught up with Mendel. Until this moment De Vries had thought that he, and not an unknown monk of an earlier generation, had discovered the long-sought secrets of heredity. In a paper read before the German Botanical Society on March 24, 1900, the Dutch botanist gave full credit for one of the most momentous discoveries in scientific history to the man to whom it belonged.

Coincidence again came into play. On April 24, just a month after De Vries made his disclosure, a German scientist, Karl Correns, went before the same society to tell how he too had recently found the work of Mendel. He too had been studying peas and maize and had been encountering the constant ratios from generation to generation. He too had believed the discovery was his own.

By further coincidence a third scientist, Erich Tschermak of Vienna, had made the same discovery at the same time. He had undertaken to repeat Darwin's experiments with peas and had found the constant ratios. On June 24, two months after Correns' report and three months after that of De Vries, Tschermak reported to the same society that he, too, thought he had happened upon something new until he read the work of Mendel.

The remarkable triple discovery undid the neglect of decades. The simultaneous recovery of Mendel's work by a Dutch, a German, and an Austrian scientist and their joint confirmation of his findings caught the attention of the world. Mendel received the scientific acclaim that had never come in his lifetime. The world, for its part, gained its first true understanding of the most immediate and ancient of mysteries— how the distinctiveness and the very form of all living things are passed down from parents to offspring. The theory of evolution at last had its base.

Chapter 3

Genes and Populations

The object is to combine certain ideas derivable from a consideration of . . . a population of organisms, with the concepts of the factorial scheme of inheritance, so as to state the principle of Natural Selection in the form of a rigorous mathematical theorem.

R. A. FISHER, 1890–1962.
THE GENETICAL THEORY OF NATURAL SELECTION.

It began to seem to Hugo De Vries, once he had rediscovered Mendel's work and made his own observations of *Oenothera,* that evolution could never get anywhere by natural selection alone. To him the sudden structural novelties that he called mutations (and whose products he was overeager to label as new species) were the chief force in evolution. Natural selection, he argued, is not a force of nature but only a sieve deciding which organism is to live and which is to die. It has nothing to do with the single steps of evolution; only after a step has been taken does the sieve act. It was clear to De Vries that novel characteristics—*mutants*—have to be put in the sieve before it can make a selection.

The Darwinians battled back: natural, gradual selection is everything, they said, and large, sudden mutations in species are meaningless in evolution's long run. De Vries retorted that "the general belief in slow changes has held back science during half a century." The battle became fierce.

The mutationists for a time thought they had found their incontrovertible proof in the phenomenon of *mimicry* (see Figure 3–1). In the Orient, for example, there lives a handsomely marked butterfly, *Danaida tytia.* Its grayish upper wings are patterned in a strong tracery of black

The Case of Mimicry

41

Figure 3–1 Mimicry occurs quite widely among animals (and even some plants). In this example, the Danaid butterfly *Danais plexippus* (left) is mimicked by the Nymphalid butterfly *Limenitis archippus*. Both butterflies have an orange ground and black and white markings. Experiments have demonstrated the function and effectiveness of this mimicry.

and its lower wings are etched in brown. In some of *Danaida*'s territory, the butterfly *Papilio agestor* also lives. Its wings bear the same coloring and markings as *Danaida*'s and are even very nearly the same shape, though they are slightly wider: in every important way *Papilio* is an excellent mimic of *Danaida*. The latter has another mimic in southwest China. Here *Neptis imitans* is just as close a replica, with the same striking colors and designs. Even a careful observer—or a careless bird—may mistake the mimics for *Danaida*. And this is the point of the mimicry. For all its delicate appearance *Danaida* is a tough, rubbery insect. Naturalists have seen it flutter away unharmed after being seized and distastefully dropped by a bird. So the birds avoid *Danaida*. On the other hand, *Papilio* and *Neptis* are tender morsels. They have found safety in mimicry of unpalatable *Danaida:* the more they resemble it, the better their chance of escaping being eaten.

Studying such wonderful resemblances, the mutationists decided that they could have arisen only by mutation. How else could an elaborate design on the wing of a butterfly come into being? Mimicry, they said, is the outstanding proof of mutation, or the "discontinuous" origin of species.

Mathematical Evidence

The dispute was a standoff until such men as Sir Ronald Aylmer Fisher, J. B. S. Haldane, and the American geneticist Sewall Wright entered the fray with a new weapon, mathematics. Such things as hereditary units, change, degrees of difference, and alterations in natural populations are subject to mathematical analysis and test. Fisher, a statistician, mathematician, and later professor of genetics at Cambridge, brought mathematical analysis to bear on the mutationists' pet phenomenon of mimicry. His calculations showed that only natural selection could bring about such intricate adaptations as the matching of mimic to model. The double occurrence of such insect patterns and shapes by the randomness of mutations is so unlikely as to be mathematically impossible.

Nor could mutation explain the proximity of model and mimic, which are always found in the same regions and in the same season. Often *Danaida* and its imitators are captured flying together. If their similarities had arisen by mutation, why should not the same patterns have occurred in other butterflies in other places? Fisher also pointed out that the mimic resembles the copied species no more than is necessary. Beneath the obvious, eye-deceiving colorings, shapes, and movements, model and mimic are as unlike as any two species.

After additional proofs confirmed Fisher's findings, natural selection was unequivocally assigned the role of evolution's prime agent. Mutation was given a supplementary role. If mutation alone could no longer be credited for the amazing adaptations of the natural world and hence for evolution, research showed that it at least supplies raw material for these changes. For without the new opportunities produced by mutations, evolution would surely stagnate, its products unable to adapt to such constant changes in physical environment as ice ages, long droughts, and the slow elevations and subsidences of the earth's crust, or such changes in the living environment as the appearance of a swifter predator, a deadlier germ, or a new competitor.

"The function of mutation," wrote Fisher, "is to maintain the stock of genetic variance at a high level." If this analysis was right, some seeming contradictions had to be resolved. Work in many laboratories was showing that most mutations are detrimental and most drastic ones usually lethal. They are steps in the wrong direction, in the sense that any change in a smooth-running, well-adjusted organism is likely to be for the worse. Most bearers of radical mutations never survive long enough to pass the changes along to offspring. This being so, how can mutations build up a "stock" for variation?

The fact is that whereas a big change in an organism is often fatal, a tiny change or adjustment may be an improvement. Thus a few mutations, generally small ones, may prove beneficial to a species. The next question for the geneticists was: how can a rare, tiny, beneficial change —say a minute change in the color or pattern of a butterfly's wing— spread through a large species? Will it not be swamped in the ordinary mating of two individuals and, later, of their descendants? Not at all, said the mathematicians. Let us assume a mutation that would offer an advantage of only one percentage point to the organism in which it arose. An advantage that small would mean the survival of 100 mutants as against 99 unmutated individuals. In a short time (as evolution goes), the mutant would replace the original as the population's normal type. Although harmful or at best useless mutations may crop up, vanish, and reappear in a species with predictable frequency, the ones that ultimately pervade a species and become part of its normal makeup are mostly beneficial.

To Fisher, the great contrast between abundant species and rare ones lay in the fact that an abundance of individuals means an abundance of possible mutations—hence, more possibilities for adapting to new conditions. With fewer possible mutants to help it cope with changes in the environment, a small species might face a dwindling future. But a numerous species such as man is likely to have a varied enough genetic pool to meet almost any change that might confront it.

The Role of Mutations

If a species had only 100 characteristics that could exist in two forms, Fisher computed, more than 1,000,000,000,000,000,000,000,000,000,000 genetic combinations would be possible when two of its members produced offspring. Mendel's conclusion that the number of combinations would increase in mathematical ratio was amply borne out. Evolution, both Fisher and Haldane realized, could head off in many directions and along tangents no one could conceive.

"It has not so often been realized," Fisher commented, "how far most species must be from a state of stagnation, or how easily, with no more than one hundred factors, a species may be modified to a condition considerably outside the range of its previous variation." In *Genetical Theory of Natural Selection*, Fisher proved that this richness of genetic variability is directly related to fitness for survival. What counts is not the plant struggling against the drought or the rabbit eluding the fox, but the nature and the preservation of the genetic material that makes it possible for the plant species or the rabbit species to win out. Organic evolution Fisher saw as the evolution of the mysterious, almost infinitely variable hereditary units whose existence Mendel had inferred.

Mendel had no way to inquire into what such units might be or where they might be located within the living cell. But in the years when his monographs were sitting unread and unknown on library shelves, scientists discovered a number of tiny, threadlike structures that exist in the nucleus of each living cell. When stained, these structures could be seen under a microscope and so were called *chromosomes* (colored bodies). Close observation revealed that they go through remarkable maneuvers (see Figure 3–2). When a cell is about to divide, they split in two and move to opposite ends of the cell. A cell wall grows between them, and in an hour, more or less, there are two cells where there had been only one. Each new cell is equipped with a full, identical set of these chromosome threads (see Figure 3–3). But when a new egg or sperm cell is to be formed, the maneuvers differ. Only half of each set of chromosome pairs goes into the next sex cell, as shown in Figure 3–4. Thus when a new individual is created by the fertilization of egg by sperm, the full chromosome complement is reestablished, half of it coming from each parent.

It was in 1902, two years after the rediscovery of Mendel's work, that the suggestion was made that chromosomes might be the containers of Mendel's hereditary units. In their coming together and pulling apart, they supplied just the kind of mechanism needed to produce Mendel's results.

A few years later William Bateson and R. C. Punnett, experimenting with sweet peas, crossed a purple-flowered plant having a long pollen grain with a red-flowered, round-grained plant. Instead of obtaining the free assortment of characteristics that Mendel found in garden peas, these English researchers found that the red flower and the round

THE UNITS OF HEREDITY

The Chromosomes

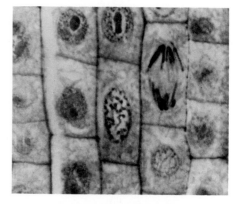

Figure 3–2 A thin section of the growing root tip of an onion shows cell division occurring in many places. The phenomenon is accompanied by remarkable changes in the nucleus, (the dark circular zone in each rectangular cell), in which the chromosomes appear as threadlike structures that divide and are pulled apart as though by magnets. This is the process called mitosis, common to plants and animals, which ensures the distribution of the entire genetic material to every cell.

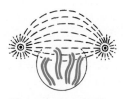

1. Chromosomes become prominent in the nucleus.

2. Chromosomes thicken; spindle grows.

3. Chromosomes divide.

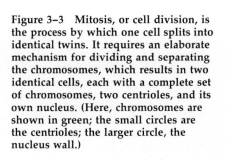

Figure 3–3   Mitosis, or cell division, is the process by which one cell splits into identical twins. It requires an elaborate mechanism for dividing and separating the chromosomes, which results in two identical cells, each with a complete set of chromosomes, two centrioles, and its own nucleus. (Here, chromosomes are shown in green; the small circles are the centrioles; the larger circle, the nucleus wall.)

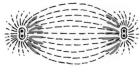

4. Chromosomes align in pairs and attach to the spindle.

5. One of each pair of chromosomes migrates to opposite end of the cell.

6. Spindle disappears; nucleus reappears.

Figure 3–4   Meiosis, or reduction division, consists of two rapid cell divisions which bring about a halving of the number of chromosomes in the formation of the sex cells (eggs and sperm). The process is shown here for four chromosomes.

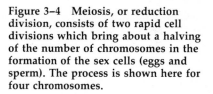

1. The chromosomes appear as double-stranded threads and thicken as in the early stages of mitosis, but then they pair up. Here the pairs are lying alongside each other.

2. Where chromosomes happen to cross, an exchange of genetic material occurs, so that the final products of the process have a gene complement different from the parent chromosomes.

3. The pairs are now separated on a spindle, each double-stranded chromosome of a pair moving apart, and the nucleus divides as in mitosis.

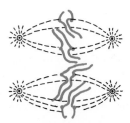

4. A new nuclear wall is formed, but the chromosomes remain distinct. Each nucleus now contains half the number of double-stranded chromosomes as were present in the original cell. A further division immediately follows.

5. Spindle formation again proceeds normally, and the split chromosomes are separated as in mitosis.

6. The final product is four nuclei, but each cell nucleus contains only half the number of chromosomes of the original cell. These are the sex cells. The full number of chromosomes is reconstituted by fertilization.

pollen grain tended to stay in constant association. Other investigators came upon the same phenomenon. Certain traits seemed to be coupled; perhaps they were controlled by the same chromosome.

Thomas Hunt Morgan was one of those finding the same kind of associated linkages. They kept cropping up in the fruit flies with which he was working. In 1910, about a year after he began studying *Drosophila melanogaster,* the little flies that orbit ripe fruit, a fly with white eyes appeared in one of the milk bottles he used for incubators. Since the wild flies have red eyes, he felt certain that this was a mutation. He bred the white-eyed male to a red-eyed female and in a short time had hundreds of red-eyed offspring, just as the Mendelian laws would lead him to expect. To bring out their underlying heredity, Morgan then bred red-eyed hybrids to red-eyed hybrids. The matings produced 50 percent red-eyed females, 25 percent red-eyed males, and 25 percent white-eyed males—but not one white-eyed female. By all indications the hereditary unit for white eyes, the mutated unit, was linked on the same chromosome with the factor that determined sex (assuming, of course, that the chromosomes were in fact the bearers of heredity). White eyes was a *sex-linked* characteristic.

It was obvious to Morgan "that there was one essential requirement for the chromosome view, namely that all factors carried by the same chromosome should tend to remain together." The fruit fly has four pairs of chromosomes. If Morgan was right, it should be possible to map the hereditary factors carried by each, and he set out to do it. It took nearly seventeen years and the breeding of millions of flies, but in the end he found that very precise locations on the chromosomes control specific characteristics in a fly. Ultimately, actual chromosome maps were made, long vertical lines on which were marked the sites of "yellow body, white eyes, echinus eyes, cross veinless, cut wing, vermilion eyes, miniature wing, sable body, garnet eyes, forked bristles, bar eyes, clipped wing and bobbed bristles." These were the descriptive names for the physical characteristics of the different flies, characteristics whose determinant factors had been narrowed down to specific locations on their chromosomes. These determining units were given the name *genes*, a name proposed by Johannsen in 1909. In one chromosome in particular were the factors determining sex differences. In many animals the sex chromosomes are strikingly different in the two sexes and easily recognizable among the chromosomes of a cell (see Figure 3–5).

Often, however, a whole group of genetic units was found to be involved in producing a single characteristic, such as the color of a stem or the weight of a fowl. In one experiment a race of fowls weighing an average of 1,300 grams was bred to a race of bantams whose weight averaged 750 grams. The offspring tended to split the difference in weight, but when hybrid was bred to hybrid there was a "wild outburst" of variation, ranging from monstrous birds of 1,700 grams down

Morgan's Work on *Drosophila*

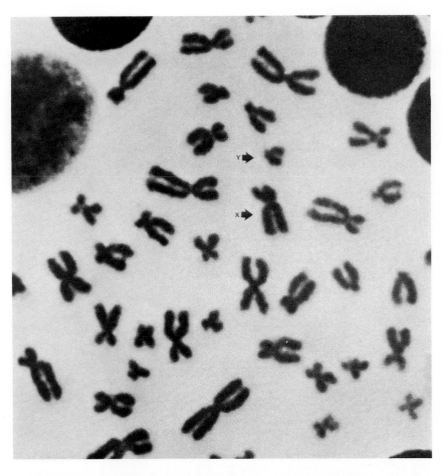

Figure 3–5 Humans have 46 chromosomes as 23 matching pairs. The sex chromosomes (labeled X and Y) are indicated in this photograph of male human chromosomes. Only males have the small Y chromosome, so in this sex the twenty-third pair cannot be matched. Females have two similar X chromosomes.

to some tinier than the bantam grandparents. J. B. S. Haldane estimated that if ten genes affected weight, they could combine in enough ways to produce 59,049 different weights. In effect, the variation would be continuous.

In all these painstaking research projects, two most important things were established. One was that inheritance is, as Mendel had already claimed, *particulate*—it operates through the transmission of definite bits of self-producing matter. The other was that it is *cooperative*—the hereditary particles, or genes, being organized in a single functional system (the gene complex), combine or interact to produce their effects. With these realizations, not only did genetics find a firm scientific base, but the relations between genetics and evolution were put on a new and satisfactory footing.

But what *was* a gene, and what happened when a gene mutated? Many scientists worked on the problem. In efforts to force changes in the submicroscopic units deep in the nucleus of the cell, they tried heat, cold, drugs, poison, and mutilation. But genes were too tough and

Muller's Work with X Rays

stable to be altered by such tampering. Then H. J. Muller, who had begun his scientific work with Morgan, got to wondering if mutation might be brought about by ultramicroscopic forces. He put hundreds of fruit flies in gelatin capsules and bombarded them with X rays. The irradiated flies were then bred to untreated ones. In ten days thousands of their offspring were buzzing around their banana-mash feed, and Muller was looking at an unprecedented outburst of man-made mutations. There were flies with bulging eyes, flat eyes, purple, yellow, and brown eyes. Some had curly bristles, some no bristles. There were flies with broad wings or down-turned wings or almost no wings at all. "They were a motley throng," said Muller. "The results of these experiments were startling and unequivocal. The roots of life—the genes —had indeed been struck and they had yielded." (And Muller's work with them won him a Nobel Prize.)

The genes had yielded some secrets of their mechanics, but their chemistry remained inscrutable. Through most of the years while Mendel and Morgan were tracing the effects of heredity's units, and while Haldane, Fisher, and Wright were establishing the sum of the continuous changing and recombining of these units as the genetic basis for evolution, bottles of a white powder were sitting on the shelves of some laboratories. The bottles were labeled *nucleic acid.* A Swiss chemist named Friedrich Miescher had discovered this substance in 1869 while breaking down some cells. The cells disintegrated, but part of their nuclei remained intact. When analyzed, this remainder was found to differ chemically from all other known cellular material.

In time other scientists found that the acid has a threadlike structure and that its molecules are huge. They also learned that it occurs only in chromosomes. When its chemical composition was worked out, the powder was renamed *deoxyribonucleic acid,* or DNA for short. Later a second nucleic acid was found, differing only slightly from DNA. It was called RNA, for *ribonucleic acid.* There the matter rested; the bottles continued to sit on laboratory shelves.

By the 1940s it was clear that the answer to the form and functioning of life had to be sought in the materials out of which chromosomes were made. These were essentially two, DNA and protein. A brilliant series of experiments at the Biological Laboratory, Cold Spring Harbor, New York, showed that when a virus, acting much like a physician's syringe, shot its DNA contents into a bacterial cell, the virus DNA took command. In twenty-four minutes it produced complete copies of itself. The virus's protein shell, comparable to the casing of the syringe, was left on the outside of the cell wall. All that entered the cell was the DNA, and it produced not only new virus DNA but new protein overcoats for the new viruses as well. All the directives for building more DNA and more protein were enclosed in the DNA or in its near-copy, the RNA. This, then, was the long-sought raw material of heredity, the basic stuff of life and evolution.

The Raw Material of Heredity: DNA

Here was a bit of matter too small to be detected in the cell except under the tremendous enlarging power of the electron microscope, yet so omniscient that it could contain all the instructions needed for building a new virus, a beetle, or a human being. All DNA is made of the same materials: *nucleotides* composed of four bases called adenine, thymine, cytosine, and guanine (and known as A, T, C, and G), plus some sugar molecules and a kinked phosphate molecule joining the sugar pieces. Therefore the secret of its marvels of creative diversity had to be sought not in its composition but in its structure; something in the way DNA was built had to account for the billions of forms it could command.

In the 1950s at the Cavendish Laboratory at Cambridge, F. H. C. Crick and James D. Watson, a young American working with him, fashioned a wire model that portrayed DNA as a helix or spiral, looking like a spiral staircase (see Figure 3–6). The sugars and the phosphate

Structure of DNA

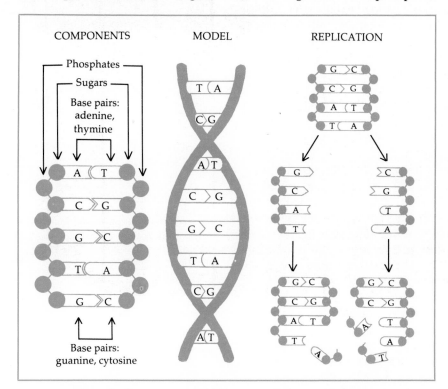

Figure 3–6 The DNA molecule is a double spiral linked by four interlocking chemical subunits—the base pairs. Replication and protein synthesis take place by the splitting of the double helix: each separate strand will then synthesize its mirror image from the unit molecules floating in solution, as shown here for replication.

made up the framework, and around them were strung the four nucleotide bases, adenine always paired with thymine, cytosine with guanine, like two kinds of repeated steps. The 46 human chromosomes, H. J. Muller estimated, contain some four billion of these bases, or steps. The order of the bases is different for each living thing. It is the endless variety of their order that explains the limitless variety of the living world. The long coils of DNA have a property uniquely their own—

their capacity for reproducing, or *replicating*, themselves. At the right time for self-replication, the helix divides down the middle. From free nucleotide units in the cell nucleus, each base picks up another unit complementary to itself, and a new coil is formed. Life now was seen to hang by a thread: it appeared to depend on self-replicating and self-varying (mutating) strings of DNA, and these self-replicating and self-varying properties coupled with a high reproductive capacity inevitably led to natural selection.

How fine these DNA variations might be, and how far-reaching their effects, became apparent as research progressed. In humans afflicted with the disease called sickle-cell anemia, the red blood cells (shown in Figure 3–7) are twisted into a sickle shape in the venous blood of a patient (where the cells are low in oxygen), but they resume their normal round form when the blood passes through the lungs and enters the arteries, replenished with oxygen. A few sickle cells make little difference, but a person who inherits a high percentage gets a serious, sometimes fatal, anemia. Nobel Prize winner Linus Pauling knew that the only parts of the red cell that are concerned in the regular taking on and giving up of oxygen are the 100 million hemoglobin molecules of each cell. "The idea burst upon me," he said, "that the molecules of hemoglobin in the red cells might be responsible for the disease—that the disease might be a molecular one involving an abnormal sort of hemoglobin manufactured by the patient because of the possession of abnormal genes in place of the normal genes that control the manufacture of normal hemoglobin."

Pauling's insight proved correct. Vernon M. Ingram decided to trace the sickle-cell disease back to its DNA source. He had to find what part of hemoglobin, a huge molecule with 8,000 atoms, was altered in a sickle-cell patient. Ingram reported, "The sole chemical difference is that in the abnormal molecule a valine is substituted for glutamic acid at one point. A change of one amino acid in nearly 300 is certainly a very small change indeed, and yet this slight change can be fatal to the unfortunate possessor of the errant hemoglobin."

All of life, it eventually became apparent, not only is built from the same basic DNA units but also is assembled by one kind of code. In 1961, Dr. Fritz Lipmann, another Nobel Prize winner, replaced RNA in rabbit hemoglobin with RNA from a foreign body—a bacterium found in human intestines—without destroying the normal function of protein formation in the rabbit hemoglobin. It hardly would be more amazing for a cat to give birth to a fish, or a plant to puppies. And yet it was not so strange. The common denominator already had been found, in the basic units that Mendel had hypothesized and their basic plan of assembly. The code, by all indications, was universal. No more striking proof of the unity of all living forms had been adduced since Darwin provided the living world with one immemorial pedigree. The universality of the self-replicating, self-varying genetic material, DNA, testifies conclusively to the oneness of life and its evolution.

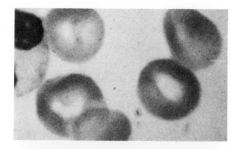

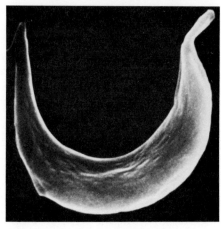

Figure 3–7   The sickle-cell trait is due to an abnormal hemoglobin (S), which differs from the normal hemoglobin (A) in only one amino acid out of the nearly 300 that constitute the protein. The red blood corpuscles in the top photograph appear normal; the bottom photograph shows the distortion that gives sickle-cell anemia its name.

The Universal Code of Inheritance

In this short history of the science of genetics, we have dealt mainly with the individual structures that bring about the accurate replication of, and occasional variation in, the genotype, the genetic material of individual organisms. In looking at the process of evolution, we must look beyond the individual to the population and the species. Individuals are born, reproduce, and die, yet the population will continue, changing and adapting to its environment.

Fisher envisaged a *gene pool* of all the individuals in a species, a pooling of the total genetic material and variability available to a species in adapting to its environment. The concept of the gene pool is an important one: the continuity we see in an evolving species is in truth the continuity and survival of the gene pool. The individuals of the species, and in particular their bodies, or phenotypes, are little more than the temporary homes of the genes they carry. The phenotype can be seen as the genotype's means of survival in a range of different alien environments.

POPULATIONS AND THE SPECIES

Genotype and the Gene Pool

Figure 3–8 A simplified visual description of the process of speciation in an imaginary frog population. In the last stage shown, two separate and independent gene pools now exist, constituting two species where one existed before.

1. The original frogs in this area interbreed with each other and constitute a single species.

2. Changes in the topography and drainage conditions of the region eventually create two distinct regions—swamp and forest—with a barrier between the two that the frogs cannot cross.

3. Over a long period of time, the frogs in the swamp and those in the forest adapt to their very different environments. As they adapt and remain isolated from each other, frogs in the two areas become very different.

4. Such differences have now been selected in the two new populations that the frogs do not interbreed even if they meet; they do not recognize foreigners as potential mates.

As the individuals in a population reproduce sexually, the genetic material is sorted, shuffled, and recombined, and so the variation among the offspring is increased. This increase in the potential for variation is the primary function of sexual reproduction. The variation available to the processes of natural selection among species that reproduce asexually is, of course, much more limited in its evolutionary possibilities.

Sexual reproduction has another advantage. If two populations that have been isolated for some time come into contact, they can hybridize. Genes can pass between them, and their differing characteristics can be combined in future generations. In time, advantageous qualities selected in one population only can pass to the other and so become available to both populations. This phenomenon is called *gene flow:* it allows the maintenance of genetic continuity between neighboring populations.

In contrast, interruption of gene flow by geographical barriers may result in *speciation,* the creation of two species where one existed before (see Figure 3–8). In this case, the variations accumulated over time in the different populations under the differing pressures of their two environments cause a genetic and phenotypic divergence between the populations. In the absence of gene flow, isolation will eventually allow large enough differences to develop between the two populations that they form distinct species. Should their ranges overlap in the future, no further interbreeding will occur. This leads us to the definition of a species as *a group of interbreeding natural populations that are reproductively isolated from other such groups.*

What is the actual effect of natural selection on a population? It is to alter the frequency with which different genes occur in the population, so that beneficial adaptive genes increase and disadvantageous genes decrease (see Figure 3–9). In practice, then, evolution is the alteration of *gene frequencies*—the alteration in the percentages in which different genes occur in a species, as a result of natural selection.

It is also important to recognize that to bring about evolutionary change, natural selection does not have to destroy less well adapted individuals *before* they achieve reproductive age. Natural selection need only bring about a *differential* reproductive rate in the population so that better-adapted individuals contribute more to the next generation than do the less well adapted. A small difference in genetic contribution across generations will bring about the adjustment in gene frequencies that constitutes the process of evolution.

If a very small population becomes isolated from its parent species, various special factors may operate. In the first place, it is possible that this small *founder population,* as it is called, is not a typical sample of its parent species so that its successors will, from the very start, carry different gene frequencies from the mother species. These differences, which will to some extent be perpetuated, are described as being due to the *founder effect.*

Gene Flow, Speciation, and Genetic Drift

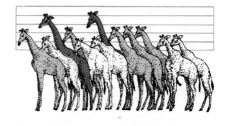

Figure 3–9 Evolution is the change in the average expression of any characteristic in a species. A simple case is the lengthening of the necks of ancestral giraffes. Because long-necked giraffes have more reliable and extensive food resources than have short-necked ones, they are more successful and have more offspring over time. As a result, the average neck length slowly increases. Eventually all individuals are relatively long-necked.

Another phenomenon, called *random genetic drift,* has been both predicted and observed in very small populations. When small populations are subject to low competition and low selection pressure, genetic drift may be expected, through random mutation over time, to lead to loss or gain of new characteristics, without regard to natural selection. However, if the population size and selection pressure increase, as they inevitably will (unless extinction intervenes), such random mutations will be eliminated in due course if they are not of positive value to the species, though some neutral qualities may remain.

It seems probable that the founder effect has been of some importance in human evolution, especially where small populations have colonized islands and multiplied in isolation. The random effects of genetic drift have probably played a much smaller part in determining the human genotype.

Sexual Selection

In discussing the action of selection and the transmission of characteristics in a population, we have made the unwritten assumption that mating occurs at random between members of the opposite sex of a population or species. Rarely is this so in practice, and one of a number of mating patterns can often be recognized. When choice enters into mating, and when mates are selected on the basis of appearance, as in many birds and mammals, we have an example of *sexual selection.* Another kind of sexual selection occurs when one male—usually, the most powerful, most impressive, or, in the case of birds, the most gaudily colored—establishes his superiority over other males and impregnates more than his share of females. He thus ensures that he contributes more genes than most of his contemporaries to the future generations of the population. In these cases natural selection operates quite specifically and intensively on certain characteristics of one sex, and in this way it brings about rapid genetic changes in a species.

Another nonrandom mating system found in animals and humans is *inbreeding* and *outbreeding.* Inbreeding occurs in small populations of animals or humans in which mating pairs share a recent common ancestor. It results in homozygous pairing of recessive genes, so that they are expressed in the phenotype. Recessive genes are often harmful, and in due course they will be eliminated by natural selection. Until then, they may be manifested by increased disease and higher mortality rates, both of which have been predicted and observed in inbred animal populations. Outbreeding is characteristic of human groups with extensive incest regulations, such as those who insist on marriage with members of other clans for political and economic reasons. This has the opposite genetic effect: variation will increase, lethal recessives will remain unexpressed and possibly accumulate, yet the population will show improved health and lower mortality.

Polymorphism and Genetic Load

All populations of plants and animals appear to carry harmful unexpressed recessive genes. These as a whole are termed the *genetic load.* The genes constituting the genetic load are expressed only in the relatively rare homozygous condition, when they may bring about a fatal genetic disease. An example of such a phenomenon is the sickle cell. The sickle-cell disease can take the form of a sometimes fatal anemia, the carriers of which die in infancy, and it is common in certain regions of West and Central Africa (see Figure 3–10). We have seen that the anemic condition is due to a rare hemoglobin, known as hemoglobin S.

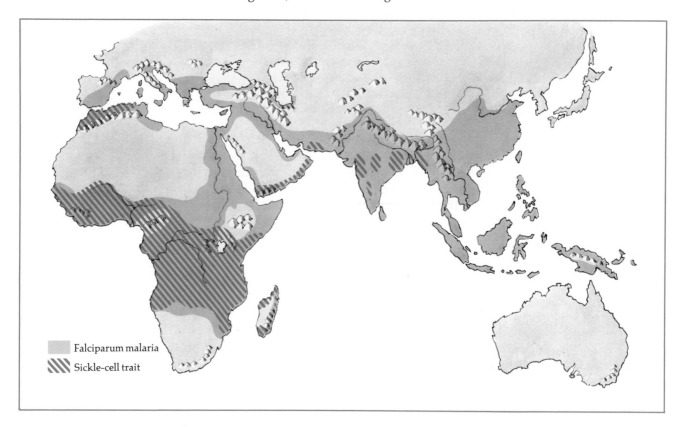

Falciparum malaria

Sickle-cell trait

The gene for this hemoglobin may be present alongside or in place of the normal gene for hemoglobin A. In many Central African populations, from 20 to 40 percent of individuals are AS heterozygotes, and 1 to 2 percent are SS homozygotes who usually die soon after birth. In the face of natural selection we have to ask why such a high frequency of the S gene is maintained. In 1954, A. C. Allison, a British doctor, showed that the sickle-cell trait in its heterozygote condition (AS) affords protection against malarial infection and that the distribution of the S gene coincides with the distribution of the *Anopheles* mosquito, which carries malaria. The S gene was being maintained by natural selection according to the balanced advantages that it offered: protection from disease for the AS carrier, death for the SS. This is an example of *balanced polymorphism*.

Today in the United States we live in an environment free of malaria, yet approximately 10 percent of the people of African origin still carry

Figure 3–10 The coincidence of the sickle-cell trait and malaria in certain parts of the Old World led to an understanding of the function of the abnormal hemoglobin S in these areas. Though disadvantageous elsewhere, in malarial areas the expression of the sickling gene gave considerable protection against the dangerous malarial parasite. The two hemoglobin forms are in balance according to the advantages and disadvantages they offer. Therefore, this instance of the phenomenon of polymorphism (the appearance of two alternative characters) is termed balanced polymorphism.

the S gene. It has become a liability and in the rare homozygous state is still a serious and often lethal condition. Clearly, what is a lifesaving adaptation in one environment is part of mankind's genetic load in another. Genes are not either "good" or "bad" but depend for their survival value on the nature of the environment in which they are expressed. We can also see how natural selection acting on genetic variability will often bring about a compromise between advantages and disadvantages, so that lethal phenotypes may be maintained in a population in balance with advantageous phenotypes. Thus it is possible that the genetic load in man as in other species represents the potential for variability, which will in the future be necessary for survival, as it may have been in the past. Natural selection operates on phenotypes—that is, on the expression of a proportion of the genotype only. Hidden genetic variability is to some extent our insurance against environmental change.

These genetic phenomena form the underlying groundwork of the evolutionary process. They are the source and the nature of the variation on which natural selection operates, and they supply the material from which novelties are selected and incorporated into the succession of diverse species.

Chapter 4

Pioneers of Prehistory

I would not be ashamed to have a monkey for my ancestor, but I would be ashamed to be connected with a man who used great gifts to obscure the truth.

THOMAS HENRY HUXLEY, 1825–1895.
DEFENDING DARWIN'S THEORY AGAINST THE ATTACK
OF BISHOP SAMUEL WILBERFORCE.

Where did man come from? Today, attempts to answer this question are regarded as an important and fascinating branch of science, one that can help us to understand a great deal about ourselves. But this acceptance of *anthropology,* the study of mankind, is recent. Not more than a hundred years ago scientific evidence of human evolution went not only unheralded and unnoticed but purposefully ignored. A few individuals discovered hints of proof that mankind has had a curious history, one that needed to be examined and explained. But it was too difficult for most people to accept any explanations that contradicted those set forth by long-established religious beliefs.

THEORIES OF HUMAN ORIGINS

The question of our origins has preoccupied human thought for thousands, conceivably for tens of thousands, of years. It is responsible for a large number of myths associated with the world's religions, each grounded in efforts to explain the creation of the earth and of mankind. Many of these explanations are exceedingly interesting and beautiful, but today much of their detail is no longer regarded as strictly factual. Instead, they are interpreted as reflections of man's past yearning to fathom mysteries he could not possibly understand, his fear of the unknown, and his often poetic attempts to construct a kind of theological prehistory to satisfy his curiosity and his need for meaning.

The story of creation as told in the Bible (Genesis 1) is a good case in point. It is seldom taken literally now. Its sweeping concepts are interpreted by most modern Christians and Jews as being symbolic of the spirit and majesty of God. Today the evidence seems unavoidable that the world was not created in six days, even though the Bible says it was, and this discrepancy no longer troubles most devout people. Still, old ideas die hard; there are men and women in the United States today who believe that the earth is flat.

Three hundred years ago most self-respecting citizens took their Bible literally. Hell was a fiery place beneath their feet; heaven was above them. Even the age of the earth was known for a fact. In 1650, Archbishop James Ussher of Armagh, Ireland, drawing on careful calculations from Biblical references, determined that the year of creation was 4004 B.C. Subsequently this date was inserted in the margins of authorized versions of the Bible, and before long it came to acquire the infallibility of Scripture itself. At about the same time, another cleric working independently of Ussher came up with the exact day and time: the morning of creation was now known to have been at 9 A.M. on October 23.

The Bible also dictated explanations for odd discoveries from within the earth. Along with the shells, petrified wood, and other ancient objects that people had been digging from the earth over the years were some curious things strangely resembling the bones of animals. Though a few authorities held that these objects had been molded into familiar forms by Satan to deceive mankind, the general notion was that fossils had been formed by natural forces in chance imitation of life. They were "stone cast in animal molds."

Figure 4–1 "And the Lord God caused a deep sleep to fall upon Adam, and he slept: and he took one of his ribs, and closed up the flesh instead thereof; and the rib, which the Lord God had taken from man, made he a woman, and brought her unto the man" (Genesis 2:21–22). A woodcut from Schedel's *World Chronicle* of 1492.

EARLY NATURALISTS

John Ray

The Reverend John Ray (1627–1705), a Cambridge University lecturer and a great naturalist, recognized that some of the fossilized shells he collected in the mountains were exactly like other shells he gathered on the seashore. Other landlocked fossils were obviously the remains of fish that must have lived only in the ocean deeps. To account for the presence of marine fossils in the mountains, Ray resorted to ingenious interpretations of Old Testament earth history. He concluded after much study that the fossils were washed up to their places of deposit when the Bible's forty days and forty nights of unceasing deluge filled the reservoirs of the world and caused the "Fountains of the Great Deep" to break forth. In the tremendous surge that overflowed the globe, he reasoned, the fish and other creatures of the sea were simply swept up rivers and carried through underground streams, right into the high mountains.

In these early days of prehistoric studies, there was not yet a body of tested scientific knowledge, and outside of a rare genius like Ray, Galileo, or Newton, there were few active scientists. The men who were interested in exploring for and collecting such things as stones and bones were usually antiquarians motivated by their own curiosity. In the seventeenth century a Frenchman named Isaac de la Peyrère made a study of a large collection of oddly chipped stones gathered in the French countryside. He then had the courage to publish a book suggesting that these stones had been shaped by primitive men who lived before the time of Adam. His book was burned publicly in 1655.

But odd-shaped stones continued to turn up. So did even odder-shaped bones. Gradually a few skeptical people began to realize that the earth had been inhabited at one time by a great number of creatures that no longer existed—huge mammoths, woolly rhinoceros, saber-toothed tigers. More digging produced more puzzles. In 1771, human bones were found in association with the remains of extinct cave bears in a site in Germany; these articles suggested not only ancient animals but ancient people, too. Their finder, Johann Friedrich Esper, was flabbergasted. "Did they belong to a Druid or to an Antediluvian or to a Mortal Man of more recent times?" he wrote. He would not face the logical answer and concluded that the fragments must have come together by chance.

Others guessed right but could not get a hearing. In 1790 John Frere found unfamiliar stone tools in the same beds with the remains of extinct animals at Hoxne, England. He recognized that they must have been made in "a very remote period indeed; even beyond that of the present world." Working in Belgian caves in 1830, P. C. Schmerling found many stone artifacts associated with the bones of long-since-vanished rhinoceros and mammoths, and in addition uncovered two human skulls. He, too, recognized their contemporaneity. These astonishing finds went generally unnoticed.

It was difficult even to get anyone to pay serious attention to the idea that stone tools were tools at all. The first person to attempt to prove in a systematic way that ancient worked stones were human artifacts was a French customs official named Jacques Boucher de Perthes (1788–1868). Interested in archaeology, he began poking about in gravel banks near Abbeville in northern France and was perplexed by the number of flint objects that not only did not "belong" in the pits because they were made of a different kind of stone, but also bore unmistakable signs of human workmanship. Many of them were carefully chipped around the edge and looked enough like axes to set even a less observant person than Boucher de Perthes to thinking. He began collecting and organizing his finds, and some years later he had what he considered an overwhelmingly strong case for the existence of human beings far older than any previously known. In 1838 and 1839, his findings were laid before two French learned societies and rejected by both. He published them anyway in five volumes that were ignored for many years.

These early investigators were laboring under two handicaps. The first was a general lack of scientific method, which often made it easier for critics to argue that tools and human bones and extinct animals had

J. F. Esper, John Frere

Boucher de Perthes

Problems of Early Investigators

gotten together by accident (or even by the sinister design of the scientist) than for the scientist to prove that they had come to their final resting place by natural means. A Catholic priest, Father J. McEnery, was to suffer from this first handicap. In 1829 he dug his way through an absolutely unbroken layer of stalagmite to find flint tools and ancient bones below a cave floor on the south coast of England. When he reported this discovery, other geologists, led by the Dean of Westminster, William Buckland, insisted that the tools belonged to ancient Britons who had dug ovens in the stalagmite floor of the cave and accidentally dropped some of their stone implements into the holes. Father McEnery's earnest rebuttal that there were no such holes fell on deaf ears; his findings, to which he had devoted some fifteen years, were not published until after his death.

A second and much more serious handicap was that scientists and laymen alike seemed almost instinctively suspicious of stone tools and fossils and from our viewpoint appeared severely limited in their thinking. They still had not the faintest notion of how old the earth actually was.

But by the end of the eighteenth century a few people were beginning to get some alarming ideas about its long history. This they read in the "testimony of the rocks," in the various layers of different kinds of sediments—river gravels, sands, and marine limestones—that they encountered, one beneath another, some of them dozens of feet thick, indicating that the layers had been laid down over long periods of time.

Figure 4–2   The universe as depicted in a woodcut, *The Creation of the World*, from Martin Luther's Bible, 1534.

Much excitement was generated in 1796 when Georges Cuvier (1769–1832), professor of natural history at the Collège de France, discovered elephant bones in the soil of the Paris area itself. Soon Cuvier and other diggers were unearthing even stranger inhabitants of an unknown and unsuspected past—reptiles big as whales, mammoths with long tusks, bears, wolves, and other creatures that bore only a superficial similarity to living species. From a few of their bones Cuvier put the animals back together with such startling realism that Balzac marveled: "Is Cuvier not the greatest poet of our century? Our immortal naturalist has reconstructed worlds from blanched bones. He picks up a piece of gypsum and says to us 'See!' Suddenly stone turns into animals and another world unrolls before our eyes."

Like the living members of the animal kingdom, such collections of ancient animals did not come in a random assortment but could be classified into species and genera. Cuvier counted ninety species, and some whole genera, that had entirely disappeared from the earth. What could have brought about such terrible decimation, he wondered, and how could the lost species have been succeeded by still others before the animals of "the present creation" appeared?

To find the answers to such riddles, Cuvier set out to learn how the fossil creatures had been entombed and to find out all he could about the earth of their distant time. He enlisted the aid of Alexandre Brongniart, a professor of mineralogy and head of the famous Sèvres china factory. For years the two studied the Paris countryside in depth.

Georges Cuvier

They discovered that layer was piled upon layer: one stony bed filled with millions of sea shells, and just below it a different formation with a scattering of freshwater or land shells. Other strata were studded with the bones of extinct giant mammals. Still others had no fossils at all.

Cuvier and Brongniart tried to interpret the puzzling succession of vanished worlds. At times, as they explained to rapt Parisian audiences, the seas had flooded into the Paris basin. At other times the salt waters had receded, and the dry land had been dotted with freshwater lakes. Again the seas had returned, and again they had rolled back. In deposits laid down during the sea eras were the shells and bones of ocean life; in sediments marking the bottoms of the freshwater lakes lay freshwater shells and the bones of land animals. There was no mixing of the land and sea deposits; one ended and the other began.

At about the same time, an English surveyor named William Smith (1769–1839) was making similar observations in his own country and coming to similar conclusions. "Each stratum contains organized fossils peculiar to itself," he reported. In 1815 Smith published a painstaking geologic map of England, showing the strata that underlie the landscape and proving again that "the same species of fossils are found in the same stratum, even at wide distances." William Smith

The implications of these studies were extremely disturbing to the men making them. Cuvier was a scientist intensely devoted to the truth, but even with the succession of species before him he could not admit that one species had arisen from another. To have done so would have denied his strong Huguenot faith in a special creation. Cuvier preferred another explanation, that a series of vast floods had wiped out the old and cleared the stage for new creations. This theory was called *catastrophism*.

It remained for another Briton, Charles Lyell (1797–1875), to synthesize from the growing avalanche of evidence another and more important theory—*uniformitarianism*. This is a long word but it embraces a very simple and logical idea: if the earth's mantle is now affected by wind and flowing water, by frost action, by volcanic activity, by faulting along lines of crustal weakness, by mountain building, then it stands to reason that such forces also have been operating in a similar, or "uniform," fashion in the past. James Hutton, in his book *Theory of the Earth* (1795), had already pointed out that the earth is of immense antiquity and shows "no vestige of a beginning—no prospect of an end." Clearly, the passage of immense amounts of time can explain the presence of such diverse strata as exist in the earth's crust. The world is constantly remaking itself, and the only reason we are not continually aware of the reconstruction is that it happens so slowly. A person who watches a few pebbles fall from a crag may not realize it, but he is watching the disintegration of a mountain. Muddy water flowing down a river can eventually move billions of tons of material from the center of a continent to the bottom of the sea. This immense layer of mud may harden and be covered in turn by other layers in a process extending Charles Lyell over great amounts of time. All of this, which seems so obvious now, was entirely new thinking at the end of the eighteenth century, a new interpretation of earth history and a new key to past and present. And to a society accustomed to believing that the earth was only about 6,000 years old, a staggering revelation.

Lyell's great work *Principles of Geology* was published between 1830 and 1833. Among its readers was a young man named Charles Darwin, who in another 26 years was to publish his even more revolutionary book. Like Lyell, Darwin organized a great amount of evidence into a theory. He was an extremely cautious man, and the evidence he used to support his theory ranged among both plants and animals but did not include human beings. He mentioned the origin of humans only once in *On the Origin of Species*, permitting himself a single timid sentence in his conclusion: "Light will be thrown on the origin of man and his history." But the implication was plain and nobody missed it.

It is impossible today to recreate the atmosphere of intellectual and moral shock that swept England in 1859 when Darwin's *On the Origin of Species by Means of Natural Selection* was published (see Figure 4–3). It was not that evolution of plants or animals was so hard to swallow. After all, man himself had been responsible, through selective breeding, for the evolution of a number of domestic animals and a great variety of crops. Then there were those peculiar dinosaur bones that people had begun digging up; they had to be explained, as did the growing evidence that the earth, instead of being 6,000 years old as the church had taught, was hundreds of thousands, perhaps hundreds of millions, of years old. No, those things were not really the problem. What was so hard to accept was the suggestion that human beings were descended from a bunch of repulsive, scratching, hairy apes and monkeys.

Those awful monkeys! As one Victorian lady is reported to have said: "My dear, let us hope that it is not true, but if it is let us pray that it will not become generally known."

In 1863 Thomas H. Huxley, a friend of Darwin and an ardent propagandist for his theory, published *Zoological Evidences as to Man's Place in Nature*. This was the first book to address itself in an orderly and scientific way to the problem of human origins. By making many telling anatomical comparisons between mankind and the apes, Huxley established that of all animals on earth, the African great apes— the chimpanzee and gorilla—are most closely related to humans. He further stated that the evolutionary development of apes and humans had taken place in much the same way and according to the same laws. From this it followed that if prehuman fossils were ever found, they would lead to even older types that would turn out to be ancestral to both apes and man. And these common ancestors would probably be found in Africa.

Darwin, confronted by the same relationship of fossil species to living ones, saw that the latter were the modified descendants of the former. Carrying the case to its full conclusion in *The Descent of Man*, which was published in 1871, Darwin was forced to propound an un-

Charles Darwin

Figure 4–3 A cruel caricature of Darwin, which appeared in *The Hornet* in 1871, labeled him "a venerable orang-outang" and cited his contribution to "unnatural history."

broken chain of organisms that began with the first forms of life and evolved to man. Here was a theory of evolution hopefully subject to proof; but where was the proof? Where were the bones of this multitude of organisms? Surely many of them should have survived in the earth, yet the fossils found up to Darwin's day supplied only the most fragmentary evidence. Where were the missing links? It was a painful time for the evolutionists. Despite all the logic in Huxley's and Darwin's views, they were difficult to support because, in Africa or indeed anywhere else, there was an embarrassing lack of fossils resembling human beings.

In all the ancient menageries that Georges Cuvier dug out of the Parisian subsoil a century and a half ago, it happened that there was not a trace of prehistoric humans. It seemed plain enough to the great paleontologist: "L'homme fossile n'existe pas," fossil man does not exist. This did not stop people from looking. Here and there, in this old cave and that old river bed, excavators ran across chipped flints and polished axes, but the bones mixed in with such finds were those of animals and not mankind. It never occurred to the finders that some of the pebble implements they collected might actually be older than modern humans—that tools had been the making of mankind as well as mankind being the maker of tools.

UNEARTHING THE HUMAN CHRONICLE

Thus, at this turning point in the history of human knowledge, there emerged two great and related ideas about the origin of nature and of mankind: that the earth is an extremely ancient place, long populated by many kinds of animals, some of which are no longer living, and that man himself, a mutable creature like the animals, has his origins far back in time. But how far back, and who those ancestors were, nobody as yet had even the slightest notion. Everything we now know about our ancestry we have learned in the last century, most of it during the last couple of decades.

From Neandertal and Spy

What the fossil hunters did not realize for a time was that they had a number of bona fide skulls of extinct humans in their possession. The most famous was the skullcap that, along with some limb bones, had been dug out of a cave in the limestone cliffs of the Neandertal (Neander valley) (see Figure 4–4) near Dusseldorf, Germany, in 1856. To experts familiar with human skeletons and skull structure, there were some very peculiar things about this "Neandertal man" (shown in Figure 4–5), as he came to be known. The skull was clearly manlike; yet it had strongly developed eyebrow ridges and a retreating forehead and was much flatter on top and more bulging in the back than the skull of any modern human being. At the time, it was easier to regard the skull as a deformed specimen of a modern human skull than to accept the possibility that human ancestors actually looked like that.

One person who examined the Neandertal skull was the renowned German anatomist Rudolf Virchow, who promptly dismissed its defunct owner as a not very ancient pathological idiot. Another physician declared that the deceased had suffered from "hypertrophic deformation." A German authority theorized that the remains were those of "one of the Cossacks who came from Russia in 1814."

Darwin heard about these remarkable bones but never investigated them. Huxley, however, undertook a thorough study of the unprecedented skull. In the condition in which it was discovered, the cranium could hold 63 cubic inches of water; complete, it would have contained 75 cubic inches, which is the average cranial volume of many modern peoples. So the brain must have been of modern size, too; and the limb bones, though on the bulky side, were "quite those of an European of middle stature. . . ."

"Under whatever aspect we view this cranium," wrote Huxley in 1863, "we meet with ape-like characteristics, stamping it as the most pithecoid [apelike] of human crania yet discovered." Neandertal man, Huxley concluded, was more nearly allied to the higher apes than the latter are to the monkeys, but for all of that he was a man. (A most successful man, as later finds were to prove: he dominated Europe for some 100,000 years until modern man took over about 35,000 to 40,000 years ago.) "In still older strata," Huxley wondered, "do the fossilized bones of an Ape more anthropoid, or a Man more pithecoid, than any yet known await the researches of some unborn palaeontologist?"

Meanwhile, a second skull had been brought to England from the Natural History Society collections in Gibraltar, where it had been discovered in a cave as early as 1848. When it was exhibited at the meetings of the British Association for the Advancement of Science in 1864, it was seen quite clearly to be a second example of a man with the hitherto unique but recognizable shape of the Neandertal skull.

For the skeptics, there was another problem that would not go away. If not Neandertal man, then who had made the stone axeheads and other crude implements that were turning up with perplexing frequency in

Figure 4–4   The Neander Valley lies near Dusseldorf in western Germany. Here, early mineworkers unearthed the now famous Neandertal bones. Today the whole valley has been mined so extensively for limestone that the site of the discovery no longer exists.

Figure 4–5   The skullcap from the Neandertal is the most famous fossil discovery ever made. Following its discovery in 1856, it was thought by many to be the skull of some pathological idiot. Today we know that it belonged to an early, but by no means primitive, member of our own species, *Homo sapiens*.

river beds and caves throughout western Europe? Advances in geology were beginning to make it possible to calculate the age of some of these implements with some precision. Reluctantly the scientific world began to realize that many of them were more than 20,000 years old and some of them more than 100,000 years old. But a convincing identification of their makers could not be made unless tools and human fossils could be found together in the same layers of debris on the floor of a cave or in the same gravel bed.

So the riddle of Neandertal man lay in a kind of limbo for twenty years. Then, in 1886, in the course of digging in a cave near Spy, Belgium, two skeletons closely similar to the Neandertal one were recovered. This time their antiquity had to be accepted without question. The human bones occurred in deposits with bones of woolly rhinoceros, mammoths, and other mammals that no longer exist, as well as with a number of chipped stone implements of a distinctive type. All of this extraordinary material was carefully removed layer by layer so that there could be no mistake about what was associated with what. At last, after half a century of groping, misunderstanding, contradiction, dispute, and ridicule, a demonstrably ancient find had been made by archaeologists working systematically and making thorough and detailed records of their excavation. The evidence was unmistakable. The Neandertal type was a man, but not a man identical with the human beings who now walk the earth.

The Gorge d'Enfer, or Hell's Gorge, is about a half mile outside the village of Les Eyzies in the Dordogne region of southwest France. In an open wood of ivy-covered tree trunks the ground is soft with moss, but

From the Dordogne: Cro-Magnon

Figure 4–6 Excavation of a rock shelter in the Dordogne called Abri Pataud. A steel grid has been constructed to enable the excavator to plot the depth and position of every fragment of archaeological evidence. The overhanging cliffs extend upwards and outwards.

among the trees jut several huge overhanging rocks. They provide ready shelter today against the spurts of spring rain, just as they doubtless did for the ancient peoples who inhabited this region 30,000 or 40,000 years ago.

It is a fair guess that in the last hundred years, more archaeologists have found more artifacts and remains of early man in the 3,500-odd square miles of the Dordogne district (see Figure 4–7) than in any other comparable patch of earth. And it was at Les Eyzies, about a mile from the gorge, in 1868, that the first acceptable proof was found that modern man had lived in prehistoric times.

The discovery was made prosaically enough by a gang of railway workers cutting into a hillside just outside the village. They dug out the earth from under an overhanging rock shelter in one of the many lime-stone cliffs that loom over the village, and with the dirt came bones and what looked like stone tools. Scientists summoned to the site soon uncovered the remains of at least four human skeletons: a middle-aged man, one or two younger men, a young woman, and a child two or three weeks old. They were buried with flint tools and weapons, seashells pierced with holes, and animal teeth similarly perforated, probably to make ornaments. The name of the rock shelter was Cro-Magnon, in garbled recognition of a local hermit called Magnon who had lived here. So the name *Cro-Magnon* was affixed to these new-found human beings.

There was nothing unusual, of course, about finding human skeletons in the ground. But two things gave this find its unique importance. First, the consensus of the geologists who subsequently examined the site was that although the remains could not be dated exactly, they had belonged to creatures living long before the beginning of history. Second, it quickly became clear that those creatures had been people who in the flesh must have looked much like modern people. These assertions, inexact though they were, made heady reading in an age that by and large was satisfied by the Biblical story of creation and that had no real concept of man's true antiquity.

The whole truth about the Cro-Magnon remains has turned out to be even more startling: the people of Cro-Magnon lived in that rock shelter some 25,000 years ago, and yet they were not simply like modern human beings; they *were* modern human beings. There was nothing apelike about them (as you can see from Figure 4–8). They had neither the beetled brows nor the sloping foreheads that had set apart all their human predecessors, including Neandertal man. The fact is that they were modern *Homo sapiens*, just as every human being on earth is today.

In the strict archaeological application, the name Cro-Magnon applies only to the people who lived in southwestern France from about 35,000 to 10,000 years ago, a period in Europe technically known as the Upper Paleolithic. But in a broader sense, the name Cro-Magnon is often used to refer to the first modern peoples everywhere. They appeared at different places on the earth at different times—the earliest date ascribed to their emergence is about 40,000 B.P. (before present)—and

Figure 4–7   Most of the sites where humans are known to have lived about 30,000 years ago are in Europe, particularly in the Dordogne in southern France. The caves in which these people sheltered themselves from the ice-age glaciers also protected and preserved their artifacts and bones for hundreds of centuries.

Figure 4–8   The Cro-Magnon skull is so typically modern that reconstruction presents no special problems.

their looks and behavior varied locally, just as the appearance and customs of Japanese and Frenchmen differ today. But they all used stone tools of a fairly sophisticated kind, and they all lived as hunter-gatherers —the last to live that way on a worldwide scale before much of mankind settled down into the agricultural age. Despite their physical and cultural differences, they can all, in a general sense, be given the label Cro-Magnon, and it will be used that way as a convenience in this book.

Considering the long duration and density of human occupation of the Dordogne, it seems fitting that the first accepted evidence of the first modern human beings should have been found there. At the time of the discovery, however, people were concerned less about where this apparently modern ancestor turned up than by the fact that he turned up at all. Since Neandertal man was not a creature anybody of the time wanted as an ancestor, the discovery of Cro-Magnon man came as an enormous relief. Cro-Magnon was certified prehistoric, and yet he was modern looking, a perfectly acceptable member of the human family tree to those who were willing to accept man's antiquity but were not able to accept evolution or acknowledge Neandertal's kinship. If mankind was as old as the Cro-Magnon remains seemed to indicate, the argument went with undaunted logic, it was unlikely that we could have been involved in Darwin's undignified and heretical evolutionary process. We must therefore always have looked the same.

Thus, the advent of Cro-Magnon man was cordially regarded by many thoughtful people of the time. The Cro-Magnon peoples were clearly ancestors of modern humans and had lived long enough ago to have used stone tools and killed animals unknown in modern times. Yet they did not seem so ancient or so different from humans of later days as to cause any serious conflict with Biblical accounts of mankind. To have achieved acceptance of the idea of prehistoric man on even these limited grounds was a major breakthrough for the science of archaeology, and this was a critical turning point for a discipline that was only just starting to clarify the mysteries of the distant past.

Dubois in Java: *Homo erectus*

When it became clear that human beings had existed in Europe for at least 10,000 years, paleoanthropology became a respectable science with some hard fossil evidence. What it lacked was any idea of where that evidence itself originated. Who were the ancestors of Neandertal man? What did they look like? Where was fossil proof of their existence?

These problems obsessed a young Dutch doctor, Eugene Dubois (1858–1940), who determined that he would be the paleontologist to solve them. Following the reasoning of Darwin and Wallace, Dubois believed that any form of creature that was in between apes and humans would in all probability have originated either in Africa, where the gorilla and chimpanzee still exist, or in Malaya, where the orangutan survives. As he put it, "Since all apes—and notably the anthropoid apes—are inhabitants of the tropics, and since man's forerunners, as they gradually lost their coat of hair, must certainly have continued to live in the warm regions, we are inescapably led towards the tropics as the area in which we may expect to find the fossilized precursors of man.''

Find them Dubois did. Within two years he had in his hands what many other men before and after him have hunted for unsuccessfully throughout their lives. What Dubois had discovered was the famous Java man, who now bears the scientific name of *Homo erectus,* a creature so seemingly primitive that Dubois himself thought at first that he was dealing with the scattered remains—a skullcap, lower jaw fragment, and thigh bone—of a fairly large bipedal chimpanzee.

The sudden extension of the span of admitted human existence, particularly on the evidence of a single specimen from a remote part of the world, had the predictable result: few people accepted it. Dubois' discovery rocked the scientific world, provoking many arguments and widespread disbelief. One thing that worked against Dubois was that like so many discoverers and inventors, he was a little ahead of his time. Sometimes a discovery is made when the world is not ready for it; sometimes even science is not ready. This was one of those times. Dubois had chosen to do his work in the East Indies, a part of the world about which next to nothing of a geological nature was known. Thus it was only natural for other scientists to be skeptical about his claims.

After Dubois' find, other remains similar to Java man were uncovered; and it gradually became clear that very primitive men—not apes or even ape-men, but men—were widely distributed half a million years ago throughout the warm and temperate regions of the Old World (see Figure 4–9). An enigmatic jaw was found in 1907 at Mauer near Heidelberg, Germany. In the 1920s and 1930s, extensive digging under the direction of Canadian anatomist Davidson Black in some hill caves

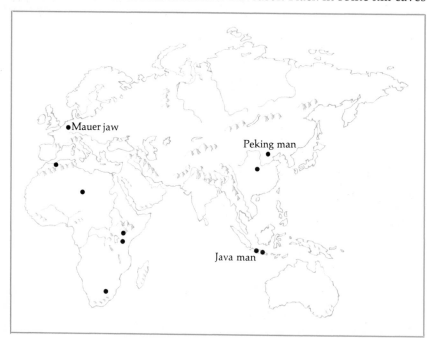

Figure 4–9 **This map shows the sites at which fossil remains of** *Homo erectus* **have been found.**

near Peking turned up a large number of bone fragments, the bones and teeth of "Peking man." These, though not so old nor so primitive as Dubois' find, suggested a human being that closely resembled Java man. Meanwhile, back in Java, other skeletal fragments just as old and as primitive were found not far from where Dubois had worked, by G. H. R. von Koenigswald.

There is a natural tendency among the discoverers of dramatically ancient fossils—fossils that appear to be about half a million or more years old—for each successful digger to think he has hit on something entirely new. For a long time there was a "Heidelberg man," a "Peking man," and a "Java man," each with its own Latin name. For one thing, the skeletal parts of these ancient people were often incomplete and very fragmentary; for another, the science of evaluating them was still fumbling its way along. It is only in the last decade or so that the growing number of finds and increasing familiarity with the fossils themselves have begun to convince scientists that, for all of their geographical dispersion, all these remains represent a single species of man that varied considerably among different locations. Java man, Peking man, and Heidelberg man were given a single scientific name, *Homo erectus* (see Figure 4–10), which places them in a different species but in the same genus as *Homo sapiens,* the name given to modern humans. *Homo erectus* was both widespread and highly successful.

Figure 4–10   Reconstruction of the skull and jaw of *Homo erectus* is based on numerous fossil finds. The general form of the face can also be reconstructed with reasonable accuracy, but we have no evidence of some important features such as nostrils, lips, and hair.

His discovery led, naturally enough, to a very troublesome question: who had preceded him? For a long time no one knew. There was an immense gap running back all the way to some possible ape ancestors known from fossils believed to be 10 to 20 million years old. Then in the 1920s, Raymond Dart (b. 1893), an anatomist working in South Africa, announced another wonderful discovery—a child's skull of a

Dart in South Africa: *Australopithecus*

Figure 4–11 This six-year-old child's skull from Taung in South Africa was recognized by Raymond Dart in 1924 for what it was—a missing link between human beings and their early apelike ancestors.

totally new type, shown in Figure 4–11. After intensive study, Dart described this find as belonging to a small creature, manlike in that it apparently ran about on the ground on its hind legs and had manlike teeth, yet apelike (but still not an ape) in some characteristics of skull and jaw. Dart christened this curiosity *Australopithecus africanus.*

The South African discoveries that later vindicated Dart's remarkable claim were made by a medical doctor turned paleontologist, Robert Broom (1866–1951), about ten years later. Broom had the knack of looking in the right place, and within a couple of years of beginning his search for early hominids like *Australopithecus,* he had many more specimens of individuals of all ages to add to Dart's single find. To his tremendous enthusiasm and energy we owe one of the finest samples of fossil hominids yet found.

During this time another remarkable man was at work 2,000 miles to the north, in Kenya and Tanzania. This was Kenya-born Louis Leakey, a passionate naturalist and anthropologist. After an education at Cambridge, England, Leakey returned to East Africa to search for early man. He had some enticing leads, including some rich deposits of fossil animal bones and stone tools that lay in a gorge cut through the plains of northern Tanzania. Buoyed by sheer faith in their own

Other Fossils from Africa and India

hunches, he and his wife Mary worked for nearly thirty years here and elsewhere before they unearthed early hominids 1.8 million years old which not only resembled the South African finds, but also were found in association with stone tools and other signs of manlike activities. The work of the Leakeys at Olduvai Gorge represents a milestone in our studies of human evolution and prehistory. Today, their son Richard carries on the Leakey tradition in northern Kenya and has taken the story of technology back a further half million years. And fossil hominid remains recently found in northeast and south Ethiopia take the record of fossil bones back beyond three million years from the present.

As work was proceeding in Africa, much earlier fossils were being discovered in India. The apelike creatures to which they once belonged have recently been recognized as the probable ancestors of the human stock. They date from 9 to 12 million years ago.

Today, discoveries are being made of fossils of all types and ages. They are at last making it possible for us to piece together an approximate lineage for mankind. Some of these more recent discoveries, to be described in later chapters, are just as momentous as the finds made by the early workers.

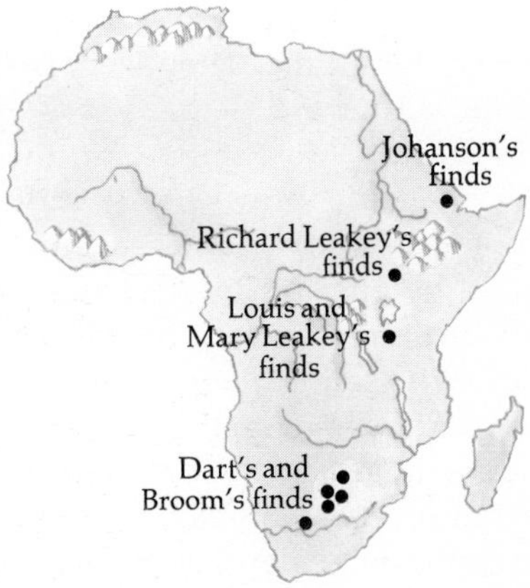

Figure 4–12 Discoveries of *Australopithecus* come from the eastern side of the continent of Africa—an area most of which has been savanna for at least 10 million years.

The wheel has come full circle. The public now accepts the enormous age of the earth as readily as it does the succession of the seasons. The problem now is to get accurate dates for human fossils, to determine their relationships more precisely, to learn how such people lived, and to discover more fossils.

PALEONTOLOGY IN PROGRESS

Man is a maddeningly poor source of fossils. As recently as 1956, the paleontologist G. H. R. von Koenigswald calculated that if all the then-known fragments of human beings older than Neandertal man were gathered together they could be comfortably displayed on a medium-sized table.

The Scarcity of Human Fossils

Why are human fossils so scarce? Why can one go to good fossil sites here and there almost anywhere in the world and find literally millions of shell remains or thousands of bones of extinct reptiles and mammals, while peoples earlier than Neandertal are known from only a handful of sites at which investigators have worked through tons of deposits, piling up other finds by the bushel basket before recovering a single human tooth?

There are many reasons. First, the great commonness of marine fossils is a direct reflection of the enormous abundance of these creatures when they were alive. It also reflects the tremendous span of time during which they abounded. Many of them swarmed through the waters of the earth for hundreds of millions of years. When they died, they sank and were covered by sediments. Their way of life helped preserve them, as did their shells, which are extremely durable and are the only parts of them that now remain. Humans, by contrast, have never been as numerous as oysters and clams. They existed in small

numbers, reproduced slowly and in small numbers, and lived a relatively long time. They were more intelligent than, for example, dinosaurs, and were perhaps less apt to get mired in bogs, marshes, or
quicksands. Most important, their way of life was different. They were
not riverside browsers but lively, wide-ranging food-gatherers and
hunters. They often lived and died in the open, where their bones
could be gnawed by scavengers and bleached and decomposed in the
sun and rain. In hot climates, particularly in tropical forests and woodlands, the soil is likely to be markedly acid. Bones dissolve in such soils,
and any early humans that may have lived and died in such an environment would have had a very poor chance of leaving remains that would
last until today. Finally, human ancestors have been on the earth only a
few million years. There simply has not been as much time for them to
scatter their bones about as there has been for some of the older species
of animals.

What is needed to catch a glimpse of a clever, elusive, uncommon
animal like early man is a quiet cave where a corpse can be gently
covered by blown-in dust or leaves and washed in soil or even sand and
mud from the rising water level of a river. Or the cave might be a large
one with a deep rock fissure at the back serving as a garbage dump into
which the dead can be placed along with the bones of game animals,
just to get them out of the way. Finally, the cave may simply be one that
is occupied steadily for a long period of time. The dirt and debris of
mere living will gradually build up the floor so that it becomes deeper
and deeper, and if people live in it long enough, their story will be
revealed—from recent to increasingly primitive—just by careful
digging downwards from one layer to another.

Not all fossil sites are cave sites; the earliest known cave occupations
are little more than half a million years old. From earlier times we find
occupation sites that were in the open, often a stream or lake shore. In
these circumstances, evidence is more difficult to come by. In other
places, fossils of human ancestors have been found scattered among
animal bones without any clear archaeological context and these are the
most rare occurrences. Indeed, as we go backward in time the fossil
record becomes dimmer, and the specimens scarcer, as might be expected. But where animal bones are found preserved (again, most
commonly near an ancient lake shore or river) there we can reasonably
expect to find fossil hominids, if the geographical area, climate, and
environment are appropriate.

The gradual revealing of the story of human evolution can be
compared to the cleaning of an old tapestry that has been covered with
mud and dirt. Let us suppose modern humanity is at the top of the
tapestry, and our most primitive ancestors are woven into it near the
bottom. The whole tapestry is fragile, increasingly so the nearer one
gets to the bottom. It must be cleaned with great care so that it will not
be destroyed. There is no assurance, if one should select a particular
spot on the tapestry to begin picking away bits of dirt, that that spot will

Fossil Sites

turn out to have a meaningful picture on it. It may be bare. It may have a hole in it. It may reveal only a fragment of one of the figures in the design, a fragment so small and mysterious as to be of no value. It may reveal an entire figure, but a totally unexpected one whose presence cannot be explained until further parts are cleaned. But the position of every piece of design on the entire tapestry—exactly where it is located with respect to all other pieces—is enormously important. In paleontology, deductions can be made about specific fossils and their relationship only when they are evaluated in the light of all other available evidence and knowledge.

To begin to understand our ancestors' fossil remains, we must know how old these bits and pieces are. Strange shapes and sizes may suggest all sorts of intriguing ideas and hypotheses about who descended from whom. But these hypotheses concerning the relationship of one odd piece of bone to another may be nailed down tightly only by reliable dating.

Dating Methods: Earth and Fossils

The critical problem of determining the age of fossils is handled in several ways. The first is through *geology*, the study of the earth itself. This branch of science is concerned with the location, size, and nature of the various layers of clay, silt, sand, lava, limestone, and other kinds of rock that constitute the earth's surface, and with their relationship to one another. It examines certain processes such as erosion, the accumulation of layers of silt at the bottom of the sea, and their compaction into rock again, by heat and pressure; it notes that these processes are taking place now at measurable rates and assumes that these same processes took place at comparable rates in the past. Analysis of these layers, or strata—a scientific discipline known as *stratigraphy*—permits the working out of a rough picture of past earth history (see Figure 4–13). From this information the fossils found in different rock structures can be arranged in order of age.

The second way to determine age is through studying the fossils themselves. Fossil types are usually not the same in different layers. They evolve through time and thus provide clues of their own, particularly if the time sequence can be worked out. The evolution of the horse, for example, is very well known through its fossils. Over a period of about 60 million years, the creature developed from an animal the size of a dog with four toes on each foot to the large animal with one toe per foot that it is today; the numerous intermediate fossil stages located in various geological strata tell this story with great clarity; any other animal or plant fossil that occurs in the same layer as one of the ancestral horses can be considered the same age. Once relative ages are established, one fossil can in this way be used to help date another.

Early investigators usually failed to realize the importance of careful analysis of fossil sites and the position of fossils. Too often they dug with reckless abandon, recovering only the largest bones and major pieces of worked stone. They did not appreciate the information that the position of things relative to one another—and the surrounding earth

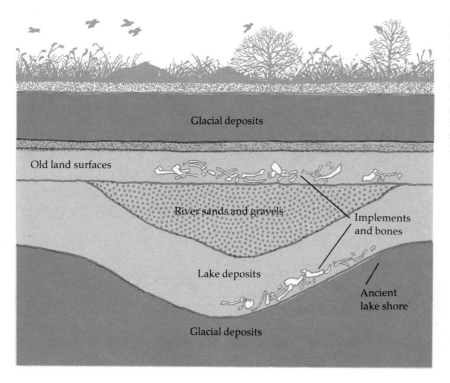

Glacial deposits

Old land surfaces

River sands and gravels

Implements and bones

Lake deposits

Ancient lake shore

Glacial deposits

Figure 4–13 Fossils are found in deposits formed by the action of glaciers and rivers or laid down in ancient riverbeds, lakes, estuaries, and seas. Some deposits are windblown and may contain volcanic ash. They are laid down in more or less horizontal beds, or strata, as shown here. Stratigraphy is the science that attempts to understand stratigraphic deposition—its form, its sequence, and its age.

itself—could give them. Many questions will occur to the curious and well-trained observer. Is there evidence of fire? Was it natural or controlled by man? Do certain kinds of animal bones predominate at one level and decrease at another, indicating a change of diet or climate? Do the deposits preserve snails, or perhaps pollen grains, which are more sensitive clues to vegetation, and hence climate, than the mineral deposits themselves?

Through the constant cross-checking and fitting together of enormous amounts of both rock and fossil evidence, science has been able to construct a rather detailed chronology of the past. But this chronology provides relative dates: absolute dates in years are at this point lacking.

As we mentioned in Chapter 1, however, atomic physics provides one technique for obtaining absolute dates. We know that certain radioactive elements discharge energy at a constant rate, known as the decay rate. Radium, for example, turns slowly but steadily into lead. Once this steady decay rate is known, it is only a matter of laboratory technique to determine how old a piece of radium is by measuring how much of it is still radium and how much is lead. One long-lasting radioactive substance is potassium 40. This breaks down into the gas argon at a constant and known rate. It is particularly useful because it is found in volcanic ash and lava. Fossils located in volcanic rock or ash or sandwiched between two layers of it can be dated with remarkable precision, because determination of the amount of argon produced (the potassium-

Dating Methods: From Physics and Biochemistry

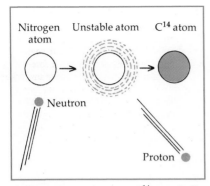

1. Nitrogen atom becomes C^{14} atom in the atmosphere.

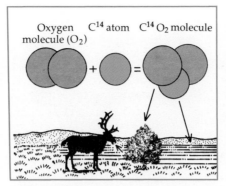

2. C^{14} and oxygen enter live organisms.

Figure 4–14 Carbon 14 is an unstable form of carbon (the stable form is carbon 12). A certain proportion of C^{14} exists in the atmosphere and as CO_2 is incorporated by plants into their bodies in the form of carbohydrates. Animals may absorb C^{14} by eating the plants. Thereafter the C^{14} disintegrates at a known rate, and the extent of this disintegration can be measured and related to the amount of C^{14} remaining, and so to the age of the organic material. So little C^{14} is left after 40,000 years, however, that the proportion in older material cannot be estimated.

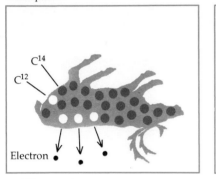

3. C^{14} atoms disintegrate.

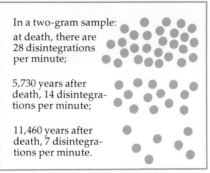

In a two-gram sample: at death, there are 28 disintegrations per minute;

5,730 years after death, 14 disintegrations per minute;

11,460 years after death, 7 disintegrations per minute.

4. C^{14} continues to disintegrate at an orderly, predictable rate.

argon ratio) will tell us when the lava or ash was ejected from the volcano. Another radioactive element is carbon 14, which reverts to the common form of carbon, carbon 12. Again the rate of decay is known and the amount of time that has passed since the radioactive carbon 14 was incorporated into vegetation and reduced to charcoal by burning can be calculated with some accuracy (see Figure 4–14).

A fourth possible dating method is based on the biochemistry of organisms. We saw in Chapter 3 that instructions for the building of new cells and new organisms are formulated and passed along by DNA. Having cracked DNA's code, scientists have begun to understand in detail two contrasting mechanisms of evolution: *genetic invariance,* the precisely accurate duplication of DNA's instructions generation after generation, which enables members of existing species to reproduce essentially unchanged, and *mutation,* the minute variations in DNA instructions that may originate new varieties of animals and plants. Today DNA is yielding new secrets to researchers. One of these is the process by which, over millions of years, mutations gradually create subtle differences in the structures of *proteins*—the basic building material of all living things—differences that can be used to determine the affinity between organisms. Some few scientists believe certain of these differences accumulate at a steady rate and so might be used to measure the evolutionary separation between humans and other species

TABLE 4–1   ESTIMATED TIMES OF EVOLUTIONARY DIVERGENCE

Species	Time of Divergence (Based on Immunological Studies)
Human and chimpanzee	4 million years
Human and gibbon	11 million years
Human and rhesus monkey	23 million years
Human and capuchin monkey (a New World monkey)	36 million years

Derived from Vincent M. Sarich, "A Molecular Approach to the Question of Human Origins," in Phyllis Dolhinow and V. M. Sarich (eds.), *Background for Man* (Boston: Little, Brown, 1971), p. 73.

Note: At present these figures diverge widely from the more reliable dates derived from potassium-argon dating of fossils.

and to work out a "protein clock" indicating when all existing lineages of animals first emerged (see Table 4–1). Though the protein clock is still a very tentative idea, it offers hope of a dating method supplementary to the better-known techniques that depend on fossils and radioactivity (see Table 4–2).

Modern Excavations

Modern work at sites occupied by early man is infinitely time-consuming and demanding. The tools of today's field worker are not so much picks and shovels as surveyor's transits, dental instruments, and small camel's-hair brushes. With such tools, it may take two weeks to excavate properly a very small area. Every scrap that is gently and patiently worked free must be mapped both horizontally and vertically; everything recorded, everything labeled. When this kind of study in three dimensions is done, the information compiled from one occupation site can be compared with data gained from another site. There may well be an overlap, permitting the matching-up of several layers from each of the two sites and a better understanding of both than was possible with one alone. Work of this sort is made still more precise when stone tools are brought into the picture, for different cultural phases are known to have had different kinds of tools and different techniques for making them.

Thus the full development of an important site may take many years, many specialists to analyze the findings in different ways, and substantial amounts of money. But the scientist will not select a site haphazardly. Something—bones or tools—must first be exposed to the erosional forces in nature to suggest that here is a site worth investigating. Then a series of test trenches are opened to expose the layered deposits, the stratigraphy, and to pinpoint concentrations of interesting

TABLE 4–2   PRINCIPAL METHODS OF DETERMINING
THE ABSOLUTE AGE OF FOSSILS

Time Period	Most Effective Method of Dating
Modern times— 2500 B.C.	Historical documents; tree-ring chronology; imported objects
Recent time— 40,000 B.P.	Carbon–14
40,000 B.P.— 500,000 B.P.	No effective method yet available: methods of relative dating used
500,000 B.P.— age of earth	Potassium-argon

Figure 4–15   A modern cave excavation in South Africa shows a section of stratified sandy deposits. Those at the bottom of the section are dated at about 55,000 B.P., those at the top about 1750 B.P. In this section layers of relatively sterile sand are surmounted by a shell midden — human food debris.

material. In these ways the paleoanthropologist vastly improves his chances of significant discoveries; otherwise he may dig out an entire hillside, using up large sums of research money in the process, and find nothing.

Does this mean that the great, exciting days of paleoanthropology are over? Not at all. It is true that the basic concepts have been es-

tablished and there can no longer be quite the sense of absolute
astonishment that greeted Lyell's concepts of geological time and the
evolutionary concepts of Darwin, or even the amazed disbelief that
greeted the discovery of Java man. Nevertheless, these are stirring
times for paleoanthropologists. Not only is the body of evidence growing almost faster than it can be analyzed, but there are still surprises in
store and problems unsolved. Each fact, each new bit of evidence that

Australopithecus africanus   *Homo erectus*

is found, speeds up the overall process of coming to an understanding of the story of human evolution.

It is the highlights of that story that will be dealt with in the following chapters of this book. First we will find out what is known about fossil apes and their possible connections with our own fossil forerunners. Then will come those predecessors themselves (see Figure 4–16): our *Australopithecus* ancestors of 6 to 3 million years ago; *Homo erectus,* the

Figure 4–16 These reconstructions suggest far more knowledge of human evolution than we actually possess. We do not have a complete skeleton of any fossil older than Neandertal man, nor do we have any direct evidence about the extent of hair in these forms. Nevertheless, the drawings do give some idea about the sequence and nature of our ancestors.

Neandertal   Cro-Magnon   Modern human

first member of the genus *Homo;* the remarkably well-documented Neandertal man and his contemporaries, those ice-age hunters of large animals; and finally Cro-Magnon man, who lives just over the hill from us in time and is really no different from us physically.

Mary Leakey (b. 1913)	1973 –	First discoveries at Hadar, by Johanson's team
	1969 –	First discoveries at East Rudolf, by Richard Leakey's expedition
	1959 –	First major discoveries at Olduvai, by Louis and Mary Leakey
Raymond Dart (b. 1893)	1947 –	Broom discovers *Australopithecus* pelvis
	1934 –	Manlike nature of *Ramapithecus* recognized
Louis Leakey (1903–1972)	1927 –	Peking man discovered
	1924 –	Dart discovers *Australopithecus*
	1907 –	Mauer jaw discovered
Eugene W. Dubois (1858–1940)	1891 –	Java man discovered by Dubois
	1886 –	Spy man discovered
Thomas H. Huxley (1825–1895)	1871 –	Darwin's *Descent of Man* published
	1868 –	Cro-Magnon man discovered
	1863 –	Huxley's *Man's Place in Nature* published
	1859 –	Darwin's *On the Origin of Species* published
	1856 –	Neandertal man discovered
Charles Darwin (1809–1882)	1848 –	Gibraltar man discovered
	1838 –	Boucher de Perthes announces discovery of ancient stone industry
	1833 –	Lyell's *Principles of Geology* completed
Charles Lyell (1797–1875)	1815 –	Smith's first geological map
Georges Cuvier (1769–1832)	1798 –	Malthus' *Essay on the Principles of Population* published
	1796 –	Cuvier discovers fossil elephants
	1790 –	Frere discovers ancient tools and extinct animal bones

PIONEERS OF PREHISTORY

There have been many great discoveries in the history of paleoanthropology and many distinguished prehistorians: only a selection are indicated in this chart. Similarly, the pioneers are more numerous than those indicated; much of the early work in prehistory was carried out by amateurs whose names are hardly known.

Chapter 5

Back beyond the Apes

It is an axiom of mine that when you have excluded the impossible, whatever remains, however improbable, must be the truth.

SIR ARTHUR CONAN DOYLE, 1859–1930.
THE ADVENTURES OF SHERLOCK HOLMES: THE BERYL CORONET.

The study of prehistoric man is, of necessity, the study of his fossil remains. To begin to understand who our ancestors were and what they were like, we must be able to interpret the bits and pieces of them that are coming to the surface in increasing numbers. Given fairly reliable methods to determine their age, we can now turn with more confidence to primate fossils for an answer to the all-important question: How do we tell monkeys, apes, and human beings apart? For present-day species this is no problem; all have evolved sufficiently so that they no longer resemble one another. But since they all have a common ancestor, the farther back we go in time, the more similar their fossils begin to look. There finally comes a point when they are indistinguishable. It is this characteristic that makes the construction of a primate fossil family tree seem essential if we are ever going to discover the line of descent from early hominid to modern human being.

We must therefore sort through the stones and bones that have survived through the ages to reveal what physical changes took place in our ancestors and how these changes led to modern human beings. Every step along the way is equally important. The new developments that characterize each new link of the chain of life that leads to mankind were made possible only by earlier developments. To understand precisely what we are, we must consider the entire chain and look behind apes and monkeys to the earlier animals from which they sprang. Traits that would later begin to emerge as distinctly human are believed to have had their origins in the anatomy and behavior of these shadowy creatures.

We must go back about 65 million years to the Paleocene epoch (see Figure 5–1), a time when human ancestors resembled squirrels more than people, and take a look at certain rat-shaped, rat-sized, insect-

THE EARLIEST PRIMATES

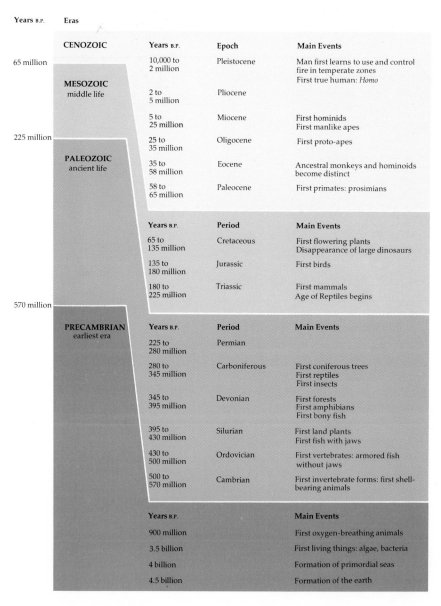

Years B.P.	Eras			
	CENOZOIC	**Years** B.P.	**Epoch**	**Main Events**
65 million		10,000 to 2 million	Pleistocene	Man first learns to use and control fire in temperate zones First true human: *Homo*
	MESOZOIC middle life	2 to 5 million	Pliocene	
		5 to 25 million	Miocene	First hominids First manlike apes
225 million		25 to 35 million	Oligocene	First proto-apes
	PALEOZOIC ancient life	35 to 58 million	Eocene	Ancestral monkeys and hominoids become distinct
		58 to 65 million	Paleocene	First primates: prosimians
		Years B.P.	**Period**	**Main Events**
		65 to 135 million	Cretaceous	First flowering plants Disappearance of large dinosaurs
		135 to 180 million	Jurassic	First birds
570 million		180 to 225 million	Triassic	First mammals Age of Reptiles begins
	PRECAMBRIAN earliest era	**Years** B.P.	**Period**	**Main Events**
		225 to 280 million	Permian	
		280 to 345 million	Carboniferous	First coniferous trees First reptiles First insects
		345 to 395 million	Devonian	First forests First amphibians First bony fish
		395 to 430 million	Silurian	First land plants First fish with jaws
		430 to 500 million	Ordovician	First vertebrates: armored fish without jaws
		500 to 570 million	Cambrian	First invertebrate forms: first shell-bearing animals
		Years B.P.		**Main Events**
		900 million		First oxygen-breathing animals
		3.5 billion		First living things: algae, bacteria
		4 billion		Formation of primordial seas
		4.5 billion		Formation of the earth

Figure 5–1 Geologic time scales are of such immense duration that it is hard fully to comprehend the great period of time during which nature and mankind have evolved. If the almost six hundred million years of vertebrate evolution is symbolized by one hour of time, then primate evolution has taken seven minutes and man's evolution occurred in the last twelve seconds of that hour.

eating mammals that were scuttling about on the ground. The Paleocene opened on a warm and placid world, with enormous tropical forests spreading much farther north and south from the equator than they do today. France and Germany were moist, humid jungles, as was much of Africa and nearly everyplace in between. Parts of North America were similarly forested, and that continent was joined to Europe across the North Atlantic. Among the inhabitants of these immense expanses of forests was a large population of long-tailed, rodentlike mammals. Their closest relatives living today are the insectivores, those small insect- and seed-eating mammals the voles, moles, hedgehogs, and shrews. Some of those early mammals began climbing into the trees, presumably because of intense competition on the ground and because there was a rich and untapped source of food up there. They soon became adept at leaping about in the trees, seeking out fruit and seeds, slow-moving grubs and insects, buds, birds' eggs, and an occasional baby bird. Mammals like this exist today in Africa and Asia and are called *prosimians*—pre-monkeys; the group includes the well-known lemurs (Figures 5–2) and lorises (Figure 5–3), including the bush baby, and the lesser-known tarsier. Modern tree shrews (Figure 5–4) represent an intermediate group with some characteristics of insectivores and some of primates. As comparison with fossils of the early forms has shown, these creatures have survived with practically no changes. Others did change. They changed so radically that their evolution is hard to believe. Those ancient prosimians were the ancestral primates; from them sprang the whole present array of prosimians, monkeys, apes, and hominids.

Why is it that our ancestors continued evolving, when a remnant of that ancient tree-living insectivore, the tree shrew, is still hanging on in the modern world? The answer is that there are two competing forces in evolution: the tendency toward change and the tendency toward stability. There is no guarantee that a species will evolve. In fact, there are enormous pressures against evolution. Nature is conservative, and a population of creatures that is getting along well in a particular stable environment will tend to stay the way it is. The forces of natural selection ensure that the vast majority of these creatures will always resemble one another very closely. Nearly all of them approach a kind of "best available model" for their particular habitat and their particular way of making a living. If they do not closely resemble that best available model, they are likely to be handicapped in one way or another, or they may not live so long as those that do resemble it. They may not reproduce themselves so successfully, and the trait that makes them different will disappear entirely or continue in a recessive state. Such a trait will appear, as we have seen in Chapters 2 and 3, only when two individuals that both carry it mate to produce offspring, some of whom may reveal it again. Those offspring may well not survive, because the full genetic complement of the nonconformist character may prove

Figure 5–2 The ring-tailed lemur (*Lemur catta*) is typical of the varied group of prosimian primates (Lemuroidea) from Madagascar. The most striking primate features of lemurs are large forward-looking eyes and long separated fingers on hands and feet.

Natural Selection and Speciation

disadvantageous: a myopic monkey or ape (myopia, short-sightedness, is believed to include a recessive genetic component) will almost certainly not survive more than a very short time in the treetops. Other offspring that carry a recessive trait not physically expressed may survive.

Most genetic variability produces endless but very slight differences in all of us. But if it is potentially dangerous in any way, why has it persisted? Why doesn't every species gradually shake out the traits in it that are nonadaptive, eventually producing only individuals that are most suitable for the life style of that species? The answer is that variability is a necessity for all life, and for two reasons. The first is that the best available model is not necessarily the perfect model. Within a species there is always a certain amount of selective pressure for improvement, for the development and intensification of traits that will fit the species even better to its environment. Indeed, more than one adaptation may be equally appropriate in a single environment. The second reason is that no environment is in fact static. There must be genetic variability in a species if it is to change in response to the changes that are taking place all around it. Therefore, for all species, what may seem like genetic excess baggage today may turn out to be tomorrow's survival kit. Too much specialization may be fatal.

The tendency toward change therefore is a strong feature of living species. When, in a general population of creatures, the environment of a group living in one particular location changes slightly, or when a group changes its feeding habits, certain physical differences may begin to appear in that group over a long period of time. If one segment of a population of creatures is separated geographically from another, or if it comes to behave differently, these modified groups of animals will interbreed less and less with the original breeding population. If a population should become truly divided—separated physically by a mountain range, an invasion of the sea, or the slow spread of a desert area—the divided groups cannot interbreed at all, and the process of becoming different will be accelerated. Ultimately, two kinds of animals will emerge where only one existed before, as we discussed in Chapter 3.

It is this evolutionary process of speciation that has been responsible for the development not only of monkeys, apes, and human beings, but also of all living things. It explains how different species today have many important characteristics that differentiate them and shape their various life styles. It is also what provides the intellectual framework that enables us eventually to identify a lineage of fossils and to determine where certain creatures developed distinctive characteristics and branched off to become a new lineage altogether.

Figure 5–3 The loris (*Loris tardigradus*) represents another group of prosimians (Lorisioidea) found in Africa and Asia. Lorises are smaller than lemurs but have very large eyes adapted for hunting insects and other small creatures at night.

The Prosimian Adaptation

Primate evolution illustrates very well the competition between the tendency toward stability and the tendency toward change. For 30 or 40 million years the prosimian stock was tremendously successful in the tropical forests of the world. Some of the ancestral insect-eating mammals evolved very little and very slowly. Tree shrews exist in their present form because there was little pressure for them to change: their environment remained fairly static, and they still fit in pretty well. Other early prosimians evolved more rapidly. The challenge that spurred that evolution may have been extremely subtle, as subtle as a slightly more intelligent or slightly stronger brother lemur, one that was a little better at catching the insect or attracting the female on the next branch. It might have been a very minor change in environment, either in climate or perhaps in the evolution of other animals, competitors, or predators. Over a long period of time, and in some places, differently adapted forms resulted. In response to the evolutionary shaping that an arboreal way of life encouraged, they began to change rather rapidly. Jumping and clinging was a better way of getting safely and quickly about in the branches than the ratlike scuttling that had preceded it. The hind legs became longer. The front paws gradually lost their ratlike claws and acquired the flat nails that are a hallmark of primates today (see Figure 5–5). All four paws began to turn into hands. The fingers grew longer and more flexible and developed tactile pads throughout their lengths. All these innovations greatly improved the ability of these new-model animals to move rapidly and suddenly in a tree—to grip a branch or to catch and hold a fast-moving insect or small lizard.

As leaping, clinging, and catching became a way of life, dependence on smelling became less important than dependence on seeing. This change was particularly necessary for an animal that lived in a three-dimensional world of trees instead of the two-dimensional world of the flat ground and that was constantly called on to make precise judgements about how far away a branch or a lizard was. In response to the growing importance of sight over smell, the head of the ancestral primate began to change. Its snout became shorter, its skull rounder. Its eyes became larger and moved gradually toward the front of the head, where vision from one eye could overlap that from the other, giving the animal what is known as binocular (two-eyed)—and eventually stereoscopic (depth-perceiving)—vision.

With stereoscopic vision came a far greater ability to judge distances than is possessed by a creature whose eyes are located on the sides of its head, as a rabbit's are. Rabbits must be alert to what may be about to attack them from the side or from behind, but they have no need to see what they eat: grass does not move and can be located easily by the mouth and nose. Nor does eating grass require a high degree of intelligence—less, certainly, than does hunting down elusive insect game in the treetops and coping with a dangerous three-dimensional environment. In time the rounder skulls of the treetop dwellers began to contain larger brains.

Within 10 or 15 million years these modifications had become sufficiently advanced that a distinct new group of animals might have been

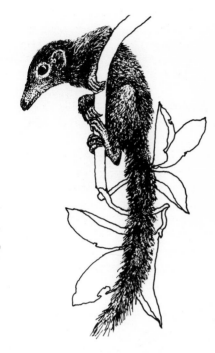

Figure 5–4 Tree shrews are found in Southeast Asia. They are very primitive mammals and are probably like the first ancestral primates. Their appearance is similar to that of the squirrel, but they are quite distinct from any rodent.

The Prosimians' Competitors

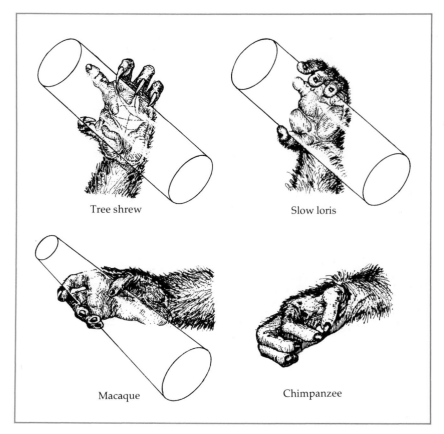

Tree shrew

Slow loris

Macaque

Chimpanzee

Figure 5–5 Hands are one of the most characteristic features of primates. One distinction between prosimians (shown in the top right drawing) and higher primates is that the former carry two or more claws at least, the latter only fingernails. The loris has claws only on its second toe: they have been retained as an adaptation for grooming— for scratching. Macaque monkeys and chimpanzees have thumbs longer than other higher primates and have a weak precision grip. The thumb, however, is usually pressed against the side of the first finger.

identified by an imaginary prehistoric zoologist. Some of the modern prosimians, particularly some of the larger lemurs, look and act very much like modern monkeys. If this new group, the monkeys, had never evolved, lemurlike creatures might still exist in places where monkeys are now found; they do exist on one island where monkeys never penetrated. This is the island of Madagascar. This large land mass that lies off Africa to the southeast was too far offshore to be reached by the newly evolved monkeys and so its early prosimian inhabitants faced no competition from these bigger-brained animals. As a result, Madagascar is still the kingdom of the prosimians, in particular, of the lemurs. In this isolated land, their evolution has resulted in something like fifteen genera (five of which have been eliminated by man since he settled there) with nineteen surviving species.

Unfortunately for the lemurs, monkeys and apes did evolve, elsewhere, establishing a fork in the primate family tree. At first, they could not be called anything more than late-model super primates; the differences between them and the older members of the prosimian populations were too small to be of much significance. But as these differences began to build up, through their survival advantage to the individuals that had them, the trees became filled with smarter, swifter, defter, altogether abler descendants. The prosimians died away in most places because they could not stand the competition.

X   Nevertheless, those first primates, the prosimians, do give us the first pieces that belong in the story of man's evolution, those at the very bottom edge of our tapestry. It was not until the late Eocene period, about 40 million years ago, that anything like a monkey showed up. What appeared then was a creature named *Amphipithecus* whose existence is known because of a small piece of jaw found in Burma. This animal is so dimly seen on this distant boundary line between prosimians and monkeys that it is hard to tell if it actually foreshadowed monkey development or not.

For a better clue, we must move ahead about 10 million years to the Oligocene era and to a spot in the Egyptian desert about sixty miles southwest of Cairo. This is a shallow dip in the landscape known as the Fayum Depression. Today it is one of the driest places on earth, but in Oligocene times the southern shore of the Mediterranean reached farther inland than it does now and the Fayum lay on the borderline between sea and forest. Apparently it was heavily wooded in parts and was laced with rivers, features that made it a fine place for proto-monkeys and apes to live and evolve. Evolve they did, and the Fayum proves it, for it contains a uniquely rich deposit of early primate fossils—not of the little prosimians that were so common elsewhere at that time, but of creatures that were beginning to look less like prosimians and more like monkeys and apes. Two in particular have caught the scientific eye as among the earliest known candidates for inclusion in the line of Old World monkeys. They bear the names *Apidium* and *Parapithecus*. (The Old World monkeys are a distinct group from the so-called New World monkeys, those of Central and South America. The New World monkeys split off from the North American branch of the prosimian line considerably farther back in time and are not at all closely related to Old World monkeys, though they resemble them considerably in form and habits. Since we know that man evolved in the Old World, it follows that the New World monkeys play no part in human evolution.)

What is it that makes *Apidium* or *Parapithecus* seem like a monkey instead of a prosimian? This gives us the first opportunity to observe how the paleontologist can deduce as much as he does from one piece of fossil evidence. Often that evidence consists mainly of teeth. Teeth are composed of the hardest and longest-lasting substances in the body. As a consequence, there are more of them than there are of bones in the fossil collections around the world, and they have been more intensively studied. It is obvious, for example, that *molars* (which are the large grinding teeth in the back of the mouth) have small conical

THE FIRST
HIGHER PRIMATES

Apidium and *Parapithecus*

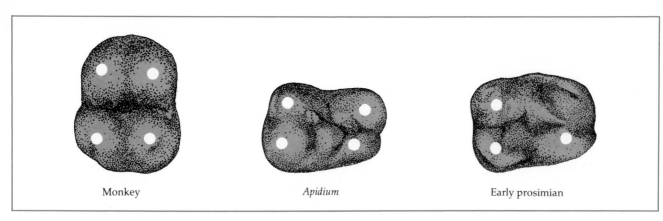

| Monkey | *Apidium* | Early prosimian |

bumps, or *cusps,* on their biting surface for chewing food. All chewing and grinding teeth are cusped, and all animal species have their own particular cusp patterns. One of these, a design of four cusps connected in pairs by small ridges, is known to occur only in Old World monkeys (though the third lower molar has a fifth cusp). So if a fossil lower molar with that unmistakable four-cusp pattern turns up, logic suggests that it belongs to a fossil monkey or to some sort of creature on the way to becoming a monkey.

Apidium and *Paraphithecus* have such teeth; prosimians do not (see Figure 5–6). Does that make *Apidium* and *Parapithecus* monkeys? Not necessarily, for elsewhere in their mouths they are more prosimian than monkey.

Figure 5–6   Molar teeth are invaluable in identifying the different groups of primates and are frequently preserved as fossils. The main key to identification lies in the arrangement and number of cusps.

Evaluating the Morphological Pattern

Comparative anatomists look for other things besides teeth that all monkeys have in common and that at the same time separate them from all other animals. Such a list of features constitutes a *morphological pattern* that characterizes a group of animals. Each genus and species of living animals has its own recognizable morphological pattern, and how closely one overlaps with others determines how closely the genera are related. For example, dogs and wolves have so many structural and behavioral characteristics in common that even a nonscientist would have no difficulty in recognizing that they are very closely related. In the same way, though dogs and wolves share with cats the traits of four legs, warm blood, caring for young, sharp teeth, and a great many others, they are much less like cats than they are like each other.

It is by systematically and laboriously studying the overall morphological pattern of fossil species that the paleontologist begins to be able to establish the relationships between long-extinct species. The evidence may be frustratingly meager, but each fragment that is added to it will either increase or decrease our knowledge of the similarity of one animal's morphological pattern to another animal's. And as the bits of evidence are sorted out, enough characteristics like the four-cusped, ridged molar pattern may finally be established for an expert to state with considerable conviction: "Yes, this fossil is a monkey, or a direct

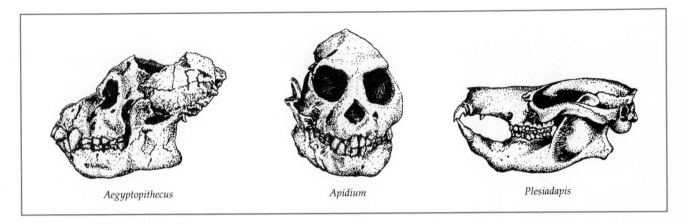

Aegyptopithecus   *Apidium*   *Plesiadapis*

monkey ancestor, while that one has too many nonmonkey characteristics and is something else.''

From this kind of detective work it has been concluded that *Parapithecus* and *Apidium* probably lie not far from the main monkey ancestral line. In addition to teeth we have another important piece of
''monkey'' evidence: an *Apidium* frontal bone. This bone lies above the
eyes and comes down around the eye sockets to form the complete
circle that gives the modern human skull its unmistakable vacant stare.
Among lower forms of primates, the frontal bones do not completely
enclose the orbit. But in *Apidium* and *Parapithecus,* as in the more advanced creature shown at the left in Figure 5–7, the frontal bones form
a full circle, or *orbital closure.* Another feature that can easily be detected
is the shortened face, indicated by the shape of the jaw. This is clearly
a feature of monkeys rather than prosimians.

Aside from these facts we do not know much about either *Parapithecus* or *Apidium*. Each was apparently about a foot high—no bigger
than a small cat—and, like many monkeys, quadrupedal, though it has
been claimed that *Apidium* had a leaping type of locomotion like some
prosimians. Was either one a direct ancestor of man? Almost certainly
not, for they were not the only primates in the forests of the Fayum nor
the earliest in date. There were a great many others, and some were not
so much monkeylike as apelike—which is another way of saying that
they were more manlike, for human beings and apes are closer in their
total morphological pattern than human beings and monkeys.

Figure 5–7 The orbits of the living
primates are surrounded by a ring of
bone that constitutes an extension of
the frontal bone joining the cheekbone.
This structure protects the large
forward-pointing eyes. *Apidium* **has
these closed orbits, as does the more
advanced** *Aegyptopithecus.* **In more
primitive primates such as** *Plesiadapis,*
**the orbit is open at the back to the
jawbone and its muscles.**

THE EARLY APES

Characteristics of Apes

When the principal differences between apes and monkeys are
spelled out (see Figure 5–8), the manlike nature of the apes is unmistakable. Many species of monkeys are built to go on all fours and do so
most of the time. Apes, by contrast, tend to be upright. This does not
mean that they always walk around on their hind legs as people do, but
simply that they can do this and sometimes do do it. More important,
they normally maintain their trunk erect except when moving quad-

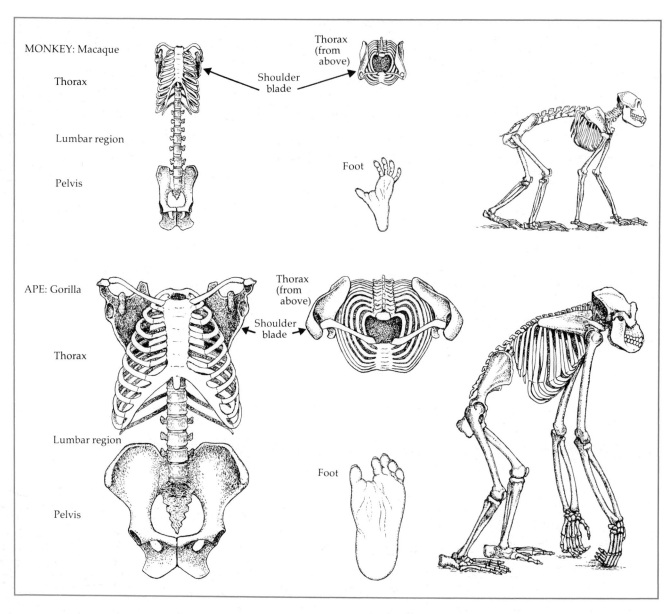

MONKEY: Macaque

Thorax

Lumbar region

Pelvis

Thorax (from above)

Shoulder blade

Foot

APE: Gorilla

Thorax

Lumbar region

Pelvis

Thorax (from above)

Shoulder blade

Foot

rupedally on the ground. Reflecting this tendency toward an erect posture, an ape has much more flexible arms and shoulders for hand-over-hand swinging and climbing. Its elbows and wrists are much more limber than a monkey's and its arms and fingers longer; the arrangement and proportions of its limb muscles are also different. Its spinal column is shorter and stiffer; its pelvis is broader; it has no tail; its head is better balanced atop the spinal column, rather than being thrust forward like a monkey's; and its brain is larger and more complex.

The main characteristics of apes are related to their feeding habits and size. Most of the food in trees is found among the small branches

Figure 5–8 Ape and monkey skeletons have much in common, but as Huxley pointed out in 1863, apes are more like humans than like monkeys in skeletal structure. Note the different proportions of limbs, the use of hands, and the form of the tail, rib cage, and shoulder blade.

and twigs at the end of the main limbs, and one of the problems encountered by any primate feeding here is that the branches are too small
and frail to bear the weight of any but the smallest animal. For other
reasons it pays to be big, as large size gives protection from predators

Figure 5–9   These photographs show
the quadrupedal doglike walk of monkeys in contrast to the hanging locomotion (called brachiation) of gibbons
(here photographed in a cage).

such as eagles and hawks, and a bigger body may mean a bigger brain (to name just two rather obvious advantages of large size). In consequence of this, a new locomotor behavior that was impractical for small prosimians appears among some monkeys and especially apes: they spread their weight through their four limbs and support themselves, not upon a single branch in quadrupedal fashion, but on a number of branches, by hanging by their arms from branches above their heads as well as placing their feet on the branches below them (see Figure 5–9). This adaptation has enabled some of the larger monkeys and all the apes to move more freely among smaller branches and at the same time to increase their size in evolution.

Gorillas, however, have increased in size beyond the point at which they can easily feed in the small branch zone of trees. When adult, they spend much of their time on the ground. In this, gorillas are not typical primates or even typical apes. The smaller and much more active gibbon probably acts more like the ancestral and probably arboreal apes that we find in the Oligocene fossil record.

Propliopithecus

These are some of the major differences that we find today between monkeys and apes. In sorting out the Fayum fossils it would be nice to have some spinal columns and leg bones to tell us if there were any apes or pre-apes among them. Unfortunately we have no such evidence, but once again we do have teeth. We have seen that certain molars in Old World monkeys have four cusps in a rectangular pattern. In apes—and in man—these same molars have in the lower jaw five cusps arranged in a characteristic Y pattern (see Figure 5–10) with a different arrangement of connecting ridges. If we can find such five-cusped molars among the Fayum fossils, we can find a hint of apes or their ancestors and, presumably, of human ancestors also. Recently such molars, with their jaws, have been found; some belong to an animal named *Propliopithecus* (see Figure 5–11).

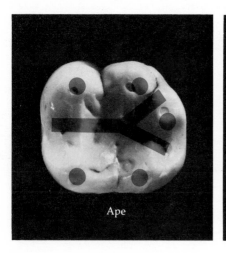 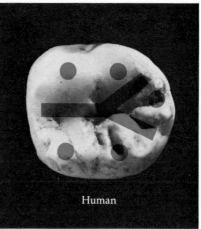

Ape

Human

Figure 5–10 The cusp patterns of the lower molar teeth enable us to distinguish apes and monkeys with ease. In contrast, humans have five cusps, as do apes. In some human lower molars, however, the fifth cusp has been lost, and it is commonly much reduced.

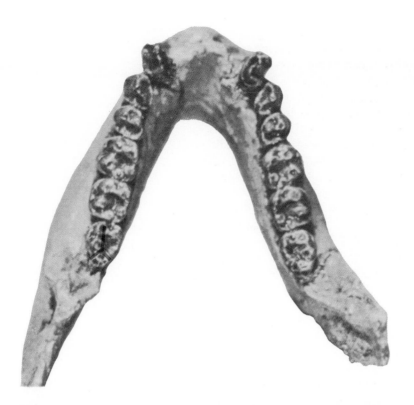

Figure 5–11 *Propliopithecus* has a five-cusped pattern on its lower molars. This very early primate appears to be a small ancestral *Dryopithecus*-like ape which may have given rise to both living apes and humans.

The existence of both monkeylike and apelike molars among the Fayum fossils makes one startling fact plain: as long ago as 30 to 35 million years, the creatures that were becoming monkeys and those that were becoming apes were already different.

In 1966 a magnificent new find of a creature closely related to *Propliopithecus* was made in the Fayum. The *Aegyptopithecus* fossil, as it was called, consisted of a virtually complete skull: head bones, upper and lower jaw, and an almost full set of teeth. The long canine teeth in the front of the upper jaw fitted the lower jaw to allow the same shearing ability that modern apes have. With this stunning find the promise of apishness made by the cusps in the lower molars of *Propliopithecus* was triumphantly confirmed by the apelike arrangement and fit of all the teeth of *Aegyptopithecus*. *Aegyptopithecus* (shown in Figure 5–7) is, in fact, the most primitive confirmable ape yet discovered. Spaniel-sized, with a skull shaped very much like that of a monkey, it may have looked more like a monkey than an ape, but the convincing evidence of its jaws and teeth prove that it was already separated from the monkeys and was following a course of its own. Whether that course led to man is, at the moment, impossible to say. A few scholars are inclined to think that *Aegyptopithecus*, despite its monkeylike skull and great antiquity, had already become too much of an ape in its dental structure, and that

Aegyptopithecus

its close relative *Propliopithecus* has at least as good a claim to being among man's ancestors, simply because it seems to have been less ape-committed and therefore to have had a greater evolutionary potential for further change.

These are sheer speculations that could be overturned at any moment by new finds, for the Fayum story is by no means fully told. Additional evidence continues to accumulate, indicating not only that monkeys and apes were distinct at a very early date, but, equally significant, that apes were beginning to differentiate among themselves. Of the four modern species of apes—gibbon, orangutan, gorilla, and chimpanzee—the gibbon is considered to be the least like a human in its morphological pattern, and the chimpanzee or gorilla the most like. In these early days, however, these distinctions were far less clear-cut than they are today, and we can logically expect to find ancestral forms which carry the characteristics of all living apes in some degree. Already there were little apes foreshadowing the gibbons, and larger ones that may have been ancestral to today's chimpanzees. It is from the survivors of these early models that modern apes have descended, and from among them, therefore, that we confidently may begin looking for our direct ancestors.

Dryopithecus

No likely candidate for man's ancestor has yet turned up from the Fayum fossil beds except *Aegyptopithecus* and *Propliopithecus*, and they are both too old and incomplete to lay positive claim to any particular living ape line. But if we jump forward another 10 million years to the Miocene epoch, some fascinating new players come on stage. One of these, *Dryopithecus* (shown in Figure 5–12), was widespread in Europe, Asia, and Africa 15 million years ago, and a number of its fossils have been dug up since as early as 1856. But the extremely limited knowledge of the times when its first fossils were found, and the near unthinkability at that time of looking for human ancestors farther back than half a million years or so, led *Dryopithecus* to be catalogued as simply a fossil ape.

Dryopithecus was back in the news, though, in the 1930s, when an African fossil ape, first called ''Proconsul,'' was discovered on an island in Lake Victoria, in Kenya. Finding the proper pigeonhole for this animal was extremely difficult. That it closely resembled chimpanzees was quickly recognized: it was obviously an ape. But then again it wasn't, for it had certain monkeylike characteristics. At last, and from a distance of some 20 million years, some wondered if this could be the first faint whisper of humanity. In all the excitement over Proconsul, it occurred to scientists to go back to museum drawers and blow the dust off *Dryopithecus*. Looked at by modern eyes sharpened by the Proconsul finds, *Dryopithecus* quickly came into new focus. Proconsul was the same kind of creature as *Dryopithecus*, with the same tantalizing blend of monkey and ape characteristics. Somewhere, a local species of this genus might have evolved into human beings.

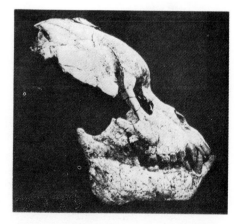

Figure 5–12 The skull of *Dryopithecus* is a typical ape skull. The ape line evolved relatively slowly after the time of *Dryopithecus*—about 15 million years B. P.

Now a new puzzle appeared, for more and more *Dryopithecus* fragments were being assembled, and these indicated that the animal came
in more than one size: some, like *Dryopithecus africanus*, were as small
as pygmy chimpanzees; others were middle-sized; still others were as
large as gorillas, and *Dryopithecus major* may indeed be the ancestor of
modern gorillas. The relationship of the *Dryopithecus* species is still
unclear, although it is now accepted that they all belong to the same
genus.

A HUMAN ANCESTOR?

With proto-gorillas and proto-chimpanzees lurking just over the
horizon, we are coming tantalizingly close to the ancestral human line.
Can we place any of these *Dryopithecus* species on it? Unfortunately,
not yet. To understand why, we must go back once more to teeth and
jaws. If you open your mouth wide and stand in front of a mirror, you
will notice two things about your upper jaw. The first is that your hard
palate, the roof of your mouth, is arched. The second is that your teeth
go back on each side in a broad curve, with the widest part of the curve
at the very back. By contrast, the hard palate of an ape is flat, and its
jaws are U-shaped. The sides of the U are parallel, with the result that
the back molars are no farther apart than those nearer the front of the
mouth.

Ramapithecus

Dryopithecus had these apelike parallel rows of molars, so we might
infer that its descendants were apes and not human beings. But what
if the broadly curving jaw was a later evolutionary development? Then
we could find that we have jumped too quickly to a conclusion. Digging
in the Siwalik Hills of India in 1932 (see page 5), G. E. Lewis discovered
a wide-curving jaw with an arched palate. He named his find *Ramapithecus* after the Indian god Rama, and on the strength of these two
manlike features (see Figure 5–13), Lewis wrote in 1937 that of all the
tangle of apelike Miocene primates, this one not only belonged to a
different genus from the others but also was the most manlike of the
lot. This was a pretty optimistic step—too optimistic, many specialists

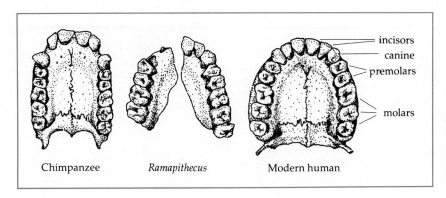

incisors
canine
premolars

molars

Chimpanzee   *Ramapithecus*   Modern human

Figure 5–13 The dentition of the
upper jaw of *Ramapithecus* is here
compared with that of an ape (a chimpanzee) and a human. *Ramapithecus*
canine teeth are relatively smaller than
ape canines, and the curvature of the
dental arcade is quite distinct.

felt, for Lewis's specimen consisted of only part of an upper jaw with a few teeth attached. To anchor the entire human line to such a small fragment of fossil seemed to be rushing things. Furthermore, there was another wide-jawed type of fossil creature collecting dust in the museums. It bore the name *Bramapithecus* and was known only by a lower jaw. With commendable caution the scientists sat back to see whether the upper-jawed *Ramapithecus* or the lower-jawed *Bramapithecus,* or perhaps another form entirely, would end up with the honors.

Nothing much happened for a quarter of a century. Then Louis and Mary Leakey, who, as we have mentioned, devoted a lifetime to fossil hunting in East Africa, discovered an upper jaw at Fort Ternan in Kenya (see page 4). Although Leakey preferred to call his find *Kenyapithecus,* the consensus of present paleontological thought is that the Kenya fossil is simply another, somewhat more primitive, *Ramapithecus.* Potassium-argon dating of a level just above the one where this new jaw lay confirmed an age of 14 million years. From the Leakey find, a fairly good upper jaw with most of its teeth could be reconstructed. With the teeth in place, a strongly human characteristic revealed itself; all the teeth were close to being the same size. Among apes, the front teeth—the incisors and especially the canines—tend to be conspicuously longer.

The matching up of the Lewis finds from India and the Leakey find from Kenya into one good *Ramapithecus* jaw was suggested by Elwyn Simons. Simons had decided to search all the fossil collections at his disposal to see if he could not find some clues that had been overlooked by previous examiners. For one thing, he was puzzled by the fact that of the two curve-jawed types then known, one (*Ramapithecus*) was represented only by upper jaws and the other (*Bramapithecus*) only by lowers. It occurred to him to put the upper and lower jaws together. They fit. *Bramapithecus* and *Ramapithecus* are the same. Thanks to Simons, the name *Bramapithecus* was dropped and *Ramapithecus* from India now has both an upper and a lower jaw (see Figure 5–14). The creature's credentials as man's oldest direct ancestor thus were cautiously advanced one step further. The age of these jaw fragments is uncertain. They may be 9 million years old; they may be 12 million. There is no convenient layer of volcanic ash in the Siwalik Hills for precise potassium-argon dating; age estimates have had to be made by comparing other animal fossils present in these strata with similar fossils in other places. But the exact date of these Siwalik fragments is not so important as their nature. They suggest that their long-gone owners had shorter, wider jaws with sets of almost even teeth much closer in appearance to those of *Australopithecus* than to the teeth of the apes that lived in India at the same time.

Reassessment of earlier finds has resulted in the discovery of yet another *Ramapithecus* jaw, this one from a site near Athens, Greece. Found in 1944 and classified as a monkey jaw, this fossil has recently been re-identified by Simons as once belonging to a European member

Figure 5–14 Side view of the upper and lower jaw fragments of *Ramapithecus* from Fort Ternan in Kenya. Note the size of the canine tooth.

TABLE 5–1 FOSSIL RECORD OF THE GENUS *RAMAPITHECUS*		
Site of Discovery	**Fossil**	**Age**
Asia: Siwalik Hills of India and Pakistan (1910–1932)[a]	*R. punjabicus:* five lower and two upper jaw fragments	9–12 million years
Africa: Fort Ternan, Kenya (1960)	*R. wickeri:* upper and lower jaw fragments, including teeth	14 million years
Europe: Athens, Greece (1944)	*R. freybergi:* lower jaw	circa 8 million years

[a] A jaw recently discovered (1974) at Candr in Turkey has also been identified by some experts as belonging to *Ramapithecus.* Its age is about 8 million years B.P.

of the genus *Ramapithecus.* This means that we have recognized what are now considered three species of the genus from the three continents of the Old World (see Table 5–1). The older, African specimen is somewhat more apelike than the later Asian and European specimens.

The bones themselves do not supply the only information about *Ramapithecus.* The environments that we can reconstruct are highly suggestive of a change in habitat. The African and Indian forms are associated mainly with forest but with some grassland species, and the European fossil with a typical grassland fauna of the period. This is most significant, for as we shall see in Chapter 8, the evolution of bipedalism was associated with adaptation from a forest environment (typical of almost all primates) to a grassland or savanna environment— not by any means treeless but with considerable open spaces of grassland in which the trees are scattered and the forest limited to river valleys and mountains.

The impressive thing about *Ramapithecus* is that each bit of additional evidence about it has tended to strengthen rather than weaken the claim being made for it. If this continues a bit longer, its position in the human ancestral line could become secure.

So anthropologists are eagerly awaiting the next *Ramapithecus* find— if it should come. They are also following Elwyn Simons' example and taking some sophisticated second looks at the bones now in their possession. As more and more of this rechecking goes on, the clouds that have obscured the Miocene primate picture are beginning to thin out. The situation is far more complicated than has been indicated in this necessarily brief chapter. (There are many forms that have not been mentioned at all: *Oreopithecus, Oligopithecus, Aeolopithecus, Limnopithecus, Pliopithecus,* to name a few.) Most exist in lamentably small

Reassessing the Fossil Picture

Lemurs and other prosimians   New World monkeys   Old World monkeys   Gibbon   Orangutan   Gorilla   Chimpanzee   Human

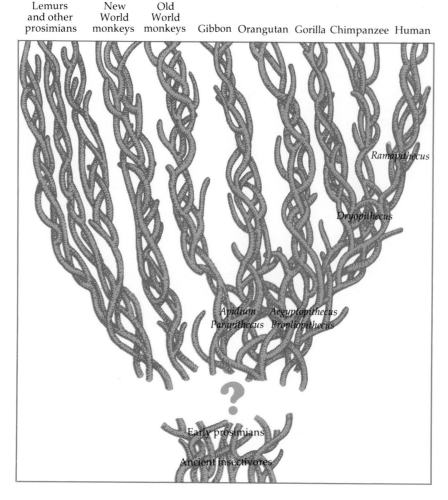

Ramapithecus

Dryopithecus

Apidium   *Aegyptopithecus*
Parapithecus   *Propliopithecus*

?

Early prosimians

Ancient insectivores

Figure 5–15   Evolutionary "trees," or dendrograms, are always greatly over-simplified and in certain ways in-accurate, but they nevertheless give a good indication of the relative age and phylogenetic relationships of the species shown. The multiplicity of lines indicates that any evolving lin-eage contains an unknown number of divergent populations which may or may not be different species. Many such populations become extinct.

fragments, and how they all relate is a question that is still being worked on. What they do make clear is that the primate family tree has nothing like a central trunk but is more like a luxuriant vine with many tendrils and shoots which grew side by side, sometimes withering and dying, sometimes branching (see Figure 5–15). One of those branches belongs to extremely ancient prosimian types, another to more advanced monkeylike and apelike types, and one to a group that belongs definitely in the ape line alone. Some of these ape ancestors were more like gibbons. Others, like *Dryopithecus,* were ancestral to the larger apes.

Much study and reorganization of the Oligocene and Miocene pri-mate fossil record is going on today. We already have a far clearer picture than was possible as recently as five years ago. That it may be turned inside out by other discoveries is always a possibility, but the more evidence that is collected to support the theory the more un-likely it becomes that it will be upset.

The Miocene, then, during about 10 million years, saw the development of a number of proto-apes. They were widely distributed through Europe, Asia, and Africa; they were evolving rather rapidly; they may well have been exceedingly numerous. Toward the end of the Miocene, since 15 million years ago, one of these creatures, *Ramapithecus*, began to show traits in its jaws and teeth that show similarities to human jaw structure and dentition and cause us to place it in the human zoological family, the Hominidae. Until a better candidate appears, *Ramapithecus* may be considered remotely ancestral to humankind. The longer its claim is allowed to stand, the stronger that claim will become.

	YEARS B.P.	FOSSIL RECORD	EARLY PRIMATES

Cro-Magnon, Neandertal, and *Homo erectus*

CENOZOIC

Early prosimians

65 million

Basic insectivores

MESOZOIC

225 million

First mammals

PALEOZOIC

First vertebrates

570 million

PRECAMBRIAN

Pleistocene
2 million —
Pliocene
5 million —

Miocene

25 million —

Oligocene

35 million —

Eocene

58 million —

Paleocene

65 million —

Early *Homo*

Earliest *Australopithecus*

Ramapithecus in Europe

Ramapithecus in India
Dryopithecus in Asia

Ramapithecus in Kenya; *Dryopithecus* in Europe

Dryopithecus in Africa

Apidium, Parapithecus, and *Aegyptopithecus* at Fayum
Propliopithecus at Fayum

Amphipithecus in Burma

HOMO

AUSTRALOPITHECUS AFRICANUS

RAMAPITHECUS

DRYOPITHECUS

PROTO-MONKEYS AND PROTO-APES

EARLY PROSIMIANS

BACK BEYOND THE APES

The time scale of primate evolution is immense. The first half of the 65 million years of primate history was the age of the prosimians, which occupied much of the Old and New Worlds. By thirty million years ago the apes were established in Africa, and for this reason we too find our origin on this continent. By about 18 million years ago the apes had spread into Eurasia.

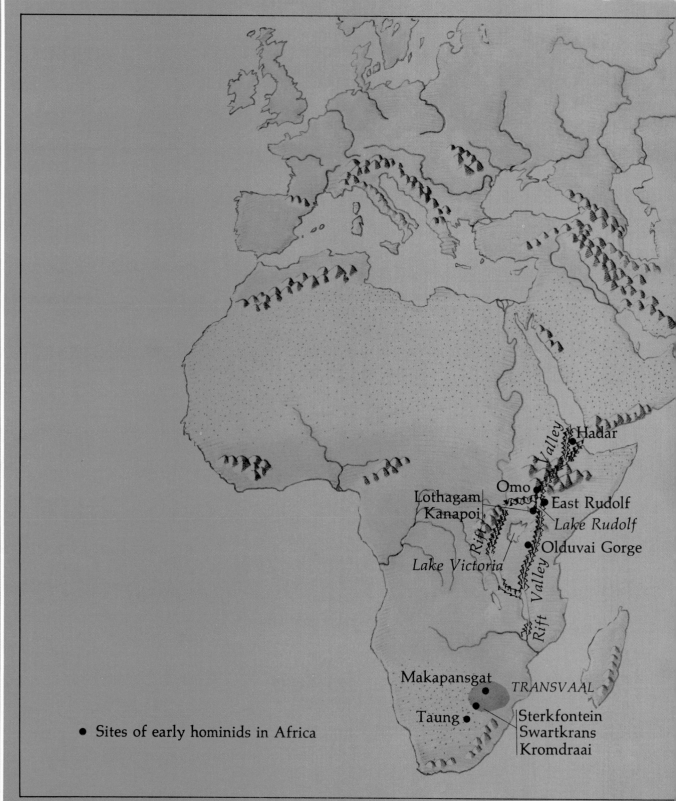

PART TWO

Makapansgat

TRANSVAAL

Taung

Sterkfontein
Swartkrans
Kromdraai

Hadar

Omo

East Rudolf

Lake Rudolf

Olduvai Gorge

Lothagam
Kanapoi

Rift

Lake Victoria

Rift Valley

Rift Valley

● Sites of early hominids in Africa

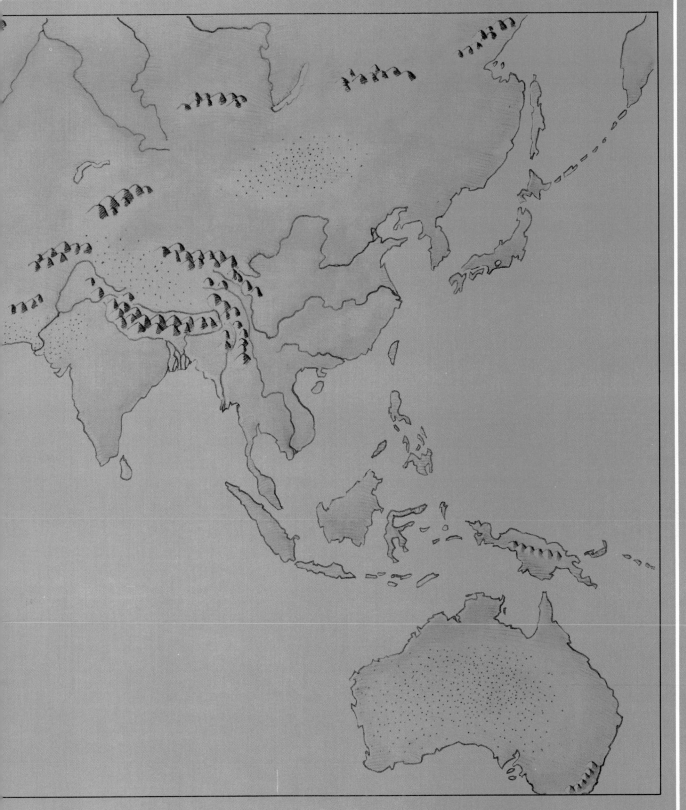

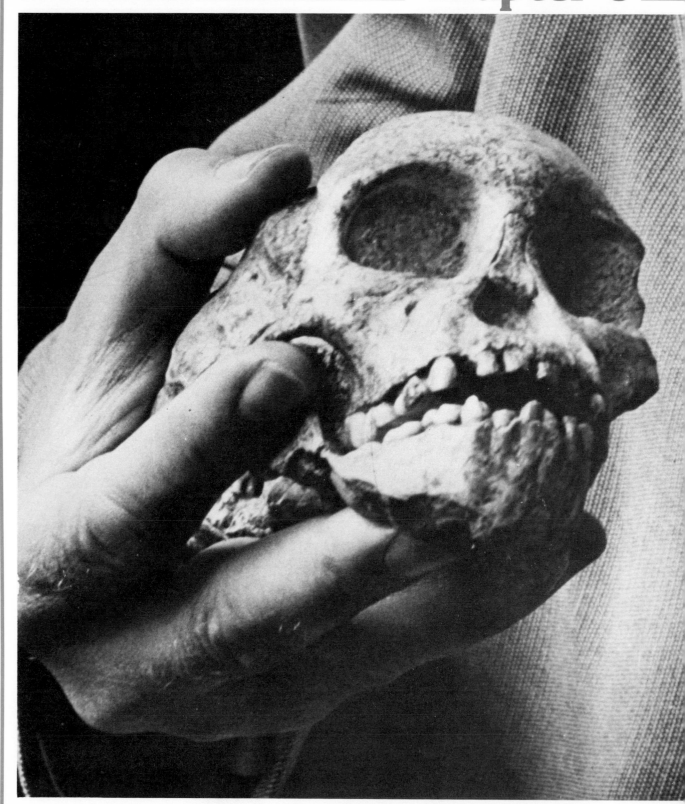

Chapter 6

African Ancestors

In each great region of the world the living mammals are closely related to the extinct species of the same region. It is, therefore, probable that Africa was formerly inhabited by extinct apes closely allied to the gorilla and chimpanzee; and as these two species are now man's nearest allies, it is somewhat more probable that our early progenitors lived on the African continent than elsewhere.

CHARLES DARWIN, 1809–1882.
THE DESCENT OF MAN.

In the last chapter we left *Ramapithecus* somewhere between apehood and manhood. How far this creature had evolved in our direction is still impossible to say, since the only remnants we have of it are jaws and teeth. We have no leg, hip, or even arm bone to tell us whether it stood erect like a man or, like an ape, used all four limbs to move around.

The importance of bipedalism—two-leggedness—cannot be over-estimated. It is much more than a mere rearing up and running about. Apes and monkeys have all sorts of structural handicaps that hamper them in this respect: they stand knees bent, unable to extend their legs fully; they walk on the sides of their feet. They can move on two legs and sometimes do for short distances, but they are not made for it. For humans, however, this is a way of life and we cannot function properly any other way. Somehow, somewhere, in the long 10 million years of the Late Miocene and Pliocene, the adaptations of bipedalism made their appearance in at least one kind of primate.

The first tangible evidence that a two-legged primate existed in the distant past came from an unexpected place, South Africa. Raymond Dart (Figure 6–1), whose name is already somewhat familiar to us from Chapter 4, encouraged his students to send him rock fragments that

DART'S DISCOVERY OF THE TAUNG SKULL (1924)

107

contained fossils. In 1924, a student brought in an unusual fossil baboon skull that had come from a limestone quarry at a place named Taung, 200 miles from Johannesburg, South Africa (see page 104). Hoping to obtain some more interesting fossils, particularly another baboon skull, Dart persuaded the quarry owner to save other bone-bearing material, and in due course he was sent two boxes of broken rock containing fossils.

Dart found nothing of interest in the first box, but his eye hit on something very strange in the second. On the top of the heap lay, not a skull, but the next best thing to it: an oddly shaped rounded piece of rock that appeared to be the mold of the inside of a skull. Scarcely allowing himself to think what this might mean, Dart went through the rest of the box and found another piece of rock with a curved depression into which this mold fitted—the skull itself. In this second rock Dart could dimly perceive the outline of a broken piece of skull and the back of a lower jaw. He was looking from the rear at the inside of something's, or somebody's, head.

A fossilized cast of the brain of any species of ape would have been a notable discovery, but one look at this antique fragment sent Dart's mind racing. Here was no fossil baboon. The animal's brain capacity appeared to be three times larger than a baboon's and perhaps even larger than a modern adult chimpanzee's. The exciting thought struck Dart that he might be holding in his hands the "missing link" between ape and man.

Dart's first problem was to free the rest of the strange skull from the surrounding stone. Working with a hammer, chisels, and a sharpened knitting needle, he "pecked, scraped and levered" bits of stone from the front of the skull and the eye sockets. After days of this painstaking dissection, an incredible face began to emerge (see Figure 6–2). Rather than the long projecting jaw and large canine teeth that clearly identify both existing and fossil baboons, this face had the relatively smaller jaw and the more nearly vertical face plane of an ape; yet it was not overhung by the low brow of an ape but surmounted by a forehead. From then on, Dart lay awake nights "in a fever of thoughts" about what kind of ape might have lived long ago in that semi-desert plateau.

Apes live in tropical forests, but there have been no such forests in South Africa for more than a hundred million years. While ice had advanced and retreated over much of the earth, and while mountains rose along the continental coasts, South Africa had always remained a dry, relatively undisturbed veld, much as it is today. Throughout prehistory, the nearest natural habitat of apes was more than 2,000 miles north of Taung. Could some different kind of ape have found a way to adapt itself to life in an arid, open land?

Dart continued his exacting labor with the baffling fossil until, on the seventy-third day of work, the stone parted and he saw before him the face and most of the skull of a child five or six years old. It had a full set of milk teeth; the permanent molars were just beginning to erupt,

Figure 6–1 In 1924 Raymond Dart startled the anthropological world by his discovery of a small fossil skull from a quarry at Taung in South Africa. The following year he named the Taung specimen *Australopithecus africanus* and boldly declared it to be a human ancestor. His claim was derided, but finds made many years later proved him right.

Evidence for
the "Missing Link"

and the canines, like those of humans, were quite small. After Dart had had time to study his find more carefully, he realized that the set of the skull suggested that this child had walked upright. One thing that made him feel sure that he was dealing with a true bipedal creature was the position of the *foramen magnum,* the hole through which the nerves from the spinal cord pass into the skull on their way to the brain. In apes and monkeys the foramen magnum is near the back of the skull, reflecting the sloping position of the spinal column in quadrupedal posture. But in the Taung skull it faced almost directly downward. This indicated that in life the Taung baby had carried its head over its spine like a rock balanced on the top of a pole. Whatever verdict the scientific establishment would eventually pass on the Taung baby, Dart was certain that the creature had stood erect.

All previous discoveries of human predecessors had proved in the end to be authentic, if early, human beings. This was true of Neandertal man, of Java man, of Peking man. All are classified as *Homo* despite certain apelike features. The child's face before Dart seemed the reverse: an ape with human features. It could not possibly be a man. It was too primitive, too small-brained. A pre-human, then, a link with the ape past? Taking a deep breath, Dart announced to the world in 1925 that he had found a human ancestor that was not yet human. He gave it the formidable name of *Australopithecus africanus* (from *australis*, southern; and *pithekos*, ape)—"southern African ape."

Because he was so confident of the significance of his find, Dart publicized his momentous news in record time. Less than four months after the skull had come into his hands, he wrote a full scientific report for the February 7, 1925, issue of the British magazine *Nature*. His report included the provocative statement, "The specimen is of importance because it exhibits an extinct race of apes intermediate between living anthropoids [apes] and man. . . . a creature well advanced beyond modern anthropoids in just those characters, facial and cerebral, which are to be anticipated in an extinct link between man and his simian ancestor." That day, in South Africa and around the world, the headlines proclaimed that the missing link had been found. Actually, it was the first link in a long chain of discoveries that would establish Africa as a possible place of origin of the human lineage.

Dart's report was intensely interesting to a number of scientists in Europe, not so much for the manlike attributes he claimed for the Taung creature as for the inexplicable presence of an ape so far south. The general conclusion was that this was a young specimen of an ancient chimpanzee-like or gorilla-like species; but how it had wandered where no ape had ever before been known to go was extremely puzzling. As a result, the Taung baby had to endure a long period of skepticism.

This recurring suspicion may seem strange. After all, anthropologists spend their lives looking for increasingly primitive, ever more apelike fossils. Why are they so reluctant to recognize one when it turns up? There are numerous reasons. For one, there are many false alarms. If this book were to catalogue all the mistaken claims about hominid fossils made by layman and expert alike, it would have to be far longer than it is. Also, there have been deliberate frauds. The most famous of these was Piltdown man, the creation of clever practical jokers who stained a modern human skull to look very old and then planted it in a dig in England along with an ape's jaw in which the teeth had been filed down to resemble human teeth. (For decades such frauds slowed the progress of anthropological thought to an extent that is hard to believe.) At the time that Dart discovered the Taung skull, the Piltdown find represented the generally held concept of our early ancestors. It suggested that early humans already had large brains but still had apelike faces—a concept that satisfies modern human vanity, with its emphasis on the special quality of the human intellect. Dart's fossil was not so agreeable. It suggested that just the opposite was true: that face and teeth began to become recognizably human while the brain was still very small. So anthropologists were naturally cautious, and the attacks on Dart were not long in coming. Dart's "baby," several critics suggested, was only "the distorted skull of a chimpanzee." Taung became something of a byword; it was ridiculed in songs and on music-hall stages.

Dart's Claims Dismissed

Figure 6–3 Dr. Robert Broom was a passionate fossil hunter and distinguished paleontologist. He kept working up to his death at the age of 85.

Despite the criticism, Dart was encouraged by a warm congratulatory letter from Robert Broom, a Scottish physician who had hunted fossils, particularly fossils of mammal-like reptiles, in many parts of South Africa. Two weeks after the letter arrived, Broom himself appeared at Dart's laboratory. He spent a weekend studying the Taung baby intensively and was convinced that as "a connecting link between the higher apes and one of the lowest human types" it was the most important fossil discovered up to that time. He said so firmly in an article in *Nature*. However, after the first flare-up of attention, Dart's baby was either forgotten or dismissed by most scientists. Dart and Broom continued nonetheless to study the skull.

The Dentition of Taung

For his part, Dart worked away at the skull almost daily for more than four years. In 1929 he succeeded in separating the upper and lower jaws, which had been cemented together in the rock-hard mass of *breccia* (a cemented mixture of sand, soil, and pebbles) that enclosed them. For the first time he could examine the entire pattern of the teeth and get a good look at their grinding surfaces.

What he found further strengthened his case that the fossil was not an ape or a baboon. In apes, the front teeth are large, because they are used both for defense and intimidating enemies, and for tearing up the large amounts of vegetable matter that form much of an ape's diet. Ape canines, in particular, are so large and extend so far that in order for them to interlock, there must be spaces between the teeth of the upper jaw (see Figure 6–4). At the same time apes' jaws are longer than humans' jaws. They are heavier, too, and the muscles needed to move them are more massive. The Taung baby, although a young individual, could be judged to be distinctly more manlike than apelike in all these characteristics. Its nicely curved jaw was shorter than an ape's and more lightly made. Its canines and incisors were relatively small and set closely together. In fact, though the molars were larger, most of the teeth could have belonged to a child of today.

In the minds of Dart and Broom, any lingering doubts about the hominid features of the creature vanished; but skeptics, they suspected,

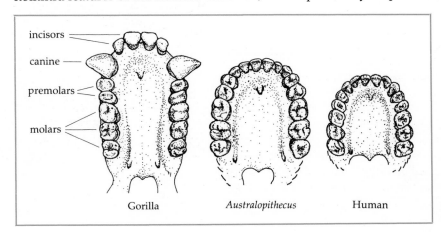

incisors

canine

premolars

molars

Gorilla   *Australopithecus*   Human

Figure 6–4 View of the palate of a gorilla, *Australopithecus*, and a modern human. Note that the gap between canines and incisors is found only among the apes.

would take more convincing. What was needed was an adult skull, and also some leg or pelvic bones to support the evidence of erectness that the position of the foramen magnum suggested. Broom was determined to find this evidence, but it was not until the 1930s that he was free to begin a serious search.

Prime Minister Smuts opened the way by offering Broom a post as curator of vertebrate paleontology at the Transvaal Museum in Pretoria. For the next year and a half, Broom was occupied digging out, describing, and naming 44 new fossil species of reptiles. He also unearthed a baboon jaw which at first appeared to be *Australopithecus*. It was not, but the publicity it engendered led two of Dart's students to tell Broom about some small skulls they had found in a quarry at Sterkfontein, a village not far from Pretoria (see page 104).

THE DISCOVERIES OF ROBERT BROOM

A Skull from Sterkfontein (1936)

Ever since the first mining camps were opened during the gold rush of 1886, the people of the Sterkfontein area had been picking up fossilized remains of baboons, monkeys, and perhaps, unknowingly, apemen. The limeworks had even issued a little guidebook, "Come to Sterkfontein and Find the Missing Link." When Broom visited the quarry, the manager, who had worked at Taung and knew about the *Australopithecus* child's skull, promised Broom that he would keep a sharp lookout for anything resembling the skull of an ape-man.

When Broom returned on August 17, 1936, the manager asked, "Is this what you're after?" and handed him two-thirds of a superb brain cast, which had been blasted out only that morning. Broom anxiously dug into the debris to try to find the skull that had served as the mold. Though he worked until dark, he found nothing. The next day, as he sorted the piles of stone, he recovered not only both sides of the upper jaw, but also fragments of the brain case. When the fragments were pieced together, Broom had most of the skull of an adult *Australopithecus*.

Broom went to the quarry at Taung and found skull of an adult Australopithecus

For three years the doctor, now in his seventies, continued to visit his fossil gold mine. One June day in 1938, the quarry manager met Broom and handed him an ape-man upper jaw with one molar in place. He had obtained it from a schoolboy who lived on a farm at Kromdraai, less than a mile away. The doctor drove over to Kromdraai and found the boy, who responded to Broom's first questions by pulling out of his pocket "four of the most wonderful teeth ever seen in the world's history." Back at the site, the boy opened his private cache and gave the doctor an excellent piece of a lower jaw. During the next two days, Broom and the boy sifted earth and found a number of scraps of bone and teeth. When the pieces were put together, Broom had most of another ape-man skull, the third. The face was flatter than that of the Sterkfontein *Australopithecus*, the jaw heavier, and the teeth larger and less human.

Australopithecus robustus at Kromdraai

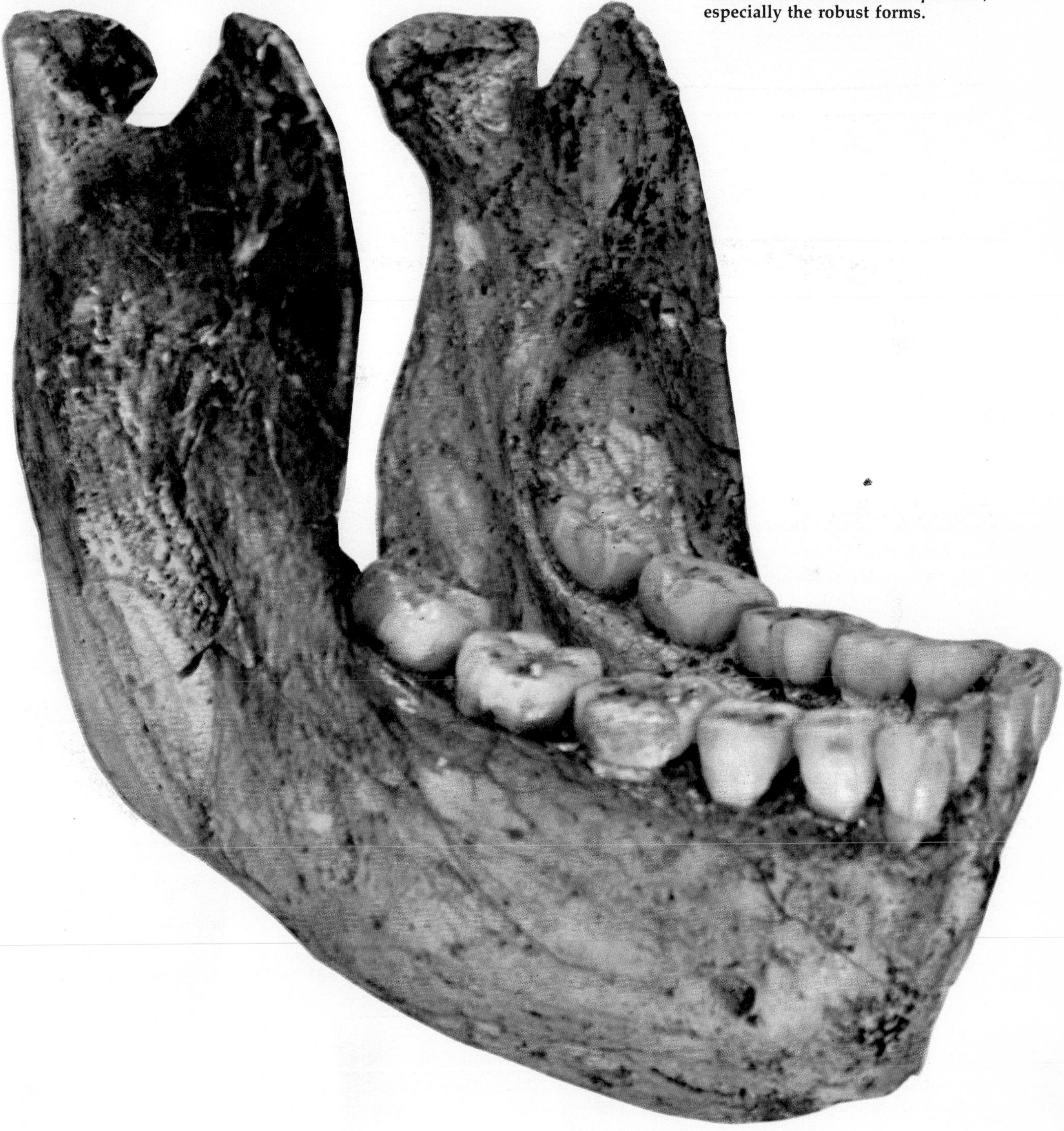

Figure 6–5 The almost perfect jaw of *Australopithecus robustus* found at Swartkrans. Note the huge molars and premolars and diminutive front teeth which characterize *Australopithecus*, especially the robust forms.

When the newest findings were published, the situation seemed even more confused. Kromdraai man differed so markedly from both the Taung child and the Sterkfontein adult that it appeared increasingly likely to Broom that there might be two species of man-apes in South Africa: the smaller, more slender "gracile" type with smaller molars that Dart had named *Australopithecus africanus,* and the heavy-jawed "robust" Kromdraai type with extremely large molar teeth. Broom established a new genus and species for the Kromdraai type: *Paranthropus robustus,* robust near-man.

Years later, when numerous fossils of both types had been recovered, a clear scientific distinction would be made between them. One of the ape-men types would be called *Australopithecus robustus* out of respect to its larger size and supposed weight of up to 150 pounds. The smaller, estimated to weigh from 80 to 100 pounds, would retain the name that it had originally been given, *Australopithecus africanus.* But when Broom set up a new genus for one small African site, his fellow scientists thought he was going too far. "Of course the critics did not know the whole of the facts," said Broom. "When one has jealous opponents one does not let them know everything." What he had not disclosed was that the fossils of animals found with the Kromdraai *Australopithecus* fossil were less archaic than the ones excavated with *Australopithecus africanus,* and represented different types. Fossil horses abounded at Kromdraai; none apparently occurred at Sterkfontein, only a mile away. Many other fossil animal species proved not to be shared between the two sites. Also, the breccia itself in which the Kromdraai creature lay seemed to be of a different age from the strata at Taung and Sterkfontein that held *Australopithecus africanus.* If the sites were occupied at various times—from several million to a half million years ago—then each might well have sustained a different species of ape-man. Broom came to the conclusion that some of his *robustus* finds were as much as a million years younger than Dart's *africanus*—and this is still considered a correct interpretation.

Broom continued to dig, and in due course he had more evidence to work with, having struck a rich find in a cave at Swartkrans (see Figure 6–5) just across the valley from Sterkfontein. The more new material he found, the more puzzled he became. Of the two types of *Australopithecus, A. robustus,* the larger, more recent man-ape, seemed more primitive. Although a million years closer to man, it was not more manlike; rather, it was more apelike (see Figure 6–6). Its jaws and molars were massive, less like those of modern man than the jaws and molars of *A. africanus* were. Its oversized grinding teeth were huge in proportion to the size of its front teeth. Also, on its skull it had a bony ridge to anchor large jaw muscles. These characteristics suggested that the creature was a vegetarian, that it chewed up large quantities of tough vegetable food, much as a gorilla does today.

Could the younger, more primitive type be the human ancestor? That just did not make sense. How could a more primitive-appearing type of ape-man occur so much later than a more advanced one? Assigning to *A. robustus* a role in human ancestry raised awkward problems.

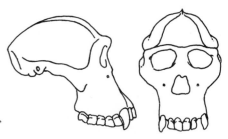

Chimpanzee

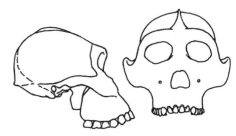

Australopithecus robustus

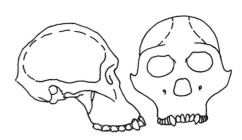

Australopithecus africanus

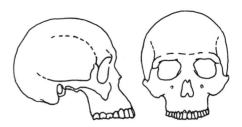

Homo sapiens

Figure 6–6 The skulls of two species of *Australopithecus* are here compared with those of a chimpanzee and a modern human being. Note the absence of the crest on *A. africanus* and its narrower face. The large ape canine is not found in *Australopithecus.* In the human specimen, note the increase in the size of the braincase and the relatively smaller jaws.

For one thing, an animal does not get specialized jaw equipment—a heavy jaw, oversized grinding teeth, a bony ridge on its skull—overnight. It could be assumed that *A. robustus* had been following an evolutionary course toward a vegetarian life for a long time. Therefore the most reasonable expectation would be that the creature would continue to do so. Very probably it would not suddenly switch to the omnivorous (unspecialized) and smaller-jawed way of life that human beings would come to lead a few hundred thousand years later. Evolution does not work that capriciously or that fast. It would be much more logical to assume that since man was known to have been an eater of all sorts of things for at least three quarters of a million years, he probably had had that trait for a much longer time.

Broom set out to calculate the age of *Australopithecus africanus*, a task which was not easy. Accurate dating is impossible in South Africa, because of the unique geological structure of the area. Most of the South African finds were made in lime-cemented breccia that had filled in ancient caves. This had to be removed from quarries by blasting, which, of course, destroyed the stratigraphic pattern. In addition, since so little was known about the geology of South Africa, whatever stratigraphic clues could be discovered could not be matched with better-known and better-dated layers in other parts of the world. About the best that Broom could do was to make a careful examination of the animal fossils associated with the *Australopithecus* remains. To Broom's frustration, not only were all of these animals extinct, but they also were not known in any other place; there was nothing he could compare them with. However, the very fact of their extinction indicated that they must have been at least a million years old, possibly much older. Making a bold guess, Broom announced that *Australopithecus africanus* was probably two million years old.

His choice of two million years turned out to be more extraordinarily shrewd than it was shaky. For the moment, however, his announcement was greeted by the scientific community with hoots of derision. What bothered other scientists who examined the fossils or read about them was not the jaws but the rest of the head. They could not believe that a human ancestor with a brain scarcely bigger than a chimpanzee's had been running around on two legs in South Africa two million years ago.

Considering that this creature was estimated to be more than twice as old as any other known hominid, it did not seem so remarkable to Dart or Broom that this peculiar mixture of ape and human characteristics should exist in a fossil. Two million years, they reasoned, might bring one pretty close to a common man-ape ancestor. That ancestor could well display a confusing and unexpected mingling of characteristics.

World War II came and went, and still *Australopithecus* was scarcely recognized in the scientific world. This was partly because Dart was a young anatomist and all but unknown to the paleoanthropological establishment, all of whose brightest stars were in the United States,

The Age of
Australopithecus africanus

England, France, and Germany; it was also partly because the brains of these South African fossil creatures just were not big enough to satisfy other scientists. Perhaps *Australopithecus* was simply an aberrant chimpanzee.

New Discoveries at Sterkfontein (1947)

Meanwhile fossil evidence continued to accumulate. Soon after the end of the war, in 1947, Broom resumed digging at Sterkfontein. One day a blast in some unpromising cave debris revealed the first of a series of important discoveries. When the smoke cleared away, the upper half of a perfect skull (see Figure 6–7) sparkled brilliantly in the sunlight. Lime crystals encrusting its inner surface caught and reflected the light like diamonds. The lower half of the skull lay embedded in a block of stone that had broken away. The glittering skull was believed to be that of an adult female. Her jaw was heavy, her forehead low, but to the trained eye there was an unmistakable quality of humanness about her. Her discovery was followed by other important finds (Figures 6–8 and 6–9): a male jaw with an intact canine tooth worn down in line with the other teeth, as human canines are; and then, in August 1947, a nearly perfect pelvis. This was, after the skull, the most important discovery. There was no doubt that it had belonged to a creature that had walked and run upright, as we do. Other finds confirmed this many times over.

Assessing *Australopithecus*

By 1949 the remains of more than thirty individuals had been recovered from the South African caves, and Wilfrid Le Gros Clark, Professor of Anatomy at Oxford University, undertook an impartial,

Figure 6–7 The magnificent skull of *Australopithecus africanus* found at Sterkfontein by Robert Broom in 1947. Although the teeth and jawbone are missing, the skull is otherwise complete and undistorted—a rare find.

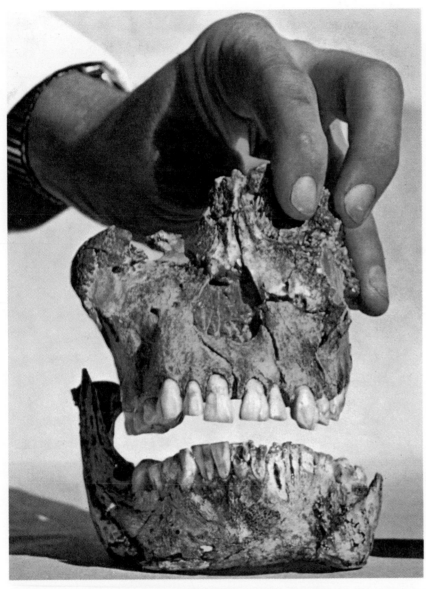

Figure 6–8 These beautifully pre-served jaws were found in 1949 by John Robinson, Broom's successor at the Transvaal Museum. This specimen has unusually large canine teeth.

definitive study. He studied the South African fossils and compared them with a series of ninety skulls of modern apes. His verdict was unqualified:

It is evident that in some respects they [the *Australopithecus* specimens] were definitely ape-like creatures, with small brains and large jaws. But in the details of the construction of the skull, in their dental morphology, and in their limb bones, the simian features are combined with a number of characters in which they differ from recent or fossil apes and at the same time approximate quite markedly to the *Hominidae*. All those who have had the opportunity of examining the original material are agreed on these hominid characters: the real issue to be decided is the question of their evolutionary and taxonomic significance.

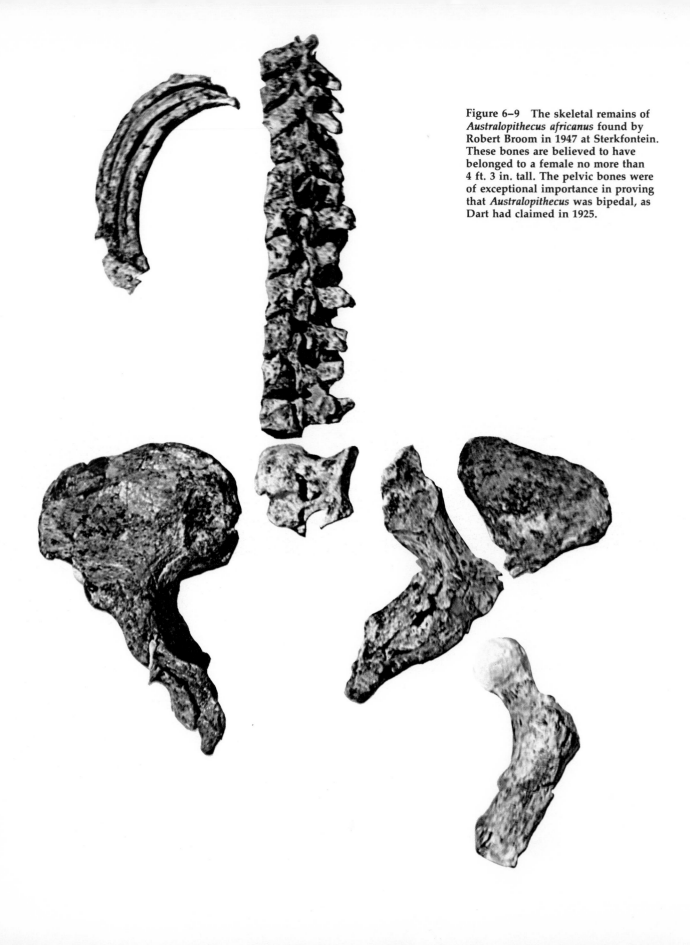

Figure 6–9 The skeletal remains of *Australopithecus africanus* found by Robert Broom in 1947 at Sterkfontein. These bones are believed to have belonged to a female no more than 4 ft. 3 in. tall. The pelvic bones were of exceptional importance in proving that *Australopithecus* was bipedal, as Dart had claimed in 1925.

By the mid-1950s a total of five sites had yielded several dozens of individuals of both *Australopithecus africanus* and *Australopithecus robustus*. The growing fossil record confirmed Broom and his assistant, J. T. Robinson, in their certainty that they were dealing with two quite different creatures. Furthermore, another South African, C. K. Brain, had made detailed studies of the sediments in the various sites, and his findings had begun to produce more evidence of the relative age of the two types. The smallest *A. africanus* specimens were invariably the older, and they seemed to evolve toward somewhat larger and slightly more manlike forms. By contrast, the robust type was bulky from the start and stayed that way. It seemed that throughout its known existence it evolved little or not at all.

Which, if either, of the two South African fossil types led to man still remained an unanswered question. Tools have been essential in human evolution, and if tools could be found associated with either type, some light might be shed on the matter.

At first, Dart and Broom were not preoccupied with stone tools. *Australopithecus* was such an ancient and controversial character that for a number of years after his discovery the argument was less over whether he was or was not a tool user than over whether he was or was not an ape. In 1947, after eighteen years as professor of anatomy at the University of Witwatersrand, Dart returned to the search for "dawn man." Analyzing thousands of fossilized animal bones found in further cave deposits 200 miles to the north at Makapansgat (see page 104), the discoverer of *Australopithecus* concluded that *A. africanus* had employed tusks and teeth for cutting tools, jaws for saws and scrapers, and leg bones for bludgeons (see Figure 6–10). His arguments, though ingenious, were not widely accepted.

Broom sought other clues, other cultural objects essential to hominid status. For years, he and his colleagues hunted for stone tools that might be associated with either the robust or the smaller, gracile man-ape. For years they found none. Then, in 1953, some simple pebble tools were discovered on a terrace in the Vaal valley, which had been formed during the same dry period in which the ape-men lived: they were fist-sized pieces of stone from which a few chips had been removed. It seemed at the time impossible that they could have been made by *Australopithecus*, whose brain was no larger than that of a modern ape, only 435 to 530 cubic centimeters. So the question of tools continued to haunt Broom and other experts.

But in 1957, once again new evidence was discovered. Working close by the cave at Sterkfontein that was yielding up a gratifying supply of *A. africanus* remains, Broom's successor, J. T. Robinson, and an archaeologist, Revil Mason, dug into a layer of red-brown breccia and found several hominid teeth and nearly 300 pebble tools. To the untrained eye these objects would have looked like naturally fractured stone, but close examination showed that chips had been flaked off two sides;

FOSSILS AND ARTIFACTS

Figure 6–10 Raymond Dart firmly believes that *Australopithecus africanus* used animal bones as a wide variety of tools. Here he demonstrates a pick (top) and a scraper (bottom).

the head of the stone was left round. A hammer stone held in a hand and guided by understanding had shaped these pebbles to cut, scrape, and possibly kill. Not only their shape and the fact that they had been worked indicated that these were tools. The Sterkfontein cave is located near the top of a hill where stones of that kind do not occur naturally. They are common in the valley about half a mile away, and since stones do not climb hills unaided, they must have been carried to the site of the cave.

The situation was not entirely clear. The site that yielded the teeth and stone tools was believed to be somewhat later in date than the site that yielded the skulls and teeth of *Australopithecus*, but there were not enough teeth from the later site to permit exact identification either with the teeth of *Australopithecus* or with those of later kinds of hominids. We are still not able to associate without any doubt this stone tool culture with the gracile *Australopithecus* from the Transvaal.

When the findings of fossils and tools were put together, even tentatively, the world was confronted with a fascinating proposition: between a million and two million years ago, South Africa contained a population of two kinds of manlike creatures. They had brains not much bigger than those of apes, but they were able to walk erect and already possessed evidence of developing intellects, since at least one kind may have been a collector and user of stones and just possibly a maker of tools.

	Holocene		YEARS A.D.	DISCOVERIES
10,000			1957 —	Robinson and Mason find tools at Sterkfontein
	CENOZOIC			
	Dryopithecus		1950 —	Definitive assessments by Le Gros Clark published
	Apidium, Parapithecus,		1948 —	*Paranthropus* found at Swartkrans
	Aegyptopithecus, and		1947 —	*Australopithecus africanus* skull and pelvis found at Sterkfontein;
	Propliopithecus			Dart discovers *Australopithecus* at Makapansgat
	Amphipithecus			
			1938 —	*Paranthropus robustus* discovered by Broom at Kromdraai
	Early prosimians		1936 —	Broom's first adult *Australopithecus* found at Sterkfontein
65 million				
			1925 —	Dart's publication on *Australopithecus africanus*
			1924 —	Dart discovers *Australopithecus africanus* at Taung

			YEARS B.P.	FOSSIL RECORD	
					HOMO SAPIENS
		Pleistocene		*Australopithecus africanus* at Taung	*HOMO ERECTUS*
			2 million —	*Australopithecus robustus* at Kromdraai and Swartkrans	*habilis* phase
				Australopithecus africanus at Sterkfontein and Makapansgat	
	MESOZOIC	Pliocene			*AUSTRALOPITHECUS AFRICANUS*
			5 million —		
		Miocene			
				Ramapithecus in Europe	*RAMAPITHECUS*
			10 million —		
	First mammals			*Ramapithecus* in Asia	
				Dryopithecus in Asia	
	Age of Reptiles			*Dryopithecus* in Europe; *Ramapithecus* in Africa	
225 million			15 million —		
	PALEOZOIC				*DRYOPITHECUS*

SOUTH AFRICAN ANCESTORS

The history of discoveries in South Africa is a fascinating story still unfolding (top right). The age of the fossils (bottom right) is still a matter of controversy because potassium-argon dating is not applicable in the area, owing to the absence of volcanic activity there during the Cenozoic (see also Figure 7-13).

Chapter 7

The Great Savanna

Ex Africa semper aliquid novi.
("Africa always has something new.")
      PLINY THE ELDER, 23–79.
      NATURAL HISTORY, BOOK VIII.

The question of whether the early hominids made tools and the continuing search for the first stone tool industries brought the attention of anthropologists to another part of Africa. During the 1950s, Louis and Mary Leakey, both distinguished archaeologists, were finding the remains of an extensive pebble tool industry 2,000 miles north of the Transvaal grasslands of South Africa (see page 104), in a dry river canyon in northern Tanzania.

DISCOVERIES AT OLDUVAI

Olduvai Gorge is an abrupt rent in the earth, some 25 miles long and 300 feet deep. Like a miniature Grand Canyon, its sides display different strata laid bare by the cutting of an ancient river. A German entomologist named Wilhelm Kattwinkel found the gorge in 1911 when he almost fell into its depths as he broke through some bush on the edge. A hasty exploration showed the place to be a rich source of animal fossils. Some of the fossils that Kattwinkel took back to Berlin were so unusual that an expedition headed by Hans Reck was sent out in 1913 to explore further. Its investigations were ended by World War I, and after the war Reck was unable to raise funds to resume operations. Eventually he wrote to Louis Leakey, the young curator of the Coryndon Memorial Museum at Nairobi, Kenya, urging him to take over, but

Leakey had to wait until 1931 before he could raise the funds for an expedition to Olduvai.

One season spent exploring the gorge was enough to convince Leakey that Olduvai was a site "such as no other in the world." He found pebble tools there the first year, long before they were discovered in South Africa, and no doubt he wondered if they could have been made by a creature similar to *Australopithecus*. For years Leakey searched the clearly stacked strata of the gorge in vain, unable to find the maker of the tools. As money and transport permitted, Leakey returned to the gorge, along with his wife and their sons. From each of the four principal beds that overlie one another from the river bottom to the surface of the plain some 300 feet above, the Leakeys eventually recovered an enormous number of animal fossils. They identified and classified over a hundred species, some of them extinct and some unknown to science until that time.

What particularly drew the Leakeys to Olduvai was the presence of the extremely primitive stone tools that were scattered in the gorge, either lying loose on the ground or working their way out of the valley's slowly eroding vertical walls. These tools were exceedingly crude. Some were large pebbles, others were fist-sized chunks; but all had a few chips struck from one end to make them jagged. Leakey recognized that this chipping had been done by some directing intellect and that the fractures were not the result of natural accident. The Leakeys found so many tools that they were able to give their tool culture a name—*Oldowan*, after the place of discovery. Yet aside from two small skull fragments and two teeth that they believed to be hominid, there was no trace of any human being. Who had made the Oldowan tools?

Figure 7–1 Olduvai Gorge is a remarkable landform as well as a fossil gold mine. In this photograph Louis Leakey points out to visitors some features of interest.

For twenty-eight years the Leakeys were engaged in one of the most persistent and unrewarding efforts in the history of anthropology. Olduvai was far from the museum at Nairobi where Louis Leakey worked, and they could seldom spend more than a few weeks a year at the gorge. The trip was expensive, and at first it took several days to get to Olduvai on the very rough road from Nairobi. The place was stiflingly hot, and water had to be hauled from a spring thirty-five miles away. There was only one way to search systematically for fossils, and that was to crawl along on hands and knees, inspecting every inch of ground. Through such work the Leakey collection of animal fossils and stone tools grew. But years went by with no sign of the men, or ape-men, who had manufactured the tools. It began to seem that the earliest known hominid, *Australopithecus*, had lived at one place, South Africa, and that the most primitive stone tools had been made at another, East Africa. It was not until the 1950s that the Leakeys were able to begin systematic excavation at Olduvai, and until July 17, 1959, all they knew was that they were the possessors of a small collection of what they believed to be the oldest implements ever seen.

On that morning Leakey awakened with a fever and headache. His wife insisted that he remain in camp. But the work season was drawing to an end and the day could not be lost, so Mary Leakey drove to the point where the party was working. As she worked slowly along the hillside of Bed I, the lowest layer of the gorge, a piece of bone exposed by recent erosion caught her eye. She recognized it as a piece of skull. Searching higher along the slope, she suddenly saw two big teeth, brown-black and almost iridescent, just eroding from the hill. She marked the spot with a small piece of stone and sped back to camp.

Leakey heard the car racing up the road and sprang up in alarm, thinking that his wife had been bitten by a snake. But as the car stopped he heard Mary shout, "I've got him!" The "him," she felt sure, was a hominid fossil—the early man they had been seeking for so many years. Leakey's fever and headache forgotten, the couple jumped in the car and drove back as fast as they could.

Mary Leakey's first impression had been right. There it was, an unmistakably hominid face. It was just beginning to emerge, along with more of those primitive tools, from the eroding slope of Bed I. Examining the teeth with the most minute care, Louis Leakey could see that the dark molars glinting in the afternoon sun were twice as wide as the molars of modern humans, but they were human in shape. "I turned to look at Mary, and we almost cried with sheer joy, each seized by that terrific emotion that comes rarely in life," Leakey commented later. "After all our hoping and hardship and sacrifice at last we had reached our goal . . . we had discovered the world's earliest known human." The Leakeys went to work with camel's-hair brushes and dental picks. The palate to which the teeth were affixed came into view, and then fragments of a skull emerged. In order not to lose a single precious scrap, the couple removed and sieved tons of *scree*, a fine rock debris, from the slope below the find. At the end of nineteen days they had about four hundred fragments.

Discovery of
Australopithecus boisei
(1959)

Figure 7-2 Louis Leakey had the inestimable advantage of being married to a remarkable woman and distinguished archaeologist. Mary Leakey worked with him at Olduvai from 1935, and today she still carries on her painstaking research in the Gorge.

While the delicate task of assembling the bits and pieces went on, the Leakeys continued to excavate the site. Not only had they discovered the oldest hominid skull found to that time in eastern and central Africa, but also they had unearthed a campsite of this ancient creature. Scattered on what had been the margins of an ancient lake were many tools made of stone flakes and chunks, along with waste chips. Lying about too were the fossil bones of animals that the residents of the campsite had killed and eaten—rats, mice, frogs, lizards, birds, snakes, tortoises, some young pigs, and parts of antelopes. Nearly all these bones were broken; the near-human skull and a *tibia* and *fibula* (the two bones of the lower part of the hind leg) that appeared at the same site were not. It seemed clear that the hominid had killed the other animals. But there were no remains of giant beasts at this site.

The skull that took form from the fragments uncovered at the campsite was that of a nearly mature male (see Figure 7–4). The fact that the wisdom teeth were unworn and the suture joining the two halves of the skull had not yet closed indicated a young adult. In brain size and in general appearance the young male broadly resembled the larger

Figure 7–3 Louis Leakey was somewhat eccentric, yet he was a great discoverer, a passionate and brilliant man. In this photograph he is searching for minute fossils under the scorching Tanzanian sun.

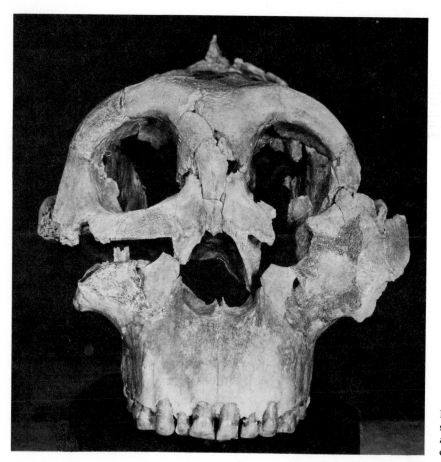

Figure 7–4 *Zinjanthropus*, the immense skull found by Mary Leakey at Olduvai in 1959. It is now classified as *Australopithecus boisei*.

Australopithecus robustus of the south. Yet, as Leakey studied the skull more closely, he saw significant differences. The face was not so apelike as the faces of the robust South African specimens. The palate was deeper and arched somewhat more like that of modern man. The molars Mary Leakey had seen protruding from the hill were extraordinarily large and heavy, but detailed study confirmed that they were, in their structure, undoubtedly hominid teeth. It had the characteristic massive face and teeth and rugged low cranium of *A. robustus* but appeared to be even larger and more specialized. These differences led Louis Leakey to set up a new genus for this early tool user, and he named him *Zinj-anthropus boisei*. (*Zinj* means "eastern Africa" in Arabic; *boisei* honored Charles Boise, who had helped to finance the Leakeys' search for early man.) Later, it was decided that the skull was more properly referred to as a new species (*boisei*) of the genus *Australopithecus;* the creature is now normally called *Australopithecus boisei.*

The approximate age of the Leakeys' fossil could fortunately be determined because it was found sandwiched between two layers of volcanic ash. Scientists extracted radioactive potassium from minerals in the volcanic ash covering *A. boisei* and also from an older volcanic bed that underlay the site. When they analyzed these layers by the then-new method of potassium-argon dating, they were able to fix the startling age of about 1,750,000 years, an age repeatedly confirmed by further potassium-argon tests. This dating of the fossil was extraordinary in itself. It also had a valuable side effect: suddenly Broom's claim of an age of two million years for the early South African *Australopithecus africanus* changed from being a wild guess to an inspired deduction. Careful comparison of the Leakeys' find with the other *Australopithecus* specimens began to suggest that *A. boisei* may have been ancestral to the later *A. robustus* from South Africa, separated from him by about thirty thousand generations in time and half a continent in space.

The question of which of the early hominids (shown in Figure 7–5) began to use tools, and when, continued to haunt paleoanthropologists. The more familiar the investigators became with both kinds of the robust type of *Australopithecus,* the more certain it appeared that this type was less manlike than the graceful little *A. africanus* species, whose brain was larger and whose jaws and teeth were smaller and more delicate. So long as the only association between australopithecine fossils and tools had been the inconclusive evidence from South Africa, it seemed safe to assume that *A. africanus* was the toolmaker. Then came the bombshell from the north that turned that assumption upside down: the Leakeys' discovery of an extremely ancient robust type in a living site full of tools. On the basis of the stratigraphic association at Olduvai, the more primitive-looking species of *Australopithecus—A. boisei*—now appeared to be the first tool user. The apparently more apelike hominid, therefore, seemed to be an immediate ancestor of man. Like it or not, students of evolution had no choice but to accept

The Age of Australopithecus

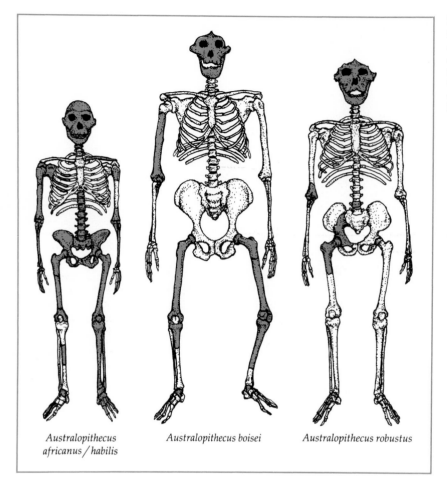

Australopithecus
africanus / habilis

Australopithecus boisei

Australopithecus robustus

Figure 7–5 These skeletons of *Australopithecus africanus* (including *habilis*), *A. robustus* from South Africa, and *A. boisei* from East Africa are reconstructed from fragments of many individuals. In the case of *A. boisei*, the drawing is highly imaginative as we have *very* limited skeletal remains.

that solution. But, as has been the case so often in the study of ancient man, an unwelcome answer to a particular question can, with the help of new evidence or a new look at old evidence, become more acceptable. In the case of Olduvai this happened with dramatic suddenness. Only a year after they had found the first skull, the Leakeys found another.

Early in 1960 the Leakeys' son Jonathan uncovered some teeth and bone fragments of another hominid. Found at broadly the same geological level as *A. boisei* and not far away, these bones, Louis Leakey realized, represented a creature far closer to mankind than the heavily built *A. boisei*. Two years passed before further specimens were found to confirm this interpretation, but by 1964 the Leakeys and their collaborators were ready to announce their new discovery.

Though as old as *A. boisei*, the new fossils represented a quite distinct species. It was clearly of the gracile type and even more humanlike than the gracile South African specimens. In fact, it seemed sufficiently human to be separated from the three known *Australopithecus* species altogether. Leakey and his co-workers described the fossil species as a

Discovery of
habilis (1960–1964)

true human that deserved to be classified in the genus *Homo*. He christened his find *Homo habilis*, "handy" man; now he really had discovered
the toolmaker.

That this *habilis*, and not the super-robust *A. boisei*, was indeed the
toolmaker has now been widely accepted. The Leakeys subsequently
collected from Olduvai a whole series of *habilis* fragments indicating
that this type lived there for more than half a million years, using much
the same primitive tool culture the entire time. (Later, *Homo erectus*
fossils also were discovered at Olduvai; they span a period from more
than one million to less than half a million years ago and strongly suggest that one type of creature evolved into the other.)

Habilis earned neither name nor credentials easily. He was primitive
and small brained. Many anthropologists preferred to identify him as
an advanced type of the gracile *A. africanus* not deserving of *Homo*
status at all. Many still identify him in this way. His qualifications as a
distinct species have been in question from the day he was christened.

Does *habilis* mark another spot on the line of the primate family tree
where a fork is indicated? It all depends on how one looks at him. If he
is an offshoot of *A. africanus* and if *A. africanus* continued to evolve in
South Africa after his appearance further north, then *habilis* does represent a fork. If *habilis* is simply a descendant of a southern form whose
manlike qualities became more recognizable over the course of time,
then there is no fork, just a slow evolution of one type into the other.
Obviously, this kind of problem can be settled only by reliable dating
of all the discovery sites, but, alas, we still have no good dates we can
attribute to the Transvaal deposits.

Although many anthropologists believe that the second way of
looking at *habilis* seems to be the more logical, the matter of how *habilis*
should be classified is still not clear. Was he a human or not? Should he
be called *Homo habilis* or *Australopithecus habilis?* Compared to the certified human beings that came after him, he seems scarcely human;
compared to the more primitive types that preceded him, his human
credentials suddenly improve. This disconcerting shift of perspective
always will occur when the eye runs down a series of fossils that are related to one another through direct descent. The differences between
them are differences in degree—not in kind—and obviously will become more pronounced as one takes one's example from more separated
time zones. Some of the more obvious characteristics of *Homo* are comparative: an "increasingly large" brain, a "less pronounced" bony ridge
over the eye with a "higher" forehead, a "more delicate" jaw, and
"longer" legs. But in a continuous series, where does one draw the line?

That question continues to arise, but it is conceivably the wrong
question. Since all creatures are bundles of characteristics, many of
which may be evolving at different rates, drawing a line that is based
on these characteristics will always cause trouble. The British anatomist
Sir Arthur Keith chose to draw the line marking the appearance of
humanity at a point where the brain capacity touched 750 cubic centi-

Classifying *habilis*

meters. Anything below that, according to Keith, was not a man; anything above it was a man, with *Homo sapiens* up around the 1,200–1,600 cc range (see Table 7–1). More recently, Sir Wilfrid Le Gros Clark put the minimum at 700 cubic centimeters. Clark's choice, unlike Keith's, was not an arbitrary one; it reflected the state of the fossil record at the time—there were no accepted "human" skulls known to exist with cranial capacities of less than 700 cubic centimeters. Implicit in this situation, of course, was the possibility that an apparently human specimen with a slightly smaller brain might be discovered any day. What would one call it, and if a still smaller one showed up, what would one call *it*?

Habilis laid this problem right on the scientists' doorstep. The great difficulty in deciding whether or not he was human lay in the fact that the so-called "type specimen," the first one to be found and named *Homo habilis* by the Leakeys, had a brain capacity estimated to be about 657 cubic centimeters—just under the limit. Since then three other

TABLE 7–1 COMPARISON OF CRANIAL CAPACITY

	Range of Cranial Capacity (cc)	Average Cranial Capacity (cc)
Lemur	10–70	—
Chimpanzee	282–500	383
Gorilla	340–752	505
A. africanus	435–530	450
A. robustus	—	500
A. boisei	—	530
habilis	600–684	642
Homo erectus	775–1,225	950
Modern adult human	1,000–2,000	1,330

Note: Measurements of cranial capacity are given in cubic centimeters (cc—a cubic centimeter is about the size of a sugar cube); the size of the brain itself is usually somewhat smaller because the cranial cavity also contains other structures. The above figures are approximate: for lemurs, the figures refer to several species of different size; for the two African apes, they are based on rather small samples; and in the case of the fossil groups, the samples are extremely small and may prove to be misleading (only single specimens of *A. robustus* and *boisei* are known and measured). Specimens included under *A. africanus* and *habilis* are from the sites listed in Table 7–2. In the case of modern humans, rare extremes exceeding even the approximate range given above have been found; the average figure is based on a limited number of samples. Slight variations of these figures will be found in other authors.

As a general rule, species of animals with larger brains are more intelligent that those with smaller brains, but this does not hold among species of different body size. Within a species, variations in brain size are not known to be related to intelligence among normal individuals.

habilis skulls from Olduvai have been measured by two experts, Phillip V. Tobias and Ralph Holloway. They came up with surprisingly uniform figures for these *habilis* skulls. They range in capacity from 600 to 684 cubic centimeters and average about 642 cc. Too small-brained for a human? Certainly too large-brained for a typical South African gracile *Australopithecus*, whose mean cranial capacity is only about 450 cubic centimeters.

With brain size and tooth shape and length of leg all evolving at different rates, it is difficult to define these sequential species on the basis of these characteristics. Nevertheless, classification and naming are necessary. The best way to deal with this problem may be to assign a point in time, rather than a set of physical characteristics, to mark the emergence of a new species. Of course, if one chooses to classify in this way, he must recognize that he always will be plagued by some blurring of characteristics.

A recent proposal of this kind placed the dividing line between the ancestral *Australopithecus* and the descendant *Homo* at 3.0 million years before present (B.P.) (see Figure 7–6). If this boundary line is accepted, then we should put the 1.75-million-year-old *habilis* into the genus *Homo* and call the species *H. habilis*. Some anthropologists take an opposite view, since they do not believe that the East African *habilis* fossils

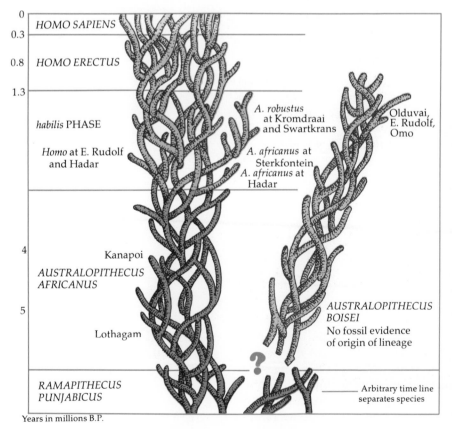

Years in millions B.P.

Figure 7–6 This diagram of the hominid lineage symbolizes the complexity of the evolutionary process and indicates the amount of variability (shown by the horizontal dimension) present at any one time. The *habilis* fossils, referred to as the "*habilis* phase," may be classified as late *Australopithecus* or early *Homo*. The successive species are separated by time lines. These are arbitrary divisions, but they represent the only effective way of subdividing such a lineage into successive taxa. *A. robustus* is believed by the author to have evolved locally from the South African *A. africanus*; some consider *A. robustus* an offshoot of the *A. boisei* lineage. We have no fossil evidence of the origin of *A. boisei* before 3 million years B.P.: it is reasonable to assume that it shares a common ancestry with *A. africanus* in view of their numerous similarities.

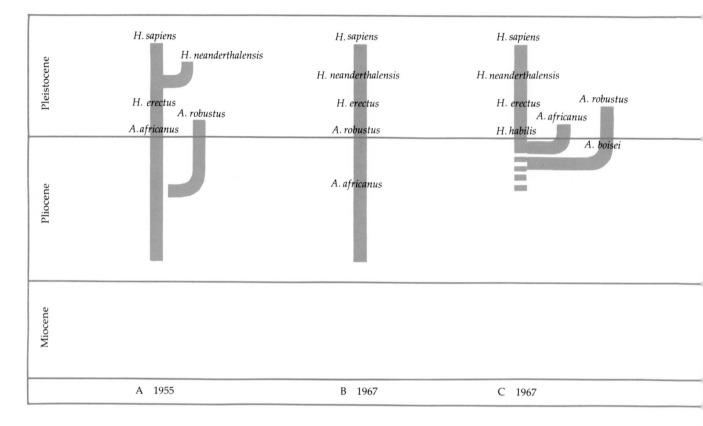

are sufficiently different from the South African *A. africanus* fossils to warrant specific distinction. In this case both groups of fossils are considered regional variations of the single species *Australopithecus africanus* (see Figure 7–7).

The debate about where to pigeonhole *habilis* began with his discovery in 1960, and it was still continuing inconclusively toward the end of the decade. Only part of the trouble lay in the difficulty of fitting him according to his physical characteristics. Equally troublesome was the absence of anything to compare him with. There was only that solitary skull of a strange super-robust contemporary—*A. boisei*—from Olduvai and a bunch of undated South African fossils. Looking back over *habilis'* shoulder, deeper in time, was impossible. There simply was nothing known that was definitely older than he was. Although many scholars suspected that the gracile South African fossils might be older, they could not prove it.

This lack of anything more than two million years old bore on the problem that bothered Broom: the apparent succession of the two different kinds of *Australopithecus*—*africanus* and *robustus*—in South Africa. Until their discovery, the prevailing opinion among scientists had been that not more than one kind of bipedal human ancestor ever had lived during any one period on earth. There is only one kind of hominid today, and the presumption was that evolution and competi-

Relating Gracile and Robust
Australopithecus

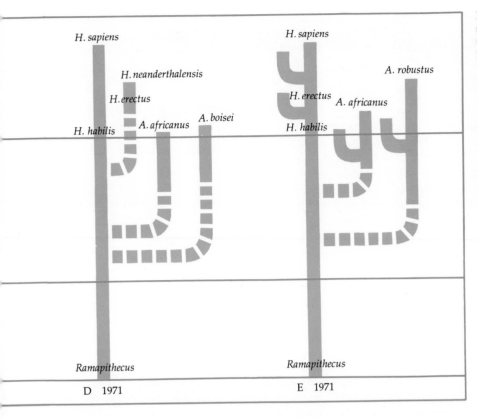

Figure 7–7 Diagrammatic representations of some earlier hypotheses of human evolution. The earliest, prepared by Le Gros Clark (A), is little different from the scheme presented in Figure 7–6. By 1967, views were diverging greatly: Loring Brace proposed a very simple scheme (B), whereas Tobias' was more complex (C). By 1971, new finds caused paleontologists to add even more branches to the hominid tree. Louis Leakey's scheme (D) has three main side branches; John Napier's has two, with some additional dead ends (E). The multiplication of branches may well be due to an erroneous understanding of natural population variation.

tion always had made that so. But as more and more fossils were recovered from South Africa, this belief was shaken. The robust and gracile types were sufficiently different to suggest that they represented two distinct species, even genera—unless, as a few people once believed, the big ones were males and the small ones females of a single species. (This is a fascinating idea but it is not supported by the evidence. If the theory is correct, then at some places and periods the population seems to have consisted of nearly all males; at others it seems to have been almost all females! Inasmuch as modern primate groups consist of both males and females, this fact is hard to accommodate.)

Does the evidence suggest that two erect hominids existed simultaneously? South Africa does not give us a good answer as the sites are of different ages. But if we look at the two types from Olduvai, a surprise confronts us. *A. boisei*, the robust specimen from Olduvai, is so very robust that there is absolutely no question that it and *habilis*, who is extremely gracile, are different. Yet they certainly coexisted, and on the same living floor.

This was the state of the art in the middle 1960s: man's ancestry had been pushed back to about two million years, at which time a creature who made tools and bore the name of *habilis* had turned up in East Africa. Although the Leakeys did not think so, other scientists believed that *habilis* was probably descended from *Australopithecus africanus*.

But until the dating problems of this species could be solved, there could be no certainty to this view. *A. boisei* presented, for the time being, a less intricate problem. The trouble with the big Olduvai skull was that it was the only one of its kind. Was it a single freak? Or did it represent a third hominid?

There was only one way to clear up the mystery, and that was by finding more fossils, by dating more precisely the ones that had been unearthed, and by digging deeper into time. In the hope of doing this, an ambitious international expedition was organized in 1967 to look for hominid remains in Ethiopia. Its destination was a remote spot in the southern part of the valley of the Omo River just north of Lake Rudolf (Figure 7–8), one of the most desolate places anywhere south of the Sahara and one of the hottest. The area had several attractions. For one thing, it had been visited thirty-five years before by one of the leaders of the new expedition, the French paleontologist Camille Arambourg, and had been found to be rich in animal fossils. For another, it bore a striking resemblance to Olduvai. It, too, is part of the Rift Valley geological complex, a giant crack in the earth that, running north–south through Africa, once was marked by chains of lakes and rivers and edged by towering escarpments. Much of the Rift Valley is dry now, its lakes shrunken, some of its cliffs worn away, its stones baked in the sun. There is no river at all today in Olduvai Gorge except during flash floods, although the gorge itself was made by a river. At Omo, as at Olduvai, deep-cut riverbeds speak of ancient days and long-vanished landscapes. The Omo River still runs down from the Ethiopian highlands and empties into Lake Rudolf, just over the border in northern Kenya. Lake Rudolf itself has grown and shrunk twice in the last four

FROM OMO AND EAST RUDOLF

Figure 7–8   This view of the Omo Valley in southern Ethiopia shows uplifted fossil-bearing deposits of the Shungura formation.

million years. It is still a sizable lake 185 miles long, but it has shrunk considerably from its original size and continues to do so. The brutal arid lands around it are largely unexplored.

The Rift Valley is an unstable area on the earth's surface where the earth's crust is still moving. It has long been a center of volcanic activity and is pockmarked by cones and craters. Due to neighboring volcanic activity, Olduvai has its invaluable layers of datable volcanic ash; so does Omo. Both places supported more life in the past than they do now. Laced with rivers, much greener, carrying a far larger animal population, each provided the lush water-edge environment, the forest-becoming-savanna, that the early hominids are believed to have preferred.

But Omo is also different from Olduvai, and the differences are what made it particularly appealing to the new expedition. At Olduvai, the most accurate and useful pages of the volcanic timetable are crowded into an 800,000-year period that is not quite 2 million years old and not much over 100 feet thick. At Omo the strata being investigated are more than 2,000 feet thick and span a far longer period of time. Moreover, they contain a great many layers of volcanic ash at varying intervals, some of them only 100,000 years apart, some more widely spaced, each datable by potassium-argon methods. Together, they can be used by scientists to step backward into time and into the earth, layer by layer, determining an approximate date at each step.

One does not have to dig at Omo to go deeper into time. The strata have been heaved up in the past and now lie at an angle to the earth's surface. One need only walk along to find successively older layers revealing themselves.

The Omo succession begins a little over 4 million years ago and continues to about 1.5 million years B.P. This date conveniently overlaps with the deposits at Olduvai which begin at 1.8 million years B.P., so that the two sites between them give us an almost unbroken succession for the last 4 million years.

In this area of great promise, the members of the 1967 expedition settled down with high hopes. Arambourg picked the spot he had worked before and knew to be productive. A second group, under the direction of an American, Clark Howell, went a short distance up the Omo River to tap a previously unexplored area. A third group, headed by the Leakeys' son Richard, picked another untapped spot across the river from Howell. As it turned out, Richard Leakey's choice was the only one that proved unfruitful. There was plenty of material there, but his side of the river contained layers that were not old enough to be of interest to the expedition. He decided to disassociate himself from the project and returned home to Kenya to do some prospecting.

The other members of the expedition persevered where they were. Immediately they began recovering extinct animal fossils of extraordinary richness and variety. The great number of dated layers at Omo made it possible to trace the evolutionary changes that had taken place in some eighty species of mammals. Six genera and eight species of

Figure 7–9 Richard Leakey has had astounding success in finding fossil hominids in the desert regions east of Lake Rudolf in Kenya. Today his research is carried out with a large team of experienced scientists and with considerable resources. With more than 150 fossil hominids found, his success is unprecedented.

The Omo Hominids (1967–1974)

extinct pigs laid their secrets bare in the strata. Twenty-two different kinds of antelope were discovered, and several extinct saber-toothed cats. Altogether, over 150 species of fossil animals are now known to have been at Omo. These discoveries were so varied and told such a clear story that matching fossils from other places with those from Omo became a distinct possibility.

In addition to all the useful pig and antelope fossils found at Omo, traces of hominids began to appear. The French group first found a jaw. Both parties found teeth, eventually over 200 of them; then came other jaw fragments, parts of two skulls, and several arm and leg bones. It has been a spectacular haul and, for several reasons, an enormously significant one. First is the great age of the oldest specimens, more than twenty teeth: 2.5 million years. These teeth are almost certainly those of a small gracile hominid resembling the South African *A. africanus.* If further analysis should prove they are indeed of the gracile type, it will mean that a good approximate date has at last, after nearly fifty years, been provided for that elusive creature, even if it refers to a different and distant population. Also of significance was the fact that remains of this hominid were found along with super-robust fossils some half a million years older than *A. boisei* at Olduvai. Furthermore, other specimens continued to turn up in various layers right up to 1.5 million years ago. *A. boisei* apparently lived at Omo for at least a million years.

Meanwhile, Richard Leakey's decision to return to Kenya proved to be one of the most fateful moves in paleoanthropological history. He flew south in a helicopter, across the border into Kenya and along the eastern shore of Lake Rudolf (see page 104). In one of those classic episodes in which an adventurous young man follows a hunch to good fortune, Leakey spotted some likely sites from the air and set his helicopter down almost on top of what is turning out to be one of the richest mines of hominid fossils ever located.

The results of Richard Leakey's first years at East Rudolf were sensational: three superb skulls, more than two dozen *mandibles* (lower jaws) or parts of mandibles, some arm- and leg-bone fragments, and some isolated teeth, amounting to over one hundred specimens in all. Much of this material is of the super-robust *A. boisei* type and dates from a little over two million years ago to about one million years ago (see Figure 7–10). When these East Rudolf fossils are combined with the Omo finds, there is enough material in the way of young and old individuals, both males and females, and enough variation in dentition, for the outlines of a variable population of the super-robust *Australopithecus boisei* to begin to reveal itself.

Having a population to study instead of an individual fossil is enormously important. No two people today are exactly alike; no two *Australopithecus* creatures were either. It is for that reason that drawing conclusions from a single fossil is risky. Measurements can be taken of it and theories built up as a result of those measurements; but this

Robust Hominids at East Rudolf (1969–1974)

Figure 7–10 This skull of *Australopithecus boisei* found by Richard Leakey at East Rudolf is similar in many ways to that found by his mother at Olduvai (Figure 7–4).

information may be misleading because the fossil may not be typical. It is only when a large number of specimens are available that all their variations can be taken into account and a norm derived. If a visitor from outer space were to describe and name *Homo sapiens* by examining one skeleton—that of a short, squat, heavy-boned Eskimo—he certainly would be excused if he set up another species on the basis of a second skeleton discovered later a few thousand miles away—that of a six-and-a-half-foot, slender-boned Watusi tribesman from central Africa.

That is why the *A. boisei* population that is emerging is so valuable. It begins to reveal some of the limits of variability beyond which none of its members go. Any creature that does exceed those limits in any way can be presumed to be something else. And those limits are now well enough defined to make it quite clear that the gracile *Australopithecus* specimens *are* something else; doubt about the distinctiveness of the two forms is now dwindling.

Furthermore, the *A. boisei* population seems to be different from the robust types of South Africa, which also exist in sufficient numbers to constitute a variable population with norms of its own. Like *A. robustus* (shown on page 114) *A. boisei* had a bony crest along the top of its skull, but its crest is more pronounced for the anchoring of even bigger muscles to work a more massive jaw containing larger molars. This complex of features indicates a life adapted to the eating of large amounts of coarse, tough vegetable matter. This way of life apparently was not conducive to rapid evolution, since *A. boisei* existed in East Africa for nearly two million years, possibly even longer, without changing much. The picture that *A. boisei* gives us is that of a creature that became stable and well-adapted to its own niche until challenged by another hominid.

Unfortunately for *A. boisei*, there was another hominid, and the challenge came.

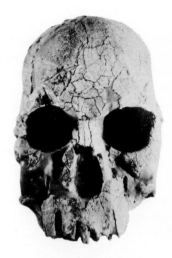

Figure 7–11   Most unusual of Richard Leakey's finds from East Rudolf is this skull, known simply as ER 1470, which may be well over 2.0 million years old. It has some features of *Australopithecus africanus* but an unusually large cranial capacity of 775 cc.

Gracile Hominids at East Rudolf (1969–1974)

Richard Leakey's East Rudolf finds include late gracile fossils (see Figure 7–11). For a million years this type was contemporaneous with *A. boisei;* coexistence of the two creatures has been confirmed without question. At first their paths—their ways of making a living—almost certainly did not cross. As time went on this situation must have changed. Though *A. boisei* did not evolve significantly, the gracile hominid did. Its brain became larger, and this feature apparently spelled disaster for all the robust *Australopithecus* populations, both north and south. *A. boisei* disappeared in East Africa about a million years ago; *A. robustus,* we believe, had disappeared in South Africa by the same time. There are, in fact, no reliably dated robust specimens anywhere that are less than a million years old. The number of differing kinds of environments that the emerging gracile hominid could occupy was increasing along with his brain and his capabilities as a hunter, and in this growing adaptability he apparently forced his lumbering cousins off the face of the planet.

What is the gracile type that appears at East Rudolf? Richard Leakey suggests that some specimens are similar to *habilis* from Olduvai; this opinion has been seconded by others. Leakey will not give species names to his finds; he simply calls all robust types *Australopithecus* and all gracile types *Homo*, regardless of age, preferring to leave the more precise naming of species to others. This is a wise attitude. The entire *habilis* story is not yet told.

In 1972 Richard Leakey found a skull and limb bones that may be over 2.6 million years old; he tentatively identified the skull as *Homo*. This would bring *Homo* back to the age of those twenty 2.5-million-year-old gracile *Australopithecus* teeth found by the Omo expedition just across the border in Ethiopia. Five hundred miles to the northeast, near the Awash river in northern Ethiopia at a place called Hadar (see page 104), new discoveries are giving these advanced forms an even earlier date. A French-American expedition led by Maurice Taieb and Don C. Johanson has found a partial but well-preserved gracile skeleton of *Australopithecus* that is probably only a little less than three million years old. They have also recovered jaws and leg-bone fragments closer to 3.5 million years old. These finds have yet to be studied in detail, but they clearly show that fully bipedal hominids with relatively modern teeth had already evolved by three million years B.P. They carry so many modern characteristics that their discoverers consider some of them to belong to the genus *Homo*. Now, at last, we find the gracile type and *Homo* overlapping in time. Since their physical characteristics also begin to overlap and mix confusingly, so that it is hard to say which is one and which is another, this is probably one of those times when we can see one type of fossil hominid evolving slowly into another. These new discoveries are moving the center of gravity of human evolution further north and leaving the South African fossils as samples of what look like relict populations, which were no part of the mainstream of our evolution and which were to be replaced later in South Africa by more modern forms from elsewhere.

Discoveries at Hadar (1973–1974)

But we are still faced with the question of where these different types evolved: whether one is African, perhaps, and one of Asian origin. Some evidence relating to this question comes from two more discoveries, from another part of the Rudolf valley. Predating the fossils from East Rudolf and Ethiopia, we have an arm bone found in 1965 by a Harvard University expedition at Kanapoi at the south end of Lake Rudolf. It is some four million years old and is probably hominid, and may have belonged to a gracile type. Then there is a half mandible, which clearly belongs to a gracile type, that was found in 1967 at Lothagam, west of Rudolf (see page 104); its age: 5.5 million years. Finally there is a single molar, worn, but probably hominid, which was found at Ngorora, Kenya. Its age: an astounding nine million years. It seems plausible from this slender evidence that Africa is the home of the lineage which leads to man while the robust *A. boisei* was

Origins of Gracile and Robust Hominids

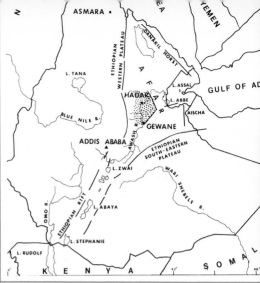

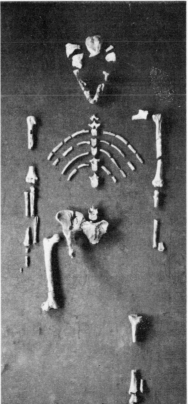

Figure 7–12 Important hominid remains have been recovered from the extensive stratified deposits at Hadar (top) in the Afar region. Near where the people are sitting in the middle photograph, Don C. Johanson (at the bottom left) discovered the first bones of an important skeleton. In 1974, after three and a half weeks of mapping, collecting, and sieving, the bones were gathered (bottom row, middle photograph). "Lucy," as the skeleton is called, lived by a lake about 3 million years ago. She was only 3.5 to 4 feet tall and died when she was 19 to 21. The most nearly complete fossil hominid yet found, she seems too small and her teeth and pelvis too primitive to be called *Homo*; Johanson believes she is "best referrable to *Australopithecus africanus*." Further study of "Lucy" should permit better understanding of the anatomy of early hominids and their means of locomotion. Also found in the region was a complete palate, dated at around 3 million years. In the bottom right photograph it is compared with a cast of a *Homo erectus* palate (left) that is perhaps a million years old. Their similarities suggest that the Afar palate is a specimen of *Homo*. Recent finds such as these and skull 1470 (Figure 7–11) have led Richard Leakey to predict that "within the next 5 to 10 years man will be able to look back, as a species, and see where he came from."

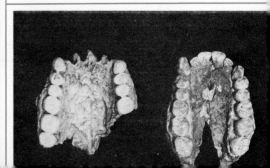

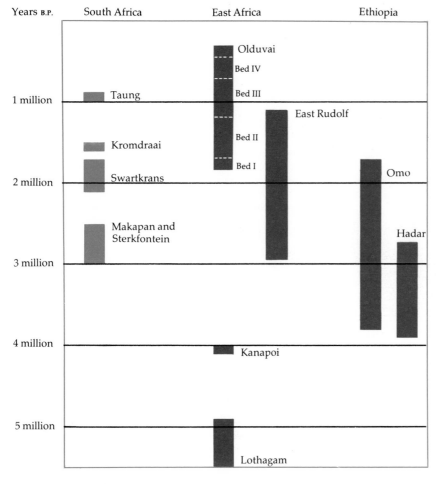

Years B.P.   South Africa   East Africa   Ethiopia

Figure 7–13 The approximate time spans of some of the deposits mentioned in the text. The South African dates are generally less reliable than those for East Africa and Ethiopia. The South African deposits usually represent a short time span that falls somewhere in the range of time indicated. (The age of Taung is very uncertain; until recently it has been claimed to be about 3 million years.) The East African and Ethiopian deposits are deep, and the range indicated is the range actually represented by the deposits: fossils are found at all levels.

an immigrant from elsewhere. Precisely where he first evolved, we have at present no clear indication.

Another of the fascinating surprises at East Rudolf is the presence of stone tools that could be as much as 850,000 years older than the oldest from Olduvai—and better made. Presumably, they were crafted by those gracile types that Richard Leakey calls *Homo.* Tools also show up at Omo, documented by potassium-argon dating to be 2.1 million years old. This raises again the question of whether *A. boisei* was a toolmaker. He may yet turn out to have been if not a toolmaker at least a user of tools, but one whose dependence on them was never great because of his supposed vegetarian diet.

Such a limitation in technology could explain why *A. boisei* did not survive. Increasing tool use is correlated with better manual dexterity and with the evolution of a more complex brain. If *A. boisei* had ever been interested in extending his diet to include much meat, his preoccupation with tools would probably have been greater, not only to

**Evidence of
Early Stone Tools**

slice and chop, but also to kill. But these specialized activities were already being pursued by the gracile *A. africanus*. By two million years ago and possibly earlier, East African *A. boisei* and South African *A. robustus* were already doomed to disappear, for the competition was to become too much for them. *A. africanus* competed not only for the best vegetation and fruit, but also for living space (perhaps sleeping trees); he even may have hunted the much slower robust species. For some millions of years they might have observed their smaller, livelier, more intelligent and increasingly dangerous cousin, oblivious of the fact that their successor was evolving right before their eyes.

While this scenario may settle the problem of where the small and large species of *Australopithecus* went—the small becoming the genus *Homo*, the large becoming extinct—it still leaves us with the question: Does *Australopithecus* qualify as a "missing link"? In the sense that he appears to lie in the shadow land between human and ape, yes, he does. But *Australopithecus* comes in more than one kind, and the names that scientists give the various kinds have changed in the past and may change again, reflecting the differing ways in which the fossil evidence is interpreted.

Let us review what the fossil evidence has told us about *Australopithecus*, bearing in mind that the following description is tentative.

Australopithecus was not an ape. He lived either on the edge of the forest or out on the open plain, but always within a day's walk of water. He was there a long time, certainly for four million years, maybe as many as five or six million years. He spent his days in small troops of males and females with their attendant children, plus some infants carried by their mothers. He walked on two legs as we do, but possibly with a less efficient gait than would be employed by a free-striding modern human being. He could run well, and did, to catch lizards, hares, rats, and other small prey. His world was thronged with animals, as East Africa is today: enormous herds of antelope, zebra, and other herbivores. He moved among them, watching the smaller gazelles for a sick or crippled individual that he might kill, alert to the possibility of picking off a newborn calf. *Deinotherium* (a type of elephant now extinct), rhinoceros, and the powerful black buffalo he sensibly avoided.

His world also contained the lion, leopard, hyena, and a large, now-extinct, saber-toothed cat. All preyed on him from time to time. But he moved in compact bands, carried sticks, bone clubs, and crudely chipped rocks, and he exhibited a strong sense of group defense in the presence of any threat. All these things made it possible for him to go about his daily business of searching for roots, berries, insects, and whatever larger game he could manage to catch, without serious threat from the big cats, which generally preferred to prey on antelope, as they still do. He may even have been able to drive single leopards or

AUSTRALOPITHECUS
REVEALED

Daily Life

lions away from kills they had made; he certainly could have done this to hyenas, provided the hyenas were not too numerous. When he had killed or scavenged game, he used sharp-edged chopping tools that he had freshly prepared from pebbles to cut it up, and he smashed the bones with hammer stones to extract the marrow.

He was agile, keen-sighted, alert. He was more intelligent than the baboons with which he shared the savanna, and he had nothing to fear from them, although a single *Australopithecus* male would probably have been no match for a single male baboon: *Australopithecus* was

Figure 7–14   This reconstruction of *Australopithecus africanus* required a good deal of imagination on the part of the artist, Jay H. Matternes, since we have no direct evidence of the soft parts of the body. The assumptions made, however, are reasonable, and the result is probably not very misleading.

lighter and less powerful, and lacked the baboon's powerful jaw and canine teeth.

The gracile-type male was between four and a half and five feet tall and weighed perhaps between 60 and 80 pounds; females were somewhat smaller. The color of his skin is unknown; it was probably dark and lightly covered with fine hair. His face was similar in some ways to that of an ape. His jaw stuck out more than a modern human's, and he had no chin to speak of. His nose was wide and flat, scarcely projecting; his forehead was low and sloping, the bony ridges over his eyes prominent. The top and back of his head were very small by modern standards—markedly so, compared to that large forward-thrusting face.

Judging by the smallness of his brain and by its presumed proportions, he probably could not talk, but he certainly must have been capable of a number of expressive nonverbal sounds, such as those we find among most primates, which others of his kind understood. He also communicated by means of a subtle and varied range of gestures, body movements, and facial expressions.

Where *Australopithecus* went at night is not known. In savanna areas with forest edges or scattered trees he may well have taken to the trees to avoid predators, since night is the time when the latter would be most active and the sleeping *Australopithecus* most vulnerable.

How do we reconstruct even this sketchy description of the life of *Australopithecus*? What makes it even likely to be true? That is a very large question that cannot be answered satisfactorily by simply positing a mode of life. As we have seen, the evidence is beginning to accumulate—evidence of the vegetation, climate, and fauna, and of the food remains and stone tools used by our ancestors, as well as the bones themselves that tell us so much. But there are more behavioral clues than these, and we shall turn to them in the next chapter.

In the discussions that follow in Chapters 8 and 9, we shall be using the generic term *Australopithecus* to refer to the common ancestor of both *A. africanus* and *A. boisei*. The similarity between these two species indicates clearly a common origin in an early bipedal hominid. The story of human evolution, however, is concerned with the nature and fate of *A. africanus*. His heavily built cousin *A. boisei* has no further part in this history and therefore will not be referred to again. In later chapters, therefore, the term *Australopithecus* can also be taken to refer to the gracile *A. africanus*.

If we are to take the story of *Australopithecus* any farther back, we shall have to turn again to *Ramapithecus*. A glance at page 99 will remind us that our evidence of this genus spans the period from 14 million to 8 million years B.P. Obviously the molar tooth from Ngorora also falls into this period. Here again we have a situation where the evidence of two successive forms shows them to blend together. Many of the characteristics of the teeth of *Ramapithecus* are very close indeed to those of *Australopithecus*. If, as many now believe, *Ramapithecus* is the ancestor of *Australopithecus*, then we can conveniently draw the line between them at about 6 million years B.P. This is a time at which we can expect to find fossils intermediate in character between the small and still mysterious *Ramapithecus,* and the gracile *Australopithecus* we are coming to know quite well.

There, for the moment, the story of early hominid fossils ends. There are many unanswered questions. The presence of *Ramapithecus* in India, for example, suggests the possibility that man did not originate in Africa after all, that he may have been evolving in a number of places. This is one view, but there is evidence against it, too. Louis Leakey's Fort Ternan find (Chapter 5) locates *Ramapithecus* in East Africa at least two million years earlier than the age of the fossils found in India; and most important, it places him in a country where *Australopithecus* specimens of great age are beginning to be discovered (see Table 7–2). Many anthropologists feel that it is reasonable to continue to argue the case for Africa as the breeding ground of man. *Ramapithecus* populations may well have radiated out from Africa to India and perhaps to other places over a period of several million years. But this is no guarantee that they went on to produce hominid descendants in those places. Until fossil evidence confirms that they did, it seems more logical to assume that the center of early hominid evolution was the place where the majority of the fossils are: Africa.

More recent or more intact—or simply more—*Ramapithecus* finds could clarify this problem. They also could improve that species' claim to hominid ancestry, to say nothing of the light they might throw on the development of bipedalism. Without a good *Ramapithecus* skull or key postcranial bone, there is no way of determining if the creature was an erect walker. We need, too, a gracile skull, a leg bone, and a pelvis from the period between 8 and 4 million years ago. These might give us some information about the timing of the evolution of bipedalism, its manner, and perhaps its rate there; we are in the dark about all these things at the moment. A significant postcranial find of a super-robust *Australopithecus* type might reveal whether that animal ever developed the advanced bipedalism we find well-documented at Sterkfontein. Richard Leakey's discoveries of fragmented leg bones from East Rudolf suggest a distinctive kind of bipedalism different from that of modern humans: the fragments of arm bones from there and the Omo are heavy and long, and suggest that they were heavily muscled and so could have regularly played some part in locomotion.

The illuminating deductions about lines of descent that can be made from skulls, teeth, and jaws have tended to obscure the fact that these parts do not say so much as they might about how their owners lived. We can speculate as we have done in the preceding pages, but that is all. It would be fascinating to know for sure what *Australopithecus* was really like. If all the known *Australopithecus* bones in the world were assembled for the making of one skeleton, that skeleton would be a patchwork of adult males, females, and juveniles, and some parts would still be lacking. The first really complete set of bones belonging to one

From *Ramapithecus* to *Homo*: One Theory

TABLE 7–2   FOSSIL RECORD OF *AUSTRALOPITHECUS*

Type	South African Finds	Age (million years)[a]	East African Finds	Age (million years)[b]
Gracile				
africanus	Taung (Dart, 1924)	circa 1.0	Kanapoi (Patterson, 1965)	4.0
	Sterkfontein (Broom, 1936, 1947)	3.0–2.0	Lothagam (Patterson, 1967)	5.5
	Makapansgat (1948)	3.0–2.0	Hadar (Taieb and Johanson, 1973–1974)	2.9
habilis[c]			Olduvai (M. and L. Leakey, 1960)	1.8–1.5
			East Rudolf (R. Leakey, 1969–1974)	2.7–1.5
			Omo (Howell, 1967–1974)	3.5–1.9
			Hadar (Taieb and Johanson, 1973–1974)	3.3–2.9
Robust				
boisei			Olduvai (M. and L. Leakey, 1959)	1.75
			East Rudolf (R. Leakey, 1969–1974)	2.6–1.2
			Omo (Howell, 1967–1974)	3.7–1.8
robustus	Kromdraai (Broom, 1938)	2.0–1.5		
	Swartkrans (Broom, 1949)	2.0–1.5		

[a] Dates attributed to South African sites are based not on potassium-argon analysis but on comparative analysis of fauna. Nevertheless, these dates probably do bracket the times during which lived the populations that the fossils represent.

[b] Most of the dates attributed to the East and Northeast African sites are based on at least a few potassium-argon determinations and, although there may be some errors in them, they can be relied on rather more than those for the South African sites.

[c] For this table, all gracile hominids from East Africa that fall into the genus *Australopithecus* have been grouped under *habilis*, except the oldest. The exact status of many of these fossils is quite uncertain since details about them have not been published in full. Descriptive and analytic studies of many of the more recently discovered fossils are still awaited.

human ancestor are of a Neandertal man, and they are about 60,000 years old. When we consider *Australopithecus* and *Ramapithecus,* we are talking in a time range of from 2 to 14 million years ago. No wonder the fossils are so rare. No wonder they exist in such tantalizingly small fragments. The real wonder is that they tell us as much as they do.

If we accept the argument for a *Ramapithecus* ancestor, plus the other evidence offered in this chapter, we may conclude that:

1. Hominids have been separate from apes for probably 15 million years.
2. They had evolved into at least two different kinds by about 5 million years ago.
3. One kind continued to evolve, producing the bigger brain and primitive culture of *Homo.*
4. These developments enabled *Homo* to supersede his relative by about a million years ago.
5. Thanks to the evolution of his culture, *Homo* has lived in unique supremacy on earth ever since.

There are other theories built on the evidence we have presented. Some authors still recognize only one interbreeding species at any one point in time (in which case the robust forms are the heavily built males, and the gracile forms the females). Others believe there were at least three, if not four, separate lineages evolving alongside each other in Africa alone. The two-species theory presented here is, however, the most popular, and it seems to fit the existing evidence most efficiently.

OVERVIEW

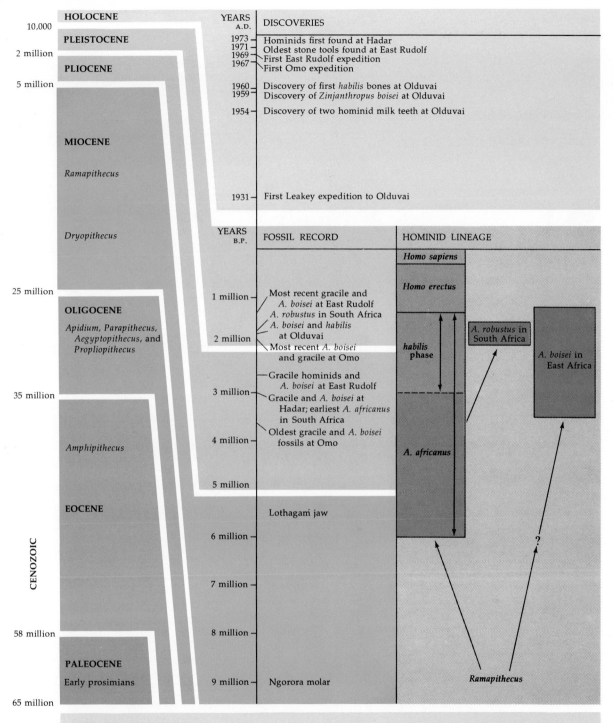

	YEARS A.D.	DISCOVERIES
HOLOCENE	10,000	
PLEISTOCENE	1973	Hominids first found at Hadar
	1971	Oldest stone tools found at East Rudolf
	1969	First East Rudolf expedition
PLIOCENE	1967	First Omo expedition
	1960	Discovery of first *habilis* bones at Olduvai
	1959	Discovery of *Zinjanthropus boisei* at Olduvai
MIOCENE	1954	Discovery of two hominid milk teeth at Olduvai
Ramapithecus		
Dryopithecus	1931	First Leakey expedition to Olduvai

Timeline scale (left): 10,000 · 2 million · 5 million · 25 million · 35 million · 58 million · 65 million — CENOZOIC — OLIGOCENE (*Apidium, Parapithecus, Aegyptopithecus,* and *Propliopithecus*) · EOCENE (*Amphipithecus*) · PALEOCENE (Early prosimians)

YEARS B.P.	FOSSIL RECORD	HOMINID LINEAGE
		Homo sapiens
1 million	Most recent gracile and *A. boisei* at East Rudolf; *A. robustus* in South Africa	*Homo erectus*
2 million	*A. boisei* and *habilis* at Olduvai; Most recent *A. boisei* and gracile at Omo	*habilis* phase
3 million	Gracile hominids and *A. boisei* at East Rudolf; Gracile and *A. boisei* at Hadar; earliest *A. africanus* in South Africa	*A. africanus*
4 million	Oldest gracile and *A. boisei* fossils at Omo	
5 million		
6 million	Lothagam jaw	
7 million		
8 million		
9 million	Ngorora molar	

A. robustus in South Africa   *A. boisei in East Africa*

Ramapithecus   ?

THE GREAT SAVANNA

The story of discoveries in Northeast and East Africa is as exciting as that of South Africa and new discoveries are reported every year. Dating of fossil deposits is far more secure in these areas than in South Africa because there has been much volcanic activity since the Early Miocene and potassium-argon dating is therefore possible. Many of the deposits, however, are very thick and span a considerable time range (see Figure 7–13).

Chapter 8

Walking and Toolmaking

The greatest events come to pass without any design; chance makes blunders good .... The important events of the world are not deliberately brought about; they occur.

GEORGE C. LICHTENBERG.

Fossils can provide a very good indication of the course of evolution, but they are less good at indicating precisely how evolution came about. This has been a source of frustration to experts for many years, so much so that some have begun to look for answers elsewhere than in the fossil record. One alternative field that seems fruitful is the study of man's close living primate relatives, particularly the closest of all: the chimpanzees.

Many scientists consider chimpanzees the least specialized of the great apes, the one that probably most closely resembles the ancestors from which all other apes—and man—have sprung. In other words, if we go back far enough along the hominid line, the ancestor we ultimately encounter may be not unlike a modern chimpanzee in certain aspects.

LOCOMOTION OF NONHUMAN PRIMATES

Early Work with Primates

There is nothing new in the idea of studying primates to learn about human beings. As far back as the 1920s, Robert Yerkes was observing domesticated chimpanzees in the United States, and Sir Solly Zuckerman was looking at hamadryas baboons in the London Zoo. Both made important contributions to the field of primatology, but they and others gradually came to realize that if the intricacies of primate society were to be properly understood, the animals would have to be studied in the wild.

Organized field work on primates did not really catch hold until the late 1950s, when a large number of young field workers led by anthropologists, many of them destined to gain international reputations, began pouring out all over the world from universities and museums in a dozen countries. They studied langurs and rhesus monkeys in India; gorillas, chimpanzees, baboons, and many forest monkeys in Africa; and most recently, the gibbons and orangutan of Southeast Asia. Some studies of New World monkeys were begun in Central and South America.

Primates turned out to be much harder to study than anyone had imagined. Many of them, like the mountain gorilla, live in inaccessible places. Many stay in the tops of trees in dense forest, where they are nearly invisible. Others, like the orangutan, are extremely rare. Most are shy. There is also the problem of what to look for and how to interpret it. Different species act differently in different areas, under different ecological influences, and even under different population densities.

Prejudices have had to be unlearned. For a hundred years or more, both scientists and adventurers cast the gorilla as a dangerous forest monster that beats its chest in rage and utters chilling roars of defiance through enormous teeth. George Schaller, a zoologist, and Dian Fossey, a primatologist, have since proved that while it can do these things, the animal is actually shy and gentle.

Thanks to long and devoted field observations, chimpanzees are now better understood. One distinguished observer is Jane Goodall, who started her career as a secretary to Louis Leakey. Leakey knew of a troop of chimpanzees that lived in a hilly forest tract near the Gombe Stream, a river running into Lake Tanganyika in western Tanzania. He was interested in anything that had to do with primates; furthermore, he believed that the present-day stream, with its forest and forest-edge environment, closely resembled the environment of Olduvai two million years ago. He persuaded Jane Goodall to undertake a study of the Gombe troop.

Goodall and the Gombe Stream Reserve

When Goodall arrived in the Gombe Stream Chimpanzee Reserve in 1960, she set up camp near the lake shore and began to spend her days roaming the forest, looking for chimpanzees in an area of about fifteen square miles. Her plan was to watch the animals discreetly, not getting too close, just accustoming them to her presence as a preliminary to closer acquaintance. Many months later she was still watching from a distance, still treated with suspicion by the shy chimpanzees. Ultimately, after a period of rejection that would have discouraged a less dedicated person, she was accepted, not by all the chimpanzees but by many of them (see Figure 8-1). She became very friendly with a few of them. Eventually she spent thousands of hours with them, sometimes in actual physical contact—handing out bananas, playing with a baby—more often just sitting quietly and watching a society of unimagined subtlety and complexity gradually unfold.

Two years later, when a photographer, Hugo van Lawick, arrived to take pictures of the animals, he had to undergo a similar process of scrutiny, of familiarization and slow acceptance, before the animals would act naturally in his presence. But in testimony to the chimpanzees' intelligence, they associated him with their human friend and accepted him in only a month. Goodall's studies and van Lawick's pictures of the Gombe troop (published in a book called *In the Shadow of Man*) reveal the chimpanzee to be an animal whose nature and social organization are provocative of all kinds of speculations about the emergence of mankind.

Ordinarily, when we look at the great apes, our vision is clouded because we see them through the distorting glass of modern human eyes and in a setting that has become so overwhelmingly humanized that the apes tend to look a great deal more simple-minded, a great deal more vulnerable, a great deal less competent than they actually are. But take man back a few million years, divest him of all his accomplishments and social progress—all the things that now threaten the survival of the chimpanzee and gorilla—and the gulf between mankind and ape shrinks. Humans become less, apes more, particularly when the work of scientists like Goodall, Fossey, and Schaller reveals how subtle and complex primate societies are.

With that in mind, we can go back to a time before there were human beings, look at the primates as a group, and try to understand why it was not a prosimian or a monkey but an ape, and just one type of ape, that would evolve in a direction that no other primate has ever taken. As a starter in this inquiry, we must learn something about primate locomotion, for it is in the different ways that primates got about in the trees that the first clue to hominid evolution may be found.

We have seen that the small ratlike insectivores that invaded the trees from the ground some 75 million years ago got around much as squirrels do today. Among those that would turn into bona fide primates, there was a rather rapid evolution. Paws turned into hands with prehensile fingers for gripping. Some groups developed a way of getting about that depended on a slow but sure four-handed movement, characterized by a grip whose strength was out of all proportion to the size of the animal. Pottos still move this way, as do slow lorises, and both have powerful hands and feet for grasping and clinging.

Another means of locomotion was, as we have seen, leaping and clinging. Some of the early prosimians were great jumpers. They had long legs—in proportion, as long as those of kangaroos—and very short arms. Most of them were extremely small; some of the surviving species still are: the tarsier of the Philippines is no larger than a kitten. In time, following the process of natural selection, many of the prosimians became bigger. Exactly why has not been determined, except that there are forces at work in all species that encourage the selection of larger-sized individuals if there is no offsetting advantage in being

Figure 8–1 Jane Goodall has been a pioneer in the study of wild animals. By undertaking a long behavioral study of wild chimpanzees since 1960, she has contributed greatly to our understanding both of chimpanzees and, by implication, of ourselves.

The First Primates

smaller. For one thing, larger, more aggressive males have an advantage over smaller ones in competing for females. For another, an increase in size may protect an animal like a small prosimian from being eaten by certain small snakes or hawks that are not powerful enough to take on bigger prey. In fact, a predator could encourage the evolution of larger animals in a population by killing a disproportionate number of the smaller ones and eliminating them as breeding stock.

Increased size brings problems with it, however. A large body is harder to hide than a small one. It also needs more food. If the food exists in the form of fruit or tender leaves and shoots at the tips of branches, a balance will have to be maintained at the point where the advantage of being bigger is not outweighed by the disadvantage of being unable to get far enough out on the twig ends to reach the best food. In short, there is an optimum size for a particular way of making a living. If the selection pressure for larger size is great enough, then the way of making a living may change. Thus a leaper may become a reacher, with longer arms that enable it to spread its weight among three or four branch ends, thereby reducing the weight on any single branch. Grasping hands with flat nails then become essential: claws will do for a very small climber but not for a bigger one, as they cannot carry the animal's weight.

Under these influences larger, heavier, longer-armed, more dexterous primates began to appear in the Oligocene epoch about 30 million years ago, as we saw in Chapter 5. Their food preferences began to be different. Accordingly, they sorted themselves out in different parts of the forest, in different kinds of trees, even in different parts of the same trees. Some of these longer-armed primates became quadrupeds, running easily along the branches on all fours. These were the monkeys. Others, whose arms became still longer, tended more in the direction of reaching, climbing, hanging, swinging. Some of these were to become the apes.

This difference between quadrupedalism and *brachiation* (as the swinging movement of the apes beneath the branches is called) may seem insignificant. It is profoundly important. Although monkeys often sit upright and occasionally even stand on their hind legs, most monkeys are not really upright animals. They get down on all fours to move about. Also, although they have well-articulated fingers and toes, they walk along the branches on the palms of their hands and feet. Thus, they may pick up an object with great dexterity when they are sitting still, but their particular quadrupedal mode of locomotion compels them to drop it when they run. Apes, because of their habit of reaching, climbing, and swinging in trees, are essentially more erect animals then monkeys and have greater freedom of arm movement.

If an animal evolves a greater degree of erectness and arm flexibility, it can do more sitting, standing, and reaching—and also more grasping, plucking, holding, examining, carrying. The more often a hand performs these acts, the better it gets at doing them. A chimpanzee, as

Quadrupedalism versus Brachiation

Jane Goodall discovered, has the manual dexterity to strip the leaves from a twig (in other words, to make an implement) and deftly insert that twig into a small hole in a termite mound so that it can lick off the termites that are clinging to the twig when it is pulled out. This remarkable act of food-gathering (shown in Figure 8–2) requires not only precise manipulation but also intelligence. This is another way of saying that increased dependence on hands has an evolutionary effect on the brain: it gets bigger and becomes more complex. It is therefore significant that apes are, as a group, conspicuously more intelligent than monkeys, whose hands are dexterous enough, but whose quadrupedal way of life limits their use and thus limits the stimulation that use of the hands has on the brain.

Apes have the potential to be erect animals; they are smarter than monkeys and they use their hands more. Why didn't all of them become hominids? This is an extremely complicated problem. Perhaps the best way to answer it is to put oneself back in the equatorial forest of 20 million years ago and try to visualize the situation as it was at that

Figure 8–2   One of Jane Goodall's important observations was that of chimpanzees fishing with short straws or twigs for termites in mounds. What was so startling was that the chimpanzees prepared the twigs by stripping leaves and breaking them at a certain length: in fact, they made a tool to a recognizable pattern.

time. The apes had already differentiated into several species; we know that, because their fossils tell us so. But the differences were not as great as they are now. All four of the surviving ape species—gibbon, orangutan, chimpanzee, and gorilla—are larger than they once were; all but the gibbon are much larger. All of them are longer-armed, the gibbon and orangutan considerably so.

The gibbon and orangutan are Asiatic species. By a great number of external and internal measurements, including genetic ones, they turn out to be remarkably different from chimpanzees and gorillas. In fact they are in some ways less like a chimpanzee than a man is. This indicates a separation far back in time, probably before the separation of man, gorilla, and chimpanzee.

Both the gibbon and orangutan are tree-dwelling animals today. Millions of years of climbing and swinging and a total reliance on the fruits that grow in jungle trees have brought them to an extreme point of arboreal specialization. When they do come to the ground they move slowly and uncertainly. In the trees, however, they are superb, each in its own way. The gibbon (which we saw in Figure 5–9) is an airy flier that hangs from branches, swinging from one to another in a breathtaking arc, grabbing the next branch just long enough to launch itself in the direction of a third. With this animal, arms and hands are everything. Its fingers are extremely long, specialized to serve as powerful hooks to catch branches. As a result of this finger specialization the gibbon has the poorest manual dexterity of any ape. And being the smallest ape, it has the smallest brain.

The orangutan is quite different (see Figure 8–3). It is much larger: adult males weigh over 150 pounds, compared to the gibbon's 10 or 15 pounds. Obviously an animal of this size cannot go careening through the branches. Orangutans have developed four extremely prehensile hands adapted for seizing or holding, and their limbs are so articulated that they can reach in any direction; they have, in a sense, four arms. There is almost nowhere in a tree that an orangutan cannot safely go, despite its great bulk, by careful gripping and climbing.

When these specialized animals are compared with the general-purpose monkey-ape model that was probably ancestral to all, it is clear that the gibbon and orangutan have evolved in a direction different from the one that might have led them to humanness. Each is far too specialized for arboreal life to become anything but a more extreme example of what it is now.

Gorillas and chimpanzees, on the other hand, have not travelled the exclusively arboreal route: they are both in different degrees adapted to ground-dwelling. Whatever specialization has taken place in the gorilla (Figure 8–4) has been in the direction of a great increase in size, along with a dietary switch from the fruit and leaves found in trees to a more generalized menu of fresh bark, larger leaves, roots, bamboo shoots, and other plants—herbal as much as arboreal vegetation. These two specializations go together. For living so much on the ground to

Asiatic Apes: Gibbon and Orangutan

Figure 8–3 The orangutan of Indonesian Sumatra and Kalimantan (Borneo) is the most seriously threatened of the great apes. He has immensely long arms and relatively short legs with short thumbs and big toes. He is mainly arboreal but does cover considerable distances on the ground in emergencies.

African Apes: Gorilla and Chimpanzee

Figure 8–4   The largest of the apes is the gorilla. It spends most of its time on the ground, and, if it climbs trees, it is confined when full grown to the strongest boughs. Although its appearance is terrifying, the gorilla is a very gentle creature and will attack only if threatened or wounded.

eat the things the gorilla does eat, size and strength have been selected so that other animals will not attack. Because the gorilla is so large, it needs a great deal of just the kind of coarse green stuff that it finds in large quantities in the places it inhabits. Today this great ape might be called an ex-brachiator. It retains the equipment for climbing and reaching—the long arms, the deft hands, the good brain—but it is too bulky to brachiate. Young gorillas are frisky and venturesome in the trees, but their elders are essentially ground animals. Having carved out a successful niche for themselves there, they are under no evolutionary pressure to evolve further.

Of all the great apes, the chimpanzee is, as has been mentioned, the least specialized. In size it is a neat compromise: small enough to get about in trees, and big enough to take care of itself on the ground against predators, particularly since it travels in troops. As a result, it is at home in both worlds. Although it is still a fruit eater whose favorite staple is ripe figs, it will eat a wide variety of other things, including some meat: birds' eggs or fledglings, insects, lizards or small snakes, occasionally a young baboon, arboreal monkey, or bush pig.

Chimpanzees as Tool Users

Although chimpanzees are tool users and toolmakers in a limited way, they do not *need* tools. Nevertheless we know that the chimpanzee can develop a tradition of elementary tool use. We cannot know when chimpanzees first learned to fish for termites with straws (as we saw in Figure 8–2) or how long this took to become an established activity. Jane Goodall has shown that it is something that each new generation learns from the previous one. The youngsters have an opportunity to learn from their elders: they watch them intently, often copying what they do.

Another talent Jane Goodall observed among the Gombe chimpanzees was for throwing things. Her accounts reveal that this activity was well established in the Gombe troop; a number of individuals tried it, and under a variety of circumstances. Even often woefully inaccurate throwing seems to be useful to a chimpanzee. In chimpanzee life there is a great deal of bluffing and aggressive display. During such activity an animal will jump up and down, wave its arms, hoot, shriek, charge forward. This behavior looks especially disconcerting if it is accompanied by a shower of sticks or trash or stones. The fact that throwing is useful explains why it is now established as part of the species' behavior.

At its present stage of throwing development, the chimpanzee is scarcely a star athlete, by human standards. Through lack of practice it cannot throw far, nor can it count on hitting anything more than four or five feet away. But the performance does not have to impress humans, only other chimpanzees, baboons, leopard, and the like. For that audience it is extremely effective. Throwing clearly has selective value, and we can speculate that if chimpanzees are left to themselves long enough they might become better throwers than they now are.

Even now, potential for improvement exists among certain individual chimpanzees. There was one such at the Gombe Stream named Mr. Worzle (Goodall named all the chimpanzees as fast as she could recognize them, for ease of identification). Mr. Worzle accomplished the remarkable feat of becoming a superior stone thrower as a result of being exposed to an unusual challenge. In order to attract the troop to the camp area where it could be more easily observed Goodall made a practice of putting out bananas. This unnatural concentration of food also attracted baboons that lived in the vicinity, leading to abrasive confrontations. The baboons quickly learned which chimpanzees, mostly females and juveniles, they could intimidate by rushing at them. But they never could dislodge Mr. Worzle, who stood his ground, picking up whatever was handy and throwing it at them. Sometimes it was leaves. Once, to the delight of the baboons, it was a bunch of bananas. But slowly Mr. Worzle learned that rocks were best, and as time went on he depended more and more on rocks and started using bigger and bigger ones. Mr. Worzle's response indicates the ability to improvise that exists in an intelligent and physically adept animal when confronted by a new situation or given an opportunity to deal with an old one in a new way.

Whether the chimpanzee is innately more intelligent than the gorilla is hard to say because the latter has not been studied thoroughly, but from what is known, the edge would seem to go to the chimpanzee. Chimpanzees are sociable, curious, and extroverted. They like to please. This characteristic may be deeply rooted in a pattern of social behavior that they have worked out. Living in groups, they must find ways of defusing frequent and potentially dangerous confrontations with one another. They do this by reassuring, by touching and appeasing. "I'm a nice fellow," they seem to be saying. "Look at me, watch me; you'll believe it." Chimpanzees are also copycats, and very observant ones. Their open, gregarious, let's-try-anything society encourages this.

Gorillas, by contrast, are slow, introverted animals that seem to prefer a quiet life. They seldom fight. Except for throwing leaves and branches when they are disturbed, gorillas are not known to use tools or manipulate objects to any great extent. Young ones play with objects, as do the young of many mammals, but adults never do.

Figure 8–5 Throwing stones and other objects is typical of chimpanzees trying to scare a threatening intruder or merely letting off steam.

The behavior of chimpanzees and gorillas has probably evolved no faster than their physical evolution, and we may assume that something like the present-day societies of these animals has existed for some millions of years. That the stolid gorilla has remained a vegetarian is not hard to understand. Harder, at first glance, is to see why the chimpanzee evolved into a modern ape rather than a hominid.

We have to remember, however, that the modern chimpanzee is a product of the familiar process of speciation, the gradual separating out of a single population into subpopulations, each aimed in a slightly different direction toward eventual adaptation to a different environmental *niche*. Let us assume that among primates the process starts with an unspecialized, all-purpose ape, not too different from a chimpanzee. It is probably somewhat smaller, somewhat shorter-armed, possibly somewhat more general in its food tastes than the chimpanzee of today, and hence more willing to look anywhere for things to eat. The world, in short, is wide open to it. It can go in any of several directions.

HOMINID LOCOMOTION

If in one part of this ape's range there are large forests and an abundance of fig trees, there is little reason for the animal not to stay in the trees and become increasingly specialized as a fruit eater and brachiator. In another place or at another time, the environment might be somewhat different: fewer fig trees, but an abundance of seeds, berries, tubers, insects, and other food materials on the ground. Such a situation may have existed about 10 to 14 million years ago. At that time, according to Sherwood Washburn, there was a great expanse of tropical forest extending through much of Europe, Asia, and a good part of Central Africa. This, of course, means that there also existed a comparably large amount of forest edge, with opportunities for tree dwellers to descend to the ground and eat the berries, roots, insects, and other food that abounded in the open. Such a place where two ecological zones meet is called an *ecotone*. It presents new opportunities, for if an animal adapts to the ecotone, it can exploit the food found in both zones. Advanced apelike creatures (among which we can include our supposed ancestor, *Ramapithecus*) thronged the forests, probably existing in a number of species, some of which must have lived on the forest edge. Like a good many monkeys and apes today, some of these creatures undoubtedly came to the ground when opportunities for feeding presented themselves.

From the Trees to the Ground

If it is understood that these "decisions" to come to the ground were repeated billions of times by millions of apes in thousands of different places, then one begins to get a better idea of the process: it was a gradual one, so gradual as to be imperceptible except over a great span of time. Opportunity and aptitude went together. No single decision by a single ape or group of apes had any meaning whatsoever. But in places that, century after century, provided a better living on the ground for apes able to exploit it, the animals best adapted to living and feeding on the ground were the ones that spent the most time there and whose descendants became still better adapted to this environment and life style.

Washburn emphasizes that the apes were not forced out of the trees. It is true that during the Pliocene the forests dried out and retreated so that several million square miles of living space were subtracted from the theoretical ranges of tree-dwelling apes. But the process was so gradual that at no time could it have had any effect on the evolving habits of individual animals. Variations of climate from one year to the next were all that concerned them. If a river goes dry and the trees along it die, the animals that formerly thrived there simply move away, taking their various ways of making a living with them. They do not abandon the trees because the trees disappear; they find other trees.

Tool Use and Bipedalism

Washburn's third and perhaps most striking observation has to do with the development of erect stance and tool using. Most views on this matter have always been to the effect that man was bipedal from the time he first stepped away from the trees, and that it was this characteristic that gave him the opportunity to become a tool user and tool-maker by freeing his hands to carry things. If a hominid found it advantageous to walk on two legs from the beginning, the argument goes on, then, to make it easier for him to get about in that way, natural selection would inevitably improve whatever pelvis, leg bone, foot bone, and muscles the hominid had.

Washburn suggests that the reverse is true: tool using may have preceded walking on two legs; more than that, it probably helped develop it. This is an astonishing idea, but the evidence for it and the logic behind it are impressive. We should not forget that apes, unlike monkeys, were characteristically upright even before they left the trees. Whereas monkeys ran along branches on all fours or jumped about in them, apes climbed hand over hand. They swung from branches, sat upright in them, and sometimes even stood on them. Their arms were well articulated for reaching in all directions, and the important, inter-related development of stereoscopic eyesight, larger brain, and improved manual dexterity had already begun. Apes, in short, had the physical equipment and the dawning brain potential to use their hands in new and useful ways. That certain of them did so is suggested by the fact that chimpanzees, man's nearest relatives, are simple tool users today. As we have seen, they throw stones and sticks as weapons. They use sticks, rocks, and handfuls of leaves for digging, cracking nuts, wiping themselves, and sopping up water.

If we accept that at some point in the early Pliocene certain apelike creatures found themselves becoming increasingly adapted to life on the ground, we must also accept that, being apes, they had the potential for walking erect and for using their hands. This brings up two important matters. First, the things these creatures spent their days doing—poking up roots with sticks, turning over stones for grubs and beetles, snatching at or swatting small lizards and frogs, cracking nuts with rocks—all tended to improve and develop the manual dexterity that

Figure 8–6 This chimpanzee is using chewed leaves as a sponge to raise water to its mouth.

they already possessed. Second, since they found themselves in greater danger from predators on the ground than in the trees, they were probably very slow to abandon trees entirely, doing so only as their ability to run about developed. That ability depended on leg structure. By standing up, a ground dweller could see potential enemies much better over the tops of bushes and tall grass. Over an extended period the individuals that had the longest legs and stood up the most often would be the ones that could see predators the best and run the fastest. They would be the best adapted and ultimately might abandon the trees entirely.

The critical matter here seems to be a combination of environmental pressure and timing. Populations that left the trees while still entirely quadrupeds remained quadrupedal, like the baboon. Those that became reachers (and climbers) had the potential for erect posture and hand use. Others became specialized as brachiators; the long-armed, brachiating gibbon and orangutan are now firmly established in the trees. The timing must be just right: it was the populations not wedged too tightly in any particular niche that were best able to adapt to a new opportunity on the ground. That way, they developed a competitive advantage over any later creatures who tried to follow suit. And, gradually, some of them became hominids. The others remained in the forest and went in slightly different directions, becoming chimpanzees and gorillas.

Physical Adaptations

To achieve good bipedalism, the hominid predecessor had to go through evolutionary changes in the shape and proportions of the foot, leg, and pelvic bones, and in the muscles of leg and buttock. A chimpanzee can walk quite comfortably on its hind legs, but not for any length of time. It can also run surprisingly fast. But the chimpanzee simply is not built properly for what man knows as efficient running and walking. Its legs are too short, its feet are not the right shape, its big toes stick out to the side like thumbs instead of forward to give spring to the stride, and its propulsive buttock muscles are rather small and poorly placed. What muscles it can use for bipedal walking are attached to its bones in such a way that insufficient leverage is provided to achieve a vigorous stride. The chimpanzee proceeds in a kind of waddle or rolling gait, because it must shift its body weight at each step to position it over the leg that is on the ground.

A more efficient way of walking erect is to have the legs straighter and closer together, as they are in man. This is made possible by a marked change from the shape and proportions of the ancestral leg and foot bones, and particularly the ancestral pelvis (see Figure 8–8). There has been a twisting and flattening of the two large pelvic flanges, which not only helps set the trunk more vertically on the legs, but also provides better anchorage and far better leverage for the three sets of buttock muscles that are used in walking.

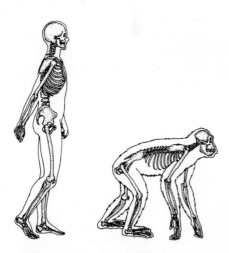

Figure 8–7 The posture of man and chimpanzee compared. The form of the skull, vertebral column, pelvis, limbs, hands, and feet reflects the means of locomotion.

Hominids gradually have achieved all these changes in the direction of efficient bipedalism. But for a long time that first venturesome ape

Knuckle Walking

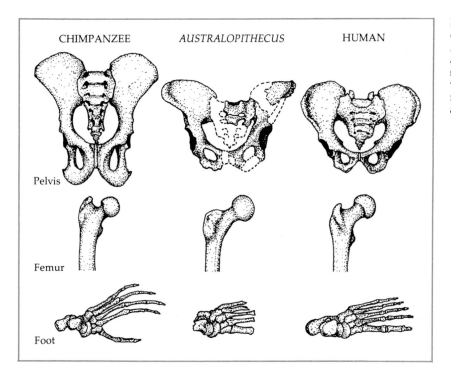

CHIMPANZEE   *AUSTRALOPITHECUS*   HUMAN

Pelvis

Femur

Foot

Figure 8–8 These comparisons emphasize the humanness of *Australopithecus*: note the shortening and broadening of the whole pelvic structure, the lengthening of the "neck" of the upper end of the femur, and the large and nonopposable big toe.

was surely more tree-bound than ground-bound. How he moved on the ground is not yet known.

It is tempting to conclude that erect walking is the final stage of a process that first had to proceed through an intermediate stage: the style of four-legged locomotion known as *knuckle walking*. Two of the great apes are knuckle-walkers today, Washburn points out: the chimpanzee and gorilla. Their very long arms and short legs enable them to stand with their backs at a slant with the ground, their arms taking some of their weight, balancing themselves easily on their bent knuckles, as shown in Figure 8–9. (As Washburn has noted, this is exactly the position a football lineman takes before the snap of the ball.) Since early hominids were almost certainly brachiators of a sort (like the gorilla, they might be called ex-brachiators), it is reasonable to assume that they did what the other brachiators did when they came out of the trees. According to Washburn, knuckle walking can be regarded as a kind of half-way step between quadrupedalism and bipedalism.

But it is not so regarded by everybody. The anatomist Charles Oxnard has pointed out that the human shoulder blade resembles most closely that of the orangutan, which is not a knuckle-walker. This suggests that the ancestral hominid was an accomplished hanger and swinger while in the trees and, being accustomed to erect posture, might have walked bipedally immediately on descending to the ground (as that other swinger, the gibbon, does now), without ever going through a knuckle-walking stage.

And if a human being is specialized for walking upright, with all the muscular and skeletal adaptations that make this possible, so is an ape

Figure 8–9 Knuckle walking is a means of quadrupedal locomotion peculiar to chimpanzees and gorillas. These animals put their weight on the soles of their feet and the outer surface of their fingers, which carry specialized, ridged, hairless friction skin, such as is found on the palm of our hands.

specialized for its kind of locomotion: a modern knuckle-walking chimpanzee has a very complex arrangement of muscles, ligaments, and bones, particularly in the wrist and the bases of the fingers, that enable it to proceed comfortably on all fours. Knuckle walking should not be regarded as an inferior or intermediate way of getting around, but simply as a different way. It is a way developed by a kind of ape that never entirely left the trees and consequently could get along with a different form of locomotion, appropriate to the animal's own needs. For another ape, one that lived on the ground in more open country and often used tools, knuckle walking was not so good. Most scholars believe that this proto-hominid never did pass through a knuckle-walking stage; it became a bipedal hominid instead.

From squatting in a tree to strolling upright in a meadow is an enormous evolutionary leap. Any explanation of the change can be only speculative. But the speculations have an uncanny way of hanging together. For a confirmed tool user, the most useful way of getting about is on two feet, since the hands are left free to carry things. Chance success with throwing stones and sticks may have led to a dawning realization that rocks and clubs were invaluable as weapons in defense, and even for bringing down small game. In due course, these talents could have made the creatures that possessed them rather formidable, allowing the animals to venture farther and farther from the safety of the trees. Eventually they could have become completely ground-oriented, with natural selection evolving creatures that were more and more adept at running on two legs.

Tool Use, Bipedalism, and Brain Development

As a bit of fossil evidence to back up early tool use, Washburn calls attention to the extreme smallness of the male *Australopithecus* canine tooth. In all other large ground-dwelling primates—in chimpanzee, gorilla, and, particularly, baboon—the male's canine is an enormous tooth, a true fang. One of its uses can be presumed to be self-defense and intimidation against the large and dangerous predators ground dwellers are exposed to. For a male hominid to be able to get along on the ground without such a tooth, we must logically supply some other means of self-defense. Washburn's answer: tools and weapons. This would mean that weapons have been vital for two, four, or five million years—long before men were men.

To an animal increasingly involved with tools, brain development becomes much more important, and changes in skull size and shape can be considered as possible results of selective pressure to provide increased brain space. By this time there is no way to separate the tangled triple influence of bipedalism, brain development, and tool using. As one attribute develops, a faster development in another takes place, and this in turn encourages a further development in the first.

The Problem of Causation

There may be disagreement as to whether tool use first stimulated walking or walking stimulated tool use, but there is absolutely no disagreement on the way both related to brain development and the importance of positive feedback between tool use and walking. *Positive feedback*—a process in which positive change in one variable component of a system brings about positive changes in other variables of that system, which in turn feed back to reinforce change in the first component—is a widely known phenomenon. Its effects are obvious in the buildup of unusually large waves in the ocean under the right conditions, when the waves themselves help create bigger waves. However, a problem is revealed when the elements that make up the evolutionary feedback model (see Figure 8–10) are broken down:

1. Out in the open, early hominids needed tools to defend themselves because they had small canine teeth.
2. They had small canines because they no longer needed big ones. Since they were becoming erect they had greater opportunities to use weapons. With weapons they were better able to defend themselves; big canines for defense were no longer necessary.

This is a classic feedback model. Once it is set up, it is not hard to see how each element in it affects the others, including that all-important by-product, development of the brain. The only trouble is that the argument goes in a circle: canines don't get small because you need tools and a bipedal stance to protect yourself against having small canines!

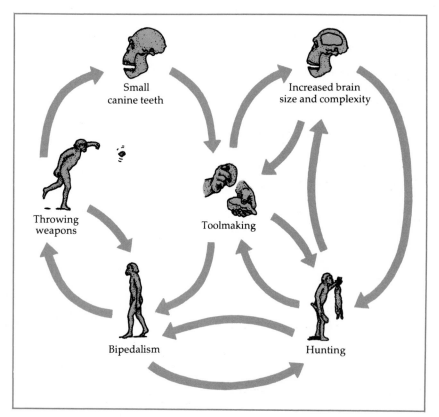

Figure 8–10 Numerous feedback systems occur in nature and are often interlocking. Negative feedback maintains stability, while positive feedback brings about major adaptive changes that constitute evolution. Shown here in simplified form is a positive feedback system that has been important in human evolution.

This circularity in reasoning has been pointed out by the British anthropologist Clifford Jolly, who notes that the more nearly perfect a feedback model is, the more nearly impossible it is to get started. If everything depends so neatly on everything else, he observes, nothing will happen. In thinking about this dilemma Jolly tried to find an element that did not depend on the others, something that got its initial thrust from some outside influence. Like many other anthropologists, he was struck by the remarkable differences between the teeth of the earliest hominids and those of the other apes (see Figure 8–11). Those small canines and incisors, together with their abnormally large molars, had to be explained in some way.

Since teeth and jaw structure obviously are related to eating habits, Jolly found it logical to seek out a shift in feeding that could account for the dental peculiarities of the ancestral hominid—a movement away from reliance principally on fruit to reliance on something else. Noting that modern man is still dependent on cereal grains, the seeds of domesticated grasses, for his diet, Jolly began to speculate that at some time in the past the ancestral hominid might have begun to eat seeds as at least a part of his diet.

Jolly's examination of this hypothesis is complicated, and some of the dental evidence is beyond the scope of this book, but its main points fall together in enough ways to make up an intriguing case for his idea. To begin with, there is the ecological niche itself: the more open country at the ecotone and seasonal variability in the weather (alternating rainy and dry seasons are necessary if a grassland is to maintain itself). Open country, with its grains, contains a large un-tapped source of food for an ape that has enough manual dexterity to scoop, pick, or strip something as small as seeds. The gelada baboons can do this today; so can some chimpanzees that have adapted to a seasonal open-country life, going out during dry periods when the yield of food in the forest is low. There is no reason why a hominid ancestor could not also have done it.

What is needed to become an efficient seed eater? Very large molars, for one thing, to grind up large numbers of small, hard objects, together with plenty of enamel on the faces of the teeth to withstand the grinding. Also a proper hinging of the jaw and powerful muscles are essential to develop power for easy crushing, together with enough flexibility to permit the side-to-side motion that is necessary for grinding. But all the flexibility in the world at the back of the mouth will do no good if rotary movement is limited by the interlocking of large canine teeth in front. If you will help yourself to a small mouthful of peanuts or sunflower seeds and proceed to chew them up, you will notice two things. First, as you swivel your jaw to grind up the seeds, your front teeth will move as much as or more than your back ones. If you try to check this front-tooth movement, as a set of oversize canines would tend to check it, you will find the side-to-side movement of your back teeth limited. Second, you will find that the highly arched roof of your mouth, together with a thick and flexible tongue, acts as an efficient

The Seed-Eating Hypothesis

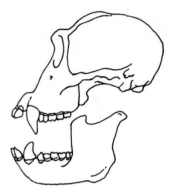

Chimpanzee

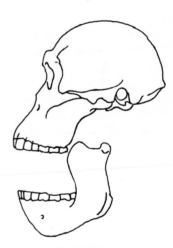

Australopithecus

Figure 8–11 The most striking difference between a chimpanzee skull and that of *Australopithecus* lies in the dentition. The *Australopithecus* teeth are of even height and wear relatively flat; the jaw is powerfully built to grind as well as crush. In addition, the braincase is larger and the skull better balanced than in the chimpanzee.

mechanism for constantly pushing the mouthful back under the molars for further grinding until the food is in a condition to be swallowed. The combination that has just served you well—extremely large molars, small canines (which are found in both males and females), rather small incisors, and an arched palate—is characteristic of *Australopithecus* but not of apes.

Here, Jolly suggests, lies the clue to the peculiar dental evolution of the earliest hominids, and also the initial thrust to get the feedback process started. If there is a wealth of small food objects like seeds to be eaten in a new environment, and a selective advantage in the evolution of smaller male canines in order to exploit this diet more efficiently, smaller canines will result.

"But," an alert skeptic will say, "what about baboons? Don't baboons have very large canine teeth for protection on the ground? If they became seed eaters, why didn't they lose those teeth too?" The answer to this question goes back to the fundamental difference between hominids and monkeys. One has the erect inheritance and potential for tool use that the other lacks. If a hominid can develop a talent for protecting himself with weapons or at least intimidating potential attackers, he does not need those big canines at all. Savanna baboons do need them—and they still have them. Gelada baboons, however, show some modifications that support Jolly's hypothesis. They are seed eaters, and their molars are larger, their canines smaller, than those of other baboons that eat more succulent food, such as the lower stems of grasses.

Jolly's comparisons, while not conclusive in themselves, make an arguable theory for the appearance of the "third ape" on the ground and out in the open at an early date. That creature probably had a talent for using tools and weapons that not only made possible the modification of molars and canine teeth to adapt to a diet emphasizing seeds, but also encouraged further tool use, manual dexterity, and bipedalism, all of which combined to stimulate the further development of the brain.

Sherwood Washburn, like some others, does not support the seed-eating thesis. He thinks diet will not explain how *Australopithecus* evolved his peculiar dentition of large molars and small canines. In Washburn's view these features must be traced to other specific activities—to the gradual increase of tool and weapon use and the development of hunting. Jolly may agree with Washburn on the importance of tool use, but mainly to explain how human teeth evolved from *Australopithecus* teeth. Jolly is looking further back; he is interested in finding how *Australopithecus* teeth evolved from ape teeth.

From these arguments we can conclude that seed eating was probably more important at an early stage of hominid evolution and tool use was more important later on. There is no doubt that at some point tool use and toolmaking became the critical factor in an increasingly swift shaping of mankind and also in the increasingly important role that hunting would play in hominid life.

The origin of tools in human evolution must have occurred through the process of trial and error. The nearest we can come to reconstructing it is to remind ourselves that there was a time when our ancestors could do less with tools than chimpanzees can do now. They must have worked their way through a similar but not necessarily identical limited capacity to shape something for a purpose—a grass stem for poking into a termite mound, a chewed-up mouthful of leaves to serve as a sponge, a stick or branch as something to be brandished in an effort to intimidate, a rock to throw.

A group of not-too-large apes will seem more formidable standing erect because they will appear to be larger. The brandishing of sticks or branches will enhance that effect, and may have been enough, on occasion, to swing the balance in a set-to with hyenas over possession of a kill. The earliest use of implements by man's ancestor, as a ground-adapted scavenger-hunter, may have received its strongest impetus from its value in threat displays against competing species. For an immensely long time, the found implement was the only type of implement, picked up and then thrown away when its immediate use was over. But there must have come a stage at which *Australopithecus* (or his ancestor) began to recognize more and more clearly the usefulness of certain objects and, as a result, tended to hang onto them longer, to the point where he may have begun carrying them around much of the time. The great abundance of wood, and the fact that it is softer and easier to work than stone, suggests that the earliest hominids may have used wood a great deal. They also probably used the long bones of some of the larger animals. But the great triumph of our ancestor as a creator of culture is seen most clearly in the legacy he has left us of worked stone. All the oldest surviving artifacts, it should be pointed out, are implements for cutting and chopping, not weapons.

The Earliest Stone Industry: The Oldowan

The magnet that drew Louis and Mary Leakey back to Olduvai Gorge year after year was the existence there of large numbers of extremely primitive stone implements. Mary Leakey made the study of these objects her special province. Her first monograph on the stone culture at Olduvai covers material taken from the gorge's lowest strata, known as Beds I and II, and a time period that extends from not quite two million years ago to about one million years ago (see Table 8–1).

It has been possible to reconstruct certain details of the lives of the creatures who lived at Olduvai so long ago from the hundreds of thousands of bits of material that they left behind—some stone, some bone; some large, some extremely small. No one of these things, taken alone, would mean much, but when they all are analyzed and fitted together like a gigantic three-dimensional jigsaw puzzle, patterns begin to emerge that speak across the gulf of time.

Mary Leakey found that there are two stone-working traditions in Olduvai. One is the Acheulian (to be discussed in Chapter 11) and the other is the *Oldowan,* the older and more primitive of the two, which produced mainly what anthropologists for a long time called pebble

TABLE 8–1 STRATIFIED BEDS AND FOSSILS AT OLDUVAI GORGE

Approximate Age (Years)	Bed	Fossils and Industry
100,000–400,000	Upper beds	*Homo sapiens*
400,000–700,000	Bed IV	Fossils of *Homo erectus* Late Acheulian hand-axes and cleavers
700,000–1.2 million	Bed III	No fossils Few artifacts
1.2–1.65 million	Bed II	*Homo erectus* and *habilis* Early Acheulian and Oldowan tools
1.65–1.8 million	Bed I	*Australopithecus boisei* and *habilis* Oldowan choppers
1.9 million	Volcanic lava	

Note: The ages of the upper beds are still rather uncertain. Bed I carries the most reliable dates.

tools, but what Mary Leakey prefers to call *choppers*. The word "pebble" suggests something quite small, and her term is an improvement, for many of the chopping tools at Olduvai are of hen's-egg size or larger, some of them three or four inches across.

An Oldowan chopper (Figure 8–12) is about the most basic "man"-made, "man"-used implement that one can possibly imagine. It is, typically, made from a cobble, a stone that has been worn smooth by sand and water action. The stone selected is often that of a close-grained, hard, smooth-textured material like quartz, flint, or chert. Many of the cobbles at Olduvai are of hardened lava that flowed out of the volcanoes in the region.

Oval or pear-shaped, and small enough to fit comfortably in the hand, such a water-rounded stone could be gripped firmly without hurting the palm when used. What an early toolmaker had to do to turn it into a tool was simply to smash one end down hard on a nearby boulder, or balance it on the boulder and give it a good whack with another rock. A large chip would fly off. Another whack would knock off a second chip next to the first, leaving a jagged edge or perhaps a point on one end of the stone. With luck this edge would be sharp enough for *Australopithecus* to cut up meat, to saw or mash through joints and gristle, to scrape hides, to sharpen the end of a stick. There are large choppers and small ones. The tool presumably was held as one would hold a rock while banging downward with a direct hammering or chopping motion. The small chips that were knocked off during the manufacture of choppers are known as *flakes*. Sharper than choppers, they probably were used for slicing and cutting. They undoubtedly became dull very quickly, for although stone is hard, its edges break easily.

The names of many of the ancient tools imply a way of using them. It should be understood clearly that a name like "chopper" describes a use that can only be guessed at by the archaeologist. The guess may appear overwhelmingly logical, but it is still a guess.

An implement like a chopper is recognized readily by an expert, although to you it might be indistinguishable from a stone that has been pointed or edged by nature. The ancient tool kit contains implements that are still more primitive than choppers, and with luck and skill even these can be recognized. An unworked stone that bears the marks of a great deal of banging and battering may have been used as a hammer or as an anvil. Also, the presence of stones of a kind that do not normally occur at a site can be regarded as indicative of tool use, even though the stones themselves have not been chipped. As for actual manufacture, the presence of large numbers of chips or by-product flakes in one spot is an indication that toolmaking once took place there. Choppers are by no means the most common kind of tool found in the earliest sites. Much more numerous are these smaller chips and naturally shaped stones. The latter, of course, were the principal source of tools for millions of years before it occurred to anyone to try to sharpen a stone. They are indentifiable today only by the context in which they are found. As one French prehistorian has remarked, "Man made one, God made ten thousand. God help the man who hopes to distinguish the one in the ten thousand."

The culture that Mary Leakey's work at Olduvai reveals was left by a 1.8-million-year-old hominid that most anthropologists believe was too small-brained even to talk. Just as the intricacies and subtleties of chimpanzee or baboon society turn out to be much more complex than anyone realized a generation ago, so does the culture of the early bipedal hominids. The Leakeys concluded that the creature responsible for turning out this varied tool kit was of the genus *Homo,* and therefore should be called *Homo habilis,* because of the elaborateness of the culture Mary Leakey unearthed, not because of the size of the brain. If he could make tools rather than merely use them, and make them to a regular pattern, then he was a human.

Perhaps the most impressive of all the things Mary Leakey has turned up at Olduvai are *occupation floors.* These are places where hominids lived for extended periods of time, dependent on the local vegetation and the local game. They are, in effect, nearly two-million-year-old camp sites and are identifiable by heavy concentrations of fossil material, stone tools, and debris, which are confined to a depth of only a few inches. The earth those hominids squatted on is still there, with the remains of what they made and ate scattered about.

Figure 8–12 An Oldowan chopper is usually made by striking some flakes from a rounded cobble to give a cutting edge. It is the simplest stone implement.

Occupation Floors

Gradually, and without disturbing anything, blown dust, encroaching vegetation, rising water, and mud covered each of these occupation floors. Thus, the objects that two million years later the Leakeys were to uncover laboriously and catalogue remained exactly where they were dropped. Elsewhere in Olduvai the artifacts and bones are spread through layers of sand and clay that may be several feet deep. In these places it is clear that river action has moved them about, swirled them together, and dumped them from time to time and that their position relative to one another is not very meaningful. But as one lays bare an occupation floor, one hopes to learn something about the life that its owner lived.

What did *Australopithecus* leave there? At one site, he left a lot of fish heads and crocodile bones, together with fossilized papyrus plants, indicating that at that site, at least, he was living next to water and getting some food from it. Other sites contain the bones of flamingos. This says that the nearby water was a lake, shallow and slightly alkaline as many East African lakes are today, since only such conditions produce the tiny shrimps flamingos eat.

Ten occupation sites have been identified at Olduvai, out of about seventy fossil- or tool-bearing sites scattered along a twelve-mile stretch of the gorge. On one floor the cultural debris is arranged in a most peculiar manner. There is a dense concentration of chips and flakes from tool manufacture mixed in with a great number of small, smashed animal-bone fragments, all crowded into a roughly rectangular area some fifteen feet wide and thirty feet long. Surrounding this rectangle is a space three or four feet wide where there is hardly any of this cultural junk; the ground is nearly bare. But outside that space, the material becomes relatively abundant again. How can we account for this extraordinary arrangement? The most obvious explanation is that the densely littered central section was a living site surrounded by a protective thorn hedge, inside which the hominids who lived there relaxed safely while they made their tools and ate their food, tossing out over the hedge whatever they did not simply drop on the floor.

At another site is a roughly circular formation of stones, about fourteen feet in outside diameter. What other stones there are on that occupation floor are widely and haphazardly scattered. By contrast, the circle is a dense concentration of several hundred stones carefully arranged in a ring by somebody—somebody who also took the trouble to make higher piles of stones every two or three feet around the circle. That this configuration survives after nearly two million years is staggering. This ancient arrangement of stones brings to mind a shelter of a kind that is being made today by the Ova Tjimba tribe of southwest Africa. They, too, make low rings of stones, with higher piles at intervals to support upright poles or branches, over which skins or grasses are spread to keep out the wind.

Although the predictable debris is found inside the stone circle,

The First Shelters

indicating that some activity took place there, there is more evidence of a wider variety of activities having taken place outside. This makes sense. The interior dimensions of this somewhat irregular circle are only about eight feet by ten or twelve feet, which would have made the enclosure rather crowded if it had been an area in which all kinds of activities were carried out. Furthermore, the group that used the shelter included some extremely good hunters or scavengers. The surrounding area contains the fossilized remains of giraffes, hippos, and many antelopes, and the tooth of the ancient kind of elephant deinotherium. Those people were eating big game and they may have found it more convenient to do their eating out in the open rather than in the confines of the shelter.

Whether they actually killed those large animals, whether they chased them into swamps and helped them die, whether they brought home meat from found carcasses, whether they preempted the kills of other carnivores, the chronicle of Olduvai does not say. But it makes clear that when an extremely large carcass became available it was cut up and eaten. There are two sites at Olduvai Gorge known to have been butchering sites (see Figure 8–13). One contains the skeleton of an elephant, the other that of a deinotherium. Since those animals weighed several tons each, it was obviously impossible to move them; the thing to do was to settle down at the carcass and chop and chew away at it until its meat was gone. Judging from the evidence at these butchering sites, that is exactly what happened. At each there is an almost complete skeleton of a huge animal, its bones disarranged as if they had been tugged and hacked apart. Lying among the bones are the discarded choppers and other stone tools that did the hacking.

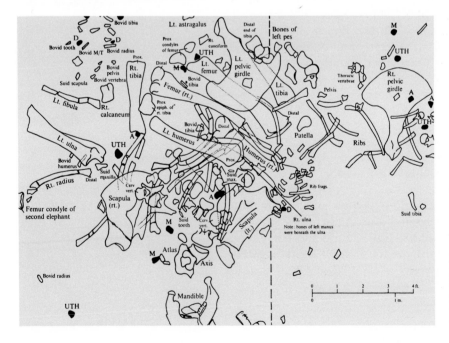

Figure 8–13 This plan of part of the living floor of a butchery site in Bed I of Olduvai Gorge shows stone tools (solid black) and almost the entire skeleton of an elephant, together with other food remains.

Certain Olduvai sites are rich in antelope bones, some with their skulls cracked open at the precise point on the front where the bone was thinnest. Others are crammed with the shells of large tortoises. One is littered with snail shells. Another contains a giraffe head, but nothing else belonging to that animal; clearly, it was brought home to be eaten.

The clues are many, and enthralling. What do we make of little concentrations here and there of very small bones, most of them broken into tiny pieces? Would any hominid have collected handfuls of skeletal fragments of mice, shrews, small birds, and lizards and then carefully placed them in piles? It seems wildly unlikely, and Mary Leakey concluded that these strange little heaps are probably what is left of hominid feces. Our ancestors were eating those small animals whole, bones and all, much as a modern human might eat a sardine. The bones were ground up into very small fragments by chewing, then passed through the intestines and deposited where they were found.

The First Stone Tools: East Rudolf

This wealth of fantastic information coming from Olduvai indicates without question that by about two million years ago hominids were living in a remarkably advanced state of culture, at a level that no one a few decades ago would have believed possible. Since progress in the early Stone Age was slow, the beginnings of the Oldowan tool industry are probably far older than Olduvai—how much older no one yet has the slightest idea. In 1969 word began to trickle back from East Rudolf and Omo that there were tools there, too. The first official news came out in 1970, when Mary Leakey published a paper describing some implements from her son Richard's East Rudolf dig at Koobi Fora. The next year two experts who went to Koobi Fora to help Richard Leakey analyze his site—Glynn Isaac, a prehistorian, and Kay Behrensmeyer, a geologist—confirmed another surprise: animal bones and Oldowan choppers and flakes had been discovered in an occupation floor that is possibly three quarters of a million years older than the floors in Bed I at Olduvai.

What is particularly promising about Koobi Fora, along with other nearby sites in East Rudolf, is that when the geology and dating of the whole are worked out and one place properly linked to another in time, it will be possible to correlate the area's exceptionally rich hominid fossil remains with its tool industry finds and to learn more about *Australopithecus* as a creature that made and used tools possibly over 2.6 million years ago.

We know that toolmaking and hominid evolution go hand in hand. But the earliest steps are unknown. At first it would have been impossible to distinguish between a worked tool and a found one, something *Ramapithecus* might have been experimenting with while he began to discover the advantages of walking erect.

OVERVIEW

		MODERN CHIMPANZEE	MODERN HUMAN
Physical characteristics		Average height of 4.3 to 5 feet	Average height of 4.11 to 5.8 feet
		Large projecting canines; rectangular jaw	Nonprojecting canines; curved jaw
		Cranial capacity ranging from 282 to 500 cc	Cranial capacity averaging 1,330 cc
Habitat		Spends much of its time in the trees	Ground-dwelling
		Tropical rain forests of Central Africa	All climatic zones
Diet		Mostly fruit, but does eat a large variety of foods, including small animals	Omnivorous
Locomotion		Brachiation and quadrimanual climbing in the trees; mostly knuckle walking on the ground	Bipedal
Tools		Not dependent on tools, but does modify naturally occurring objects to use as a sponge, to fish for termites, and to threaten others	Dependent on tools; extensive technology

Time scale (left margin):

10,000
2 million
5 million
10 million
15 million
20 million
25 million

HOLOCENE

PLEISTOCENE
A. robustus and *boisei* extinct

PLIOCENE
Earliest Oldowan tools at East Rudolf

MIOCENE
Earliest *Australopithecus*

First *Ramapithecus*

First *Dryopithecus*

OLIGOCENE

Apidium, Parapithecus, and *Aegyptopithecus*

HOMO ERECTUS

AUSTRALOPITHECUS AFRICANUS (circa 2.75 million B.P.)

Physical characteristics	Males about 4.5 to 5 feet tall; females somewhat smaller
	Moderate-sized canines; curved jaw
	Cranial capacity ranging from about 430 to 530 cc
Habitat	Ground-dwelling, perhaps sleeping in the trees
	Tropical savanna
Diet	Probably seeds and small animals in addition to fruit, leaves, etc.
Locomotion	Bipedal, although possibly not as efficient a walker as later hominids
Tools	Used naturally occurring wood, bones, and stones and worked stones—the crude Oldowan tools—for chopping, cutting, and hunting

WALKING AND TOOLMAKING

The evolution of walking and toolmaking are central processes in human evolution. Although we are not descended from chimpanzees, there is good reason to suppose that the common ancestor we share with them was much more like a chimpanzee than a human. The fossil evidence of *Australopithecus* enables us to discover how far along the way to humanity this creature had travelled in these all-important characteristics.

Chapter 9

Social Organization and Hunting

As unto the bow the cord is,
So unto the man is woman;
Though she bends him, she obeys him,
Though she draws him, yet she follows;
Useless each without the other!

HENRY WADSWORTH LONGFELLOW, 1807–1882.
THE SONG OF HIAWATHA, x.

As we have seen, there is a great deal of dispute and uncertainty about when, why, and even how our ancestors became bipedal terrestrial creatures. But vitally important characteristics of hominids must surely be traced to the unique introduction of a forest ape to the savanna. One such characteristic is social organization, the kinds of groups that those first ground-exploring apes probably moved in.

THE BASIS OF SOCIAL ORGANIZATION

We cannot know at this late date what these groups were like, but we can make some shrewd guesses about them. Since early hominids were most closely related to ancestors of chimpanzees, and since they probably shared the savanna environment with ancestors of baboons, it may be useful to look for clues in the social organization of living descendants of both these animals.

Although chimpanzees and baboons differ from each other in important ways, they have many characteristics in common. Of these, certainly the most interesting is that their societies are highly organized. Far from being a structureless collection of rushing, squalling animals, chimpanzee and baboon societies are remarkably stable, usually serene and quiet, with order maintained through a complex interrelationship of five main factors. The first is the mother–infant bond. The second is the animal's age, which regulates its progress from one role in the troop to another. The third is *dominance,* how high each animal ranks socially in the group. The fourth is *kinship,* the continuing recognized relationship of an animal to a brother or a sister or a mother. The fifth is the adult male–female relationship and relationships between adults of the same sex.

Thinking about these five factors, one quickly sees that they are among the most important regulators of human society, as well. Thus, for a very long time (we may assume) and for many different species—for man, for chimpanzee, and for baboon—the problem of life has been, and is still, largely the problem of getting along with one's fellows in a group.

Sherwood Washburn and David Hamburg, looking at primate behavior from the point of view of an anthropologist and a psychiatrist, respectively, recognized the importance of group life when they wrote:

> The group is the locus of knowledge and experience far exceeding that of individual members. It is in the group that experience is pooled and the generations linked. The adaptive function of prolonged biological youth is that it gives the animal time to learn. During this period while the animal is learning from other members of the group, it is protected by them. Slow development in isolation would simply mean disaster for the individual and extinction for the species.

What is meant by "prolonged biological youth"? A kitten has become a cat by the time it is a year old. A male baboon, by contrast, takes six years to grow up, a chimpanzee anywhere from ten to fifteen years, a human even longer. As a result, family ties among these primates tend to be strong and long-lasting. This slow development is necessary if a higher primate is to learn all the things it must to fit itself into the complex society into which it is born. In a society in which an individual must deal with many daily choices and varied personal interchanges, a long period of youthful learning is an absolute necessity.

This learning period looks suspiciously like play, and it is. For a chimpanzee, childhood play is the equivalent of going to school. It watches its mother look for food, and looks for food itself. It watches her make nests, and makes little nests of its own—not to sleep in, just for the fun of it. Later, during a long adolescence, it picks up from its peers the physical skills it will need as an adult as well as the more intricate psychological skills involved in getting along with others: it learns not only how to interpret the moods of other chimpanzees but also how to respond to other individuals. Any chimpanzee that cannot learn to communicate fully with its fellows almost certainly will not live to grow up, for communication is the essential bonding of any society. All this time the learner is finding its own place among its peers, first in play, later in more competitive activity that will help determine its rank several years later as an adult. In sum, there are two sources of learning, two sets of relationships, that make up primate society. One of these is the family relationship (mother–infant–

Figure 9–1 Chimpanzee mother and son have a bond that is as close as that between human mother and child, though not so long-lasting, and as vital to the young chimpanzee's health. As with humans, the quality of chimpanzee mothering varies and affects the personality of the young.

Learning in Childhood

Figure 9–2 Play is important in chimpanzee social development, as it is among humans. Here, two young chimpanzees play together on a branch.

sibling). The other is the larger relationship of an individual animal to all the other members of the troop.

One of the most striking aspects of a baboon troop is the phenomenon of male dominance. In many of the baboon troops that have been studied so far, there is a dominant individual to which the other males habitually defer. (Often two animals, sometimes as many as three or more, will team up to hold a top position that neither could hold alone.) Below the top male (or males) the other adult males usually arrange themselves in descending order of authority. There is always a certain amount of minor jostling for position, and even some prolonged and bitter struggles for places at the top; nevertheless, once a dominance hierarchy is established, it tends to be a remarkably stable structure. The high-ranking animals move confidently through their troop; the others defer to them as a matter of course in confrontations over food, females, selection of sleeping sites, grooming and being groomed, and so forth. This sure deference is important. It is the behavior of subordinates in the troop, rather than the constant ferocity of their superiors, that ensures the society's day-to-day stability. A low-ranking animal is subservient. It knows its place.

The situation is not so clear with chimpanzees as it is with baboons. Among chimpanzees, dominance is a relaxed matter; the animals are tolerant of one another, and exact status is often blurry. Among many baboons it is more rigidly enforced. The difference is believed to stem largely from differences in the living conditions of the two species. A savanna baboon troop moves on the ground, where there is strong selective pressure to produce big, aggressive males to protect the troop against predators. As a result, there is marked *sexual dimorphism* in baboons; that is, the males are noticeably different from the females

Dominance

Figure 9–3 Hamadryas female with young, and male. The male is larger and heavier, and he carries a magnificent mane, which makes him look even larger.

(see Figure 9–3). They are much larger (often twice as large) and much stronger, have far bigger canine teeth and jaws, are a great deal more combative, and are less tolerant of lapses in behavior or threats to their status. They are also very jealous of females in heat. These traits tend to create an authoritarian society in which a mere stare by a dominant male will remind a subordinate of the realities of its status.

Why are there not more fights among baboons, particularly in large troops of several dozen animals where the steady penetration of husky post-adolescents into the adult male group should make a continuously stable hierarchy highly unlikely? And why doesn't every youngster have to start at the bottom and work its way up?

Deeper study by baboon experts gave some answers to these questions. Better knowledge of blood relationships within the troop began to reveal that the stability of the group does not depend so much on the males as it does on certain high-ranking females. True, those females draw some of their status from their association with dominant males, but they also constitute an ongoing aristocracy of their own, based on mother–daughter and sister–sister ties. Once established, this aristocracy tends to perpetuate itself. The privileged—and usually related—females generally congregate at the center of the troop, which is the preferred spot because it is the safest from predators. There they groom each other sociably, bringing up their infants in an atmosphere of comfort and security that is denied low-ranking females. The latter are forced to hang about at the edge of the group, alert to the possibility of a bite or slap if they do not move aside for a higher-ranking animal. Unable to enter permanently into the established matriarchy at the center, they pass their timidity and generally low self-esteem on to their babies. As we might expect, the babies reared by the dominant mothers grow up with a far greater chance of achieving dominance themselves. They learn confidence and assurance from their mothers. Their friends from infancy are other well-born youngsters. They go to the right schools, as it were, make the right contacts, have all the right opportunities for successful baboon careers.

Chimpanzee social life is more complex than that of baboons, because there is more opportunity for individual expression. Since they live in the forest and are largely relieved of the threat of ground predation, chimpanzees need not be so combative nor so cohesive as savanna baboons, and they are not. Nor, for the same reason, do they exhibit the degree of sexual dimorphism that these baboons do. Although they do have dominance hierarchies, these are not so rigidly enforced. Chimpanzee society is more innovative, more relaxed, more tolerant. Free of sexual jealousy, it is marked instead by a casual promiscuity. When a female is in heat and anxious to mate, any interested males in the troop will line up and amiably wait their turn—which should come soon, since copulation takes only a few seconds and is performed casually, sometimes while one of the protagonists offhandedly munches a banana and curious youngsters look on or tug at the performing male.

Figure 9–4 Confrontations among savanna baboons usually result in one individual either presenting in defeat or scampering off. These two baboons are well matched and both are threatening very strongly, with their mouths wide open to display their powerful teeth.

Figure 9–5 Female baboons are always attracted by the sight of an infant. A female with an infant will usually become dominant to one without an infant. Here the subordinate female is approaching the mother submissively with her rump lowered to denote friendly intentions.

The dominance hierarchy is not the sole determinant of relationships in a primate troop. Communication plays a central role in social life, and the possibility of receiving communications from others implies awareness of others. It seems clear that the degree of awareness exhibited by chimpanzees and baboons is such that they are not merely conscious of the activities and status of each other, but see deeper into personality. They show special preferences; that is, they prefer to spend time with particular members of the troop, who may be their kin. In both species we see what looks very like friendship: certain pairs and trios (sometimes of different sex, but more often of the same) spend much time together and share experiences and food sources. When meat is obtained, quite a rare delicacy, chimpanzees will share after the provider has had first pick; baboons will move aside to make room for a friend to get at the kill. It looks as if these primates are in some small way responding to each other's needs, even when adult and outside the mother–infant relationship. What we see is an extension of the innate altruism that rearing an infant implies, to reciprocal altruism between adults. Insofar as the members of a troop help one another, this behavior has an obvious adaptive value for the social group as a whole. This is a fascinating example of the way we so often see in the social life of these highly intelligent primates an intimation of what we consider to be typically human behavior.

We take the unit of the *nuclear family*—father, mother, children—for granted, and naturally enough, for it has been central to our society for so long that we tend to forget that there was a time when it may not have existed in its present form. If, in searching for hominid family beginnings, we use as a likely model the chimpanzee family, with its relaxed affections and its prolonged mother–infant and sibling–sibling ties, then we must account somehow for the introduction of a father into the unit. For in chimpanzee society there are no social fathers, nor can biological fathers be identified. There is plenty of food in the forest (no need for a fatherly provider), and there are almost no predators (no need for a fatherly protector). Where, then, does the human father come from?

This brings us to consider an important physiological difference between the nonhuman primates and mankind. Although all primates have an *estrous cycle* (which in women is called the menstrual cycle) and although all cycle within approximately a four-week period, humans alone lack the phase of "heat," or *estrus,* that is common to the majority of mammals. This, in higher primates, is a period of about three to five days when the female is ovulating, shows (in the case of the chimpanzee and some monkeys) pronounced swelling of the perineal (genital) region, and actively solicits male sexual attention. Female chimpanzees present themselves for mating at this time only,

Friendship

Figure 9–6 Grooming, an important pastime of adult chimpanzees, besides maintaining the hygiene of their soft fur promotes social bonds: it is an opportunity for expressions of affection, especially by a lower-ranking to a higher-ranking animal. Mothers regularly groom their young from birth.

EVOLUTION OF THE FAMILY

The Estrous Cycle

and are very receptive to males. During this phase of estrus the female will probably mate with all the adult males in the vicinity. Humans are exceptional in having lost this complex of physiology and behavior associated with ovulation. Women can and do initiate sexual activity at any time of their cycle, and men are unable to determine, through any such sign as the female chimpanzee shows, the stage of any female's cycle. This is a very striking and important development in human evolution.

It seems clear that the loss of estrus must be associated in some way with the development of the more permanent relationship between men and women. Humans generally form relatively permanent male-female bonds and enjoy a mutual attraction that may last for some time (beyond one month) and does not depend on the female's monthly cycle at all. But how and when humans achieved this is a total mystery. One suggestion is that any change in the environment or the social structure of the troop that has the effect of throwing a male and female together over an extended period of time might cause the slow development of a continuous sexual interest between them. It might then follow that the periods of the female's sexual receptivity could gradually become longer and longer under the stimulation of such conditions of extended male–female intimacy, until the periods themselves overlap, making her continuously attractive and receptive.

But that period of extended intimacy between a male and a female— where and why does it originate? It does not exist among chimpanzees, where males prefer the company of males. It is absent in the East African savanna baboon. However, it is present in some other baboon societies, notably among the gelada and the hamadryas species, and among some langurs. The gelada and the hamadryas baboon live in open country that is not only generally drier but also has greater seasonal variations in climate and hence in the availability of food than the country familiar to the forest-edge baboon, which finds itself living in an environment of relative abundance the year round.

Here environmental difference coincides with differences in social organization, a coincidence observed by the noted British ethologist John H. Crook. Crook has studied the social organizations of many animals, including certain African weaver birds and antelopes as well as baboons. What struck him is the apparent uniformity with which *all* of these otherwise entirely different creatures react to similar environmental change. So striking were his findings that he has used them as the basis for a hypothesis: *under similar environmental conditions, social animals will tend to develop similar social organizations.* Crook's conclusions about social organization are based on complex and subtle evidence that is beyond the scope of this volume. However, a look at three different African baboon societies should make his point clear.

Man himself is the best example of adaptability. Thanks to the human brain—and its by-product, culture and technology—a human being can live near the North Pole with a body that is essentially the

Role of the Environment

Figure 9–7 On the savanna of the Amboseli Reserve in Kenya a water hole and the relatively lush vegetation surrounding it attract baboons and other animals.

same as the body of another human living on the Equator. Baboons, too, are extremely adaptable animals. They have not become as physically specialized as many other animals, and they are thus able to fit themselves to a wide variety of living conditions. With no material culture to rely on, however, baboons must fall back on changes in their social organization in order to adapt to different environmental conditions.

Of three baboon species, the East African savanna species lives in the easiest surroundings: close to trees to which it can flee and in which it can sleep, and in a climate where there is a year-round abundance of food. In this setting the troop is the all-important social unit; family relationships, except for mother–infant ties, are secondary. The nearest thing to a *social father* is a dominant male that, as a matter of course, exercises authority over some or all of the females in the troop. This male may be the *biological father* of many of the infants.

By contrast, geladas are confined to mountain slopes in Ethiopia. There the climate is harsher, seasonal change is greater, trees are very rare, and food availability is more chancy. Male-female relationships, too, are very different from those that prevail in the savanna. The animals are found in large herds that, in areas or seasons of poor food supply, break down during the day into a number of wide-foraging separate units, each containing a single adult male with one or more females and assorted young. The value of this arrangement is obvious: during times of food shortage, adequate food for females and young is far more important for the survival of the species as a whole than is food for extra males. More ground must be covered. So long as there is one strong male to protect the females, other males can be regarded as so much surplus baggage, useful only for replacement or for forming new families of their own with young females. With this social structure the relationship between a particular male and females is far more durable than it is among savanna baboons. In that respect it resembles the human nuclear family unit more closely than does the organization of the savanna baboon troop. Significantly, when the wet season comes to the dry Ethiopian hills and food starts to be more abundant, the one-male groups begin to coalesce into larger, more conventional multimale troops.

Hamadryas society is different again. This baboon lives in country even drier than the gelada's terrain, in rocky sections of Ethiopia and the near-desert of Somalia. In this environment one-male groups are the rule the year round. The male–female relationship is more close-knit than among geladas. Each hamadryas male is continuously jealous of its harem, requiring its females to stay very close to it at all times. When it moves, they move—or get bitten.

Now, hominids are not baboons and are not even very closely related to them. Nevertheless, Crook's thesis is provocative. If social organization is shaped by environment (Crook would have it understood that the shaping does not take place directly but over a long period of time, initiated by and reinforced by selection), then it can be argued that an ape, in moving out of the forest to live in seasonally dry country, could have modified its social organization to conform to the requirements of that environment. Further, it could have done so in the way that other primates are known to have done. These modifications obviously would have varied from place to place. Just as baboons have differing life styles, surely hominids did, too, depending on where they lived and on how severe the seasonal food- and water-getting problems were. Where such problems were at their worst, extra male hominids may be considered to have been just as expendable as surplus male baboons, and one-male family units may have resulted.

This speculation supplies a father figure for our small-toothed, open-country, erect ape—a figure that was missing in the easygoing chimpanzee-like society that hominids most probably had before they left the forest. It was not the peculiarly human characteristic of round-the-clock sexual attractiveness and receptivity that introduced the father to the family (although, later in evolution, such receptivity may have become one of the forces that encouraged him to keep coming back to it). One the contrary, at the stage of which we are speaking, as we try to identify the beginnings of a human family structure in a creature that is not yet a human, the determining factor may well have been environmental. If so, the long-term association of a male with certain females was an economic one. Under certain conditions we have outlined, one-male groups were the most efficient arrangement for survival.

This search for a father has been roundabout, and the evidence for the explanation offered here is entirely circumstantial. Nevertheless, the search for an acceptable argument is necessary. We have heads of families now, and have had for a long time. The father—or more properly, the male family head—plays a key role in so many developments that are peculiarly human that the emergence of human beings simply cannot be conceived of without his presence at some point far back in time.

One-Male Groups: Hominids

The question really becomes: how far back? Crook's hypothesis seems to suggest that the male–female bond is a very old one, since it is based on the fundamental issue of environment and therefore could logically be expected to begin to manifest itself soon after the first exposure of hominids to a ground life where seasonal food shortage was any kind of a problem. That could take us back to the earliest *Australopithecus* or perhaps even *Ramapithecus,* but here guesswork takes over.

Those who disagree with this say that to explain family formation it is not necessary to look that far back, or as far afield as baboons. They prefer to keep their eye on that closer relative, the chimpanzee, and attribute the beginnings of family formation to meat eating and food sharing—traits that chimpanzees display in a feeble form. These activities, says Sherwood Washburn, a strong advocate of this view, were the influence that led to the development of more permanent male–female bonds. Since a developing taste for meat leads to an improvement in hunting techniques, and since the practice of hunting begins to get involved with more effective tools and weapons and with more efficient bipedalism, the Washburn model implies a somewhat later date for family formation. It implies that the family evolved as a response to unequal access to food resources.

EVOLUTION OF MALE AND FEMALE ROLES

Everyone is agreed that the changing role of the male in hominid evolution, however it emerged, is an important one. It has had its effect on the evolution of different and appropriate male and female roles in daily living, the division of labor; on the development of teaching elaborate and appropriate new skills to the young; on the development of the concept of a home base; and on the matters of hunting, food-gathering, and food sharing. All are interconnected. Together they make for a complex feedback system.

Physical Differences

Differing roles suggest evolutionary shaping to fit those roles. For example, men are usually bigger and stronger than women now, and they surely have been for millions of years. These attributes are predictable for protectors and hunters; the relationship between role and physique is simple and direct. But men can also run faster than women, and here the reason is neither simple nor direct. If speed on foot were merely a matter of size and strength, then the largest and strongest man would be the faster runner. Since this is demonstrably not the case, there must be another reason why a lithe woman should not be so swift as a bulkier man: she cannot be if she is going to be the mother of larger-brained children. The best-designed pelvis for bearing such children is not the best-designed for running, or even for the most efficient walking.

As we saw in Chapter 8, hominids became capable of efficient bipedalism because of marked changes in the shape and proportion of leg and foot bones and, particularly, of the pelvis. But changes in man's pelvis have not made the open space in its center any bigger. In order to achieve that, the whole pelvic structure would have to get bigger, and that change would defeat the evolutionary process of developing a compact, efficient pelvis for bipedal walking. The pelvis of the human female cannot be as compact as the human male's (Figure 9–8) without being too small to permit passage of the head of her baby. The female pelvis is therefore a compromise—not compact enough for the most efficient walking but large enough for the birth of a large-brained infant. As hominids became more human and larger-brained, the pelvic opening might have become even larger than it is. That it did not is due to the demands of bipedalism and one cause of the difficulties in childbirth that the modern woman experiences.

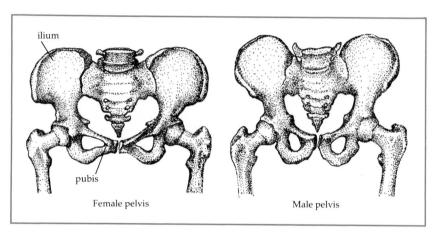

Female pelvis   Male pelvis

Figure 9–8 Among humans the greatest skeletal difference between the sexes is found in the pelvis. The most important differentiating feature is the female's large birth canal, which causes numerous minor differences in the shape of the bones that constitute the pelvis. Especially noteworthy is the breadth and form of the blade of the ilium and the angle below the pubic bones.

Prolonged Youth and the Female's Role

When hominids entered the savanna, we can be sure that they began to evolve differences in the roles played by males and females. Since hominids were more intelligent than baboons, hominid females were even more closely tied to infant care. Not only did hominid infants mature more slowly, but they were becoming more helpless at birth. This is because one of the solutions to the small-pelvis, large-brain problem is for the female to give birth to the infant at an earlier stage in its development before its head gets too big, and go through a correspondingly longer period of caring for the infant. Clearly the human infant enters the world much earlier in his development than other primates, at a stage in which his brain and body are too unformed to let him walk and forage for himself. (See Table 9–1 for a comparison of chimpanzee and human development.) At birth the human brain is one-fourth to one-third its eventual size; the baboon brain is three-quarters grown.

Ape and monkey infants have feet as well as hands that enable them to hang onto their mothers' fur. Within a day or two, a baboon baby, for example, can cling unaided to its mother's hair while she moves around in search of food and water; within twelve months the baboon is more or less on its own. The human baby, by contrast, is utterly dependent on his mother. He has to be carried and supplied with almost all his needs for at least two years; it may be six years before he is as able to take care of himself as a baboon is at twelve months.

With influences like these at work, it is logical to assume an intensification of the differences in the roles played by hominid males and females, particularly as females become more and more necessary to their infants for longer and longer periods of time and more dependent on males, with whom they were beginning to associate longer. Longer association encourages mutual support. New behavioral twists become possible, one of them being the slow beginnings of food sharing.

Providing Food: Hunting and Gathering

Baboons rarely share food; chimpanzees sometimes do. The food shared in either instance is meat. Hominids also may have had traces of the meat-sharing trait when they left the forest. On the savanna, with males becoming increasingly good walkers and extending the range of their activities accordingly, the chances of their finding small animals to kill, and later beginning deliberately to hunt them down, obviously grew. The incentive to share food must have grown accordingly. A man cannot eat an entire baby antelope on the spot. What he might well do is share it with other hunters then and there, and carry what is left back to the infant-encumbered females with whom the hunter is associated. Because hunting involves chasing prey, sometimes for considerable distances, some group members must be left behind, most probably females and infants. "Behind" should be at best a place where those less mobile members of the group are reasonably safe, and at worst a place that the hunters can find again—in short, the beginnings of a home base.

Hunters are not always successful. As often as not, they return empty-handed. As a result, in nearly all hunter-gatherer societies they supply only part (usually less than half) of the group's food. Therefore it is the females' responsibility to see to it that there is a dependable supply of fruit, seeds, nuts, and other vegetable materials. Food-gathering is a behavior very different from that which we find in monkeys and apes. These creatures pick and eat food as they need it. Food-gathering implies that more food than is immediately required is picked and placed in containers. In addition to evening out the ups and downs in the food supply created by the unreliability of hunting, such things as nuts and grain, unlike quickly rotting meat, keep a long time and may be rationed out in small quantities as needed.

In some such way, the sharing of food got its start, along with the development of appropriate male and female roles for its procuring. These are roles that would endure for some millions of years. They are commonly found in hunter-gatherer societies today.

Behavior of *Australopithecus*

How far this division of labor had progressed by the time of *Australopithecus* is debatable. Certainly its progress was uneven. For a female to be an efficient gatherer of small food objects she must have baskets or gourds or containers made of large leaves or pieces of animal skin. There is no evidence that *Australopithecus* used any of these, but the lack of evidence does not mean they were not used, for all such materials are perishable.

TABLE 9–1   DEVELOPMENT OF HUMANS AND CHIMPANZEES

Age	Characteristic Behavior	Percentage of Adult Brain Size
Human Child		
At birth	Depends completely on mother for food, transportation, and protection Exhibits grasping reflex: automatically grabs an object that touches his palm Stretches arms outward, then together over his chest, in a grasping gesture, when his head falls backward Vocalizes by crying	25 percent
3 months	Raises his head when lying down, supporting his weight on his forearms Turns body from back to side Vocalizes through cooing	35 percent
6 months	Sits up unsupported Exhibits coordination: reaches purposefully for an object and grasps it Vocalizes through babbling one-syllable sounds	45 percent
9 months	Stands upright when supported Crawls on all fours Takes a few steps holding on to an adult	50 percent
1 year	Stands upright and walks unsupported Responds more to play objects than to playmates Responds to verbal commands and says first words	60 percent
2 years	Runs upright Moves quickly from sitting to standing position Uses a cup as a drinking tool Plays as much with playmates as with play objects Exhibits great interest in objects Speaks with a vocabulary of more than 50 words and uses two-word sentences	70 percent
4 years	Actively practices motor skills: running, jumping, hopping Plays extensively with other children Has the ability to understand and use language with precision	80 percent
8 to 9 years	Learns to cooperate with others and masters control over impulses and aggression within a group Thinks in abstract terms and exhibits great interest in solving problems	95 percent
12 to 14 years (puberty)	Exhibits increasing interest in the opposite sex	100 percent

Age	Characteristic Behavior	Percentage of Adult Brain Size
Chimpanzee		
At birth	Depends completely on mother for food, transportation, and protection Exhibits grasping reflex: clings to its mother's chest with hands and feet Stretches arms outward, then together over its chest in a grasping gesture	65 percent
3 months	Sits up unsupported Exhibits coordination: reaches purposefully for an object and grasps it	70 percent
6 months	Stands upright when supported Moves about on all fours Takes a few steps holding on to an adult	70 percent
9 months	Stands upright and walks unsupported Actively swings through trees, leaping from branch to branch Plays with other young chimpanzees	70 percent
1 year	Runs upright and on all fours	70 percent
2 years	Engages in social activities with chimps of all ages except infants	75 percent
4 years	Completely independent of mother for food and transportation Plays much of day with other chimps and its mother Makes and uses tools to obtain food and drink Begins to vocalize using noises to express fear, excitement, anticipation of food, and pleasure during grooming	85 percent
8 to 9 years (puberty)	Spends increasing amount of time in social grooming and in feeding itself as it devotes less time to play Begins sexual interest and activity	100 percent

Could *Australopithecus* have invented such an object? All that can be said is that some time prior to one million years ago female hominids had probably already begun collecting and keeping more food than they could eat at the moment themselves. Some experts consider that the brain of *Australopithecus* was too small for him to have been engaged in making and using containers. And yet the existence of rather sophisticated toolmaking techniques recently proven by Mary Leakey should make anthropologists extremely cautious about making firm pronouncements on what early hominids could or could not do. The more we learn about our *Australopithecus* ancestors, the more capable they seem to have been.

HUNTING

One area of their lives in which our ancestors were marvelously successful was hunting; many of our physical characteristics and some of our most deeply ingrained emotional traits stem from our long career as hunters. Although the development of agriculture and the dramatic rise of civilizations in the last five thousand to ten thousand years tend to obscure it, our ancestors almost certainly lived by hunting and gathering for more than a million years, perhaps for two or three million years. Out of the last three million years of their evolution as bipedal hominids, our ancestors probably spent 99 percent of their time as hunters.

How did the first hominids practice hunting as a way of life? How and to what extent may it have developed in the early years of our ancestors' existence? In order to begin to answer these questions, we can look again at the behavior of our closest relative, the chimpanzee.

Hunting among Chimpanzees

A hunting chimpanzee, Jane Goodall reports, is unmistakable. Compared with other chimpanzee behaviors, there is something a little out of the ordinary about hunting behavior, something purposeful, tense, and inward that other chimpanzees recognize and respond to. Sometimes they just watch the hunter intently. Sometimes they move to adjacent trees to cut off the escape of the quarry, a young baboon or small arboreal monkey. On several occasions observed by Goodall, the quarry was a young baboon whose screams usually brought adult baboons rushing to its defense. In the ensuing hullabaloo the youngster more often than not escaped. But she saw chimpanzees eating infant baboons often enough to realize that there was a small but fairly steady toll taken of them through the year.

Chimpanzees are excited by meat and clearly very fond of it. They chew it long and reflectively, usually with a mouthful of leaves added. Wads of this mixture are occasionally given to other begging chimps. Sometimes the carcass is shared by the successful hunter, who will tear off pieces and hand them out. The curious thing about meat eating and meat sharing is that when these activities are going on, regular dominance patterns do not apply. A high-ranking chimpanzee that would not hesitate to assert itself over a lowly one for possession of fruit will respect its right to the possession of meat. Apparently there is some-

Figure 9-9 The upper chimpanzee is holding the rib cage of a small monkey; the two lower chimpanzees are begging from him. When he has eaten enough, the hunter will share the remains of the kill.

thing about having killed an animal that gives an individual the right to keep it.

The revelation that chimpanzees hunt and eat meat—and share it as well, albeit often reluctantly—has enormous implications in explaining the development of hunting and sharing among hominids. It now becomes possible to speculate that these traits were brought to the savanna from the forest. We no longer have to puzzle, in any case, over how a propensity for meat eating got started in a creature with a fruit-eating ancestry; it was probably there, as we now know it is in most primates. All it needed was encouragement in a new environment.

That environment, the African savanna, was inhabited by other meat eaters that still roam and hunt there: lions, leopards, cheetahs, spotted hyenas, and wild dogs. By observing the hunting practices of these carnivores, we may, as George Schaller proposes, gain some insight into how *Australopithecus* developed hunting techniques to satisfy his inherent desire for meat. Schaller has written: "Since social systems are strongly influenced by ecological conditions, it seemed [to me] that it might be more productive to compare hominids with animals which are ecologically but not necessarily phylogenetically [evolutionarily] similar, such as social carnivores." Lions, hyenas, and wild dogs all are social animals that have developed two vitally important traits: they hunt in groups, and they share their food.

Cooperative hunting has many advantages; Schaller lists no fewer than five that give a group of hunters a big edge over an individual working alone. First, the group is consistently more successful in killing. Two or more spotted hyenas, working together, kill an animal at the end of a hunt more than three times as often as a single hyena does. Second, a group can kill larger animals than one hunter can. The most dramatic example of this (shown in Figure 9-10) is probably the wild

Social Carnivores: Cooperation

dog, which, working as a member of a pack, can bring down zebras that weigh up to 500 pounds, though the dogs themselves weigh only about 40 pounds each. Third, *all* the food caught by a group will probably be eaten on the spot, so that none is wasted. This is often not possible for a single animal, which eats as much as it can and then must wait until it is hungry again. By that time scavengers may have found the carcass and finished it. That is why the leopard, a solitary hunter, is put to the trouble of hauling its kills into trees where hyenas, jackals, and dogs cannot reach them. The fourth advantage is what Schaller calls division of labor. Here he cites the example of a wild dog that will remain behind to guard pups in the den while others are off hunting for food that they will bring back in their bellies and regurgitate for the pups—and also for the adult guard. Finally, there is a power ranking on the savanna based on size, with the lion at the top, the leopard next, followed by the hyena and wild dog. But numbers can overbalance size. Frequently, a lioness is unable to defend the carcass of a giraffe against a dozen hungry hyenas.

Figure 9–10 African wild dogs cooperate to stampede zebras, hoping to flush a laggard. They succeed in cutting out one zebra that is weaker than the others. As the rest of the zebra herd runs off, the pack closes on the quarry.

Another advantage that we might cite is the wider range of hunting methods that is open to a group than to a single animal. Among these is a kind of relay-race effect achieved by wild dogs. One or two adults will start a chase by running right after the prey, keeping constant pressure on it. As it flees, it is apt to run in a wide circle, which enables trailing dogs to watch the action and then save steps by cutting across the arc of pursuit and close in for the kill. Another example: lions are very good at driving prey toward hunting partners lying in ambush. They are also adept at surrounding it, so that whichever way it bolts there may be a lion in a position to attempt a kill. A group hunting together can sometimes maneuver the quarry into a cul-de-sac: out onto a promontory, into a swamp or a river, into a gully from which it cannot escape. Hominids, through their history as hunters, probably have used all these techniques.

Another very important aspect of social carnivores' behavior is food sharing. Lions fight and snarl—and, though rarely, kill each other—over their food (a trait that suggests incomplete social evolution: that is, they may have learned to cooperate in the field but not yet at the table). Hyenas and wild dogs are much better adapted in this respect. Dogs are extraordinarily scrupulous; the pups in the pack, being slower runners, are likely to be the last to arrive at a kill. The adults usually content themselves with a few bites, then move aside to let the youngsters have their fill before settling down for their own meal. This sometimes means that they go hungry and must hunt again, but good care of pups has great survival value for a species in which mortality among adults seems to run high.

Social Carnivores: Food Sharing

Cooperation and sharing, then, confer strong benefits on social carnivores. For savanna-living hominids these same benefits could have accrued. The more widely they ventured, the greater would have been their chance of coming upon small prey animals such as hares, fledgling birds, and the newborn young of larger herbivores. Not only would they be increasingly stimulated to chase and kill these creatures but, even more important, they would be encouraged to be on the lookout for them and to think more and more about how and where to find them. Hominid ambitions perhaps grew as they realized that crippled or old individuals of even larger species were within their capabilities as social hunters. But the bigger the game, the greater the need for cooperation. And with proportionally larger amounts of meat on hand as a result of successful cooperation, the greater the opportunity and the incentive to share it.

Australopithecus as Hunter and Scavenger

Here, again, positive feedback could have operated. The more successful a particular kind of behavior is in an animal intelligent enough to remember its actions, the more likely that animal will be to continue to try what has worked before. Each animal prey caught strengthens the urge to look harder for more prey. This phenomenon was observed by Jane Goodall among the Gombe chimpanzees. A chance catch of a young baboon would stimulate a good deal of hopeful hunting energy.

Figure 9–11 Shaking sticks, two scavenging hominids bully a timid cheetah, hoping to chase it from a kill it has just made.

But because of their poor success as hunters, their misguided enthusiasm, and the large number of alternative food sources, the chimpanzees would be discouraged quickly by failures. Hunting would cease to arouse interest until the next lucky kill rekindled the urge. Stimulated by more frequent success in the open and perhaps also by a greater need to hunt and scavenge because of a less stable food supply there, hominids could have made hunting, which was unimportant to the survival of chimpanzees, into a pattern of behavior that was increasingly vital to their survival.

Sharing, just as much as cooperative hunting, would have improved the survival chances of a hominid. It is painful to watch a sick or injured baboon trying to keep up with the troop. Other baboons do not feed or look out for it in any way; being largely seed, grass, fruit, and root eaters, they have to spend most of the day feeding themselves. Therefore the sick individual must manage on its own, and even though the other animals may move slowly throughout the day, the disabled one still may not be able to forage because it is devoting all its strength merely to keeping up. In such a situation it will get weaker, find it harder to keep up, and eventually be picked off by a hunting carnivore. Bringing back food to a place from which a disabled individual does not have to stir for a critical few days might mean the difference between life and death—particularly for a hominid whose maturation and learning processes are very slow and whose experiments with a meat diet, though they might result in great nutritional advantages, may expose it to the ravages of unfamiliar internal parasites. A baboon with a broken leg or a case of dysentery is almost certainly a dead baboon. A similarly stricken hominid might have survived.

So combine the peculiar attributes of a hominid with the cooperative hunting and food sharing of a social carnivore, and the result, in its slow, earlier stages, could produce something like *Australopithecus,* a hunter that goes about its business in a new way—on two legs and with weapons—its wits constantly being sharpened thereby until it eventually becomes a very efficient hunter indeed.

Because apes and monkeys are diurnal (active during the day), Schaller, like virtually everybody else, assumes that the early hominids were, too, and that they did all their hunting and scavenging in daylight. This speculation is overwhelmingly logical. For one thing, the night is dangerous; a small hominid out scavenging after dark would have been all too likely to run into saber-toothed cats, and lions, leopards, or hyenas, which hunt at night. For another, bipedal hominids were tall enough when standing up to see considerable distances, and they were also mobile enough to cover a good deal of ground. This suggests that they observed sharply what was going on around them and that much of their activity was directed towards scavenging. Too slow to run down healthy large animals by themselves, they probably relied on hyenas and wild dogs to do that for them, and then ran up in a noisy group and drove the hunters away. Finally, they would have found less competition from other hunters during the day.

By late *Australopithecus* times, about two million years ago, it is almost certain that hominids were sufficiently skillful hunters to make all but the largest herbivores afraid of them. It is likely that they competed with hyenas and wild dogs, fighting with them over their kills and over the found carcasses of large dead animals. In those fights, numbers, aggressiveness, and weaponry undoubtedly decided the issue.

Still, hunting started on a very modest scale, limited to the chance finding of small animals. Equally important, probably both in the earliest stages and thereafter, was scavenging, finding game already dead, either from natural causes or killed by other animals capable of being intimidated and driven away. This might be called the opportunistic side of meat eating, and here, once again, hominids probably resembled social carnivores. Although a lion will drive hyenas off a fresh kill, the hyenas are capable of gathering reinforcements to drive away the lion. Two or three lions will turn the tables again.

Hunting and Language

If animals are to cooperate during hunting, aggression between individuals must be discharged or suppressed. David Pilbeam suggests that aggressive behavior among male hominids became reduced as a result of the emergence of one-male groups and male–female pairs. He also believes that the beginning of language—a sophisticated level

of communication that could convey something more than mere feelings—would have led to greater trust, greater understanding, and
greater cooperation between individuals. Language development,
Pilbeam says, "would have made possible for the first time in primates
the reward and reinforcement of nonaggressive behavior patterns."

On this point there is some dispute. Pilbeam's remark carries the
implication that language was developed very early, possibly as early
as *Australopithecus.* Other experts disagree. Although they concede that
language may be a useful moderator of aggressive behavior (you curse
somebody or complain instead of hitting him with a club), they do not
concede that it was necessary in stimulating nonaggressive behavior.
That, they maintain, resulted from family formation, long mother–
infant relationships, and food sharing, long before language came
along. In fact, they insist, *Australopithecus* was too small-brained to
have been able to talk. They contend that speech was beyond the

Figure 9–12 *Australopithecus* lived
in a savanna environment with
animals that were not very different
from those we see today. In this
reconstruction, *Australopithecus* has
been placed in a modern setting; one
individual bends for a drink while
two others make stone choppers.

capacity of hominids before the emergence of *Homo erectus* a little over a million years ago.

Furthermore, early hominids may not have needed to talk. The real value of language, in addition to the enormous stimulation it gives to brain development, is that it permits the conveying of symbols referring to objects in the environment and ideas that are beyond the power of grunts and gestures to communicate. Nonverbal communication (which we will examine further in Chapter 13) can be surprisingly subtle and does permit a remarkably high degree of communication among such animals as chimpanzees; but while we may assume that *Australopithecus* knew more than a chimpanzee and thus had a need to communicate more, how much more is hard to say. Like everything else, language origins were gradual and slow in coming. We simply do not know, and never will, how or when language began. Schaller sensibly observes that speech is not necessary during hunting. Carnivores do not communicate while so engaged; indeed, some of them hunt at night, using stalking techniques that require silence and make visual communication difficult.

Having made the many keen observations about the lives of social carnivores that have provided a base for our discussion here, Schaller prudently backed off with the observation that there are many styles of hunting among them and that at present there is no way of telling which, if any, were adopted by hominids, or even if different hominids did different things at different times. Nevertheless, the analogies are there, and they are extremely provocative—so much so that Schaller decided to turn himself into an *Australopithecus* for a few days to find out more about what these early hominids may or may not have been able to do.

Schaller and Lowther's Experiment

Selecting the Serengeti Plain in East Africa as an environment whose climate and large herds of grazing animals are still very close to the presumed conditions of a couple of million years ago, Schaller and a fellow scientist, Gordon Lowther, conducted two experiments as hunting-scavenging hominids. The first experiment was conducted on the open savanna, where the two men walked, a hundred yards apart, for a total distance of about a hundred miles over a period of several days. Their main target was baby gazelles, which, in the first week of life, do not run but crouch in the grass. They found eight and could easily have caught them all. An excellent food supply for an early hominid, but there was a catch to it: five of the young were spotted within a few minutes of one another at a place where pregnant females had gathered to deliver their fawns. Since birth among most of the plains herbivores is concentrated into very short periods, Schaller concluded that catching gazelles was a poor long-term proposition: marvelous for a few days, poor the rest of the time.

However, he and Lowther stumbled over some other things on that same walk: a hare they could have caught, a couple of adult gazelle carcasses partly eaten, a cheetah making a kill that they could have preempted. Conscientiously adding up all the bits and pieces, including some scraps of brain from one kill gnawed almost clean, they came up with 75 pounds of meat.

Their second experiment was conducted in a woodland strip edging the Serengeti's Mbalageti River and lasted a week. There they had better luck. Choosing as their territory the riverbank where the herds came to drink, they ran into competition from 60 or 70 lions that were also hanging around. They found four lion kills, but these had all been picked so clean that there was nothing left but some brains and the marrow in the larger bones. As tool-using hominids, they could have recovered the marrow by smashing the bones open with rocks. They found a partly eaten buffalo that had died of disease, and they could have recovered about 500 pounds of meat from it. In addition they found an 80-pound zebra foal, abandoned and sick, and an oddly acting young giraffe that they discovered was blind when they succeeded in catching it by the tail. It weighed about 300 pounds.

But the game supply was as unpredictable for *Australopithecus* as it is now. It rose and fell seasonally, according to drought, disease, and migration. To cope with this, hominids must have been under some selective pressure to become increasingly artful hunters, to learn how to stalk, ambush, and kill healthy animals when there were no old and sick ones to be had. It is unlikely that they used any one hunting technique but rather they developed a varied repertoire of methods of obtaining meat, whether by hunting or by scavenging. Then there were always seeds, nuts, roots, and fruit for them to fall back on—just as hunter-gathers do today.

To make a direct comparison between the *Australopithecus* hunting-gathering life and that of certain modern hunter-gatherers like the Kalahari Bushmen is misleading, according to Schaller. The Bushmen have been pushed into a semi-desert area where there is almost no game at all; the bulk of their food has to be vegetable. Small and relatively unintelligent though they must have been, early hominids may have gotten more meat than modern Bushmen. Whether they did or not is not the important point. What counted in the long run was the activity of hunting itself. The challenges of hunting stimulated the brain. One of the strongest influences in the intellectual evolution of man, as Sherwood Washburn keeps emphasizing, was undoubtedly his activities as a hunter. But Washburn thinks it is a mistake to look to the social carnivores for hunting models; he maintains that to account for a hunting tradition in early hominid behavior one need look no further than the chimpanzee, with its natural inclination to hunt. That inclination was germ enough, according to Washburn. It changed our ancestor by enlarging his horizons and his mental capacity. Gradually he learned to hunt better, to think and plan better, and to use and make better tools.

From observing the behavior of other animals and examining the evidence of tool use in this and the preceding chapter, we are now able to make some behavioral speculations about *Australopithecus*. We have

A Reconstruction

an image of a social hominid with a group structure and, possibly, the beginnings of a family, its society intricately organized, probably on dominance lines originally. This hominid had moved from the forest into more open country; there it exploited an ever-widening range of foods, including seeds. It had brought with it to the savanna the ape's potential for bipedalism, for tool use, and for meat eating. On the savanna there were very real advantages in developing these traits, and it exploited them all. From the fossil evidence we know that it was an efficient erect walker by three million years ago, and it may have been bipedal long before that. Distinct male and female roles, of protector-hunter and homemaker-gatherer, respectively, were surely beginning to assert themselves. Here we find ourselves once again in the circle of positive feedback, for these roles not only were necessary for protection and sharing in order to take care of larger-brained, slower-developing infants and their mothers, but also were made possible by the larger brains that this new way of life, with its reliance on sharing, bipedalism, and tool use, encouraged.

The size of the area through which hominid groups might move to exploit all kinds of food resources began to grow as their physical ability to roam these ranges increased. Opportunities for new sights and experiences grew correspondingly. So did the selective pressure to evolve larger brains capable of storing more and more information about that larger world. With increased movement came the stimulus to carry things for greater distances, itself a further stimulus to bipedal walking —and to further exploration.

There is absolutely no way at present of calculating the range of an *Australopithecus* band, and it must surely have varied from place to

Figure 9–13 As part of their experiments on hunting-scavenging hominids, Schaller and Lowther themselves smashed animal bones to recover the marrow and stalked a blind giraffe.

place and from good year to bad. It was almost certainly measured in the scores, and may well have been in the hundreds, of square miles. With that expanded range went all the advantages that could accrue to a mobile group living in it: the ability to escape local disasters of drought or flood, to take advantage of local bounty as it developed seasonally, and, most important, to remember where, when, and how to exploit that large domain. Simply by increasing the options available, a large-brained hominid that could walk respectable distances increased its chances for survival.

Estimates of the number of individuals in an *Australopithecus* band range from a dozen or so up to fifty. These estimates are based on the known sizes of chimpanzee, gorilla, and baboon troops, and on the practical size limits that would be put on (and, incidentally, are still put on) hunter-gatherer bands by the day-to-day problem of finding enough food and water for all their members.

As to how long *Australopithecus* lived, that too is a subject for speculation. A chimpanzee has a life expectancy of about 25 years in the wild, although it has the physiological potential to live as long as 60 years. *Australopithecus*, of similar size and close lineage, could be expected to have the same potential. But as is the case with chimpanzees, this potential apparently was severely reduced under actual living conditions. The paleoanthropologist Alan Mann has been examining the rate of tooth development among immature specimens of some South African gracile fossils and the rate of tooth wear among adults of that same population. His studies indicate that none of the gracile *Australopithecus* whose teeth he examined got past 40 and that only about one in seven lived as long as 30 years. Their mean lifespan, he estimates, was about 20 years, which says a good deal about the hazards of life for *Australopithecus*. In the absence of modern medicine and technology the mean lifespan of modern man is probably about 30 to 35 years, while in the West it is now about 70 years.

Movement to the savanna may have led to the evolution of human beings, but it would be millions of years before this revolutionary development would have any payoff in easier living or greater longevity. Meanwhile, the evolution of the bipedal hominid *Australopithecus* continued, slowly, over millions of years. As we have seen, the fossil evidence suggests that there were two distinct species of this genus (and no doubt many varieties within each species). The huge *Australopithecus boisei* eventually became extinct, while the smaller *A. africanus* was becoming the world's cleverest hunter and continuing to change and evolve more complex social institutions, more sophisticated technology, and a more effective means of communication. The hominid which had evolved by about 1.3 million years ago carried a brain that had about twice the volume of the brain of the earliest members of the genus *Australopithecus*. This far more manlike hominid we now call *Homo erectus;* it was the first true human. We shall now turn to the evidence for the further evolution of this lineage which was to lead eventually to ourselves.

OVERVIEW

	MODERN BABOON	MODERN CHIMPANZEE	MODERN HUMAN
Habitat	Open country, usually close to trees in which it sleeps	Spends much of its time in the trees; tropical rain forests of Central Africa	Ground-dwelling; all climatic zones
Diet	Primarily vegetation, but also small animals	Mostly fruit, but does eat a large variety of foods, including small animals	Omnivorous
Locomotion	Quadrupedal	Brachiation and quadrimanual climbing in the trees; mostly knuckle walking on the ground	Bipedal
Subsistence	Picks and eats food as needed; some hunting and sharing of meat	Picks and eats food as needed; some hunting and sharing of meat	Hunting, gathering, agriculture, husbandry, and extensive mechanisms of exchange
Social organization	Strict dominance structure. Multimale troops, which, in some species, when food is scarce break into groups with one dominant male, one or more females, and youngsters	Relaxed dominance structure. Casual promiscuity; prolonged mother–infant ties; no father figure	Variable systems of dominance. Prolonged male–female ties; prolonged mother–infant ties; various kinds of family units

Timeline (left axis, CENOZOIC):

- 10,000 — HOLOCENE
- PLEISTOCENE — *A. robustus* and *boisei* extinct
- 2 million — Earliest Oldowan tools at East Rudolf
- PLIOCENE
- 5 million — Earliest *Australopithecus*
- 10 million
- First *Ramapithecus*
- 15 million — MIOCENE
- 20 million — First *Dryopithecus*
- 25 million — OLIGOCENE
- *Apidium, Parapithecus,* and *Aegyptopithecus*

AUSTRALOPITHECUS AFRICANUS (circa 1.75 million B.P.)

Habitat	Ground-dwelling, perhaps sleeping in the trees; tropical savanna
Diet	Mostly small, some large animals; possibly seeds in addition to fruits and leaves
Locomotion	Bipedal, although possibly not as efficient a walker as later hominids
Subsistence	In addition to picking and eating as needed, hunted small animals and probably gathered food. Appears to have shared food
Social organization	Probably weak dominance hierarchies. Probably beginning to divide labor between the sexes—with males hunting and females gathering food and caring for the young; prolonged male–female bonds

SOCIAL ORGANIZATION AND HUNTING

Our ancestors were certainly more typical primates than we are, so that we can learn something about *Australopithecus* by comparing modern humans with monkeys (e.g., baboons) and apes (e.g., chimpanzees). This chart indicates some of the main features of the social organization and behavior of these three species and compares them with what we can deduce about the nature of our ancestor *Australopithecus*.

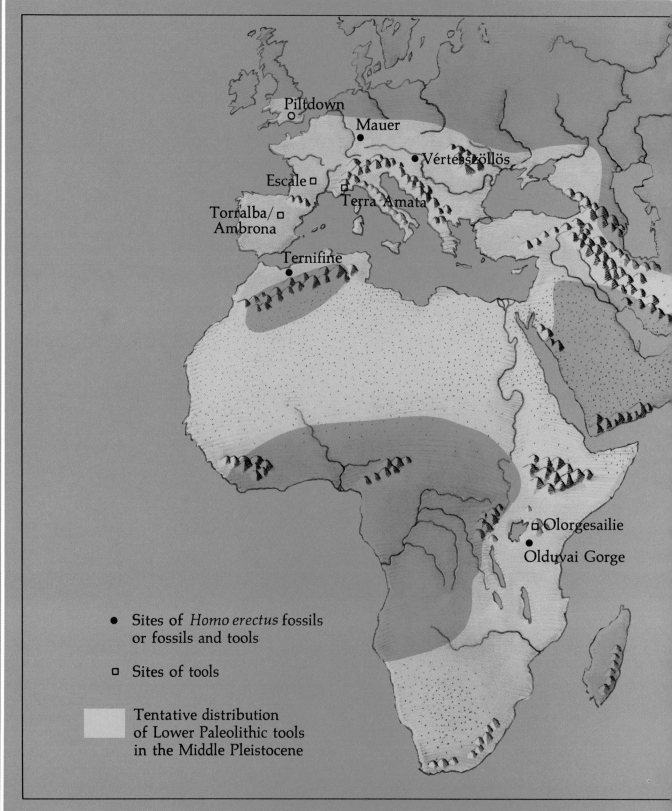

PART THREE

Piltdown

Mauer

Vértesszöllös

Escale

Terra Amata

Torralba/
Ambrona

Ternifine

Olorgesailie

Olduvai Gorge

● Sites of *Homo erectus* fossils
or fossils and tools

□ Sites of tools

Tentative distribution
of Lower Paleolithic tools
in the Middle Pleistocene

HOMO ERECTUS

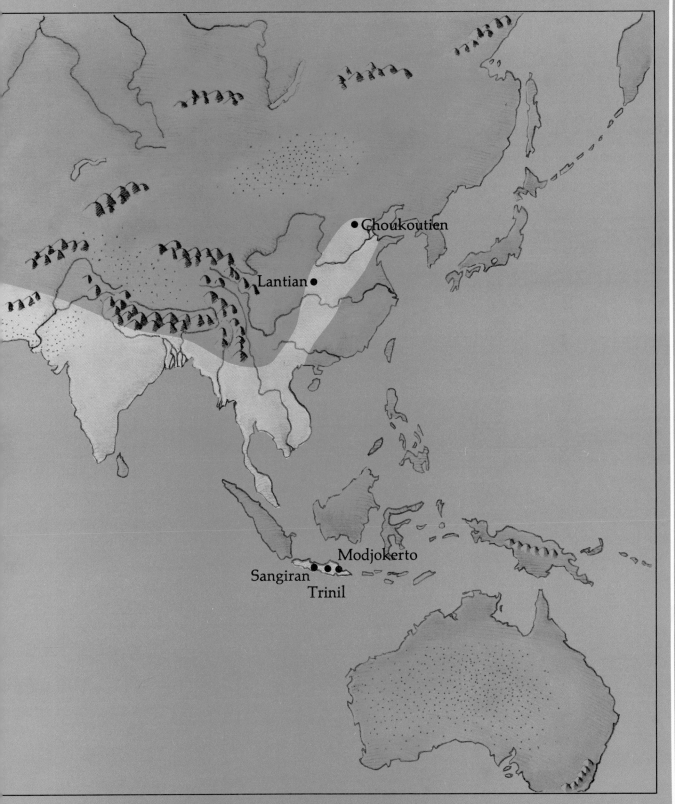

Choukoutien

Lantian

Modjokerto

Sangiran

Trinil

Chapter 10

Discoveries of the First Humans

Then felt I like some watcher of the skies
When a new planet swims into his ken;
Or like stout Cortez, when with eagle eyes
He stared at the Pacific — and all his men
Looked at each other with a wild surmise —
Silent, upon a peak in Darien.
　　JOHN KEATS, 1795 – 1821.
　　"ON FIRST LOOKING INTO CHAPMAN'S HOMER."

Since most of what we know about early man is based on fossil evidence, it may be worth noting that fossil finds, as far as their impact on knowledge goes, fall into two rough categories. There are the discoveries of previously unknown fossil types, finds that provide brand-new insights into the evolutionary picture, and there are those that merely confirm or enlarge information about a type of fossil already discovered. It is the first kind—the heart-stopper, the producer of wild surmises—that makes newspaper headlines. But the second kind should not be underrated, since, to the scientist, it is perhaps at least as important. In order to get a good idea of the characteristics or dimensions of a species, one must have a series of fragments or whole skeletons from a number of individuals. Without such a series, a single fossil may be simply a curiosity, a provocative and exciting one, no doubt, but still one that cannot be fitted with any sense of certainty into the overall order of things until a number of like fossils can be found and examined. It is the patient, more obscure, and always time-consuming comparative studies of later finds, often made years after the original one, that eventually turn the wild surmises into scientific conclusions. The subject of this chapter is the fossil evidence of *Homo erectus*.

In the mid-1800s the Western world's interest was focused on the present and the future. It was an age of human progress and accomplishment, of prosperity, and of inventions to make life easier and more civilized: running water and lighted streets, iceboxes, sewing machines, elevated railways, lawnmowers, typewriters, and even telephones. It is understandable, then, that the new theory about mankind's descent from prehistoric apes provoked doubt and opposition. In this atmosphere of progress and self-approval, the claim that mankind was merely an offshoot of the ape was rejected by much of the public and by many eminent scientists as well.

People were beginning to accept the idea of evolution, but only as it applied to the lower animals. Scientists agreed that the world is very old and that geological strata provide a clear record of past ages on earth. Many accepted Darwin's thesis that modern species of animals are descendants of more primitive ancestors, for the lines of descent could be traced in the fossils clearly visible in ancient beds of rock. In fact, there were some fossil remains that spanned enough time and were sufficiently well represented in collections to illustrate their evolution from prehistoric to modern forms. But human evolution was something else. No one had yet found any fossils proving a link between the apes and humans. Most of those who doubted our primate origins did so not merely through acceptance of the Biblical account of Creation, but also because there was no convincing fossil evidence to support Darwin.

Some scientists took the lack of any fossils of intermediate human-like apes as proof that no such creatures had ever existed. At the other extreme, some of Darwin's early supporters rushed forward with fanciful pedigrees for mankind, making up in enthusiasm for what they lacked in evidence. Even believers in human evolution were confused by the outpouring of rival experts' family trees for man, full of imaginary apish ancestors with scientific-sounding Greek and Latin names.

Eugene Dubois was born in Holland in 1858, into this atmosphere of often bitter debate over human origins. Although the Dubois family was conventional and religious, the home atmosphere was not one of narrow-minded provincial piety, and the boy's interest in science was encouraged. Dubois went to medical school and then, choosing academic life over medical practice, became an instructor in anatomy at the Royal Normal School in Amsterdam. He was fascinated by the many different family trees that were being published in both learned and popular journals and was much influenced by the work of Ernst Heinrich Haeckel, a German zoologist who had predicted in some detail what *should* be discovered about the course of human evolution (see Figure 10–2). For six years Dubois delivered his lectures and gave no hint of the wild idea that was taking hold of him: to establish man's place in evolution and set the record straight once and for all, by finding a fossil of a primitive creature that was the clear forerunner of humans.

THE WORK OF EUGENE DUBOIS

Nineteenth-Century Background

Figure 10–1   An 1883 photograph shows Eugene Dubois as a teacher in Amsterdam.

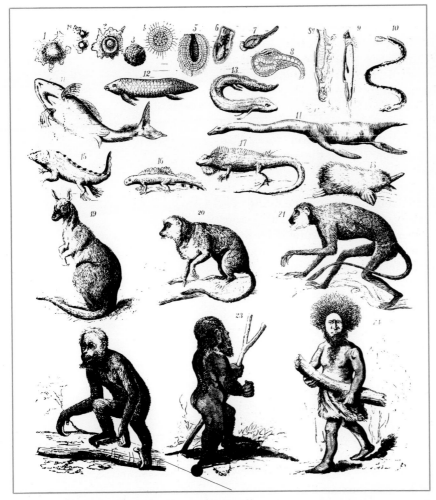

Figure 10–2 Ernst Haeckel's work on the ancestry of mankind was one of the first attempts to deal with the specifics of evolution. Although his genealogical chart, which starts with a blob of protoplasm and ends with a Papuan, is filled with misconceptions and fictitious creatures, it is in some ways surprisingly accurate, considering the dearth of knowledge in his day.

Dubois took up this new vocation by going over all the clues he could find. One important clue was the existence of Neandertal man. As we saw in Chapter 4, the first Neandertal fossils had been discovered in 1848, ten years before Dubois was born; and for twenty years the Neandertal remains were the only trace of a primitive skeleton in the human closet. Although some experts assumed Neandertals to have been very primitive people, not even Darwin's strongest supporters classified them as missing links. Their large braincases led most scientists, as we have seen, to maintain that they were either simply the remains of modern people who had somehow been oddly deformed, or a strange, extinct race of *Homo sapiens*.

Dubois, a firm believer in evolution, considered the Neandertal fossils to be definitely human but very ancient. To him they suggested that the search for even more primitive creatures should be carried out in some region of limestone deposits and caves similar to the European

Dubois' Search for the Missing Link

habitat of the Neandertal; but they also suggested that Europe was not the place to look for a missing link. The creature that provided the evolutionary link between ape and human being, Dubois reasoned, must have lived long before the Neandertals, at a time when Europe was far too cold to permit their survival. The forebear he wanted to find, he concluded, must have lived in a tropical part of the world untouched by the glaciers of the ice age.

Other clues as well pointed to the tropics. Darwin had suggested that our tree-dwelling progenitors lived in "some warm, forest-clad land"; Alfred Russel Wallace had also recommended that our forebears be sought in a tropical zone. Wallace had lived in Malaysia for eight years, and he had noticed that the islands of Sumatra and Borneo are the home of both the gibbon, the oldest and most primitive living ape, and the orangutan, one of the most advanced and intelligent species of ape. He wrote, "With what interest must every naturalist look forward to the time when the caves of the tropics be thoroughly examined, and the past history and earliest appearance of the great man-like apes be at length made known." Wallace's curiosity about these islands and their caves proved contagious, and Dubois began to think seriously of going to the Dutch East Indies to explore these caves himself. The more he read about the geology and natural history of the region, the more convinced he became that the missing link would be discovered there. The islands once had been part of continental Asia; before the seas had inundated the lower land, turning the mountaintops into islands, animals could have wandered down freely from the north.

At the age of 29 Eugene Dubois set out to solve the mystery of human origins, to find the fossil of a creature with both apelike and human traits that would prove the relationship between humans and the apes. Dubois' planning focused on Sumatra, which was then under Dutch rule and therefore a practical place for a Dutch citizen to launch an archaeological expedition. In 1886 he told some of his colleagues at the University of Amsterdam that he had reason to believe he would solve the mystery of human origins. They tried to dissuade him, and one even politely suggested that Dubois was slightly mad. His requests for financial backing were turned down flatly by both private philanthropists and government bureaucrats. But Dubois was determined to get to Sumatra, and finally he was sent there by the Dutch East Indian Army, in which he had enlisted as a doctor.

For the first two years in Sumatra, his investigations of a great many limestone caves and deposits yielded only teeth that were too recent to interest him; they belonged mainly to orangutans. When word came in 1890 of the discovery of a very ancient skull at Wadjak, Java, Dubois persuaded the government to send him to that neighboring island. The colonial government, showing a new interest in his work, supplied him with a native crew of convict laborers and two Dutch officers to oversee them. With such backing, excavations proceeded on a grand scale.

Dubois managed to buy the Wadjak skull that had brought him to the island, and then he promptly found another. Both were modern in appearance and too recent to have belonged to a missing link. But the region was extraordinarily rich in fossils of many kinds, and Dubois set up several digging parties at different locations. By 1894 he had shipped to the Netherlands 400 cases of fossil bones, including specimens of many extinct and previously unknown animals.

At one site to the north, Dubois' foreman reported an unexpected problem. He had found that for many years natives of the area had been digging up fossils and selling them to Chinese merchants as "dragon bones" to be ground into powder for an ancient and popular Chinese medicine. (In addition to fossilized bone, the ingredients for these medicines included tiger's claws and whiskers, bat dung, and rhinoceros horn.) The local fossil hunters, unwilling to give up a profitable business with the Chinese, would not sell any of their finds to Dubois' party. To make matters worse, the foreman soon discovered that his own workmen were stealing the fossils they unearthed and carrying them off to sell to the local traders. When called upon for help, the colonial government issued an order outlawing the sale of any fossils to Chinese merchants in Java.

To Dubois, the most promising site on the island seemed to be an exposed and stratified embankment along the Solo River, near the small

Discovery of Java Man (1891)

Figure 10–3 At this bend in the Solo River at Trinil, Java, Dubois excavated the terraced bank where the bones of Java man were found at a depth of forty-eight feet.

village of Trinil in the center of Java (see page 199). Here, in the months when the river was low, Dubois could survey a 45-foot-high bank of ancient river deposits, clearly defined layers of fine volcanic debris and sandstone.

In a stratum about four feet thick and exposed just above the stream level, Dubois came upon a rich store of animal fossils: a stegodon, an extinct hippopotamus, a small deer, an antelope. Soon he also uncovered a fragment of a lower jaw that he felt certain was human rather than animal. Before he could pursue this highly interesting find, the rains set in and he had to abandon his excavations until the following autumn. In August 1891 he and his crew set to work once more, digging down through the strata with hoes, hammers, and chisels—crude implements by later standards, but Dubois was one of the first scientists ever to attempt a systematic search for fossils. In September he found his first fossil of a primitive primate: a single, apelike tooth.

On first inspection, this fossil seemed to Dubois to be the wisdom tooth of an extinct giant chimpanzee. Later, in comparing it with molars of other apes, he noted a strange wrinkling of the crown, suggesting that it was, instead, the tooth of an orangutan. As Dubois mulled over the molar, the digging went on for another month. Then, only three feet from where the tooth had been unearthed, and in the same layer, a workman uncovered a heavy, brown rock that looked like a turtle's shell. After the earth was brushed away from the new find, it looked more like part of a skull. "The amazing thing had happened," wrote the English paleontologist G. Elliot Smith; "Dubois had actually found the fossil his scientific imagination had visualized." It was the evidence he had crossed half the world to find.

The skull (see Figure 10–4) was unlike any ever seen before. Clearly, it was too low and flat to be the cranium of a modern man. After detailed study of both the skullcap and the tooth, Dubois reported: "that both specimens come from a great manlike ape was at once clear." Despite his expert knowledge of anatomy he found the skull peculiarly hard to place more precisely than that.

Figure 10–4 The brown skullcap of *Pithecanthropus erectus* was Dubois' greatest find. It was to be nearly forty years before another skull of this kind was found.

Shortly after these finds were made, the rains came again, the river rose, and digging had to be suspended until the following year. When digging at the Trinil site could begin again, Dubois cut a new excavation in the same deposit about thirty-three feet from where the strange cranium had been buried. There, ten months after the apelike skull was found, he discovered another, even more surprising, primate fossil. This one (shown in Figure 10–5) was unmistakable. It was the left femur, or thighbone, of a primate that had walked erect! It resembled a human thighbone in almost every respect except that it was heavier than the thighbone of a modern man. In October, another tooth quite like the first turned up. Could the curious teeth, the problematic skull, and the unexpected thighbone all have belonged to the same individual? The implications were staggering.

The creature whose anatomy was indicated by bones and teeth like these was exactly the sort that Ernst Heinrich Haeckel had suggested as a human precursor. Haeckel had named his hypothetical ancestor *Pithecanthropus* (from the Greek *pithekos*, "ape," and *anthropos*, "man"). Dubois studied and measured the apelike skull and the humanlike femur from Java, and in 1893 he announced his conclusion: the skull and femur had belonged to the same creature, who had possessed a skull intermediate between ape and human, and a leg fully adapted for upright walking. Deliberately, and almost provocatively, Dubois announced that he had discovered the real *Pithecanthropus*. To point up the distinctive thighbone, he added the species name *erectus*, upright. By appropriating this name for his Java find, Dubois boldly filed his claim to have found, as he cabled to his friends in Europe, the "Missing Link of Darwin." He attributed to it a late Pliocene age.

The bones of *Pithecanthropus erectus* were one of the greatest fossil finds ever made, and even though he had only these few incomplete specimens Dubois fully realized their immense importance. As we have seen in Chapter 4, we now believe that *Pithecanthropus erectus* was actually one of the first human beings, a vital link in the chain of human evolution, but not the half-ape fossil Dubois had supposed it to be. Its age we now believe to be the Middle Pleistocene—between 800,000 and 900,000 B.P. (see Figure 5–1).

Figure 10–5 The first femur that Dubois found appeared very modern and indicated an upright posture. The growth of bone on its inner surface is an unusual condition that is also found in modern humans but has no evolutionary significance. Today there is some doubt as to whether the femur belongs with the skullcap.

The Java Man Controversy

Before Dubois could show his discoveries to colleagues in Europe, his precious fossils became the focus of a raging scientific controversy that embroiled him throughout the rest of his life. His first cabled reports were met with skepticism. Some critics insisted that the fossil bones did not belong together at all and suggested that Dubois simply had made the mistake of mixing the skull and teeth of an ape with the thighbone of a man who had died nearby. One member of the Netherlands Zoological Society, writing in a Dutch newspaper in 1893, ridiculed Dubois' jigsaw-puzzle methods, asking whether more finds at the site in Java might not eventually lead to announcements of an even stranger creature: if another, more human, skull was discovered within fifty feet of the other bones, this unfriendly commentator queried, would this mean that *Pithecanthropus* had two skulls, one apelike and one manlike?

To those unwilling to acknowledge any link with any form of anthropoid ancestor, *Pithecanthropus* was pure insult. Clergymen hastened to assure their flocks that Adam, and not the crude half-ape half-human brute unearthed in Java, was the true ancestor of man. Dubois was denounced from pulpit and platform. Scientists were almost as angry and skeptical. The combination of apelike head and upright posture ran directly contrary to the belief that the development of a larger, better brain had come first in the separation of the human stock from earlier anthropoids. A being with a human head and an apelike body was expected, not the reverse.

The arrival of the fossils themselves for close inspection did not settle the arguments. Only six weeks after Dubois reached Holland in 1895, he presented *Pithecanthropus* to the Third International Congress of Zoology at Leiden. Almost at once, a great quarrel broke out over where to place this Java "ape-man" in the scheme of evolution. Opinion seemed to harden along national lines: most Germans believed that *Pithecanthropus* was an ape that had manlike characteristics; most Englishmen thought it was a man that had apelike attributes; and the Americans tended to lean toward a transitional form more along the lines Dubois had suggested.

Dubois gave his colleagues as much detailed knowledge of *Pithecanthropus* as he could. He exhibited the bones at scientific meetings throughout Europe, showed them to any scientist who wanted to examine them, and published detailed descriptions. He had to acquire the skills of a dentist, photographer, and sculptor in the process. In order to make accurate brain casts, he spent weeks learning to use a fine dental drill, with which he could clean away minute stone particles inside the skullcap. He invented a special "stereorthoscope" camera, designed to photograph the fossils in various planes without distortion. For the public he sculpted a life-size reconstruction of *Pithecanthropus* (see Figure 10–6), ordering his son to pose for him during a school vacation. He patiently defended *Pithecanthropus*, carting the bones around in a battered suitcase, and seemed to develop an almost personal attachment to the fossil ancestor whose bones were a constant companion.

In spite of all Dubois' efforts, the attacks on *Pithecanthropus* continued. Dubois took them personally. Deeply hurt by the refusal of other scientists to accept his interpretation of the fossil bones, he withdrew the remains of *Pithecanthropus* from the public realm, hid them under the floor of his dining room, and became almost a recluse.

In 1920 the discovery of an ancient skull in Australia led scientists to urge that *Pithecanthropus* be let out of solitary confinement, but Dubois was obstinate. He added to the problem by announcing for the first time that he had the two Wadjak skulls and no one could see them, either. At this point Henry Fairfield Osborn, head of the American Museum of Natural History, appealed to the president of the Dutch

Figure 10–6 Dubois' model of Java man holds an antler.

Academy of Sciences in the hope that this material, essential to science, would be made available. Soon afterward, in 1923, Dubois opened his strongboxes for Alés Hrdlička of the Smithsonian Institution, and thereafter again exhibited *Pithecanthropus* at scientific meetings. He also released a cast of the *Pithecanthropus* skull that indicated a brain of about 900 cubic centimeters, well above the range of 275 to 750 cubic centimeters of the apes and below the range of modern humans (approximately 1,000–2,000 cc).

Today there still remain some unanswered questions about Dubois' discovery. Did the bones really belong together? To suppose that two different primates—an unknown species of ape and an unknown species of man—had lived in Java at exactly the same time, and had died within forty feet of each other at Trinil, seemed to Dubois far more improbable than to suppose that the various bones belonged to one creature with both apelike and human characteristics. Scientists are still arguing the point. The skull is unquestionably that of an early man, but one tooth at least may have belonged to a prehistoric orangutan and some experts still suspect that the thighbone might have come from a higher stratum and belonged to a more modern form of man.

Because of the great controversy over whether *Pithecanthropus* was a human, an ape, or an ape-man, a true missing link, Dubois' brilliant detective work in locating the fossils seemed only to add to the mystery of human origins instead of solving it. While anthropologists argued over the bones of Java man and Dubois withdrew into his home in Holland, the controversy was being settled elsewhere.

On October 21, 1907, a new clue to man's past turned up in Germany. On that day, two workmen were digging in a huge commercial sand pit near Mauer (see page 198). Several fossils previously had been unearthed there, and geologists from Heidelberg University had asked the owner of the pit to save any bones that were found, particularly anything that looked human. This day, digging nearly eighty feet below ground level, one of the workmen struck a large jawbone with his shovel and split it in half. The jaw (see Figure 10–7) looked human, but it seemed much too large to belong to a man. Professor Otto Schoetensack of the university was notified and took possession of the jaw, which he cleaned, repaired, and studied with growing excitement. The fossil was so wide and thick that, without its teeth, it might have been mistaken for the jaw of a large ape. But the teeth were remarkably like the teeth of modern humans. They had bigger roots and were slightly larger than our teeth, but they showed all the characteristics that distinguish modern human teeth from those of the ape, including small canines and molars worn flat by chewing. In a monograph describing the find, Schoetensack created a new species of man on the basis of this lower jaw—*Homo heidelbergensis*, or Heidelberg man. Today the fossil is considered simply a European example of the once widespread species *Homo erectus*.

TWENTIETH-CENTURY DISCOVERIES

Heidelberg Man: The Mauer Jaw (1907)

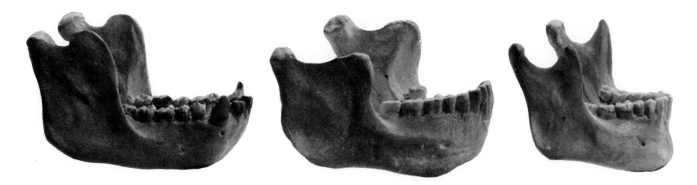

Figure 10–7 The Heidelberg jaw (center) is here compared with the jaw of a chimpanzee (left) and that of a modern human being (right).

From the jaw alone, it was impossible to tell very much about what Heidelberg man looked like. Much more revealing was the place where Heidelberg man was discovered. The fossil jaw had lain in strata of rock where other extinct animal fossils also were found. Because the era when these animals had lived was known, the Heidelberg jaw could be roughly dated: it belonged to someone who lived in the Early Pleistocene. This discovery was the first hint that man had come so far north, into the wintry climates of Europe, at so early a date. Today we attribute to the Heidelberg jaw a date of over 500,000 years B.P.

Despite the importance of the Mauer jaw, it was too small a piece of evidence to throw much light on Heidelberg man's place in human evolution. It was nearly two decades before another fossil like it was found, this time in Peking.

Search for Peking Man

The discovery of "Peking man" in 1927 involved a piece of scientific detective work almost as remarkable at Dubois' exploit in Java. Peking man was added to the human family tree simply because a small band of scientists had gone to China determined to hunt him down. Even after Dubois' success in Java, the prospect of searching for primitive man in China could appeal only to people prepared to spend their lives hunting for a needle in one haystack after another. A Canadian physician, Davidson Black, was sure that he might unearth a human ancestor in China if only he looked long and hard enough. So in 1919, when he was offered an appointment as professor of anatomy at Peking Union Medical College, which was being set up with funds from the Rockefeller Foundation, he eagerly accepted.

Black's conviction was based both on geologic evidence showing that the ancient climate and geography of China were quite suitable for a primitive human being's existence there and on the theory that patterns of evolution are closely related to climatic conditions. There was also a single, tantalizing piece of fossil evidence that some early primate had once inhabited China. In 1899 a European doctor had chanced upon an unusual fossil tooth among some dragon's bones that were about to be ground up for medicine in a druggist's shop in Peking. The tooth was among the more than a hundred bones the doctor picked up in various

Chinese drugstores and sent to paleontologist Max Schlosser. Schlosser identified the tooth as "a left upper third molar, either of a man or a hitherto unknown anthropoid ape" and predicted hopefully that further search might turn up the skeleton of an early man.

Black's hopes to find time for fossil hunting were dissolved by an advisor from the Rockefeller Foundation, who warned him to concentrate on anatomy, not anthropology. So it was not until 1921 that the search for early man in China actually began. That year a group led by John Gunnar Andersson, a Swedish geologist, began to dig at a site 25 miles southwest of Peking, near the village of Choukoutien (see page 199). Excavations were proceeding at a rise called Chicken Bone Hill near an old limestone quarry, when Andersson was told by his workmen that there were much better fossils on the other side of the village, at Dragon Bone Hill, beside another abandoned quarry.

The Chinese had been digging "dragon bones" out of this spot and others like it for hundreds of years, and no one will ever know how many powdered fossils have passed harmlessly through the alimentary canals of dyspeptic Chinese mandarins. Whatever the losses may have been to paleontology, some of the limestone caverns in the hillside were still richly packed with interesting material. There were bits of broken quartz among the limestone deposits around an ancient cliffside cave. The quartz would not naturally be associated with limestone, Andersson knew; it must have been brought there—perhaps by some toolmaking peoples of the past.

A great many fossils were dug out of the rock and shipped back to Sweden for study. Twenty different mammals were identified, many of them extinct species. Andersson's toolmaker was not so easily found. A likely tooth turned up, but it was identified as the molar of an ape. Finally, in 1926, when one of Andersson's associates had given up and returned to Sweden and the digging had stopped, a closer study of this molar and another tooth found later suggested that they might be human. The teeth were sent back to Andersson, who turned them over to Davidson Black for his expert appraisal. Preoccupied though Black was with medicine, he had never lost interest in the Choukoutien digs. He was certain that the tooth came from a human of great antiquity, and he persuaded the Rockefeller Foundation to support a large-scale excavation of the site.

Peking Man Discovered (1927)

Work started up again at Dragon Bone Hill in 1927. At some remote time in the past, water had honeycombed the limestone of the hill with caves and fissures. The caves in turn had filled with the deposits of running water and with the debris of collapsing roofs. By the twentieth century, when modern quarrying cut away one face of the hill, the former caves appeared only as fossil-bearing rock distinct from the limestone. Digging in this hard, compacted fill material proved difficult; blasting was often necessary. Just as much of a problem was the troubled political condition of China. Antiforeign riots were flaring, and Chiang Kai-shek's armies, moving to the aid of Shanghai, were still far from the city. Bandits controlled the countryside around Peking. For weeks at a time they isolated the dig from the city. On October 16, 1927, three days before the first season's work was to end, Birgir Böhlin, field supervisor, found another early human tooth. As he hurried to Peking to take it to Black, soldiers stopped him several times without suspecting that he carried a scientific treasure in his pocket.

Black studied the tooth exhaustively. Struck by its size and its cusp pattern, he became convinced that it was a very ancient human molar. Without waiting for any further proof, Black announced the discovery of a new genus and species of prehistoric man: *Sinanthropus pekinensis*, Chinese man of Peking. Scientists were startled, and although Black travelled around the world to let them examine for themselves the evidence (which he carried on a watch chain in his waistcoat pocket), many refused to recognize Peking man as a legitimate ancestor on the evidence of only a few teeth.

When Black returned to Peking in 1928, his belief in the antiquity of *Sinanthropus* was vindicated. His associates were waiting with fragments of a primitive human jaw they had dug out of the cave. And as tons of earth were excavated from the hillside and sifted for signs of fossil fragments, bits and pieces of teeth and several small fragments of human bone came to light.

Then, in 1929, W. C. Pei, a Chinese paleontologist working with Black, turned up the first skull of *Sinanthropus*. Work was about to be closed for the year, when Pei opened up two caves at the extreme end of a fissure. On the floor of one was a large accumulation of debris. Pei brushed some of it away, and suddenly, partly surrounded by loose sand and partly embedded in travertine (a water-formed rock), there lay revealed the object of all the searching—a nearly complete skullcap. Even at first glance, Pei felt certain that it was a skullcap of *Sinanthropus*. After removing the skull and part of its stone bed from the cave, Pei carefully wrapped it up, set it in the basket of his bicycle, and pedaled the twenty-five miles to Black's laboratory in Peking. Black showed Pei's discovery to Roy Chapman Andrews, an American scientist. "There it was, the skull of an individual who had lived half a million years ago," Andrews wrote. "It was one of the most important discoveries in the whole history of human evolution. He could not have been very impressive when he was alive, but dead and fossilized, he was awe-inspiring."

Black spent the next four months freeing the skullcap from the surrounding stone. When it was entirely clean he separated all its bones, made a cast of each one, and then reassembled the pieces. For the first time Black was able to make a reliable estimate of the brain capacity of *Sinanthropus*. It came to about 1,000 cubic centimeters, marking its owner as definitely humanlike in this respect.

The news made headlines all around the world. Excavations at Choukoutien were reorganized on a broader basis and went on for almost ten more years, finally taking on the proportions of a grandiose engineering project.

Figure 10–8 The excavation of the cave filling at Choukoutien was a gigantic undertaking. Work continued at the site from 1927 until 1937.

As work advanced a whole hillside was sliced off, revealing deposits 160 feet deep (see Figure 10–8). They can be visualized in comparison with an apartment building about sixteen stories tall, each story packed solid with blown-in debris combined with the abandoned rubbish of long-departed tenants. Layer on layer, the Choukoutien caves were filled through the ages with strata of clay, with soil carried in by the wind, with limestone drippings, with rock fallen from the ceiling—all sandwiching other layers of human and animal debris. It is clear that large carnivores occupied the caves for long periods of time. Bones of extinct creatures like the cave bear and a giant hyena, together with the remains of animals on which they preyed, occur at certain levels. At others, it is equally clear that human beings drove the carnivores out and took over the caves for themselves. At first the animal and human layers alternate fairly regularly, but toward the top, humans take over permanently.

A total of 1,873 workdays was devoted to dynamiting and removing some 20,000 cubic meters of rock and earth and sorting through the debris for fossils. The findings comprised an encyclopedia of prehistory that has given us a great part of our knowledge of the first human beings. By 1937, parts of more than 40 men, women, and children had been unearthed; these fossils included 5 complete skulls, 9 fragmentary skulls, 6 facial fragments, 14 lower jaws, and 152 teeth.

Black organized the work, kept detailed records of all the finds, classified them, and made casts, drawings, and photographs of the heavy volume of material pouring into Peking. Tragically, he did not live to savor the full bounty of Choukoutien. He died of a heart attack in 1934, but he had seen enough of the excavation to realize its extraordinary significance.

The Rockefeller Foundation sought carefully a successor and chose Franz Weidenreich, then a visiting professor of anatomy at the University of Chicago. Before the Nazis drove him from his native Germany, Weidenreich had completed world-famous studies of the evolutionary changes in the pelvis and foot that made possible our upright posture. His studies underwrote the contention of Darwin and Huxley that mankind is a descendant of some ancient anthropoid stock but not of any recent genus.

After Weidenreich's arrival at Choukoutien in 1935, only two more seasons of undisturbed digging were carried out. Fighting between Chinese and Japanese guerrillas broke out nearby, and the archaeologists had to take refuge. With the approach of World War II, Weidenreich concentrated on making accurate drawings and casts of the Peking skulls and published detailed photographs and descriptions of every important fossil. He began a classic series of studies of Peking man—*The Mandibles of Sinanthropus, The Dentition of Sinanthropus, The Extremity Bones of Sinanthropus, The Skull of Sinanthropus*. All four supported Black's conclusion: *Sinanthropus* was indeed a human, though a very primitive one; he was not a link between apes and humans. What,

Intensive Work at Choukoutien

Figure 10-9 Franz Weidenreich (left) succeeded Davidson Black at Peking Union Medical College in 1934 and pursued the excavations at Choukoutien with equal fervor.

Assessment of Peking Man

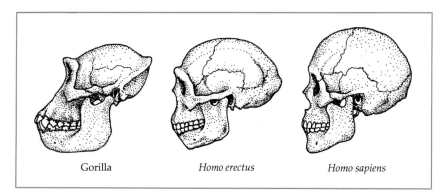

Gorilla   *Homo erectus*   *Homo sapiens*

Figure 10–10 Skulls of a female gorilla, Peking man, and a modern Chinese (all equally reduced). Note the size and form of the braincase in relation to the jaws.

for Weidenreich, placed him solidly in the human race was his undoubted ability to walk upright on two legs. "Apes, like man, have two hands and two feet, but man alone has acquired an upright position and the faculty of using his feet exclusively as locomotor instruments," said Weidenreich. "Unless all signs are deceiving, the claim may even be ventured that the change in locomotion and the corresponding alteration of the organization of the body are the essential specialization in the transformation of the prehuman form into the human form."

The teeth and dental arch of *Sinanthropus* testified further to his status. The canines were not the projecting fangs of the ape, and the dental arch was curved, not oblong. Still more evidence lay in the skull. Weidenreich arranged the skulls of a gorilla, Peking man, and a modern human in a row, so that even a glance revealed their striking differences: the extremely flat skull of the gorilla, the somewhat higher skull of Peking man, the rounded skull of modern man (see Figure 10–10). In the low vault of the gorilla skull a brain averaging about 505 cc is housed; the higher dome of Peking man held one of about 1,000 cc; the high cranium of the modern human encloses a brain averaging about 1,330 cc. Because Peking man's brain was so small, some scientists questioned his human status. Weidenreich cautioned that brain size alone is no absolute determinant. One species of whale, he pointed out, has a brain of about 10,000 cubic centimeters, but this amounts to one gram of brain for each 8,500 grams of body weight, compared to our one gram for each 44 grams of weight. "Neither the absolute nor the relative size of the brain can be used to measure the degree of mental ability in animals or man," he added. "Cultural objects are the only guide as far as spiritual life is concerned. They may be fallacious guides too, but we are completely lost if these objects are missing."

Culture at Choukoutien

At Choukoutien cultural objects were not missing. The continuing excavations produced thousands of chipped-stone tools. They were simple, with only a few chips removed, but they were made to a pattern. In the largest cave that was explored, 100,000 stone tools and fragments, most of quartz, were found. Some of them lay with charred bits of wood and bone. The charring, it was evident, had not resulted from some accidental fire, for the hard-baked red and yellow clay of ancient hearths often underlay the carbon. Peking man had mastered the use of fire. The charcoal in some of the hearths was as much as 22 feet deep—dramatic evidence that the first humans did not permit the fires to die out. There were also some tools fashioned from animal bones and antlers, as shown in Figure 10–11.

The bones of thousands of animals were strewn about in the caves. Nearly three quarters of them belonged to deer, which must have been the favorite meat of Peking man. There also were bones of giant sheep, zebra, pigs, buffalo, and rhinoceros, and traces of monkeys, bison, and elephant and even of such river dwellers as the otter. All of the mammalian bones came from species long since gone from the earth. About 20 feet below the lowest outer threshold of the big cave, the expedition found Peking man's garbage dump, a stony amalgam of thousands of scraps of bone, stone chips, and hackberry seeds. All in all, by his fires and his handiwork as well as by his bodily structure, Peking man indubitably established his right to a place in the human genus.

This assessment corroborated Black's earlier conclusion that Peking man was humanlike. In 1929 Black had compared his Peking skull with Dubois' detailed description of Java man. He concluded that the skulls were two specimens of the same type of human being. In each, the bones of the skull were thick, the forehead was low and sloping, and massive brow ridges jutted out over the eye sockets. Dubois, however, had insisted that Java man was not human but was a missing link between apes and humans.

In 1931, on an upper terrace of the same Solo River whose banks had harbored the bones of Dubois' *Pithecanthropus*, fragments of eleven somewhat more recent skulls had been excavated by Dutch geologists. This discovery encouraged G. H. R. von Koenigswald, a young German paleontologist, to keep searching for more specimens of Dubois' Java man. Eventually, in 1937, in a region to the west, called Sangiran, he found pieces of three more skulls, definitely human and definitely very old—and presumably remains of the same type of Java man that Dubois had found forty years before. When the most complete skull was assembled, it scarcely could have been more like Dubois' fossil. "It was a little eerie," said von Koenigswald, "to come upon two skulls . . . which resembled each other as much as two eggs." In 1936, von Koenigswald had excavated a child's skull, which later proved to be that of a two-year-old *Pithecanthropus*.

In 1939 a historic meeting of Peking man and Java man took place in Weidenreich's laboratory, when von Koenigswald paid a visit and brought his Java fossils along to compare them with the Choukoutien finds. Von Koenigswald described this unique occasion in a later memoir:

We laid out our finds on the large table in Weidenreich's modern laboratory: on the one side the Chinese, on the other the Javanese skulls. The former were bright yellow and not nearly so strongly fossilized as our Javanese material; this is no doubt partly owing to the fact that they were much better protected in

Relationship of Java Man and Peking Man

Figure 10–11   Two antler tools. Bone and antler tools were found in abundance at Choukoutien.

their cave than the *Pithecanthropus* finds, which had been embedded in sandstone and tufa. Every detail of the originals was compared: in every respect they showed a considerable degree of correspondence.

The two scientists concluded that *Pithecanthropus* and *Sinanthropus* were indeed close relations. "In its general form and size [the Peking skull] agrees with the Java skull to such an extent that it identifies *Pithecanthropus* too, as true man, and a creature far above the stage of an ape," said Weidenreich, upsetting the judgement of Dubois that *Pithecanthropus* came long before man.

The assessment of von Koenigswald and Weidenreich was later corroborated by Sir Wilfrid Le Gros Clark. *Pithecanthropus*, Le Gros Clark noted, appeared slightly more primitive, with his brain of about 900 cubic centimeters and his slightly heavier jaw. In addition, the animals he killed and ate were a little older than those at Peking, and no tools were found with *Pithecanthropus*. Despite these differences the two ancient beings were strikingly alike.

Von Koenigswald and Weidenreich had agreed that Java man and Peking man differed little more than "two different races of present mankind," and Le Gros Clark came to the same conclusion. The Oxford authority proposed dropping the *Sinanthropus* classification, which implied that Peking man constituted a separate genus, for it was doubtful that the two formed even separate species. He suggested that both should be identified as *Pithecanthropus*, and distinguished only by their specific names, *Pithecanthropus erectus* and *Pithecanthropus pekinensis*, or more simply as Java man and Peking man.

The ageing Eugene Dubois bitterly opposed Le Gros Clark's conclusion, continuing to insist that his own find was quite distinct from all others. But von Koenigswald and Weidenreich were little disturbed by his protests. More upsetting was the rumble of an approaching war.

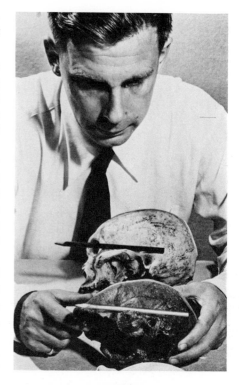

Figure 10–12   G. H. Ralph von Koenigswald worked in Java in the 1930s and managed to find more specimens of Java man. He also discovered fossil hominid and ape teeth in Chinese drugstores.

Fate of the Java Man Fossils

In Java, von Koenigswald knew that it was only a matter of time until the island would be seized. He quietly gave some of his most valuable fossils for safekeeping to a Swiss geologist and a Swedish journalist, neutrals in the conflict between Allies and Axis. (The journalist put the teeth in milk bottles and buried them one night in his garden.) When the Japanese occupied Java in 1942, they demanded that von Koenigswald give up his fossils. He did surrender a few, but he also substituted cleverly faked plaster casts for some of the originals.

At the end of the war, von Koenigswald tracked down and reassembled all of the fossils. "My happiness was complete," he said, "when I learned that my precious specimens had been saved. Large parts of my collections, many of my books, and all of my clothes had been stolen, but Early Man had survived the disaster." Von Koenigswald later exhibited Java man in New York and then took the precious bones to the Netherlands and then on to Frankfurt, Germany, where they now remain.

Fate of the Peking Man Fossils

Peking man was not so fortunate as Java man. By the autumn of 1941, the scientists working at Choukoutien could not misread the signs of war. After some debate about what to do with the fossils, the Chinese scientists appealed to the president of the Peking Union Medical College to have the irreplaceable remains of Peking man taken to safety. It was arranged to have the collection sent to the United States. The boxes of fossils were entrusted to a detachment of Marines who were evacuating Peking. At 5 A.M. on December 5, nine Marines, with their baggage and Peking man, went by special train to the port of Chinwangtao, where the steamship *President Harrison* was waiting for them.

But the rendezvous was never kept, for on December 7 Japanese bombs were dropped on Pearl Harbor and total war came violently to the Pacific. Somewhere between the Peking depot and the *President Harrison*, the boxes with all that existed of Peking man—fossil pieces representing about forty individuals—disappeared. They never have been found. It seems that Peking man, after lying buried at Choukoutien for nearly half a million years, reappeared for only twelve short years before disappearing again, perhaps forever. Fortunately, a superb series of casts was prepared in Peking and these have been saved. We also have Weidenreich's outstanding descriptions and photographs.

The fate of Peking man remains one of the great international mysteries, but his standing is secure. However fleeting and violent his reappearance, his bones and those of Java man offered incontrovertible proof of mankind's lengthy existence. These ancestors emerging from the past were not what their descendants expected them to be, for they were crude, primitive, and low of brow. But not only did they live successfully in their environment several hundred thousand years ago; they also walked like human beings and bore a human intelligence. In short, they were human beings, not forms transitional between animals and mankind.

THE MEANING OF THE FOSSILS

By the time anthropologists were able to resume the search for early man after World War II, the ancestry of man had been traced, as we have seen, to forebears more primitive and apelike than Java man. Yet there was still no clear conception of the human lineage, or the relationships between the various fossils found in different parts of the world. Had the human body evolved toward its modern form more rapidly than the human brain, or had the brain outstripped the body in early human evolution? Were there many different species of early humans, evolving at different rates and in different ways in various parts of the world? Or was there a single, consistent pattern governing human evolution worldwide? In part, these crucial questions could not be answered yet because the answer was obscured by the most peculiar human fossils of all—the skull and jawbone of a creature known as Piltdown man.

Piltdown Man: The Great Hoax

When they turned up in a gravel pit on an old farm in Sussex, England, in 1911, the Piltdown fossils were seen as an important new clue to man's past. The discoverer of Piltdown man was an amateur archaeologist named Charles Dawson. Dawson reported that while taking a walk near a place called Piltdown Common, he spotted unusual brown flints being used to mend the road. He asked where they had come from and was led to a nearby farm where workmen were digging gravel. The gravel pit looked to him like a possible source of fossils, and he asked the men to save any old-looking bones they might unearth. On his later visits to the farm he retrieved several parts of a seemingly ancient human skull. Dawson told his story and showed the fossils to A. Smith Woodward of the British Museum, and together the two made an exhaustive search of the gravel pit. They found many fragments of the skull, apparently smashed and scattered by the digging operation, as well as half of a slightly damaged jaw. On December 18, 1912, the two men introduced Piltdown man to the members of the Geological Society of London. Smith Woodward formally named this creature *Eoanthropus dawsoni*, or "Dawson's dawn man."

At first sight, Piltdown man was a complete surprise (see Figure 10–13). He had the skull of a modern human—an imposing braincase and a vertical forehead with slightly ridged brows. But he also had the more primitive-looking jaw of an ape. This jaw was almost exactly like a chimpanzee's, except that the molars were ground down the way a human's teeth are worn by chewing and the canine was missing. Unfortunately, the small section of the jaw that could have proved whether it fit the skull, a structure called the *condyle,* had been broken off.

Piltdown man was so strange that astonished anthropologists were forced to completely revise their ideas about evolution. The small braincase and manlike thighbone of Java man had suggested that the human body had evolved more rapidly than the brain. Because he was originally considered to be of Pliocene (and later, Middle Pleistocene) age, Piltdown suggested the opposite: that the brain evolved first. Just as some scientists had doubted that the different parts of Java man belonged together, there were now skeptics who felt that the Piltdown skull did not go with the jaw. But many of the world's leading experts welcomed Piltdown man into the family of human ancestors.

Over the years, troubling discrepancies began to be noted in the Piltdown fragments. The maturity of different parts seemed to vary, and one expert complained that Piltdown man was not only human-brained and ape-jawed, but appeared to have a middle-aged skull, a young jaw, and an elderly set of teeth! But the downfall of Piltdown man did not come until the 1950s, when so many genuine fossils of early man and his ancestors had been found that Dawson's discovery was seen to stand out like a transistor radio in a collection of stone hand-axes. All the other fossils confirmed that man's brain had evolved toward its modern form somewhat more slowly than the rest of his physical equipment. Piltdown man must be, then, an evolutionary freak—or could it be a fraud?

The first scientist to test the latter idea was J. S. Weiner, then a lecturer in Oxford University's anatomy department, which was headed by Sir Wilfrid Le Gros Clark. Weiner tried out his suspicions of Piltdown man on Le Gros Clark, who doubted at first that the fossils could

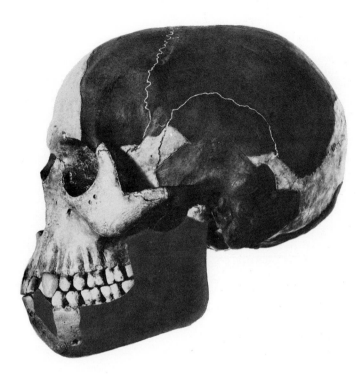

Figure 10–13   The fraudulent Piltdown skull led scientists astray for forty years in their understanding of human evolution. The black shaded area of the skull and jaw are the original fragments.

be fraudulent. Then Weiner took a chimpanzee jaw from the anatomy department collection, filed down the teeth to resemble those of Piltdown man, and stained his handiwork to make it look like a fossil. Placing the jaw on Le Gros Clark's desk, he said he had found it in the anatomy collection and asked what it could be. The resemblance to the Piltdown jaw was remarkable. Convinced now that Weiner must be right, Le Gros Clark joined him in initiating a thorough re-examination of Dawson's discovery.

Recently devised tests that could determine the age of fossil bones by measuring the amount of fluorine they have absorbed from the ground water showed the Piltdown jaw and skull to be of different ages, and when a magnifying glass was used on the teeth, file marks showed up clearly. In 1953 Weiner and Le Gros Clark and others announced that the jaw was a hoax.

After further tests, the rest of Piltdown proved to be fraudulent as well. Fragments of several different modern skulls, along with what turned out to be an orangutan's jaw (and a few genuinely ancient animal bones to suggest the age of the deposit), had been planted in the gravel bed. Who put them there, and why, has never been determined, though the circumstances suggest that Dawson could have been the perpetrator, but a number of young paleontologists also had the knowledge and the skill needed to have carried out such a hoax. Dawson died in 1916, 37 years before the forgery was finally detected.

Whoever did contrive the Piltdown hoax went to great pains to carry it out. All the fragments were antiqued with potassium dichromate, a chemical that gave them the dark brown color of fossils. The forger, besides filing down the teeth and knocking off the telltale condyle joint of the jaw, had also removed the canine tooth, which is long and pointed in an orangutan. (Soon after Dawson announced his discovery of Piltdown man, Smith Woodward, the anthropologist to whom Dawson had first taken the bones, made a model of what he thought Piltdown man's canine ought to look like. When Dawson revisited the gravel bed, a worn canine tooth almost identical to the model "turned up.")

Once the Piltdown puzzle was disposed of, scientists began to perceive more clearly the basic pattern of our evolution from the prehistoric apes; Java man and Peking man, and many more recent finds from other parts of the world, fell into place. A great many new fossils and living sites of the species have been discovered in recent decades. Almost as important as the new finds is the fact that scientists have arrived at a far better understanding of what these fossils signify. As improved methods of dating (see Chapter 4) were devised and a clear scheme of classification developed, it became possible to see beyond small variations in anatomical detail and envision the first human beings evolving together as the single species *Homo erectus* spread over many parts of the world. Today, Java man, Heidelberg man, and Peking man are considered varieties of this single species.

Another thing also became clear. The evolution of man is definitely *mosaic* in kind; that is, the different parts of the body did not evolve

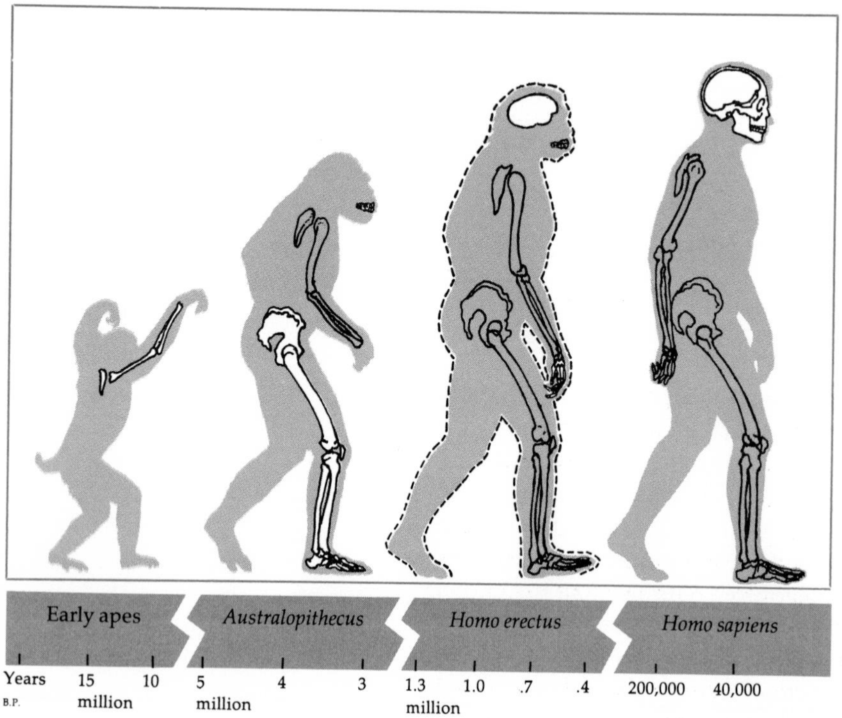

The Pattern of Human Evolution

Figure 10–14 Evolution of the entire human body did not occur at one period. Different organs evolved at different times. These diagrams show the succession of evolutionary developments that produced the present-day form of *Homo sapiens*.

toward *Homo sapiens* together, and at the same rate (see Figure 10–14). The evidence from *Australopithecus* and *Homo erectus* together made it clear that the locomotor apparatus—the human pelvis, legs, and feet— had evolved long before the brain and jaws. Small-brained *Australopithecus* was fully bipedal and very like human beings from the waist down; flat-crowned *Homo erectus* was almost indistinguishable from modern humans in the anatomical structures that equipped him for bipedalism. It was only during the later evolution of *Homo* that the head took on its present shape.

In 1955 several jaws and part of a skull were discovered in a sand pit in Ternifine, Algeria (see page 198), showing that *Homo erectus* once had inhabited North Africa. In 1960 a *Homo erectus* skull turned up in East Africa in the rich layers of deposits of Bed II at Olduvai Gorge, where Louis and Mary Leakey had already found the bones and tools of his ancestor. Three years later, a fossil skull somewhat older and more primitive than those of Peking man was discovered in China, near the town of Lantian, 600 miles southwest of Peking. At the same time, the Chinese obtained more fossils from Choukoutien, including a fine skull. (The cave site has now been made a museum.) In 1965 a quarry in Vértesszöllös, Hungary, thirty miles from Budapest, yielded part of a *Homo erectus* skull that had been larger brained than any discovered up to that point.

As all these fossils were compared and studied, it became apparent that there were some broad similarities among them; allowing for the fact that they came from such widely scattered places and that they might differ in age by as much as a million years, the similarities seemed much more striking than the individual variation. Once the classifiers recognized this, they were able to clear up the confusion caused by the initial naming of the fossils, each with its own separate genus and species. Names like *Pithecanthropus* and *Sinanthropus* were discarded: *Homo erectus* encompassed them all. The great wave of discoveries in recent years has demonstrated the wide range of living sites and physical characteristics of the classic *Homo erectus* type, and has shown that over the million years of his existence he slowly evolved toward a form indistinguishable from early *Homo sapiens*. The skull found at Vértesszöllös, for example, borders on the modern, while the skull from Lantian is almost too primitive to be put with the rest.

In the search for the first humans, much of the initial excitement over the discoveries of the fossil hunters centered on human skulls. Along the way, however, scientists have accumulated a vast store of other fossils: tools and artifacts the first people made and used, such as those unearthed in Choukoutien, and the bones of the animals that were their contemporaries. At some sites, as we shall see in Chapters 11 and 12, no human bones were found, but the artifacts told much about the people who used them. No fossil bones of *Homo erectus* have been discovered yet in India or the Middle East, but tools like those he used elsewhere have been found, and he is assumed to have lived there as well.

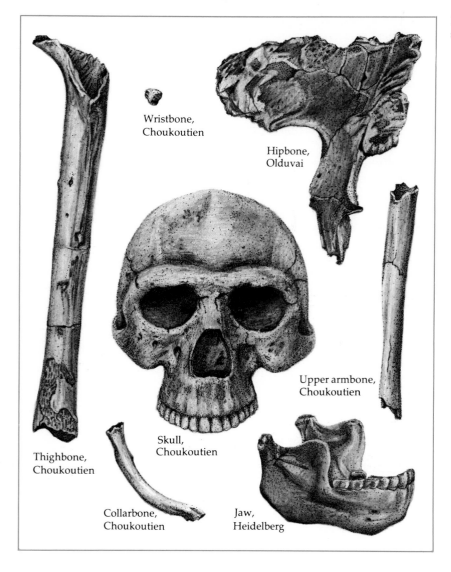

Wristbone,
Choukoutien

Hipbone,
Olduvai

Upper armbone,
Choukoutien

Thighbone,
Choukoutien

Skull,
Choukoutien

Collarbone,
Choukoutien

Jaw,
Heidelberg

Figure 10–15   A representative
selection of fossils of *Homo erectus*.

In some places, the combination of human bones and artifacts has presented a puzzle. The fossils found at Vértesszöllös, for example, suggest that their owners were highly advanced for *Homo erectus,* and yet, mysteriously, they used more primitive types of tools than their smaller-brained contemporaries in other parts of the world. So long as any such puzzles and questions remain, the fossil hunters will go on hunting.

But the search for evidence of *Homo erectus* already has provided an enormous amount of information about the first human beings. Some of the discoveries, indeed, provoked bitter and prolonged controversies among the experts. But in recent years the quantity of evidence accumulated by the fossil hunters has come to be recognized as material for the portrait of a distinct species; a record left behind by the first humans has been assembled by their modern descendants in an extraordinary tale of scientific detection.

Left timeline (CENOZOIC):

Years	Epoch / Events
10,000	**HOLOCENE**
	A. robustus and *boisei* extinct
	PLEISTOCENE
2 million	Earliest Oldowan tools at East Rudolf
	PLIOCENE
5 million	Earliest *Australopithecus*
10 million	
	First *Ramapithecus*
15 million	**MIOCENE**
20 million	First *Dryopithecus*
25 million	**OLIGOCENE**
	Apidium, Parapithecus, and *Aegyptopithecus*

YEARS A.D.	DISCOVERIES
1965	*H. erectus* at Vértesszöllös
1960	*H. erectus* at Olduvai
1955	*H. erectus* at Ternifine
1953	Piltdown man shown to be a hoax
1936	New finds in Java
1929	First skull of *Sinanthropus*
1921	Excavation begins at Choukoutien
1911	Piltdown man revealed
1907	Mauer jaw discovered
1894	Dubois' book on *Pithecanthropus*
1891	Dubois discovers *Pithecanthropus* skull in Java

YEARS B.P.	FOSSIL RECORD	HOMINIDS
200,000	*H. erectus* at Choukoutien (Peking man) and at Ternifine	**HOMO SAPIENS**
	H. erectus at Vértesszöllös	
600,000	Mauer jaw (Heidelberg man)	
	H. erectus at Trinil and Sangiran (Java man)	
1 million	First Olduvai *H. erectus* fossils; *H. erectus* at Lantian	**HOMO ERECTUS**
1.4 million	*H. erectus* at East Rudolf	
1.8 million	*A. robustus* in South Africa; *habilis* and *A. boisei* at Olduvai	**HABILIS** phase
	Java man at Modjokerto; Sangiran	
2.2 million		
2.6 million	Gracile hominids and *A. boisei* at East Rudolf	
3 million	*A. africanus* in South Africa	**AUSTRALOPITHECUS AFRICANUS**

THE FIRST HUMANS

Discoveries of *Homo erectus* have been made throughout the Old World since the first finds of Java man in 1891. His predecessors, indicated here as the *habilis* phase, were intermediates between the ancestral *Australopithecus* and himself. Whether we call these creatures true humans (and classify them as *Homo habilis*) or as late members of the genus *Australopithecus* (and classify them as *Australopithecus habilis*) is subject to disagreement. The evolutionary process was a continuous one; there were no evolutionary events that clearly demarcate changes in our lineage and can guide us in this problem. The subdivisions of this lineage and the names given to those subdivisions are arbitrary. It is not the naming of these ancestors but their nature that is the subject of the science of paleoanthropology.

Chapter 11

Bones and Stones

Man is a tool-making animal.
BENJAMIN FRANKLIN,
1706–1790.

On a late spring day about 400,000 years ago, a band of perhaps twenty-five men, women, and children stopped at a sandy cove on the Mediterranean coast. They were looking for a place to stay, and they chose a spot atop a sand dune protected by a limestone cliff, at the mouth of a valley. Today, the city of Nice, France, rises around their ancient campsite, but archaeologists have unearthed the place, called Terra Amata (see page 198), where these twenty-five primitive visitors once made a brief stopover. From the assortment of fossil bones, stone tools, and imprints left behind and from the consistency of the sand in which this record was deposited, archaeologists have been able to determine that the group stayed only about three days. Further, they can describe, in extraordinary detail, just what the visitors did there before moving on. It is possible to tell what kind of shelter they built, what sort of meals they ate, how they made their tools, and even, from imprints on the floor of the hut, where they slept and what they slept on.

The story of the discovery begins in October 1965, when a construction site near the cliff road to Monte Carlo attracted the official prehistorian of Marseilles, thirty-year-old Henry de Lumley. De Lumley's interest in the site had been whetted eight years before when laborers

TERRA AMATA

Site and Excavation

225

preparing the ground for new apartments uncovered a stone tool and a few flint flakes. But at that time the contractors went broke, and no further work was done until 1965. That year, bulldozers moved in again, and de Lumley stood by, watching the site carefully. As a bulldozer sheared off about three feet of ground, some objects glinted in the sunlight. De Lumley spotted what he quickly recognized as beach pebbles that had been shaped by human hands.

In France, where prehistoric artifacts may crop up anywhere, archaeology takes precedence over new construction—for a time, at least. The bulldozers backed off, and a few days later de Lumley and his wife Marie-Antoinette, an anthropologist, nailed to the fence around the project an official notice warning off all trespassers, including construction workers, on pain of fine and imprisonment.

Now began a battle against time. It called for a massive effort. Before long more than three hundred archaeologists, students, and interested amateurs were involved, and between January and July of 1966, this army of diggers, equipped with everything from bulldozers to trowels, quickly dug down almost fifty feet, through hundreds of thousands of years of geologic history, until they uncovered an ancient beach that bore traces of human habitation. The meticulous work of excavating the beach site took the diggers down through a richly rewarding layer of sediment eight feet thick, after which they went down another sixteen feet without finding any further sign of man. In the end, they had sliced vertically through more than seventy feet of the Terra Amata hill.

While inching down through the eight feet of Paleolithic deposits, each digger worked on a small area. The site had been divided into sections a meter (39 inches) square, marked off by strings tied to stakes around the edges of the excavation. Thus the dig was carried out horizontally, layer by layer. The diggers drew to scale on graph paper the plans of their particular squares and marked the exact location of each discovery. In this way the location of every relic found could be precisely identified, for relative position, as we have seen, reveals much about the identity and purpose of a fossil. The subsequent juxtaposition of all of the charts, coupled with photographs and casts of the finds, enabled de Lumley to reconstruct the various levels of the ancient habitation.

In five months, de Lumley's team exposed 35,000 objects, which were recorded by means of 1,200 charts, 9,000 photographs, and 108 square yards of casts. In all, the Terra Amata site afforded one of the most unexpected and valuable archaeological treasures ever found in one small area. "It is as if we are reading a book," de Lumley said while the rewarding work of excavation was still in progress. "Each layer is like a page that we read, and as we read, we know the story of early man."

The first page to be read was the 20-by-40-foot floor of a hut. Several holes, about a foot in diameter, within this floor space suggested that the roof of the hut had been held up from the inside by two or more

Huts and Living Floors

posts, perhaps the trunks of dead trees washed up on shore. In the center of the dwelling was a hearth, a fairly compact area of baked and discolored sand partially surrounded by pebbles that someone had placed there to protect the fire from the northwest wind, still the prevailing wind in Nice today. The fact that the hut was such a drafty affair as to require a windbreak of this sort led de Lumley to surmise that it may have been made of saplings or branches. A circular area around the fireplace was free of litter, suggesting that the inhabitants slept there. Only a few steps away from the hearth, de Lumley uncovered a toolmaker's workshop, in the middle of which was a flat stone. Here, he guessed, the toolmaker had sat; tools and chips lay scattered about the seat. The most dramatic of all the discoveries was a nine-and-a-half-inch footprint (Figure 11–1) made by an adult whose heel had slipped slightly as he stepped in the mud.

If there had been no other discovery, this occupation floor alone would have been enough to excite anthropologists everywhere. But the richness of the site exceeded de Lumley's dreams. No fewer than twenty-one levels of habitation came to light, layered one on top of another. Each reveals part of a fascinating story.

Huts had stood in three locations: at one time or another, four had been built on a sandbar, six on the beach itself, and eleven on a dune. They had been built over the course of perhaps a century, although the eleven on the dune, not so old as the others and built one on top of the next, had apparently resulted from as many consecutive visits to the cove by the same band.

The dune where the later camps had been set up was evidently an ideal spot, protected by a limestone cliff and close to drinking water from a spring nearby. The huts there (see Figure 11–2) were all elongated ovals in shape, but they varied in size, measuring from 26 to 49

Figure 11–1 Footprints of early humans are extremely rare. This one from Terra Amata is about 400,000 years old. It is a rather broad right foot (heel to the bottom).

Figure 11–2 This drawing reconstructs the kind of huts that Henry de Lumley excavated evidence of at Terra Amata.

feet long and 13 to almost 20 feet wide. Their shape could be determined from the bracing stones still lying in a ring around many of the living floors and from the imprints of a series of what must have been stakes or saplings stuck into the sand very close together around the edge to form the walls. At the center of the huts lay the hearths—shallow pits, either unlined or with pebbled surfaces—each shielded by its little stone windscreen (Figure 11–3), which seemed to corroborate de Lumley's original belief that the structures were drafty, sapling-walled constructions.

The size of the huts suggested to de Lumley that the groups of inhabitants had been relatively small, some consisting of perhaps no more than 15 individuals. On this basis he conjectured that the groups were made up of men out on a short hunting foray. This opinion, however, is not shared by most authorities, who point out that it would not have been feasible for the men to transport, in their arms or on their backs, an appreciable quantity of meat over any great distance to the women and children of the band who had been left behind.

No human bones were found to provide proof for either opinion, but something of the life of the more recent dwellers could be visualized through the details extracted from the living floors (see Figure 11–4). In a corner of one of the later huts, not far from a hearth, lay a large, smooth stone scarred with tiny scratches. To de Lumley's eye those scratches indicated that meat had been cut on the stone with a smaller piece of sharp stone; bones of many different animals were found nearby.

Close to this "kitchen" area de Lumley came upon another unusual find: specimens of fossilized human excrement. *Homo erectus,* it seems, was not the most hygienic of men, though, to his credit, a kind of toilet zone does seem to have been set up in the hut. Analysis of fossil pollen found in the feces indicated the time of year the hut had been built and occupied—late spring or early summer, when certain flowers, among them yellow broom, were in blossom and shed their pollen over everything that the prehistoric campers ate.

It was also a time when many game animals would have been abundant on the flood plain of the Paillon River, not far from the campsite. Surely the presence of game was no coincidence. The first human groups were above all hunters, and the Terra Amata bands must have chosen the site in the late spring because hunting was good there at that time.

The animal remains found throughout the site corroborate that speculation. There were bones from birds, turtles, and at least eight kinds of mammals. The hunters did not spurn rabbits and rodents, but they preferred larger, meatier prey. Many bones were those of the young of big game. Red deer were represented in greatest numbers, followed in descending order of abundance by an extinct species of elephant; wild boar; ibex or wild mountain goat; Merk's two-horned rhinoceros, now extinct; and the extinct wild ox. Only the wild boar still lives in the environs of Nice and it is smaller than its forebears.

Figure 11–3 On one of the Terra Amata hut floors, a windscreen of stones still shields a shallow hearth (left).

Figure 11–4 An antler, together with pebbles and tool chips, lies on the hut floor at Terra Amata.

The visitors obviously concentrated on hunting while at Terra Amata, but they also had a taste for seafood. Shells of oysters, limpets, and mussels, creatures that are fairly readily scavenged, are found at the site. The presence of some fishbones and fish vertebrae indicated that the dune campers may have fished occasionally as well.

The occupants of the earlier huts, on the beach and sand bar, differed in several ways from the people who camped on the dune. For whatever reason, they built bigger fires. They seem also to have been less competent toolmakers. They left behind several examples of their rather crude skill, including such pebble tools as a pick, flaked on one face only, rough *bifaces* (oval cobbles chipped on two sides of one end), scrapers, cleavers, choppers, and projectile points.

The Dune Campsites

The dune dwellers made many of the same kinds of tools as did their predecessors but employed a more advanced technique of manufacture —flaking chips off a core and then shaping the chips, rather than the core, into tools. They apparently travelled to find proper materials: a projectile point fashioned from a kind of volcanic rock found only in the Esterel region, some thirty miles to the west, was unearthed at a dune site.

The dune dwellers used tools manufactured from bone as well as stone. The leg bone of an elephant had been hammered to a point. Another bone tool had been hardened in fire, and the fragment of a third was blunt with use. A fourth tool had a long, sharp end and may have been employed as an awl to pierce hides, perhaps to make clothing. Around one hearth impressions in the sand, unmistakably those of animal skins, indicated that *Homo erectus* either sat or slept on hides.

The discovery of several pieces of red ocher, worn to a nub, suggested that the first humans may also have decorated their bodies, perhaps even for ceremonial purposes. The ocher may, however, have had a more practical application: some peoples living in sunny areas today still mix it with fat and use it as a sunburn preventive.

One of the most intriguing finds was a spherical imprint in the sand. Was it left by a bowl? De Lumley thinks so and believes that the bowl, presumably of wood, would have been used to store water. He theorizes that the hut dwellers might also have cooked in such a container, filling it first with water and then adding hot stones ("potboilers") to raise the water temperature, a method of boiling food followed until recently by many American Indian tribes. The possibility that the *Homo erectus* tool kit included vessels provides rich ground for further speculation. They may well have been used by women and children to gather nuts, berries, and seeds, thus facilitating the division of labor that is the hallmark of developing human society.

The people who built the huts apparently never stayed long in them. De Lumley could determine this fact from the state of the living floors; they had not been compacted much. Had the hunters been around for more than several days, they would have pounded the ground with their feet.

The dig at Terra Amata was a tour de force of modern archaeology. Not only did it reveal uniquely the life of *Homo erectus,* but it disclosed much about the climate, geography, flora, and fauna of his times. The results of studies by paleontologists and geologists, for instance, made it possible to reconstruct the countryside of Nice at the time of the hunters' visits. Terra Amata was colder and more humid then. The Mediterranean was about eighty-five feet higher than it is today, and the sea covered most of the plain of Nice and partly filled what is now the Paillon River valley. That is why Terra Amata, once on the shore of the sea, now overlooks it from a hillside.

Where the hunters of Terra Amata went after their short visits, and why, after visiting the cove for many years, they never came back, are mysteries still. But what has happened to their ancient settlement is no mystery at all. When the last bit of archaeological evidence had been carefully lifted from the ground in July 1966, the bulldozers inexorably closed in. Today, luxury apartments stand where *Homo erectus'* huts stood more than 400,000 years ago; Terra Amata continues to be one of the oldest occupied spots in human history.

Other Clues

CHARACTERISTICS AND ACHIEVEMENTS

What sort of people visited this cove on the coast of Europe 400,000 years ago? The finds at Terra Amata, although extraordinarily useful for what they do tell us, include no hints—other than the single human footprint in the soft sand—about the anatomical makeup of these European members of the genus *Homo.*

Anatomical Development

As we have seen, fossils of *Homo erectus* are now known from many areas of the Old World, from Peking in the east to Heidelberg in the west, and south to Olduvai Gorge and Java. These fossils clearly indicate that anatomically comparable human populations existed more than a million years ago on both the east and west sides of the Indian Ocean. Toward the top of Bed II at Olduvai (see page 166) lies a fine example of *Homo erectus* more than a million years old that falls well within the range of variation of finds from Choukoutien in China. As we discussed in Chapter 7 in the lower levels of the gorge, which date back nearly two million years, are fossils indicating the presence of an advanced species of *Australopithecus.* Perhaps most important of all is what was discovered higher in Bed I and at the bottom of Bed II: Louis and Mary Leakey's "*Homo habilis*," whose skull and teeth seemed to be intermediate between Olduvai's *Australopithecus* and its *Homo erectus.*

Physically, *Homo erectus* represented a considerable step away from his more apelike ancestors. Although *Australopithecus* had evolved a larger brain, relative to his size, than modern apes have and was able to make primitive tools, he was still comparatively small—pygmy-sized in many cases. His pelvic and leg bones indicate that while he could run well enough, his walk may have been different from ours and possibly less efficient, though on this subject there is still considerable controversy.

Homo erectus, by comparison, was a superb walker and probably moved with a springy stride. He stood straight-backed, and his legs were long and straight. In fact, the leg bones of *Homo erectus* that have been unearthed are not easy to distinguish from those of modern man. From this it is assumed that the rest of his skeleton was also much like a modern human's. (It should be emphasized that so far, since we do not have all representative bones, this is only an assumption.) As to his size, the best evidence suggests that females stood just under, and males probably over, five feet tall. No complete set of *H. erectus* hand bones has been found, but his skill at making tools suggests that he had hands like ours, capable of both power and precision grips.

While *Homo erectus* was not built quite like his forebears, neither did he resemble us exactly (see Figure 11–5). His bones were heavier and thicker than a modern man's, and bigger bones required heavier and more powerful muscles to move them. These skeletal differences, how-ever, were not extreme. Below the neck the skeletal differences between

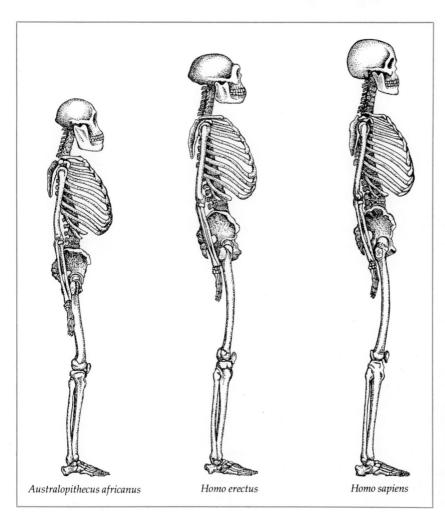

Australopithecus africanus   *Homo erectus*   *Homo sapiens*

Figure 11–5 Though stockily built, *Homo erectus* was becoming very modern in most features and distinct from *Australopithecus*; the differences in the skull are the most striking. In addition, *Homo* probably had longer legs and shorter arms than his ancestors. Stature is a very vari-able characteristic, and some living races of *Homo sapiens* are smaller than the average *Homo erectus*, some individuals of which were very large.

Australopithecus

Homo erectus

Figure 11–6 Although imaginative, these reconstructions probably give a reasonable approximation to the posture and form of *Australopithecus africanus* and *Homo erectus* (see also Figure 7–14).

Homo erectus and modern man could be detected only by an experienced anatomist.

From the neck up, however, *Homo erectus* looked markedly different from *Homo sapiens*. From the fossils we possess we can deduce that *Homo erectus* had a low, rather narrow, sloping forehead; thick, jutting brows; and a massive jaw with no chin. His lower canine teeth, which were still a little larger than ours, showed a slight tendency to interlock with the teeth of his upper jaw. His head was very robust, yet, with the exception of his eyebrows, these primitive aspects were less pronounced than they had been in his forebears. The cusp pattern and shape of his molars sets them about midway between *Australopithecus* and *Homo sapiens*. Also, the basic proportions of *H. erectus'* head had begun to change. His jaw became relatively smaller as his demands on it lessened with the inclusion in his diet of more easily chewed, cooked food. In addition, his head became higher-domed than that of *Australopithecus*, and his forehead receded less. His brain was expanding. Taken together, these changes tended to humanize his looks; nevertheless, his face was probably the least modern thing about *Homo erectus*.

Far more than increased height, erect stature, human gait, or improved grip, the remarkable change in *Homo erectus'* brain and behavior clearly marked him as the first of human beings. The sharpest difference between *Homo erectus* and all the primates who preceded him was the large size of his brain and the complexity of behavior this made possible. While the size of the braincase cannot always be relied on as an

The Brain

accurate measure of brain power, it is generally true that among animals of similar size, species with large brains are more intelligent than those with small brains. The capacity of a modern ape's skull—even a great ape like the gorilla—averages only about 450 cubic centimeters. The cranial capacity of *Australopithecus* was little larger; even with the skulls of the advanced *habilis* included, it seems that the braincase of *Australopithecus* measured between 435 and 685 cubic centimeters. *Homo erectus,* however, had a braincase of between about 775 and 1,225 cubic centimeters, putting the brainier members of the species well within the range of modern man, whose cranial capacity varies between the extremes of 1,000 and 2,000 cubic centimeters.

Sheer size in brains is important for two reasons. Most obviously, a small brain simply cannot hold as many brain cells as a large one can. Less obvious, but more important, is that the true quality of a brain must be measured by the complexity of the linkages between cells. Inasmuch as the possible number of linkages increases very rapidly as the brain gets larger, it is clear that a big brain can be a much more sophisticated instrument than a small one.

Homo erectus' brain was not only larger than earlier primate brains but also probably far more complex in internal organization. As a general rule, apes and humans share the same basic pattern of brain configuration; certain parts in the brains of both are known to be associated with the same certain functions. Toward the rear are areas that have to do with vision, while on the sides and top are areas concerned with memory, bodily sensations, movements of the body, and so forth. But a comparison of the brains of modern apes and modern humans shows that the larger human brain has quite different proportions, with larger and more complex individual cells, enlarged centers for such functions as speech and memory, and many more internal interconnections between brain cells (see Figure 11–7). Scientists consider the internal pattern of organization as important as size in making the human brain what it is. In fact, certain people born with very small brains, a condition known as *microcephaly,* show distinctly human behavior, including speech, even though their brains may have fewer cells than does the brain of a large gorilla.

There are no fossil brains, of course, to show what the brain inside *Homo erectus'* skull was like, but there is indirect evidence. The shape of his brain as determined from a cast of the inside of his skull was somewhat different from a modern person's. His head was narrower, slanting inwards above the ear at the sides, and his crown was lower, so that the central and side parts of his brain were reduced in size. His forehead sloped back, making his forebrain also considerably smaller than a modern human's. These are facts we know. But it is exceedingly dangerous to go on to make inferences about the function of *Homo erectus'* brain from its shape. For insight into how his brain had evolved, we must rely on our knowledge of the things he could do.

A restructuring of the brain was already evident in *Australopithecus,* for he made tools and showed other signs of manlike behavior, but the great change came with *Homo erectus.* When it came, it gave him the

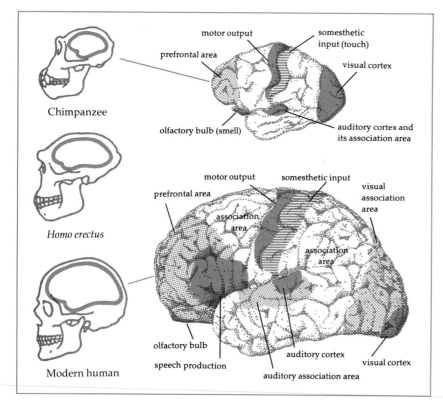

Figure 11–7 A comparison of ape an human brains shows that the human brain is much bigger and its cortex more extensively and deeply folded. The human brain also has a much greater area of cortex not associated with sensory input and motor output but containing very extensive and complex memory and association areas. The form of the brain of *Homo erectus* can only be guessed at from the shape of its skull.

mental equipment that distinguished him as a human being. The proof of this lies in what he did with his better brain. In some ways, *H. erectus* simply went farther along paths his forebears had started; for example he became a much better toolmaker and tool user than *Australopithecus* had been.

Territorial Expansion

In other ways, *Homo erectus'* accomplishments were completely novel. He expanded his range northward from the tropics, and as he did he was confronted with the problems and challenges of surviving in a severe and wintry world. These challenges stimulated new cultural and social adaptations and, in all probability, speeded up the evolution of the species.

As the early populations of *Homo erectus* multiplied, some of the first human groups stayed on in the tropics, developing the skills, language, and social organization that enabled them to flourish as hunters of big game on the savannas. But as their numbers increased, their range expanded. They did not migrate in the sense of pulling up stakes and immediately moving hundreds of miles to a new location. Instead, the expansion into new habitats was accomplished by a process anthropologists call *budding*. A few individuals would split away from a prospering group and found their own autonomous band in nearby territory, where the food resources were perhaps somewhat less plentiful. If they could make a go of it, their population would grow, and later generations might split off into other marginal areas.

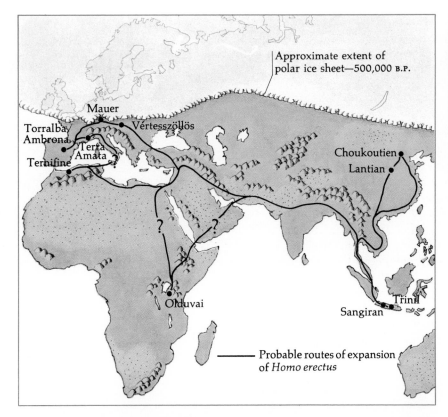

Figure 11–8 *Homo erectus* was much more widely dispersed than *Australopithecus* and was the first primate to survive the winters of the north temperate region. During interglacial periods he reached at least latitude 49° north. This map shows the sites of some major finds and gives an idea of the routes of expansion and gene interchange. *Homo erectus* may have occupied many other areas as well. We do not know if he originated in one particular area.

Homo erectus' dispersion across several continents occurred during a time of great change in the world's geography and climates. In a series of cold waves that represented what we now call the Ice Age, snow-fed glaciers spread over the northern continents, while rainfall may have increased greatly in the tropics. Between these cold spells, the glaciers melted away and temperatures were often warmer in Europe and Asia than they are today, while the tropics may have experienced long periods of drought.

With so much of the world's water locked up in ice and snow, sea levels dropped greatly at times, and land bridges between continents appeared. Java, now an island in the Indonesian archipelago, was for a long time connected to the Asian mainland. Similarly, Africa might for a time have been linked to Europe and Asia across Sicily, as well as through Egypt and Ethiopa (Figure 11–8), at the same time as tropical rains are believed to have produced great stretches of grassland and lakes in the now uninviting North African desert. It is not yet known exactly when and where these land bridges appeared, nor which ones *Homo erectus* may have used. In part, the problem stems from the fact that for tracing early migrations we depend on the age of skulls and skeletons found in various regions of the world. Evidence on this point changes as improved methods of dating are applied to finds and the deposits containing them. It is possible, however, to sketch a reasonable picture of events based on the best evidence available.

At the time when *Homo* evolved from *Australopithecus,* a vast tropical corridor of woodland and savanna surrounded the Indian Ocean, running up the east coast of Africa, across the Indian subcontinent, and down into the Indonesian archipelago. Because of the wide dispersal of early *Homo erectus,* we can safely assume that his ancestors had been living in many parts of this corridor, either dispersing through it from some universal ancestral home or evolving in several of its parts. Evidently, *Australopithecus* was firmly established in both Africa and Asia before *Homo erectus* evolved, so it is impossible to say whether more advanced forms first appeared in the east or the west.

Like his forebears, *Homo erectus* probably drifted back and forth throughout the tropics, with new bands branching off from more settled populations as their numbers increased. Some of these new bands also spread north, probably along several different routes at different times. Some dispersed north from Java into China; others spread north from Africa across land bridges to Europe, or entered Europe after skirting the Mediterranean by way of the Middle East, Turkey, and the Danube.

Whenever it began, the expansion from the tropics into Europe had been completed by 750,000 years ago and into China by perhaps a million years ago. Living sites that old have been unearthed in several places. The oldest hearths, going back some 750,000 years, may be those in a cave at Escale, in southern France; and as we have seen in Chapter 10, fire was used extensively at Choukoutien about 400,000 years ago. What led the first human beings to brave the winters in these places can only be guessed. It may have been the pressures of multiplying human populations; it may have been man's search for new or more fertile hunting grounds. In any case, changes in the world's geography and climate facilitated the northward expansion of *Homo erectus'* range.

Once the human tribe became so widely dispersed, it was forced to adapt to a new diversity of changing climates and environments. *Homo erectus* was probably forced to retreat from his northern outposts many times during the cold of this changeable age. The fossil record clearly shows that numerous animal species less adaptable than man perished during the times of advancing ice.

Confronted with such trying conditions, the first humans were **Use of Fire** forced to meet the challenge of winter with their wits. How they first learned to tame fire and use it to their advantage will never be known. There are two possible explanations. One is that they learned to capture and carry fire when nature offered it, as when a volcano erupted, when lightning struck in the dry grass of the plains, or when some outcrop of coal or shale oil burst into flames by spontaneous combustion. Early man must have seen blazes many times. Fire has a fascination even to sophisticated modern people, and perhaps this fascination has always existed in the human race. Perhaps an earlier human being approached a natural fire fearfully but curiously. He could easily have managed to hold a burning twig and, in touching that twig to a shrub or tuft of grass, could have multiplied the flame. One can imagine the sense of power and wonder that he must have experienced then. The warmth of fire is felt quickly, and even the inexperienced *Homo erectus* must have imagined its usefulness in a cold cave and attempted to bring the fire indoors with him. Another possible theory for the discovery of fire connects man even more closely with its actual production: he may once have accidentally made fire himself while chipping flint tools with iron pyrites. Sparks struck in this way may well have landed in piles of leaves used as bedding, or in the hair of animal skins, and begun to smolder.

However fire was discovered, having captured it, the first humans learned to keep it going in their hearths. Undoubtedly these early fires must have gone out many thousands of times before people became wise enough to keep supplies of fuel on hand, and skillful enough to invent methods for preserving hot embers, perhaps banking them with sod (as is still done in some remote corners of the world where the matchstick has not made its appearance). When a fire went out, the loss must have been keen and the wait a long one before a natural blaze could be captured again.

Homo erectus seems to have been slow to learn the secret of making his own fire, if he ever learned at all. Only by continuous friction between certain woods, or by sparking from certain rocks such as flint and iron pyrites used in combination, can fire be made. So far no firestones have been found among the relics *Homo erectus* left behind. The earliest known firestone, a round lump of iron pyrites grooved by repeated strikings, dates back only 15,000 years, hundreds of thousands of years after the last of these early humans. Even in modern times, some primitive hunter-gatherers have not known how to make fire.

Nevertheless, once people learned to use and control fire, the idea surely would have caught on rapidly and *Homo erectus* would have begun to live by fire, at least throughout the northern world. In the north he could not have survived without it. On the winterless plains of Africa, where human beings could thrive in the open without any need of fire, relics of its use date back to only about 50,000 years ago (though it may be older).

Excavations at the great cave of Choukoutien have given a remarkable view of the importance of fire to the first humans. When groups of *Homo erectus* first arrived there about half a million years ago, they may have spent their first few winters along the crevices and ledges of the cliff, wrapping themselves in hides while building some sort of makeshift shelters against the bitter winds. Choukoutien was the kind of site these first northerners picked out wherever they settled; it was not far from water, and it gave them protection and a commanding view of a grassy plain where herds of grazing animals could be spotted.

The great cave in the cliff offered a good place to come in from the cold, but the humans had to fight the animals around them for possession of it. The oldest and deepest layers of fossils in the cave show that *Homo erectus* made his home there, and was driven out again, many

Evidence from Choukoutien

times over many generations. At a certain point, however, the fossil deposits show that humans took full and permanent possession of the cave; this is the point at which the evidence of fire becomes continuous. Fire had become the key to man's control of the cave. His flaming brands and the light of his all-night fires kept even the most savage competitors such as the giant cave bears at bay.

Besides the protection it afforded, fire was a key to survival in other ways. The origin of cooking was undoubtedly the result of an accident: food that fell into the fire turned out to be tasty and tender when retrieved and allowed to cool. Once *Homo erectus* discovered the art of cooking, he seems to have cooked much of what he caught. The Choukoutien cave floor was littered with charred bones of sheep, large horses, pig, buffalo, and especially deer. Roast meat not only was more appetizing and tender; it offered increased food value, for heat breaks down some of the chemical compounds of tough meat and releases nutritious juices.

Homo erectus discovered other practical uses for fire. It broadened his choice of tools and weapons. The observation that bone or antler grows hard in the heat of a campfire, or that green wood does not always burn completely and instead hardens, must have led man to employ fire in toolmaking. Among the bones fossilized at Choukoutien were pieces of fire-hardened tips of antlers, which probably served as hammers for chipping away the rough edges of split-stone tools and fashioning cutting edges on them; the points of wooden spears found at other sites had likewise been hardened in fire to increase their piercing power. Similarly, sticks could have been tempered with flame before they were sharpened for use as digging implements.

Although we cannot know for certain how *Homo erectus* used fire, the evidence he left behind in places like the Choukoutien caves allows us to make logical assumptions about that aspect of his behavior. With an increasingly well-developed brain, and with growing prospects of foresight and reflection, *Homo erectus* almost certainly had within his reach the simple mental processes required to capture fire, keep it alive, and roast and hunt with it.

STONE TOOLS

From what has been said so far in this chapter, *Homo erectus* might be labeled as a kind of "migratory worker," a fellow who returned to certain sites with some regularity. He probably made his rounds according to the seasons, living on game, fruit, and vegetation as they became abundant within his range. Most of our specific knowledge about his habits is based on his occupation sites, and these are especially rich in stone tools.

In the drawers of museum and university collections around the world are hundreds of thousands, possibly millions of prehistoric stone tools. This abundance may seem amazing when we consider the extreme scarcity of fossils of the human beings who made them, and yet it is entirely logical. Stone is one of the most enduring substances on earth, and tools were almost invariably made of the hardest kinds of stone. Once made, they were virtually indestructible, whether they happened to fall into the mud of a swamp or slowly were covered by rubbish in the floor of a cave. Since the oldest stone implements that can be recognized as such today are not much more than two million years old, we must assume that practically all that have ever been made are still lying around somewhere. It is not surprising that a good many of them have been found, any more than it would be surprising for some archaeologist of the future to stumble over a quantity of Coca-Cola bottles entombed quietly where they had been dropped, one by one, beneath the pier of a waterside amusement park.

Another reason for the abundance of stone tools is that whereas each individual had only one skull to leave behind, he had any number of stone implements. He or she made them quickly and easily. As fast as he broke them or lost them or blunted them, he made new ones, starting when he was a child and continuing throughout his life. So even among the beginners in the tool business, one toolmaker might have produced anywhere from dozens to hundreds of tools before he died. Of course, we do not know what the rate of tool production at that early date was, or how many members of a band made tools. It may be that only a few of the most able ones did, although the likelihood is that, once toolmaking had become characteristic of hominids, it was common to all.

Certainly by the time of *Homo erectus*, toolmaking was universal. Not only had humans become much more dependent on tools by then, but they were also making better ones. This, in turn, changed their way of life and tended to increase their dependence on this developing tool technology.

Much attention has been paid to the question of tool use, and sophisticated experiments have been conducted by several paleoanthropologists. J. Desmond Clark, Louis Leakey, and S. A. Semenov, for example, tried to work out a scientific basis for determining how tools were used. The method was to make several duplicates of a specific tool, use each one in a different way—chopping wood, cutting flesh, skinning animals, scraping hides, digging roots—and then examine their edges under a microscope to see if the different uses had produced different kinds of wear. As a by-product of this study, a great deal of practical knowledge was gained about what kinds of tools are best for what kinds of jobs.

The Oldowan Industry

In addition to being named according to their presumed use, stone tools are classified according to their workmanship, or their presumed method of manufacture. As seen in Chapter 8, chopping tools, which were first found by the Leakeys in East Africa, constitute the so-called Oldowan industry. Similarly worked tools bear that name no matter what part of the world they are found in, China, Hungary, or South Africa.

The Oldowan industry lasted for at least a million and a half years, perhaps much longer. How it got out of Africa, if that is really where it first arose, is unknown. The most probable route for the exportation of the Oldowan industry was through the Middle East, and from there it could have branched out into both Europe and Asia.

It was not until 1963 that a relatively clean and undamaged Oldowan site was opened up in Europe: Vértesszöllös, in Hungary (see page 198). Four different occupation levels were detected. They are thin, suggesting that small groups lived there only briefly. Although some layers are merely scatterings of debris, the debris is significant. It includes not only a number of burned objects indicating the use of fire, but also tools in considerable abundance, and the smashed bones of some fifteen different species of small animals. Among the tools are many flakes and choppers, simply chipped on one or two edges and primitive enough to qualify as Oldowan. Even more significant was the eventual discovery of ancient human footprints and parts of a human skull suggesting a form no longer typical of *Homo erectus* but not yet fully *Homo sapiens*.

The types of tools found at Vértesszöllös are much the same as those found at Choukoutien, but the site is probably older than Choukoutien and was inhabited some 500,000 years ago. Most other sites associated with *Homo erectus* or his descendants are characterized by a different kind of tool industry.

Materials and Techniques

This is the *Acheulian* industry, a new style in toolmaking that made its earliest appearance about 1.4 million years ago. (In its earliest forms it bears several names like "Chellean" and "Abbevillian," but "Acheulian" is the principal style and the principal name that covers it through most of the world and for several hundred thousand years.) The name comes from the small town of Saint Acheul in the Somme Valley in France. The Acheulian was a clear step forward. It spread rapidly, probably from Africa into Europe and eastward as far as India. To understand what gave the new style its novelty, it is necessary to learn something about the various ways in which stone can be shaped.

Rocks of a coarse, granular composition, like granite, are almost useless for making chipped tools; they do not fracture along smooth, clean edges but tend to crumble. Certain other rocks, like common feldspar, tend to break only along certain fracture lines and hence cannot be controlled by the toolmaker.

The ideal stone from the point of view of the toolmaker is a stone like flint or chert: hard, tough, and of a smooth, fine-grained consistency. Stone of this type behaves somewhat like glass; it shatters rather than crumbles, and chips can be knocked off it that are razor-sharp. Flint was the most common of the desirable tool stones in western Europe, and the typical Acheulian implement was a flint hand-axe. In many places where flint was unobtainable, quartz, quartzite, and other rocks were used.

In a very real sense the presence of good tool stone helped to determine the distribution of peoples during much of the Paleolithic era. That is one reason why so many of *Homo erectus'* artifacts are found in

Figure 11–9 A plausible reconstruction of a *Homo erectus* group. After butchering their prey where they killed it and carrying the meat back to camp in manageable chunks, hunters hack it into still smaller pieces before throwing it into the fire. They apparently shared the meat, made more digestible by cooking.

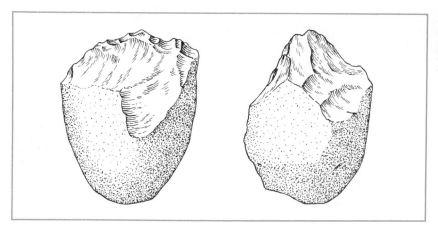

Figure 11–10 It is not difficult to see how a simple chopper (left) developed into a very primitive hand-axe (right). Both these tools are from Olduvai.

or near rivers, which are an almost endless source of pebbles and pieces of rock.

Combining various kinds of stone with various ways of working it produces a surprising variety of results. The more fine-grained the stone, the flatter and more leaflike the flakes that can be chipped loose from it. The size and shape of these flakes can be further controlled by the ways in which they are separated from the original stone. They may be knocked loose by a hammer or pried loose by a pointed stick or bone. The angle at which the hammer blow is struck can be changed to produce either a small, thick flake or a large, thin one. Also, different kinds of hammers produce different kinds of flakes. Relatively soft hammers of wood or bone produce one kind, hard stone ones another, and a wooden point pressed against the edge of the stone will produce still a different kind. Even the way a tool is held while it is being made will affect the kind of flake that can be struck from it: when it is held in the hand, the results are not the same as when it is balanced on a rock.

Every ancestral craftsman must have had a good deal of skill, based on necessity, on years of practice, and on an intimate knowledge of the natures of different stones. For each has its own qualities, and these may vary further depending on whether the stone is hot or cold, or even on whether it is wet or dry. But the basic principles of toolmaking are fairly simple. If you decide to try it, you may be surprised at how hard a blow it takes to crack or flake a stone, but if you do it right, the stone actually will behave in a predictable way.

Given all these variations in technique and material, there are still only two basic categories of tools: *core tools* and *flake tools*. To make a core tool, take a lump of stone and knock chips from it until it is the desired size and shape; the core of stone that remains is the tool. A flake tool, as its name implies, is a chip struck from a core. It may be large or small and its shape may vary, depending on the shape of the core from which it was struck. It may be used as it is, or it may itself be further flaked or chipped, somewhat in the manner of a core tool. In any event, the flake itself, and not the core from which it was struck, is the tool.

Core and Flake Tools

In the earliest days of toolmaking, flake tools were very simple. Whatever happened to fly off a core would be put to use if it had a sharp edge. In general, flakes were used as cutters because their edges were sharper than the edges that could be produced on core choppers, which were more useful for heavy hacking. As time went on, more and more skills were developed in the manufacture of flakes, and eventually this was to become a much more sophisticated method of toolmaking than the core technique.

As the Acheulian culture progressed, core tools underwent a great deal of refinement. The characteristic implement of the Acheulian is the *biface,* a tool whose cutting edge has been flaked more carefully on both sides to make it straighter and sharper than the primitive Oldowan chopper. This may seem like an awfully small improvement, but it was

The Acheulian Industry

Figure 11–11 Toolmaking is not simple but requires skill and much practice. Most people, however, can learn to make simple tools. These photographs show Francois Bordes making a chopping tool.

Bordes begins with a rounded quartzite lump and a smaller hammerstone. With

two or three blows he can produce a rough but serviceable cutting edge. Such

tools as this were a basic weapon and hunting implement for over a million

years. They have been discovered in Africa, the Middle East, Asia, and Europe.

Having knocked the end off a large flint
nodule, Bordes has prepared a striking

platform from which, using a hammerstone, he proceeds to strike off several

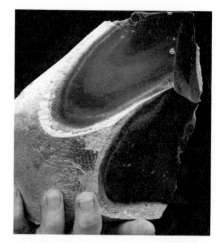

large flakes, roughing out the general
shape, He then switches to an antler

hammer (fifth picture), working both
sides of the tool to thin out and retouch

the edge. The final product, with long,
straight, sharp edges, is one of the tools

used for hundreds of thousands of years
by *Homo erectus* and early *Homo sapiens*.

a fundamental one and it made possible much more efficient tools. The
purpose of the two-sided, or bifacial, technique was to change the
shape of the core from essentially round to flattish, for only with a
flat stone can one get a decent cutting edge. The result was the hand-
axe, the typical and most well-known implement of the early Stone Age.
The first step in making an Acheulian hand-axe was to rough out the
core until it had somewhat the shape of a turtle shell, thickest in the
middle and thinning to a coarse edge all around. This edge could then
be trimmed with more delicate little scallops of flaking. The cutting
surfaces thus produced were longer, straighter, and considerably
keener than any Oldowan chopper could offer.

One technological improvement that permitted the more controlled
working required to shape an Acheulian hand-axe was the gradual

**Figure 11–12 Making a hand-axe
is more difficult than making a
chopping tool, as these photographs
of Bordes illustrate.**

implementation, during the Acheulian, of different kinds of hammers. In earlier times, it appears, the toolmaker knocked flakes from his stone core with another piece of stone. The hard shock of rock on rock tended to leave deep, irregular scars and wavy cutting edges. But a wood or bone hammer, being softer, enabled its user to control his flaking to a much greater degree. Such implements left shallower, cleaner scars on a core and produced sharper and straighter cutting edges. In time, the use of stone on stone was pretty much restricted to the preliminary rough shaping of a hand-axe, and all the fine work around the edges was done with wood and bone.

Figure 11–13 Many of the developed Acheulian hand-axes were carefully and well made. Tapering to a slender tip, this 200,000-year-old hand-axe was shaped with a stone hammer. Then its edges were refined with a hammer of hard wood or bone, whose more resilient blows yielded smaller chips.

Acheulian hand-axes were usually pear-shaped or pointed and ran somewhat larger than chopping tools. Some have been recovered that were more than 2 feet long and weighed upwards of 25 pounds. Obviously these were far too heavy and cumbersome to have been used for the kind of cutting and scraping that the smaller ones were designed for. One suggestion is that they may have been fitted to broomlike handles and poised over traps, set to fall and split the skulls of animals that triggered them.

Another type of implement that appears for the first time in the Acheulian is the *cleaver*. A cleaver had a straight cutting edge at one end and actually looked much more like a modern axehead than the pointed hand-axes did. It was probably used for heavy chopping or for hacking through the joints of large animals.

Present-day knowledge of the early development of the Acheulian industry is somewhat general, somewhat sparse, and somewhat disorganized. An extremely useful source of what information we do have is Olduvai Gorge. The Olduvai living floors tell us a great deal not only about the evolution of *Australopithecus*, of *habilis*, and of *Homo erectus*, but also about the development of the associated stone industries. As we ascend the strata in the gorge, we pass from a simple Oldowan industry with little more than a variety of choppers to a much more varied tool kit. In Bed II we come across the first bifaces, witnesses to the beginnings of the Acheulian culture. Here we find some eighteen different kinds of implements including—in addition to the choppers and simple bifaces—scrapers, burins (chisels), awls, anvils, hammerstones, and round stone balls. The marked increase of scrapers in Bed II suggests the beginning of an industry in hides and leather, which needed preparation with this kind of tool. There is also a huge amount of so-called débitage, or waste: the small flakes and chips that would naturally accumulate in a spot where implements were being made over a long period of time—and that would begin, over time, to suggest the basis of a new type of tool industry.

Further matching-up of tools with fossil evidence from this confused early period will undoubtedly take place and lead to further clarification. For the cultural evidence from the Middle Pleistocene onwards is varied and rich. It reveals the development of a large number of subcultures during the long span of the Acheulian. These have many names, each usually identifying a particular local way of toolmaking. Mankind obviously was moving in many directions in his culture by this time, and as these different threads met, crossed, tangled, disappeared, and emerged again, the fabric of human society began to become increasingly complex and increasingly widespread. Acheulian tools of one type or another are found in all major river valleys of western Europe and Africa.

One thing that should be borne in mind is that the more highly **Cultural Adaptation** developed a culture is, the more quick and the more complex will be its response to local conditions. By the middle of the Acheulian, the

sophisticated toolmakers of that time were capable of living on the sea-shore, in the temperate forest, on temperate grasslands, or on the sub-tropical savanna. Whatever specialized tool kits they needed for a successful life in these places, they made.

However, when we realize the immense period of time over which these changes took place—a period of at least a million years—we get a strong sense of cultural stagnation. Life then was entirely conserva-tive; it crept on from millennium to millennium without apparent change. In some places there appears to have been no cultural develop-ment: *Homo erectus* was still using the same stone tools in China that his ancestors had used a million years earlier. Yet he had evolved physically. It therefore seems very probable that this period saw very important developments in aspects of material culture other than stone tools—in containers, shelters, clothing, traps—and, of course, in social organization and language.

Figure 11–14 These photographs show another well-developed Acheulian tool, a 200,000-year-old side scraper. Chipped depressions in its top, visible in the full view, provide grips for the thumb and fingers. The long, almost straight right-hand edge shown in the profile view is the working edge.

OVERVIEW

	HOLOCENE	YEARS B.P.	EVIDENCE OF BEHAVIOR	ARCHAEOLOGICAL ERAS
10,000				**UPPER PALEOLITHIC**
			Fire used in Africa	**MIDDLE PALEOLITHIC**
	Peking man			
		250,000		
	Günz glaciation		Fire used extensively at Choukoutien; Terra Amata inhabited	
	Java man (Trinil and Sangiran)			
1 million	**PLEISTOCENE**	500,000		
	A. robustus and *boisei* extinct			
		750,000	*Homo erectus* expansion into Europe; hearths at Escale	
	habilis at Olduvai	1 million		**LOWER PALEOLITHIC:** oldest period of Old Stone Age
	Java man (Modjokerto)		*Homo erectus* expansion into China	
2 million		1.25 million		
		1.5 million	Earliest appearance of Acheulian tool industry	
		1.75 million		
3 million			Oldowan tool industry at Olduvai	
		2 million		
	PLIOCENE			
4 million		2.5 million	Earliest Oldowan tools at East Rudolf	
		3 million		
5 million	Early *Australopithecus*			

BONES AND STONES

Assigning absolute dates to geological and archaeological events between 50,000 and 1.5 million years ago is particularly difficult. The dates given here are based on a wide range of geological and paleontological evidence.

Chapter 12

Hunting and the Evolution of Society

It is far from easy to determine whether Nature has proved a kind parent to man or a merciless stepmother.

PLINY THE ELDER, 23–79.
NATURAL HISTORY, BOOK VII, 1.

HOMO ERECTUS, THE HUNTER

At Olorgesailie in southwestern Kenya, archaeologists have found dramatic evidence of the success the first humans achieved when they took up hunting, a way of life that came to separate them clearly from their primate relatives. The fossil remains at Olorgesailie tell an engrossing story about a creature at work who was no apelike hominid, but man the hunter.

In an area only 21 yards long and 14 wide, archaeologists unearthed bones and teeth of at least 50 adult and 13 juvenile baboons of a now extinct genus (*Simopithecus*); mixed with them were more than a ton of stone tools and cobbles. It was evident that a massive, organized slaughter had been conducted on the site and that the logistics and details of the hunt had to have been worked out well in advance, since both the stones and the tools had been taken to the spot from sources twenty or more miles away. It is possible to reconstruct what must have happened at Olorgesailie a half-million years ago.

Olorgesailie: A Scenario

It is night. Concealed by the darkness, a band of hunters steals up on a group of baboons asleep in trees. Having positioned themselves in a circle around the trees, the hunters hurl at their sleeping victims the cobbles they have brought with them. The baboons are big-boned, formidable creatures, the males almost the size of the human hunters.

251

They scramble down from the branches and fight fiercely, their long, sharp canines flashing. But teeth are no match for the hunters' weapons, and when the baboons give up the fight and try to escape, they are clubbed or stoned to death. The hunters proceed to butcher the dead baboons with stone cleavers and hand-axes, and in the morning light the attack ends with a feast.

The significant aspect of the Olorgesailie baboon hunt is the logic and efficiency with which it apparently was executed. Humans, like other primates, normally sleep by night and are active by day. In order to take the sleeping baboons by surprise the hunters had to stay awake until a late hour. They had to find and import the stones and clubs for the attack and prepare them beforehand for use as weapons and tools, making an ample stockpile of armaments; and they had to work out a careful battle strategy. In short, there probably was nothing casual about the hunt. It must also have taken a great deal of courage to bring off, since if it did occur at night, nocturnal predators would have been on the prowl, as eager perhaps to eat the somewhat vulnerable hunters as these were to make a meal of the baboons. By the time of the Olorgesailie baboon ambush, human beings already had become very skilled hunters. They had taken a long time to reach this level of skill.

The Hunter's Diet

As we saw in Chapter 9, the fossil evidence shows that *Australopithecus* groups consumed a wide variety of animals, some of which they presumably caught and some of which they may have scavenged. But they evidently lacked the ability to be thoroughly consistent hunters. The picture changed dramatically with *Homo erectus*. Although the first true human continued to rely heavily on plants for nourishment—as do practically all modern humans—he possessed both the cunning and the equipment necessary to assure himself of meat on a fairly regular basis. If hunting had been merely an occasional exercise for his predecessors, it became for *Homo erectus* a major occupation.

Like all evolutionary change, this crucial development was a slow matter of advantage and capacity reinforcing each other. Humans did not become hunters because some individuals decided they liked meat. Instead, a creature able to catch, eat, and digest meat was favored, at a particular time and place, in the competition for survival. Hunting makes available far more food per square mile of the African savanna than wild plant life alone can provide. As vegetarians, humans can make use of only a limited number of the things that grow in the ground—mainly roots, nuts, fruits, berries, and some tender shoots. The most abundant plants—the grasses of the savanna and the leaves of forest trees—cannot be digested by the human stomach. But the animals that live on the things that humans cannot digest may themselves be both edible and nourishing. Through hunting, previously inedible greens, converted to edible meat, became available as a food source for humans.

Hunting not only increased the amount of food available to man; it also provided a better food. Meat, particularly when cooked by the fire that our ancestors slowly learned to tame, is a much more concentrated form of nourishment, a more efficient source of energy, than wild vegetables, fruits, and berries. Venison, for instance, yields 572 calories (a measurement of the energy available in food) per 100 grams of weight, whereas the same weight of most fruits and vegetables yields well under 100 calories. So one medium-sized animal would have provided, in a compact, easily carried form, the same amount of energy as the results of a whole day's foraging for greens. (Nuts yield more calories than most meats and were undoubtedly a vital part of early man's diet when and where he could find them; but they grow only in certain localities, and most of them are seasonal, whereas game is widely available throughout the year.)

Another very important factor in the development of hunting and the evolution of *Homo erectus* is the seasonality of vegetable food in the temperate regions. In tropical savanna regions with their biennial wet and dry seasons, the supply of vegetable foods is more or less continuous, as the success of the vegetarian savanna monkeys demonstrates. In north temperate zones by contrast, there is a real dearth of vegetable foods after the nuts and berries have been consumed in the fall. In the winter and early spring, meat would have been an absolutely essential and major part of the diet of *Homo erectus* groups that had expanded into the temperate zones. Correspondingly, hunting was to become an essential adaptation for any groups who were to succeed in the bitter winters of northern Eurasia.

Skin Adaptation

Because meat-eating brought clear-cut advantages for survival, individuals who had to some small degree the physical or mental traits that made them better hunters were favored in the process of natural selection over those who did not. Most of the physical traits required for hunting probably had been acquired by *Homo erectus'* predecessor, *habilis*. He walked erect and was a good runner, although *Homo erectus* became taller and thus could run faster and see farther. Furthermore the hands and arms of his ancestors were possibly adapted for fairly accurate throwing, a fundamental hunting skill.

Another major physical change that supposedly had occurred by the time of *Homo erectus* was the adaptation of his skin. When hominids started diverging from the apes and monkeys, they probably were as hairy as those animals are now. As our ancestors evolved, their hair must have grown less dense and the sweat glands in their skin more numerous. By the time of *Homo erectus* the skin probably had become relatively hairless and had developed a far greater number of sweat glands. This change sharply differentiates humans from other primates. Today, while we still have as many hair roots as apes, our hair is generally much shorter and finer, and over large areas of our bodies it is almost invisible. Conversely, we have from two to five million sweat glands, far more than are found in any other primate.

Scientists are not sure why this change in body hair took place, but it seems connected with an increasing ability to sustain strenuous physical exertion. As we have seen, most meat-eating animals hunt at night. As hominids ancestral to man moved from the protective forests onto the open savanna and became daytime hunters, they faced a problem new in animal evolution. They were to generate a great deal of body heat (*metabolic heat*) in the hunt, just at the time of day when the temperature of the air was high and so the cooling effect of the air low. This meant that to maintain a constant body temperature, essential to any primate, a very efficient cooling mechanism was required. A logical evolutionary adaptation to this biological need would have been the increased development of sweat glands and reduction of hair cover. During heavy exertion or in hot weather, the sweat glands bathe the body in moisture. Evaporation of this moisture cools the surface of the skin and the blood just below it. Dense hair would inhibit evaporation and would get matted and clogged with dried sweat. Hence, the theory goes, the marked decrease in hair density.

There are, of course, other savanna animals that sweat heavily during strenuous exertion and yet retain a full coat of hair; zebras are an example. But their metabolic rate is noticeably lower than that of humans, and their dependence on grazing allows them to lead a much less active life. Stenuous exertion is probably rare and occurs at night when predators are active.

Sweating is not an unmitigated blessing for humans. As biologist William Montagna has pointed out, sweating represents a major biological blunder in one sense, for it not only drains the body of enormous amounts of moisture requiring fairly constant replenishment, but also depletes the system of sodium and other essential elements. Montagna suggests that the moisture-producing glands "are still an experiment of nature—demonstrably useful to man but not yet fully refined by the evolutionary process."

In any case, a sweating human being certainly was better equipped to exert himself for long periods in the tropical sunlight than his ape and monkey relatives were, and it can be assumed that the dramatic changes in his skin, however they occurred, made it possible for him to engage successfully in his new way of life.

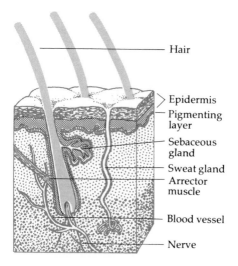

Figure 12–1 The skin is an organ of astonishing complexity. It is the barrier between the relatively closed system of a human body and its external environment; it is strong, elastic, waterproof, protective, and self-repairing. Beyond this, it serves as a sense organ, an excretory organ, a heat control mechanism (involving hair and sweat glands), and as the organ of individual identification. It responds to environmental stress, both directly (sun-tanning and healing) and indirectly (sweating).

Hunting and Intelligence

If all the important physical adaptations that equipped man for hunting had already been achieved by *Homo erectus'* predecessors, what made him so much better a hunter than they were? The answer almost certainly lies in the enormous increase in the size and adaptive capabilities of his brain. Hunting was more than a physical activity; it created a new way of life, involving language, culture, and social organization. Hunting became as much a matter of the mind as of the body.

We have seen that one indication of *Homo erectus'* increasing mental ability is the refinement and improvement of his technology. His stone tools and weapons were improvements over those of his predecessors, and we shall see that he also had wooden spears, which made hunting safer and more effective. Even if he only jabbed with the spear rather than throwing it, he still could attack an animal without getting within immediate range of its claws and teeth. And a spear embedded almost anywhere in an animal's body is likely to disable it; a stone, to be equally effective, must be thrown accurately to hit a vulnerable spot.

Perhaps as important as any improvement in weapons technology was a change in tactics. We can suppose that with his bigger brain *Homo erectus* had a greater attention and memory span. By being able to remember information from his own and his fellows' past hunting experiences, he could amass knowledge of animal behavior, plan ahead, work out strategies, and roam farther afield than his forebears without getting lost. Furthermore, he could cooperate more subtly with his fellow hunters; and this increased the chances of his making a kill. With better cooperative tactics, human hunters in organized groups could take on much larger herd animals than *habilis* had dared to. There was a definite advantage in trying for big game; more meat could be obtained for less time and labor.

HUNTING METHODS

Homo erectus' success as a hunter must have depended to a large extent on his guile and his understanding of the quarry's behavior. If so, just how did he hunt? Some of his hunting methods are documented in the remains found in excavated sites; others can be inferred by examining hunting techniques employed in modern times by hunter-gatherers. As we have shown in Chapter 9, many of these methods have close parallels in the animal world, and the similarities suggest that early man, faced with the same hunting challenges that confront most social carnivores, responded in the same way. If *Homo erectus* adapted tactics that paralleled those of other predators, he almost certainly did so unconsciously. But his growing brain enabled him to make conscious improvements in hunting methods.

He was clever enough to have looked carefully for the weaknesses of the animals he hunted, big or small. The large number of fossil remains of immature mammals found at *Homo erectus* sites indicates that the first humans had learned well the advantages of picking on the younger, weaker animals as their prey.

African hares are quick but vulnerable, and they, too, must have figured as part of *Homo erectus'* diet. How easily they can be caught by an intelligent (and agile) human was demonstrated by Louis Leakey, who ran them down and captured them with his bare hands. The technique is simple. The hunter has only to keep his eyes on the hare's long ears. When the hare is about to dodge, it lays its ears all the way back. Seeing this telltale sign, the hunter veers immediately either to the left or to the right. Whichever direction he chooses he has a 50–50 chance of picking the way the hare is going to go. If the hunter has guessed correctly, he and the animal are now on a collision course, and if he is quick he can scoop up his dinner as it goes by. If he misses, the hare usually will run for cover and freeze there. The hunter, with the advantage of the primates' highly developed color vision, can spot the animal where another predator would be fooled by its camouflage coloring; all he need do is go over and pick up his prey.

Since *Homo erectus* could not have run down much of his larger quarry, he probably used a technique that anthropologist Grover S. Krantz has called *persistence hunting*. Development of this method, too, required insight into the behavior of animals, such as the tendency of antelopes and gazelles to move in an arc when trying to escape from a pursuer, giving the intelligent hunter the opportunity to cut them off. But the key to persistence hunting is persistence: never allowing the animal to rest, but keeping it constantly in motion until it grows so tired it can go no farther; when it slumps from exhaustion, it can be killed easily. *Homo erectus* may have had to keep up the chase for hours on end. The Tarahumara Indians of Mexico have been known to pursue a deer for as long as two days. Although the Indian hunter may at times lose sight of his quarry, he never loses track of its spoor—hoofprints, droppings, and other signs of its passage—and relentlessly continues the pursuit until the deer collapses.

Stalking can bring down far larger animals than deer. Though his predecessors butchered them, possibly scavenging dead animals or bringing down weak ones, *Homo erectus* is known to have hunted and killed such formidable creatures as ancient elephants, which were considerably bigger than their modern counterparts. It seems incredible that an animal as huge and tough as an elephant could be killed with nothing but bone and stone weapons and wooden spears. Yet Pygmies still use poisoned wooden spears to hunt elephants. Normally, Pygmy hunters go out in groups, and when they come across an elephant, one hunter will attack it with his spear. As the animal charges the attacker, the other hunters dash toward it from different angles and plunge in their spears. They keep this up until the tormented animal dies. Some Pygmies even hunt elephants alone. For this feat the hunter wears no clothing, but smears his body with animal dung to mask his human smell. Once he has located an elephant herd that has paused to rest in the midday heat, he sneaks up on it, and with a favorable wind, stalks one of the beasts. When he is within three or four yards, he rushes forward and spears the animal in the neck. He must beat a quick retreat to escape the thrashings of the wounded elephant while the poison

Persistence Hunting

Figure 12–2 The close of an elephant hunt. Except that they use iron-headed rather than flint-pointed spears, these Mandari hunters of the Eastern Sudan, Africa, could be reenacting a Palaeolithic elephant hunt.

takes effect. An even more audacious method involves waiting in the bush for a herd to file past. When the last one goes by, the hunter darts between its legs and plunges a lance with a barbed head into its belly. The elephant is unlikely to be killed at once but probably will wander through the jungle, dazed with pain and becoming increasingly weary; the hunter must follow it until it weakens enough so that he can kill it.

Another hunting technique, the Leakeys have hypothesized, may have involved the use of *spheroids*. A most common object found at many sites in Bed II at Olduvai Gorge, these round stone balls are too carefully made, and represent too big an investment in time and labor, to have been used simply as thrown missiles, likely to be lost fairly readily. Mary Leakey believes that they may have been used as bolas. The bola is still seen on the South American pampas. It consists of two or more stones connected by thongs or cord. The hunter whirls these around his head and throws them at a running animal or large bird. The chance of hitting a target is far greater with a whirling bola that may be two or three feet across than with a single thrown rock. Furthermore, a single hit at a vital point is not necessary, since the weapon is also very effective simply in tangling up an animal's legs. If it misses entirely, it can be found more easily than a rock and used again.

Spheroids

If such techniques as persistence hunting were indeed used by *Homo erectus*, they certainly must have taken a serious toll of the hunter's energy, and they had the distinct disadvantage of leaving him stranded so far from camp that he could take back only a small part of the animal's flesh. A more productive method would have been the surprise attack by several hunters, as in the baboon ambush carried out at Olorgesailie.

One ambush method that *Homo erectus* clearly appears to have developed and refined was the use of bogs as traps for catching individuals or even entire herds. At Olduvai Gorge archaeologists unearthed the fossil remains of herds of extinct forms of cattle and gazelles. The animals had been driven into a swamp by hunters and killed as they attempted to free themselves from the mud. The leg bones of one still stood in the clay; the hunters apparently had butchered the rest of the carcass and carried it off.

The Ambush

By far the most dramatic proof that has come down to us of *Homo erectus'* prowess as a hunter—indeed, one of the most revealing sources of information we have about the culture of those people, in any of its aspects—lies in the sites of Torralba and Ambrona, in Spain. Here is evidence that about 400,000 years ago *Homo erectus* hunters managed systematically to kill a large number of elephants in the course of many seasons. As at Olorgesailie, from the distribution of the bones at the sites and from stray bits of evidence it is possible with some informed guesswork to reconstruct what happened, even to imagine in detail what took place during a hunt:

Torralba and Ambrona: A Scenario

Small groups of hunters are spread out on a limestone plateau on either side of a broad, grassy valley. Below are several boggy areas, key elements in the hunters' strategy. This is the fourth season the men have come, drawn by the expectation that the elephants will use this pass once again during their annual migration. The hunters are members of several bands that normally hunt and forage in separate areas during the rest of the year but join forces in autumn. The men understand the importance of cooperation and work well together. Some are even related, sisters and daughters having been exchanged between bands. And thus around the fires at night there is an air of friendship, enlivened, perhaps, by an acting out of the year's most exciting hunts.

The men are armed with fire-hardened wooden spears, bone daggers, and stone weapons. These are not very impressive arms with which to take on such big prey, but the hunters also have another weapon at their disposal, and it is a weapon they know the elephants fear: fire. One man in each group is a fire-bearer, carrying a slow-burning ember that is ready for use the moment the hunt begins.

When the men catch sight of the elephants moving slowly into the valley from the north, they hug the ground and wait for the lead beasts to come abreast of them. Then at a signal they rise and move down the slopes behind the elephants. With the wind blowing down toward the bogs, they set a long arc of fire in the grass and slowly move forward behind the line of flame. The flames close in on the trapped animals. Suddenly the ground shakes under the hunters' feet as the elephants stampede away from the crackling fire toward the bog. Three adult animals and two young ones sink into the deep, sticky mud, and the shouting men approach behind the fire to dispatch them.

As the hunters move closer, a few terrified wild horses, ensnared along with the larger beasts, charge out through the encircling flames. Several hunters leap upon the escaping prey, hanging on as they jab at the horses with spears and sharply pointed bones until the animals collapse on the smoldering valley floor.

Now the work of killing the mired elephants begins. As the elephants tire and lie still, some hunters thrust spears at the beasts; others pummel the animals' heads with stones. As the last elephant rolls over into mud, the men eagerly begin to butcher their victims. Here, in these mountains of flesh and bone, is enough meat to supply their several bands with all they could possibly eat.

Such a detailed reconstruction, though speculative, is based on the evidence uncovered at the site of the hunt. How this evidence came to light is a fascinating story in its own right. The relics at Torralba and Ambrona, like those at Terra Amata in France, first were hit upon accidentally by a commercial enterprise. In 1888 workers for a Belgian company were digging trenches in preparation for laying a water main for a railroad when they came upon a few huge bones; the bones turned out to be the remains of an extinct species of elephant (*Elephas antiquus*), which had straight, rather than curved, tusks almost ten feet

Figure 12–3 Ancient elephant bones excavated at Ambrona are jacketed in plaster and reinforced with rods to protect them during removal to the laboratory for study.

History of Torralba

long (see Figure 12–3). The bones remained only curiosities until 1907, when a Spanish aristocrat and amateur archaeologist, the Marqués de Cerralbo, began to excavate at Torralba. Off and on for four years the Marqués dug and collected fossils, including the remains of at least twenty-five elephants. He also found several kinds of stone and bone tools, sharpened tusks, and fragments of wood, apparently worked by human beings. It was the first collection of *Homo erectus* artifacts ever assembled.

Cerralbo's work was justly celebrated, and many of his conclusions were sound; his conjecture that Torralba represented the most ancient site of a human settlement in Europe held firm as late as 1958, when earlier sites were discovered at Vallonet, in France. Unfortunately Cerralbo died before he was able to publish his extensive and well-illustrated study of his work at the site. His digging was not as thorough as this literary work might have been; by today's standards it was hardly systematic. A great deal of work still remained to be done at Torralba, but it was more than half a century before anyone undertook it. Then in 1960 the anthropologist F. Clark Howell visited the fallow trenches and soil heaps. A quick examination told him that this was still rich ground, and the following year he came back to begin new excavations.

During one summer's work Howell and his assistants unearthed the remains of six additional elephants at Torralba and another dozen at the larger site of Ambrona. By the end of the third season, the diggers, under the direction of Howell's associate, anthropologist L. G. Freeman, Jr., had found more than fifty beasts. Torralba was completely excavated. Ambrona had been only about a third uncovered when Howell turned his attention to the Omo River area in southern Ethiopia. (He has remarked that he is reserving the less strenuous job of excavating the rest of Ambrona for his old age.)

The unexplored portion of Ambrona may yet reveal a skeleton of *Homo erectus,* although there is probably less chance of this at a kill and butchering site than there would be at a living site. Neither the Marqués de Cerralbo nor Howell discovered any human fossils or evidence of man-made shelters at either Torralba or Ambrona, but the picture of the hunting and butchering activities that emerged from the digs is one of the most complete we have for *Homo erectus.*

Figure 12–4 Every bone and stone at the Ambrona site was mapped, drawn, and photographed before any were moved.

Elephant Butchery

The study of fossilized pollen has revealed that it was very cold in central Spain at some point during this period of 300,000 to 400,000 years ago, so cold that the ground bore characteristic traces of frost patterning and resembled land in northern Alaska today. The summers were warm enough only to have thawed out the surface; the subsurface remained frozen the year round. Digging into this once-frozen soil, Howell found evidence that suggested to him that the hunters used fire to stampede the elephants: bits of charcoal and carbon were widely scattered across the ancient valley (Figure 12–5). The assumption that the hunters had spears as well as stone weapons is based on the dis-

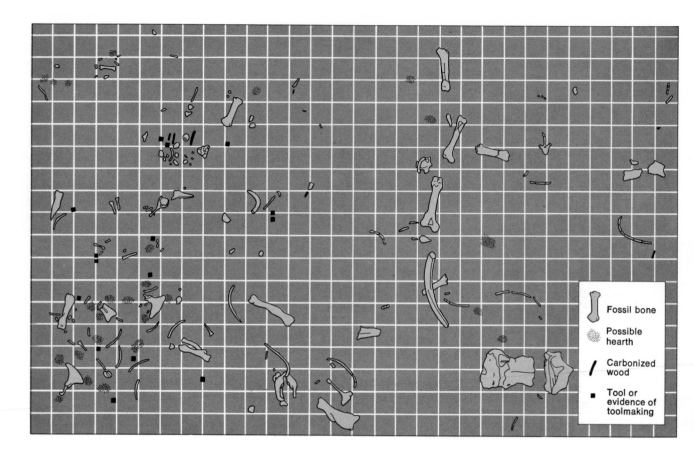

Fossil bone

Possible
hearth

Carbonized
wood

Tool or
evidence of
toolmaking

covery of small pieces of wood; some fragments, in rotting away, left hollows in the ground that could be filled with plaster to reveal their original pointed shape.

The animal bones the hunters left behind reveal how the meat was butchered—and lead to intriguing speculations about *Homo erectus'* customs. After stripping the carcasses of choice pieces of flesh, the hunters seem to have taken the chunks of meat to a second spot nearby for further processing. Here, as the debris they left behind would seem to indicate, they reduced it to smaller pieces and cracked some of the bones for marrow. What they did with the skulls is a mystery; one found at Ambrona had the entire crown smashed away, presumably so the brain could be extracted and eaten.

Once the hunters had cut up the meat, they seem to have feasted on it at other locations, marked by clusters of crushed and burned bones. But when the four-ton size of an individual elephant is taken into account, it hardly seems possible that the hunters, no matter how numerous, could have eaten anything but a very small portion of the meat. They must have carried most of it off to their base camps, perhaps in some preserved form. The smoke-curing process seems advanced, perhaps, for *Homo erectus,* but there is no reason why he could not have

Figure 12–5 Plotted on one-meter squares, the bones, tools, and charcoal at Ambrona were all recorded for each level excavated.

learned to dry his meat in the sun, as many people do today. Drying would have reduced the weight of the meat by a considerable amount, rendered it more easily transportable, and preserved it for future use. (Plains Indians used to dry buffalo they killed; the flesh of an entire cow, cut up and dehydrated, weighed only forty-five pounds at the end of the process.)

How did the hunters go about sharing the meat? The ashes, bones, and tools of Torralba and Ambrona cannot answer this question directly, but one small, indirect clue emerged from the excavations. Analysis of the clusters of splintered and burned bones showed that each pile contained examples of most of the animal species known to have been killed and butchered at the site. Thus the hunters would seem to have distributed the spoils of the hunt equally among themselves; such egalitarianism is in fact the mark of hunter-gatherers today.

In the case of one animal at Torralba, the skeletal remains of the left side only were found lying skin side up. The cranium and pelvis had been removed from their natural position within the skeleton and the other bones do not appear to have been cracked for the marrow. Could this particular elephant have been singled out for special treatment and its bones assembled in a symbolic way, perhaps as part of a ritual? A more probable explanation may be that in trying to free itself from the mud of the bog, the animal toppled onto its left side, completely worn out. It may have sunk so deeply into the muck that only its right side could be butchered. But then why was the remaining part eventually flipped over, as the position of the skeleton would seem to indicate?

Across the valley at Ambrona a tusk and five long bones were discovered lying in a straight line near other parts of the animal's skeleton (see Figure 12–6). At first it was thought that these huge bones may have served as a bridge across a boggy area, but it was determined that this particular spot was not a swamp at the time. Perhaps this arrangement had a ritualistic meaning; these hunters, like some modern hunting peoples, might well have had a deep respect for their giant prey. For lack of direct evidence of any ritualistic practice among these hunters, this suggestion, like others, must remain mere conjecture.

One thing that is quite clear is that the practical hunters were not so reverent that they avoided turning parts of their prey into tools. Among the many artifacts found at Torralba were some that had been made from animals' long bones and ribs, which had been fractured longitudinally down the middle. The pieces were then flaked by stones used like hammers to produce tools that may have functioned as picks, cleavers, or hand-axes.

Hunting and Life Style

The *Homo erectus* hunters paid at least ten visits to Torralba. Howell and his associates have not been able to determine whether the same groups were involved in each visit or how much time elapsed between the first visit and the last. Nor have they been able to pinpoint just when the hunters came. The charcoal is too old for radiocarbon dating, and the river deposits are not suitable for potassium-argon dating.

The botanical and geological evidence indicates, however, that the ancient hunters were active at least 300,000 years ago and probably close to 400,000 years ago.

Torralba and Ambrona provide one of the oldest known examples of cooperative hunting. Their importance lies in the proof they offer that *Homo erectus* was capable not only of successful team effort but also of the coordination of the diverse social activities that the techniques of butchering and processing prey involved.

The evidence also shows that *Homo erectus'* brain was advanced enough that he could plan into the future on the basis of past experience. He could memorize details about the countryside over which he wandered and remember how to get back to camp. More significant, he could perceive and follow the seasonal migrations of the animals he hunted. Hunting was no longer a hit-or-miss proposition, a matter of getting whatever game was around. Man had learned to take the in-

Figure 12–6 This view of the excavation at Ambrona shows the remarkable linear arrangement of elephant tusks and leg bones which suggests that humans were responsible for their disposition.

itiative and go where the hunting was good. The Spanish site is by no means the only proof of such carefully planned forays. The roughly contemporary cove at Terra Amata also was a camp where wandering hunters stopped briefly at a certain time each year because that was where the animals were.

The travel imposed on *Homo erectus* by his wandering prey must have had an enormous effect on his life. It forced him to cover new ground and exposed him to a variety of new experiences and sensations. All primates are curious and doubtless *Homo erectus* explored the diverse features of his enlarging world with interest. He must have had to solve new problems, such as how to transport food and water and fire as he moved from one hunting ground to the next. No direct evidence has been discovered so far to show he had receptacles of any sort (we can hardly count the inconclusive imprint of a possible bowl in the sand at Terra Amata as direct evidence); but it is inconceivable that he could have managed without at least crude skin bags made of animal hides or perhaps bowls made of wood, stone, or even clay. (It is unlikely that *Homo erectus* carried many stone tools with him; the elephant bones sharpened for use as tools at Torralba and the chips around the toolmaker's "bench" at Terra Amata suggest that he manufactured most of his implements on the spot.)

The hunters' wanderings may have played a part in *Homo erectus'* remarkable expansionary movement out of the tropics, if only in preparing him for the adjustments that the new environment would force on him. When he did begin to expand his range northward, the cooler climates he found made the taming of fire, and probably also the construction of clothing of some sort, a necessity. Both these behaviors can be related to hunting. The cold, harsh winters of the north deprived him of a year-round supply of vegetable food and put an even higher premium on his skill as a hunter. How successfully he met these challenges is widely evident. Of hearthside fires, where he cooked the meat that hunting had supplied him with, we have ample evidence in the continuous layers of ash at the cave at Choukoutien. Clothing could have been made from the pelts of animals he had killed; impressions in the ground at Terra Amata and elsewhere show that *Homo erectus* used hides for something. And the remains at the slaughtering grounds at Ambrona and Torralba are nothing if not mute testimony to *Homo erectus'* skill as a hunter.

NEW SOCIAL DEVELOPMENTS

The record of achievement left by *Homo erectus* at Choukoutien, Torralba–Ambrona, Terra Amata, Olduvai Gorge, and other sites may not seem like much for his million-year tenure. And yet in successfully adopting hunting as a way of life, human beings had taken a major step toward setting themselves apart from their animal ancestors and establishing the genus *Homo* as supreme among the creatures of the earth. This development of dependence on hunting and the expansion into temperate regions of the Old World must have greatly influenced human social organization.

The expansion into temperate zones (shown in Figure 11–8) was perhaps the high adventure of those million years during which *Homo erectus* was establishing himself as nature's dominant figure. Before the great expansion, his immediate ancestors had been evolving by the dictates of natural selection much as the other animals around them were: adapting imperceptibly to their environment, living in loose social groups, depending on a generally benign environment for food and warmth, having very little awareness of the past or thought for the future. But when *Homo erectus* spread into the world's previously unpeopled regions, this way of life began to alter. *Homo erectus* prevailed over the obstacles of new environments not because he developed new bodily equipment but because he had a better brain. By meeting the challenges of changing conditions with solutions of his own making, rather than waiting until evolution created solutions for him, mankind passed a crucial milestone: for the first time, a creature, however unconsciously, took an active hand in its own adaptation and its own evolution. The invention of a "cultural environment" was the most significant contribution *Homo erectus* made to human evolution.

Interdependence and the Family

Cultural development requires a particular social environment: it depends on the existence of a home base and interdependence among people so that their relations are frequent and stable. We saw in Chapter 9 that *Australopithecus* society must have begun to operate according to certain patterns of social dependence. As *Homo erectus* evolved, the links of dependence among individuals strengthened and became more numerous—babies depended upon mothers, youngsters upon adults, hunters upon other hunters, and men and women upon each other; eventually, groups depended upon groups.

Homo erectus probably had to cover a large territory to find his food. It has been estimated that it took as much as 10 square miles to support a single hunter; a band of 30 people would have ranged over an area of 300 square miles in supplying itself with meat. Even if *Homo erectus* was as successful in his hunting as primitive hunting tribes are today, through most of the year the kills probably provided no more than a fourth of the food the band needed to live on. The rest had to be supplied by vegetable foods, probably gathered by the women. As meat became more and more important in the human diet, women would have become more and more dependent on the men to supply it for them; similarly, the hunter's dependence on the women gatherers to supply the vegetable mainstay would have grown.

By the time of *Homo erectus,* when hunters were tackling larger and more dangerous prey than *Australopithecus* had, more hunters working together were needed, and the specialization of work had become more necessary. The division of labor between men and women, which is accepted—or challenged—in today's cultures as a traditional social arrangement, had by then become essential to survival. Men and

Figure 12-7 *Homo erectus* probably evolved a pattern of division of labor similar to that of these present-day Kung! Bushmen. While the men are out searching for meat, the women gather and dig vegetable foods.

women living separately on an every-individual-for-himself basis would almost certainly have starved; working together in distinct roles as hunters and foragers, they formed a successful economic team.

While this increasingly essential new life style was forging an increasingly stronger male-female relationship, and while larger brain size was reinforcing the infant-mother relationship, still another relationship was further developing: that of male to female to young.

Figure 12–8   Two Kung! brothers and their wives go out in the morning to find food. The men carry springhare poles, bows, and quivers of arrows for hunting; the women, one carrying two children, will gather plant foods.

This three-way interdependence was perhaps the most important of all the new kinds of social bonds. It was to become the basic unit of human society: the family.

We may suppose that a crude forerunner of the human family was to be found in *Australopithecus* groups. Interdependence and some division of labor probably began to appear, as we have seen in Chapter 9, fostering rather impermanent relationships among subgroups of men and women within the band. By *Homo erectus'* day, these subdivisions undoubtedly were becoming more clearly established. If a *Homo erectus* band encompassed 20 to 50 individuals, as most experts believe, it included perhaps three to a dozen family units.

It is tempting to think of these closely related subgroups as traditional Western families—Mom, Dad, and the children making up a tightly knit unit of their own. But all sorts of human families exist today, and the European or American nuclear type is not the most common. The earliest families may have evolved under the leadership of the father, the mother, or the uncle (all these systems are to be found today) and may have included several females for a male or, very rarely, several males for a female. What is common to all types of families is three-way interdependence. One or a few males assume some measure of special responsibility for one or a few females and their children, while the females assume special responsibility to the males and children, and it follows that the children feel a special commitment to their own elders.

This interdependence is a matter of degree. It is more noticeable now than it was in its early form, when individuals often shifted or even shared allegiance among family units, probably more easily than they do now. Children in particular perhaps tended to be viewed in those early times as the charge of the entire band rather than of their families alone. Yet the ties that distinguish families within a society must have been growing markedly stronger. Since family ties seem to be associated with sexual habits and mate-selection practices, these behaviors, too, possibly developed at that time; certainly, they have come to help distinguish humans from their animal relatives.

As we discussed in Chapter 9, the estrous cycle of hominid females must gradually have become modified so that human females became capable of year-round sexual receptivity and were always attractive to males. Men and women must have come to exert some control over their sexual behavior and could decide when, and with whom, they mated. This physical change introduced the all-important element of choice, and led to what has been called the individualization of sex. Couples could now become partners.

This "partnering" probably was not permanent nor even monogamous (involving only one male and one female), particularly if there were more men than women in the band, or vice versa. Furthermore, since hunting was communal, the sharing of meat probably was also, so that a man would not have been expected to provide all the meat a particular woman needed. Nevertheless, it seems inescapable that certain men and women would have attracted each other, become friends, and formed some sort of relationship that they and the group recognized. They would have bedded down together, kept one another company when the band was on the move, and paid particular attention to each other's needs. In addition, a man would have taken a parental interest in the children of the woman he favored, even if he did not specifically recognize them as his own; he would have gone on hunting forays with her male children as soon as they were strong enough to keep up, and would have formed close ties with these protégés as he initiated them into the skills of the hunt.

Kinship ties in the group almost certainly would have been extended by the presence of a few grandparents—men and women who were past their hunting and child-bearing days but who were honored for their skills at toolmaking or teaching, or valued simply as baby-sitters. They may also have held an authoritarian role in the band as elders. The continuity of genetic lines thus would have taken on a firmer definition.

The Incest Taboo

As these family patterns became more deeply etched into the emerging society, there undoubtedly was a more marked avoidance of *incest*. Incest inhibitions are evident in some of the apes and monkeys. Among Japanese macaques, for instance, there is apparently some sort of restraint against sex between mother and son; in chimpanzees this inhibition usually is extended to include brother and sister, although in other ways chimpanzees are entirely promiscuous in their sex lives. In modern man a taboo against incest is found in all societies (though a few societies have carefully defined exceptions). Sometime during the evolution of the early humans, then, the partial inhibition became the hard-and-fast taboo. It seems fair to suggest that as *Homo erectus* grew more aware of kinship structures within his community, a sanction against sex within the family group became more pronounced. We can suppose that the reason for this may have been to retain the stability of the family group and the broader social structure. It is clear that the bonds within the family will always be threatened by incest; and the development of bonding between descent groups (discussed below) depended upon the extension of the incest taboo to a widening group of kin. The fact that extensive inbreeding can be genetically undesirable (as we saw in Chapter 3) was surely not known to these people, yet in this respect also the taboo was certainly an advantageous behavior pattern.

Homo erectus' tendency to look around widely for mates probably grew, and eventually he reached beyond his own band to select a partner from a neighboring group. This practice, which anthropologists call *exogamy,* certainly would have had advantages. Speech would have enabled *Homo erectus* to symbolize relationships between different families and descent groups, and the development of blood ties between such groups through exchange of women would have encouraged intergroup harmony. When bands with adjoining hunting ranges are related, a practice of sharing develops; when game becomes scarce, the bands hunt freely over one another's ranges. By bringing in mates strange to the group, exogamy made family ties and identity ever more important.

Exogamy

With strong family ties and individualization came another cultural development that was vital for society's growth. This was the idea of a home base. It is all very well for apes to travel everywhere and at all times as a group: each individual does its own foraging, and the safety of the individual lies in the numbers of the group. In a society that is more complex than that of the apes, the subgroup, as opposed to the group, must frequently be the functioning unit. Subgroups of hunters or foragers are likely to be isolated from the main group for periods of time. As we have seen, there is some evidence that *habilis* invented the base camp, to which individuals or subgroups would return after dispersing to perform their specific social functions. Certainly, constant association as a group would not have been possible for *Homo erectus,* whose hunters ranged far and whose young were becoming increasingly dependent. The solution was a place, however temporary, where the children could be looked after and the fires kept burning, where the women could stockpile the fruits of their gathering, and where the men could bring their supplies of meat after a day or two on the hunt.

The Home Base

By the time of *Homo erectus* we have evidence of at least two kinds of homes: one temporary, one permanent. If the hunters were following migrating animals, the bases were used only as long as the animals were in the area. Terra Amata was a temporary home of this sort. Even there, the visitors saw fit to build huts for shelter each time they came. The eleven huts apparently built in consecutive years on the same sand dune at Terra Amata suggest a group with a well-ordered annual schedule and perhaps even a feeling of attachment for a favored spot. Choukoutien was not a temporary home. There, where in one cave the layers of hearth ashes were found to be 22 feet thick, the base must have been more or less permanent (although during some periods it may have been a seasonal home): no doubt it was in a favored location where water and game were within close range most of the year.

In their development of the idea of a home base, *Homo erectus* and his predecessor were unique among primates. Many animals mark off territories they regard as peculiarly their own, and some monkeys and apes show a preference for certain clumps of trees to sleep in within their ranges. The most highly evolved social carnivores, the African wild dogs, have a *den*—a permanent home base—to which they always return. But no other primate society incorporates either permanent or temporary bases.

With a home base, mankind had a new social blueprint. For one thing, the existence of a home meant that sick or infirm individuals no longer faced abandonment along the way; now there was a place where they could rest and mend in comparative safety. "For a wild primate," Sherwood Washburn and Irven DeVore have written, "a fatal sickness is one that separates it from the troop, but for man it is one from which he cannot recover even while protected and fed at the home base. . . . It is the home base that changes sprained ankles and fevers from fatal diseases to minor ailments."

Thus the development of the home must have affected the normal life span. Still, only a few *Homo erectus* individuals are believed to have attained the age of 40, and anyone who survived until 50 would have reached a ripe old age indeed. Most died much earlier, as is shown by evidence from the cave at Choukoutien: 50 percent of the human bones found there belonged to children under 14 years of age.

In terms of the long-range development of human society, the real importance of the home base was that it provided a medium for cultural growth. Within the safe circle of its carefully tended fire could grow a fellowship, a self-awareness and trust, a sense of community that was new on earth. There man could begin to learn more than simply how to survive; he could improve his tools and weapons and fashion a language.

INTRASPECIES AGGRESSION

Theories of Aggression

The home, for all it contributed to human growth, also could be involved in another, and much less desirable, hallmark of human society (according to some writers)—one that some observers think they can trace to the first men and before. That is modern man's unhappy tendency to do violence to his own kind.

Author Robert Ardrey, for example, has hypothesized that a person instinctively guards whatever territory he considers his own, such as that of a home base, and will defend it, violently if necessary, against all intruders. It is suggested that an inborn drive for aggression carried over from animal forebears explains all man's violent behavior, from wars to riots to throwing dishes in a domestic quarrel. Konrad Lorenz, the Austrian authority on animal behavior, argues that this innate drive will express itself one way or another; if it is not channeled productively, in society's terms, it will burst out destructively—sooner or later, but inevitably.

Most anthropologists and ethnologists today disagree with Lorenz's hypothesis. They believe that humans have no specific innate drive for aggression but merely the potential for this kind of behavior, and that this potential is shaped by society. For instance, when one person is threatened or thinks he is threatened by another, his response might just as well be to flee the threat as to fight the provoker. His culture and his experience determine which response he should make.

Anthropologist David Pilbeam does not believe that aggressive behavior is innate either in man or in the monkeys and apes. "The degree to which such behavior is developed," he states, "depends very considerably indeed upon cultural values and learning. Territoriality, likewise, is not a 'natural' feature of human group living; nor is it among most other primates."

Pilbeam's analysis is borne out by observation of several hunter-gatherer peoples living today, such as the Kung! bushmen of the Kalahari Desert in southern Africa. The Kung! are not particularly territory-minded, and among themselves they are markedly unaggressive, regarding hospitality and generosity as normal. Even more mild are the Tasaday people, discovered living in Stone Age primitiveness in the Philippine jungle. These quiet, gentle people live in harmony with their surroundings and apparently exhibit no driving aggression in any aspect of their society.

Homo erectus, too, probably was a peaceable creature. He lived by the club and spear, it is true, but only to feed himself and his kin. Sharing of food was basic to his existence, and since his possessions were limited by the kind of life he led, covetousness and greed could hardly have driven *Homo erectus* to violence.

Aggression among *Homo erectus*

Yet the possibility of conflict within or between bands cannot be entirely eliminated. Much that is known about *Homo erectus* provides a portrait of our Paleolithic ancestors as solid and industrious social human beings, sharing the burdens of a primitive existence. Yet, among the fossils unearthed on the cave floor at Choukoutien, there are reminders that they were savages, living in a savage world. Charred human bones were found, and human skulls smashed in at the base. This evidence can be explained in many ways; some archaeologists conclude that the first human beings practiced cannibalism. Savage as this act is now considered, it does not necessarily make *Homo erectus* less human. In fact, it could be taken as evidence of a forward step in human development.

Among all the tribal peoples that have been known to practice cannibalism, the act is nearly always carried out not for the sake of food, but as a ritual. Writing of some of the present-day headhunters, G. H. R. von Koenigswald has explained, "The head hunter is not content merely to possess the skull, but opens it and takes out the brain, which he eats in order by this means to acquire the wisdom and skill of his foe." From the very evidence suggesting that the first human beings ate each other, we might even conclude that they had some spiritual notion that cannibalism could increase their powers.

Conflicts between bands, if they occurred, must have been rare and unplanned in an uncrowded world that offered no natural examples of creatures systematically setting upon their own kind. It appears likely that war, greed, and cruelty were later developments. They probably came after man settled down on the land, became a more numerous species, and forged cultures that encouraged individual and group pride in possessions, territories, and beliefs, even as they fostered art, science, and humanity.

These are today's problems, of course, and there is little reason to think they afflicted *Homo erectus*. He was confronting his own challenges and, with perseverance and imagination, was solving them remarkably well. To his success we owe our flaws and triumphs.

HOLOCENE		
10,000		
		HOMO ERECTUS (circa 400,000 B.P.)
Peking man	Physical characteristics	Males just over and females just under 5 feet tall
Torralba/Ambrona and Terra Amata		Cranial capacity from 775 to 1,225 cc
Olorgesailie		More sweat glands and less hair than previous hominids
Günz glaciation		
		Heavier and thicker bones than a modern human's
Hearths at Escale		
Java man	Subsistence	Scavenged and foraged
1 million		Hunted larger animals, such as ancient elephants, than did previous hominids
PLEISTOCENE		
A. robustus and *boisei* extinct		At least in northern areas, probably hunted as a major means of getting food
Earliest Acheulian tools		Used spears and probably spheroids as weapons and the techniques of ambush and persistence hunting
	Social organization	Division of labor between the sexes and interdependence more firmly established than among previous hominids
habilis at Olduvai		
Java man at Modjokerto		Extended kinship ties, incest taboos, and exogamy probably appeared
2 million		Established temporary and permanent homes
		Probably lived in bands of 20 to 50 individuals
Earliest Oldowan tools at East Rudolf		
3 million		
PLIOCENE		*AUSTRALOPITHECUS AFRICANUS* (circa 3 million B.P.)
	Physical characteristics	Males about 4.5 to 5 feet tall; females somewhat smaller
		Cranial capacity ranging from about 435 to 685 cc
	Subsistence	Scavenged and foraged and hunted small animals in tropical regions. Primarily dependent on vegetable foods, which possibly were collected
4 million	Social organization	Division of labor between the sexes and prolonged bonds between males and females began to appear
		Lived in social groups
Early *Australopithecus*		
5 million		

HUNTING AND THE ORGANIZATION OF SOCIETY

The evolution of human society was to a great extent the result of the development of hunting to increase food resources and the expansion into the north temperate zones.

Chapter 13

The Evolution of Language

He gave man speech, and speech created thought,
Which is the measure of the universe.
PERCY BYSSHE SHELLEY, 1792–1822.
PROMETHEUS UNBOUND, II, iv, 72–73.

Speech was given to man to disguise his thoughts.
ATTRIBUTED TO CHARLES MAURICE DE TALLEYRAND,
1754–1838.

As humans' social life grew more complex, their ability to communicate must also have developed. Language, we can now see, was mankind's passport to a totally new level of social relationship and organization, the tool that allowed a human to vary expressions to meet changing conditions instead of being limited by less flexible patterns of communication, as the other primates are.

WAYS TO COMMUNICATE

When did humans learn to speak? How did they start? What did their first words sound like? Investigators have been seeking answers to questions like these for thousands of years. In ancient Egypt the pharaoh Psammetichus ordered two infants reared where they could hear no human voices. He hoped that when at last they spoke, uninfluenced by the sound of the Egyptian tongue, they would resort to their earliest ancestors' language, which he confidently presumed lurked within them. One child finally uttered something that sounded like *bekos,* or "bread" in the language of Phrygia, an ancient nation of central Asia Minor. Phrygian, said Psammetichus triumphantly, was obviously man's original tongue.

Many centuries later King James IV of Scotland tried a similar experiment with two babies. The result, he let it be known, was that his experimental subjects spoke passable Hebrew. This report must have

Early Theories of the Origins of Speech

pleased Biblical scholars of the day, for they had contended all along that Adam and Eve conversed in Hebrew. A Swede of the late seventeenth century believed otherwise: he announced that in the Garden of Eden God used Swedish, Adam Danish, and the serpent French.

As time went on, all sorts of theories sprang up concerning the origins of speech. The eighteenth-century French philosopher Jean-Jacques Rousseau envisioned a group of tongue-tied human beings getting together and stammering out more or less overnight a language they could use. Why they felt the need for one, and how they communicated with each other before they had invented the words to communicate with, Rousseau failed to mention. His contemporary, the German Romantic Johann Gottfried Herder, also espoused the notion that language was man-made, not God-instilled as most people believed. Anything so illogical, so imperfect as language could hardly be attributed to a divinity, Herder argued. But he would have none of Rousseau's ideas either. Instead, he saw language springing from the innermost nature of man, in response to an impulse to speak. Just how language took shape Herder could not say, but he imagined that it started when man began imitating sounds of the creatures around him and eventually used the imitative sounds as the words for the animals themselves. This theory, known today among those who disagree with it as the "bow-wow thesis," was followed by a number of others, similarly named and ridiculed: from the whistle-and-grunt thesis to the ouch-ouch, which claimed that language rose from exclamations of pain, pleasure, fear, surprise, and so on.

Darwin's concept of human evolution provided a new way of approaching the problem of the origin of language. Scientists now believe they have a fairly good idea of how we came to speak. Furthermore, they have some reason to believe that *Homo erectus* was the first creature to begin to depend on language for communication. Studies of animals, particularly monkeys and apes, both in the laboratory and in the wild have given an understanding of the foundation on which language is based; they have shown that there is considerably more of the ape in talkative man than most people ever stop to think about. An examination of that foundation is necessary, because understanding what communication was like before there were words helps make clear why and how language evolved and emphasizes the tremendous biological and cultural changes that it made possible.

The lower animals and insects have some intriguing ways of communicating. Honeybees, for instance, perform a kind of dance on the honeycomb that accurately transmits information about the direction, distance, and nature of a food source. Dogs and wolves use scents to communicate in addition to their barks, howls, and growls; they also use a system of visual signals that includes not only facial expression and body movement but also the position of the tail.

Communications get more complex as the social organizations of animals do, and next to ourselves the nonhuman primates have the

Communication among Animals

most intricate systems of all. Far from depending only on vocalizations, the nonhuman primates seem to rely heavily on combinations of gestures, facial expressions, and postures as well as scents and sounds. They apparently are able to lend many shades of meaning to this body-language vocabulary. Often, they use sounds as a means of calling attention to their other signals. However, there are important occasions when only sounds will do. On discovering something good to eat, for example, a monkey or ape will let out a cry of pleasure that brings the rest of the troop running; or, sensing danger, it will give a shriek that causes its companions frantically to seek shelter.

This wordless communication system serves the nonhuman primates extremely well. As social animals living in troops, they use it to keep in touch with one another at all times. More important, it enables individuals to display their feelings and to recognize at a glance the intentions and moods of others, thus averting conflict. Many of the signals used have to do with expressing the established hierarchy of dominance and submission within the troop (see Figure 13–1). A subordinate male baboon, seeing signs of aggression directed at him by a male of superior rank, backs up to the other and presents his rump in a gesture of appeasement—unless he intends to challenge the other male. Different signals, vocal and visual, keep the troop from becoming scattered when it is on the move or roaming over a territory foraging for food. Still other signals promote mating behavior or foster good mother–infant relations. A mother chimpanzee has been observed to calm her disturbed youngster simply by touching its finger lightly with hers (Figure 13–2). So complex and so delicate is this language of gesture in the chimpanzee that it cannot be said to be less evolved than our own.

Yet for all its complexity, and however well suited it may be to the chimpanzees' needs, such a communication system falls far short of human language. As far as is known, nonhuman primates in the wild cannot name specific things; they have no way of referring to their en-

Figure 13–1   A dominant male chimpanzee reassures a young male who is presenting his rump in appeasement. As a result, the younger male now feels able to turn and face his superior.

Figure 13–2   Among chimpanzees, as among humans, physical contact is the most important single means of communication between individuals. Even a touch is reassuring. This photograph is of wild chimpanzees in Tanzania.

vironment and cannot communicate thought via the complex phonetic codes—words—used by human beings. Nor do they seem able to refer to the past or future with the aid of their signals. For them, what is out of sight is out of mind.

This is not to say that the nonhuman primates' vocal signals are entirely unspecific. Some apes, for instance, indicate the desirability of the food they are eating by the intensity of their food calls. During normal feeding, chimpanzees emit food grunts; but for a favorite food they give the more excited food bark. They still cannot say "banana," of course, but they communicate something more than simply "food." Even more specialized is the danger call system of the African vervet monkeys, which have three different alarm calls for three different kinds of attackers. The vervets use a chutter for snakes, a chirp for ground-dwelling carnivores, and a *r-raup* sound to warn of birds of prey. A chirp is enough to send the vervets scrambling to the tips of branches, well out of reach of ground animals, whereas a r-raup launches them from the trees into the thickets below, where birds cannot get at them. A cry of "Watch out—eagle!" is beyond their capabilities, but it is also beyond their needs. They do not have to know whether it is an eagle or a hawk diving on them; what matters is that they get the message and flee in the right direction.

In their function, as well as in their causation, the vocal and visual signals used by the nonhuman primates can be divided into two kinds. The majority of them, and probably all their vocal signals, express inner emotional and physiological states and automatically accompany such states. They allow all members of the troop to monitor the emotional status of all other members. All signals of this sort are generated by a group of structures in the brain known as the *limbic system* (or the "emotional brain") below the level of conscious awareness, just as the human scream is generated.

Limbic and Nonlimbic Communication

In contrast to these signals, some gestures appear to communicate conscious will or intent. A chimpanzee will hold out its hand as a gesture of submissive greeting or will raise it in threat. A young baboon will anxiously present to a superior male. A mother chimpanzee will beckon her infant with her hand or repel its approach. These gestures, which are normal conscious movements, have taken on a role in communication. Because of the intentions and wishes they symbolize, they fall into a category very different from the expressions of emotion we have considered above. They are generated not by the limbic system but by the higher centers of the brain, just as human language is.

Both kinds of communication are seen in our own behavior. We, too, have a repertory of wordless signals that universally express emotions. A person has only to smile to demonstrate friendly intentions; clenched fists and jaws, scowls, and frowns are unmistakable signs of anger or disappointment; the laugh, the cry, the scream are direct expressions of inner psychological and physiological states. Humans even have acquired at least one involuntary signal the other primates do not have; this is the blush, over which most people have little or no control, but which sends a clear message about what is going on inside the brain. And when humans are most excited, they often show it by speechlessness. Such basic signals are in a different category from the many other body motions humans use, such as shaking and nodding the head, shrugging the shoulders, and clapping the hands; these are really abbreviated substitutes for spoken language and vary in meaning from one place to another.

But signals are much less important to man than they are to other animals, for they make up a much smaller part of his total communication system. Most of the information necessary for social interaction among human beings is conveyed vocally; a blind human can communicate satisfactorily. Speech, many authorities believe, is what makes humans human. Deafness from birth is tragic: because a baby born deaf cannot hear and imitate spoken words, he can learn to speak only with great difficulty, and without fluent speech he can only communicate clumsily.

The Nature of Language

Language provides a magnificently efficient and versatile system of communication. Its coded series of sounds conveys conscious thought at least ten times faster than any other method of signaling possibly can—faster than hand signs, moving pictures, or even other kinds of vocalizations. Through language a human can step outside himself and give things and people names, reflect about them and himself, and refer to them in the past and the future. Most important of all, language gives a person the capacity to share his thoughts. As Sherwood Washburn and Shirley Strum have written: "It is the communication of thought, rather than thought itself, that is unique to man, makes human cultures possible, and that is the primary factor in separating man and beast."

This insight provides one of the reasons why specialists are so sure *Homo erectus* must have had some form of language: so many of the activities he engaged in required a sharing of thought. To carry out a hunt such as that documented in the fossil evidence at Torralba–Ambrona, for instance, he must have been able to lay plans in advance; name animals, plants, and tools; identify places; and refer to both the past and future. Moreover, the division of labor that must have marked *Homo erectus'* society would have been all but impossible if men and women had been unable to communicate about their separate responsibilities or could not agree to meet at a particular spot once their food-gathering activities were over. As their society grew more complex, they would have used words to sort out family relationships and to establish ties with neighboring bands.

Furthermore, language was the new and extraordinarily efficient means by which humans acquired and passed on from one generation to the next that flexible network of learned, rather than inherited, behavior patterns that allowed them to alter their environment and adapt to new ones. This gave a simple culture a symbolic form that changed its whole nature. From this point in human evolution, culture and its medium—language—would be necessary for survival.

THE ABILITY TO SPEAK

Though it has long been clear that this watershed in evolution occurred largely because of the ability to use words to communicate symbolic meaning, it was not at all clear until recently why mankind alone, and not his intelligent close relatives among the apes, learned to speak. After all, apes have much of the vocal apparatus—lips, a tongue, and a larynx or voice box with vocal cords—that humans have. Yet as repeated experiments have shown, they cannot learn to talk as humans do.

Talking Apes?

An eighteenth-century French physician and philosopher, Julien Offroy de la Mettrie, imagined that apes were on about the same intellectual level as retarded humans and that all they needed to turn them into "perfect little gentlemen" was speech training. Not until early in the twentieth century, however, were any scientific attempts made to teach apes to talk. One couple worked with a chimpanzee called Viki, and only after six years of the most painstaking effort on their part and a great deal of frustration on hers did she manage to say, on cue, what sounded like "Mama," "Papa," "up," and "cup."

A more recent experiment, mentioned in Chapter 1, produced a more startling result. A chimpanzee named Washoe, by the age of five learned to understand more than 350 hand signals of the standard American Sign Language of the deaf (Ameslan) and to use at least 150 of them correctly (see Figure 13–3). With these, she learned to name things and express her wants and needs in terms of those names. Another chimpanzee, Sarah, learned to communicate with her keepers by selecting from a number of plastic signs, which she placed upon a magnetic

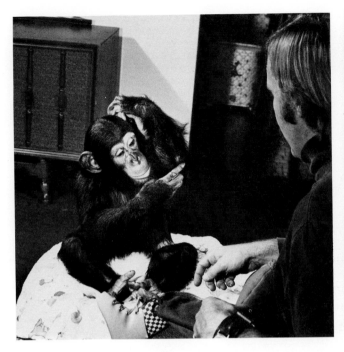 

board. A third ape is learning to communicate by pressing buttons on a keyboard. Constant training by humans enables these chimpanzees to associate visual symbols not only with objects, but also with adjectives, verbs, and even prepositions. With these symbols, the chimpanzees can construct simple sentences, which they use to express their desires. Evidently, with human help, they can learn the symbols and use a symbolic means of communication, but in all cases they do so by gesture or manipulation, rather than by means of their vocal apparatus.

Washoe's success and Viki's frustration have led to a clearer understanding of what is involved in human speech. Spoken language requires equipment, both physical and mental, that apes and monkeys simply do not have. The adult human tongue, for example, is thicker than that of the monkeys and apes, and unlike theirs, it bends in a sharp angle into the throat. In addition, the human larynx (Figure 13–4) lies farther down in the throat than the ape larynx. This means that the part of the throat above the larynx, the pharynx, is proportionately much larger in humans than in any other primates.

The pharynx serves as a combined opening for the windpipe, which goes to the lungs, and the gullet, which leads to the stomach. It is also the anchor for the base of the tongue, and it plays a fundamental part in the production of speech. For it is the pharynx that is used to modify the sounds made by the vocal cords and give them the tones that a listener recognizes as language. To provide this control, the muscles of the pharynx walls and the base of the tongue move continuously during speech, constantly and precisely varying the dimensions of the pharynx;

Figure 13–3   Two Ameslan hand signals. In the "tree" sign, one hand holds the opposite forearm upright by the elbow, and the free hand is fluttered back and forth. The sign meaning "hat" is made by first placing the hand on top of the head and then making a repeated patting motion.

The Pharynx

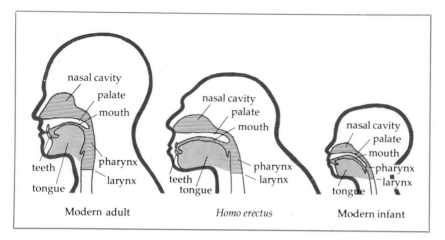

nasal cavity
palate
mouth
teeth
pharynx
tongue
larynx
Modern adult

nasal cavity
palate
mouth
teeth
pharynx
tongue
larynx
Homo erectus

nasal cavity
palate
mouth
pharynx
tongue
larynx
Modern infant

Figure 13–4 Scientists have assessed the speaking ability of *Homo erectus* by comparing the vocal apparatus of a modern adult and a baby with reconstructions of early humans. To form words, sounds must be modulated by the areas above the larynx. *Homo erectus,* however, is believed to have had a vocal tract similar to the one shown above (which was adapted from studies of Neandertal man). The larynx sits higher up in the throat than in modern adults, limiting the size of the pharynx. The tongue, being relatively long and almost entirely in the mouth rather than the throat, cannot act on the pharynx. This single-chamber system restricted *Homo erectus* to relatively slow and clumsy speech. The vocal tract of a modern newborn baby resembles *Homo erectus'* more than a modern adult's.

the greatest width of the pharynx is at least ten times its narrowest. These dimensional changes produce much the same effect on sounds that an organ achieves with its dozens of pipes of different lengths and diameters, each making a particular tone. So important is the pharynx to speech that it is quite possible to speak intelligibly without the larynx or tip of the tongue as long as the pharynx and base of the tongue are intact.

Monkeys and apes, lacking the human vocal equipment, vary the shape of only their mouths when they vocalize; there is practically no movement of the pharynx, which in them is quite rudimentary. They can produce only a certain number of distinct signal sounds—ten to fifteen in most cases—and they cannot combine them at will to form words.

The same limitation restricts the vocalization of human babies, who at birth are unable to make the vowel sounds typical of modern human speech. For at least six weeks a baby's tongue remains immobile during his cries. It rests almost entirely within his mouth, as in nonhuman primates, and the larynx sits high in his throat. This arrangement permits the baby to swallow and breathe at the same time without danger of choking. By the time he reaches the babbling stage, at around three months, the base of the tongue and the larynx have already begun to descend into the throat, enlarging the pharyngeal region. Not until then is the infant equipped physically to begin to make the speech sounds that will distinguish him from his simian ancestors.

There are other equally important reasons why human beings can talk and the nonhuman primates cannot; these reasons have to do with the brain. When a person uses his voice to communicate, he is doing more, of course, than making noise. He is codifying thought and transmitting it to others in a string of connected sounds. The coding begins in the *cerebral cortex,* the convoluted outer layer of the brain. Here there are three areas (shown in Figure 13–5) of particular importance in speech production. One is called *Broca's area.* Located toward the front

Language Centers of the Brain

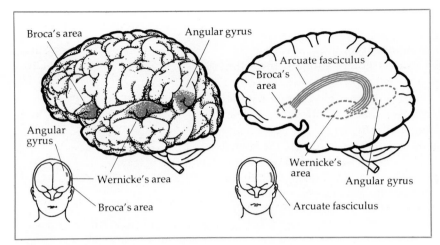

Figure 13–5 Areas of the brain cortex concerned with speech production are shown on the left. In right-handed people, speech areas occur on only the left side of the brain; in left-handed people, the speech areas are often on the right side. The drawing on the right shows the arcuate fasciculus, which links Wernicke's to Broca's areas. Wernicke's area and the angular gyrus are also involved in decoding speech.

of the brain's dominant hemisphere, it sends the code to an adjacent part of the brain controlling muscles of the face, jaw, tongue, palate, and larynx; thus it helps set the speech apparatus in operation. Injury to Broca's area produces one form of *aphasia* (loss or impairment of speech) in which articulation is slow and labored.

The second region is *Wernicke's area,* located farther back in the brain, in the temporal lobe; it is vital to the process of comprehension. Damage to Wernicke's area usually produces another form of aphasia: speech that is fluent but meaningless. A bundle of nerve fibers called the *arcuate fasciculus* apparently transmits signals from Wernicke's area to Broca's, making possible the vocal repetition of a heard and memorized word.

The third region, adjacent to Wernicke's area, is known as the *angular gyrus.* It occupies a key position at the juncture of individual portions of the cerebral cortex that are concerned with vision, hearing, and touch —the parts of the brain that receive detailed information from the world outside the body. Linked to these sensory receivers by bundles of nerve fibers, the angular gyrus operates as a kind of connecting station, permitting one type of incoming signal to be associated with others. For example, the angular gyrus makes it possible for the brain to link the visual stimulus produced by the sight of a cup with the auditory stimulus produced by a voice saying "cup" and with the tactile stimulus produced when the hand picks up the cup. The importance of these associations is clear when we think of the way children learn the words for things: when a child asks "what's that?" and is told by his parents, he matches the image of the seen object with the sound of the spoken word and thus absorbs the name for it, automatically filing the auditory note for that association in his memory bank. This process of association and memorization is the first and most basic step in the acquisition of language.

The brains of monkeys and apes are similar to humans' brains but are significantly less developed in some important areas. An ape's

The Limbic System

angular gyrus is so small that there can be very little association between information signals coming from the senses. Apparently, incoming signals are routed mainly to another part of the brain altogether: the limbic system (see Figure 13–6). All vertebrate animals, including humans, have this evolutionarily ancient region lying at the core of the brain, a kind of netherworld of neurological activity. Among other things, it activates the physical responses that go with hunger, fear, rage, and sexual activity, and it triggers the feelings that accompany these responses. If a monkey sees an enemy, for instance, the visual signal feeds into the limbic system and produces a physical reaction—the sounding of the danger call, perhaps—and also makes the animal feel fear. Similarly, sexual signals sent out by a female chimpanzee go to the limbic system of a male, causing him to feel sexually stimulated and prompting a suitable response.

In other words, information channeled to the limbic system from the outside produces an instantaneous, unthinking, adaptive response. As anthropologist Jane Lancaster has written, the limbic system "makes the animal want to do what it has to do to survive and reproduce."

Among the responses directed by the limbic system are certain vocal signals—cries of fear or pleasure, for example—which are quite distinct from language. That communication through signals like these is controlled by this part of the brain can be demonstrated by laboratory experiment. When electrodes are planted in the limbic system and related structures of a monkey and its brain is stimulated electrically, the animal responds with its repertory of cries, even though none of the situations that normally stimulate those sounds (aggressive behavior by a dominant male, food, enemies) is visible. Furthermore, other monkeys of the same species in the laboratory react to these sounds (by cringing, searching for food, taking an alert stance) just as though they were bona fide signals. Similar experiments have been performed on human subjects during brain surgery, and they react in a similar way. When the human limbic system is stimulated, the patient responds with sounds.

The sounds produced through the limbic system in both ape and human are not the sounds of speech. For that distinctive emblem of humanness it was necessary for other parts of the brain, specifically the angular gyrus and Broca's and Wernicke's areas of the cortex, to develop fully. It was in this development that emerging man left the inarticulate apes far behind.

In the cortex evolved the means of producing vocal signals that could be used to communicate intent, will, desire, just as could those gestures we referred to earlier. Language is a learned vocal and symbolic communicatory system that is cortical in origin. It can be used to refer to all kinds of objects, processes, and concepts, and indeed it is practically unlimited in its value to human society. It was probably the most important single development in human evolution, because it made possible our extraordinary cultural adaptations.

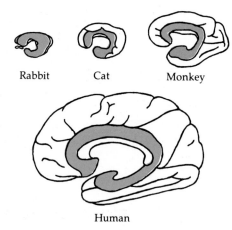

Rabbit   Cat   Monkey

Human

Figure 13–6   These drawings of the brain in partial section show the relative size of the limbic regions in different species (approximately to scale). The limbic system is the "emotional brain" in animals and humans. It is concerned with the expression and decoding of much of the nonverbal communication that plays such a big part in the social life of animals. Though it is very large and important in human beings, it is no longer the largest component of the brain as it is in other animals.

Figure 13–7   A threatening baboon displays his large canine teeth and the white areas above his eyelids. This is one response to danger: the alternative is submission or escape.

THE EVOLUTION OF SPEECH

It is obviously impossible to pinpoint the time when *Homo erectus* began to use language. In his million years on earth, he was, of course, evolving all the time; the development of speech and other human characteristics was infinitely gradual. The process may have begun long before the first man, when his ancestors started making and using tools. If *Australopithecus* had at first depended upon gestures to communicate, such hand signals would no doubt have become inadequate; the hominids literally would have had their hands full, carrying tools to chop, cut, or scrape. Thus the ability to use sounds voluntarily to attract attention and to make meaning clear would have proved a great advantage.

But in order for the process of naming things to start, the vocal apparatus had to be modified, the brain to evolve. This development must have taken hundreds of thousands of years during the evolution of *Australopithecus*. Some small mutations may have enabled *Australopithecus* to make a few voluntary sounds, giving him an edge in the competition for survival. The ability to signal one another through a more extensive repertoire of *phonemes* (speech sounds) would have been a definite advantage when *Australopithecus* creatures were gathering food or hunting. And then, as the number of phonemes grew, brain development could have permitted more precise differentiation between them and new combinations of them, so that primitive words may have taken shape. All the while the brain and vocal apparatus would have been involved in a feedback relationship with each other, changes in one fostering development of the other: the success of the cortex in forming a rudimentary sound code would have affected the vocal apparatus, and this, in turn, would have helped enlarge the speech centers of the brain, and so on until, by the time of *Homo erectus,* the rudiments of language might have appeared. At that point, the first humans were ready to begin combining a few separate sounds, or words, that represented specific elements of terrain, the hunt, the family, and seasonal changes into simple combinations that conveyed a great deal of information.

What this first human speech sounded like depends on how far the dual development of vocal apparatus and cortical brain equipment had progressed. Recent investigations have given a clue to the state of that development. Linguist Philip Lieberman has made an analysis of the character of modern speech that emphasizes the importance of man's vocal equipment. He points out that the pharynx is essential for producing the vowel sounds *a* ("ah"), *i* ("ee"), and *u* ("oo"), which are crucial to all modern languages, whether English or Kirghiz. Virtually all meaningful segments of human speech contain one or more of these sounds. Combining these vowel sounds with a wide assortment of consonants, the human vocal apparatus not only can produce an infinite number of variations but also, and more importantly, can connect them with great rapidity in the coded series of sounds that is language.

The key to this process is the putting together of separate phonetic segments into a sound that can be understood as one word. When a man says the word *bat,* for instance, he does not articulate the fragments of sound represented by the letters *b, a,* and *t;* rather he combines these elements into a single syllable. This ability to combine sounds gives the voice the ability to put together and transmit upward of thirty phonetic segments a second.

Had the pharynx developed enough in *Homo erectus* to produce the complex sounds characteristic of modern speech? Lieberman thinks not. He places *Homo erectus'* speech at a much cruder level, basing this opinion on a fascinating piece of detective work carried out with the aid of anatomist Edmund S. Crelin. Much of this work involved fossils and reconstructions of *Homo erectus'* descendant, the type of *Homo sapiens* called Neandertal man, but Lieberman feels the conclusions can be used to assess the development of *Homo erectus* as well. The two scientists compared the skulls of newborn modern human babies, modern apes, and Neandertal man. They found many likenesses; indeed, in some important ways, the babies' skulls were more similar to those of apes and early man than they were to those of modern human adults.

To obtain detailed information about the all-important pharyngeal region located at the base of the skull, Crelin reconstructed the vocal tracts of several fossil Neandertal people. Taking into account the an-

Lieberman and Crelin: The Vocal Apparatus

atomical similarities in the skulls of Neandertal man, modern apes, and human infants, Crelin was able to estimate the position of the larynx in the throats of his fossil humans: it was placed much higher than it is now. He then proceeded to reconstruct in modeling clay early man's pharyngeal, nasal, and oral cavities. Then Lieberman measured the reconstructed vocal tracts. Relating these measurements to the dimensions of the vocal tract of modern humans and its sound-making capabilities, he fed the figures into a computer programmed to calculate the resonances that corresponded to the range of shapes each vocal tract could have produced.

The results suggested that an undeveloped pharynx would have prevented early man from making the quick shifts in pronunciation that modern humans can make; he would have been incapable of using the key vowels *a, i,* and *u* in rapid combinations. Lieberman and Crelin concluded that early humans would have had to communicate verbally much more slowly than modern people—perhaps even as slowly as one tenth the speed we can maintain.

Krantz: The Brain

This assessment of early man's limited facility in language is complemented by another theory addressed to an entirely different matter. Anthropologist Grover Krantz confronted a problem that has puzzled anthropologists for a long time: why did the quality of *Homo erectus'* stone tools remain so static for so long? Over a period of many thousands of years, no matter where found, they show little sign of improvement, as though all had somehow been made with an unchanging ancient model in mind. Why did they not become more sophisticated as time went on? Krantz has posed an ingenious explanation that possibly sheds light on the acquisition of language by the first humans. He suggests that *Homo erectus'* brain was not well enough developed to allow him to begin to speak until much later in his life than a child does today. And because *Homo erectus* was short-lived, he therefore had a shorter period in which to use his language to acquire and augment the skills necessary for toolmaking.

Krantz bases his conclusions about speech and toolmaking on studies of brain size. Taking a brain volume of 750 cubic centimeters as the dividing line between mankind and his predecessors, Krantz wondered why modern human brains should now average about 1,330 cubic centimeters, a 65 percent increase over the cranial capacity of *Homo erectus* (which, in turn, was a 100 percent increase over *Australopithecus'* cranial capacity). In pondering that question, Krantz turned to the growth pattern of modern human brains. By the end of the first year of a baby's life, its brain reaches 750 cubic centimeters. This capacity, Krantz suggests, represents the threshold for speech; within half a year after that, the normal child begins to talk. Drawing a hypothetical curve of *Homo erectus'* brain development from infancy to childhood, Krantz showed that the 750-cubic-centimeter size critical to speech may not have been achieved until after the sixth year. Prior to age six, he argues, *Homo erectus* apparently did not have a big enough brain to be able to speak. His mental growth, if not his physical maturity, could have lagged about five years behind that of a modern human child. Krantz theorizes:

When reproductive age was reached, [*Homo erectus*] had no more than seven years of cultural experience, whereas when the modern man reaches reproductive maturity he has at least twelve years of cultural experience. Age estimates of known fossil men indicate a very low life expectancy. . . . Five years would be an appreciable portion of the lives of most individuals. This shorter period of full cultural participation would limit the total quantity and complexity of cultural content that is likely to be transmitted in each generation.

Even with the speech limitations proposed by Krantz and Lieberman, *Homo erectus* still would have been able to communicate a great deal about himself and the world around him. It is necessary only to listen to very young children to see how effective language in its simplest form can be. Between the ages of 18 and 24 months, only half a year or so after a child says his first words, he begins to use two-word sentences. They are neither copies of grown-up speech nor reductions of it, but the child's own inventions, conforming to what would seem to be native, universal rules of grammar. They are made up of so-called *open words,* words that can be said by themselves and still mean something, such as the nouns "blanket," "milk," and "baby"; and *pivot words,* often prepositions, adjectives, or verbs such as "on" and "hot." The child puts his words together to describe the world or to get people to act ("pajama on"), but not to express emotion.

Speech among the First Humans

Only when the child is three or four does he consistently begin to put feelings into words. Before then he relies, as the nonhuman primates must, on the workings of the limbic system to call attention to his needs. Rather than say "I'm angry," or "I'm afraid," he demonstrates physically how angry or afraid he is. He finds temper tantrums, whimpering, or crying a much easier way to communicate; that is, he finds emotions easier to act out than to explain. As any parent knows, children have little difficulty in making themselves understood. There is no reason to think that *Homo erectus,* speaking even the simplest of sentences reinforced by gestures and hand signals, could not have communicated just as well with his early version of human speech.

Whatever it sounded like, and at whatever age he began to use it, *Homo erectus'* language was a tool used in its own right—a tool to drive like a wedge into the environment, hurrying the split from nature that marked his development and foreshadowed ours. For the first time in human history, cultural evolution began to outpace biological evolution as instinct and emotion were counterbalanced by custom and thought.

HOLOCENE

10,000

Peking man

Elephant butchery

Günz glaciation
Hearths at Escale
Java man

1 million — **PLEISTOCENE**

A. robustus and
boisei extinct

Earliest Acheulian tools

habilis at Olduvai

2 million

Earliest Oldowan
tools

3 million —

PLIOCENE

4 million —

Early *Australopithecus*

5 million

AGE	MODERN HUMAN
Birth to 6 weeks	Tongue immobile during cries and larynx high in throat
6 weeks to 3 months	Base of tongue and larynx have begun to descend in the throat
	Babbling
1 to 1½ years	Cranial capacity of about 750 cc
	Begins speaking
1½ to 2 years	Uses two-word sentences
3 to 4 years	Consistently expresses feelings in words
Adult	Cranial capacity of 1,000 to 2,000 cc
	Larynx low in the throat, enlarging the pharyngeal region
	Through speech, normally able to convey thought at least ten times faster than would be possible by any other form of signaling

AGE	*HOMO ERECTUS* (circa 400,000 B.P.)
6 years	Cranial capacity reaches what is probably the threshold of speech—750 cc
Adult	Cranial capacity ranging from about 775 to 1,225 cc
	Larynx higher in the throat than it is in modern humans and pharyngeal region therefore smaller
	Probably incapable of using *a, i,* and *u* in rapid combinations, so communicated much more slowly than modern humans do

AGE	*AUSTRALOPITHECUS AFRICANUS* (circa 3 million B.P.)
6 years	Cranial capacity about 400 cc
	Probably entirely dependent on limbic nonverbal communication
Adult	Cranial capacity ranging from 435 to 685 cc
	Limbic communication paramount but first voluntary sounds of cortical origin probably appearing in certain populations

EVOLUTION OF LANGUAGE

Statements about the evolution of language are necessarily merely informed guesses, but they are based on a wide range of evidence.

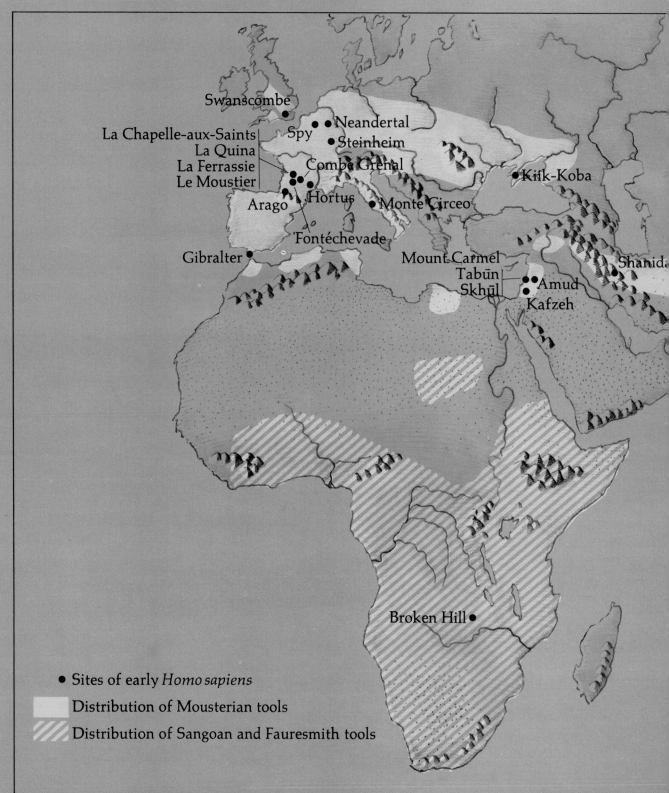

PART FOUR

Swanscombe

La Chapelle-aux-Saints
La Quina
La Ferrassie
Le Moustier

Spy

Neandertal

Steinheim

Combe Grenal

Hortus

Arago

Monte Circeo

Kiik-Koba

Fontéchevade

Gibralter

Mount Carmel
Tabūn
Skhūl

Amud

Kafzeh

Shanida

Broken Hill

• Sites of early *Homo sapiens*

Distribution of Mousterian tools

Distribution of Sangoan and Fauresmith tools

EARLY HOMO SAPIENS

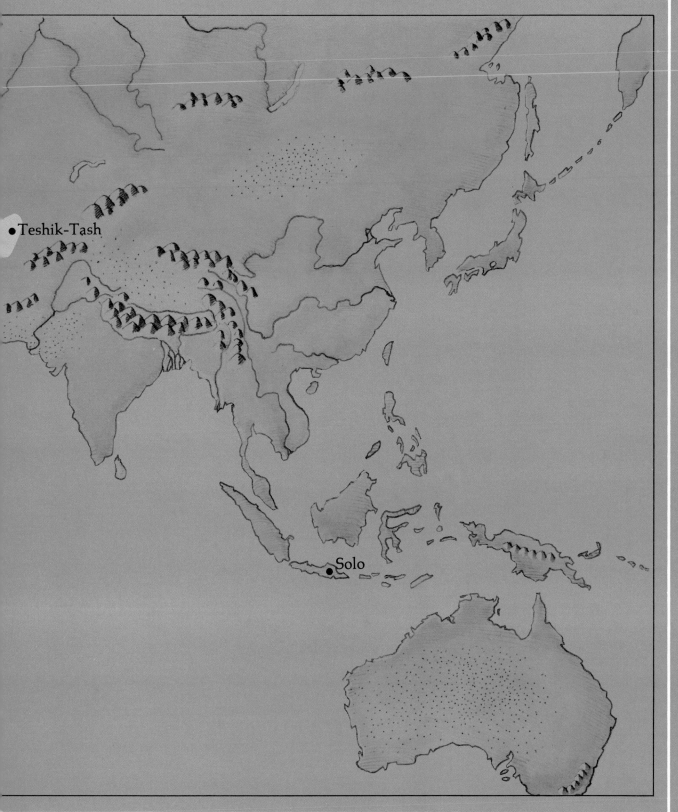

●Teshik-Tash

Solo

Chapter 14

Discovery of Neandertal

And the life of man, solitary, poore, nasty, brutish, and short.
THOMAS HOBBES, 1588–1679.
LEVIATHAN, Pt. 1, Ch. 13.

Of all the different kinds of prehistoric peoples, certainly the one who projects the clearest image is Neandertal man. For many of us he *is* Stone Age man, a shambling, beetle-browed lout who prowled the earth during the time of the glaciers. We picture him living in a snow-choked world, wearing ragged furs, speaking in grunts, and occasionally pausing to bat Neandertal woman over the head with a club before dragging her back to his cave. The reason for the persistence of this unattractive image of a life nasty, brutish, and short may lie partly in the fact that there is some truth in it. Neandertals were more primitive than we are (in some ways), they did live in cold climates (sometimes), they probably wore skins (sometimes), and they lived in caves (sometimes). That is the way they were first presented to us and that is the way they are remembered.

The Neandertals got such a poor reputation among the general public because they were grievously misjudged by the experts. Until recently, many paleoanthropologists regarded Neandertals as a brutish breed that at best represented an insignificant side branch of the human family tree. Only now is this misjudgment being remedied: there is much new evidence to demonstrate that some Neandertals, perhaps all of them, were our immediate ancestors. From 100,000 years ago to about 40,000 years ago they greatly expanded the regions occupied by

FIRST VIEWS OF NEANDERTAL

man, devised ingenious stone tools to exploit nature, developed a complicated society, and opened the door onto the world of the supernatural. Clearly, they were ancestors of great accomplishments.

Why did the experts misjudge the Neandertals? Many reasons could be given—the scarcity of fossils, errors in reconstructing bone fragments, and other technical difficulties. But perhaps more important, these problems were compounded by an accident of timing. The first fossil skull ever to be positively identified as belonging to ancient man was that of a Neandertal. It appeared midway through the nineteenth century, at a critical moment in intellectual history when old but comfortable ideas about the human past were beginning to fall apart and new but shocking ideas, such as evolution, were coming in. The old ideas could not explain the Neandertals. The new ones, which could, were generally unwelcome and almost always poorly understood. Thus, no one was prepared for the sight of a primitive-looking skeleton in the human closet, and when such a skeleton was found in Germany in 1856 (see Chapter 4), it brought on a crippling case of ancestor-blindness. Having nothing with which to compare the first Neandertal skull except the skull of a modern man, scientists of the time were struck more by the differences between the two than by their similarities. Today the reverse is true. Compared to an early *Australopithecus,* who was little different from a two-legged ape, a Neandertal man is a model of evolutionary refinement. He might be a little shorter than the average modern Westerner, and considerably heavier-featured, squatter, and more muscular than most, but in all important ways he is well on his way toward modernity.

The Discovery of Neandertal (1856)

As we described in Chapter 4, Neandertal man first turned up not far from the city of Dusseldorf, Germany, where a tributary stream of the Rhine flows through a steep-sided gorge known as the Neander Valley, "Neanderthal" in Old German. In 1856 the flanks of the gorge were being quarried for limestone. During the summer, workmen blasted open a small cave about sixty feet above the stream. As they dug their pickaxes into the floor of the cave, they uncovered a number of ancient bones. But the quarrymen were intent on limestone; they did not pay much attention to the bones, and most of what was probably a complete skeleton of a Neandertal was lost. Only the skullcap, ribs, part of the pelvis, and some limb bones were saved.

The owner of the quarry thought that these fragments belonged to a bear, and he presented them to the local science teacher, J. K. Fuhlrott, who was known to be interested in such things. Fuhlrott had enough knowledge of anatomy to realize that the skeletal remains came not from a bear but from a most extraordinary man. The thickness of the limbs and the heavy, slanted brow of the skullcap seemed very ancient to him. In an attempt to account for the apparent antiquity and odd location of the relics, he concluded that they belonged to some poor mortal who had been washed into the cave by Noah's flood.

Knowing that this judgement was bound to be disputed, Fuhlrott called in an expert, Hermann Schaaffhausen, professor of anatomy at the University of Bonn. Schaaffhausen agreed that the bones represented one of the "most ancient races of man." He had in mind an age of no more than a few thousand years; the fossil fragments could have come, he suggested, from some barbarian who had lived in northern Europe before the Celtic and Germanic tribes arrived.

Schaaffhausen can hardly be faulted for missing the truth about the bones from the Neander Valley. As we saw in Chapter 4, the scientific community of 1856 did not realize that humankind had been on earth for a substantial length of time. And no respectable scientist believed that humans had ever existed in any form other than that of modern man. Such a notion would have been directly contrary to the scheme known as the Chain of Being, a grandly conceived hierarchy for all living things. In it, every creature had a rank: starting with the lowliest worm, the hierarchy progressed steadily upward through ever more advanced species and finally reached the pinnacle of nature, man himself. Creatures positioned close to each other on this chain naturally showed some similarities; even man admittedly resembled apes in his outward form. But similarity between types of creatures did not mean that there was any genealogical connection. The separate links of the Chain of Being were thought to have been fixed forever at the Creation; species never changed and certainly never evolved from lowlier forms.

This orderly scheme still held in 1856, but it was being shaken by the appearance of animal bones unlike those of any living creatures, suggesting to some dissenting thinkers that the Chain of Being did not tell the full story of life. Extinct animals were not the only threat to the established scheme. A few primitive-looking human fossils are on record as having been found as early as the year 1700, and many finds probably went unrecorded before that. What are now known to be Neandertal remains had been uncovered in Belgium in 1829 and on the north face of Gibralter in 1848. However, unlike the bones from the Neander Valley, these finds received no publicity, and science was not forced to grapple with their significance. When Charles Darwin's *On the Origin of Species* was published in 1859, the tidy scheme of the Chain of Being was undone, and the way was open for the recognition of fossilized human ancestors of intermediate form.

We have seen (Chapter 4) what a range of responses was elicited by the discovery of the Neandertal fossils in 1856. T. H. Huxley, who was the first to accept Darwin's new theory, recognized the apelike characteristics of the skull. Nevertheless, in view of its large cranial capacity, he did not see it as an ancestral form and wrote: "in no sense can the Neanderthal bones be regarded as the remains of a human being intermediate between men and apes."

Only William King, professor of anatomy at Queen's College in Galway, Ireland, accepted the fossil as an extinct form of humanity. In 1864 King suggested that the specimen be placed in a separate species, *Homo neanderthalensis*. In giving the fossil the genus name of *Homo,* King was acknowledging a general similarity to humankind; but

Missing Links in the Chain of Being

Homo neanderthalensis?

he felt that he could not add the species name for modern man, *sapiens*, because, as he wrote, "The Neanderthal skull is so eminently simian ... I am constrained to believe that the thoughts and desires which once dwelt within it never soared beyond those of the brute."

King's assessment was closer to being correct than anyone else's, but he changed his thinking when he heard what the anatomist Rudolf Virchow had to say. In a closely reasoned paper, Virchow stated that the man from the Neander Valley was not ancient at all, but a modern man who had suffered from rickets in childhood and arthritis in old age. And, at some time during his life, had received several stupendous blows on the head. This pronouncement, coming from such a respected source, effectively silenced all further speculation.

How could authorities such as Rudolf Virchow conclude that the Neandertal bones were modern? The incompleteness of the fossil was one factor: because the skull lacked a face and a jaw, it was hard to tell what the original owner had looked like. Also, as we have seen, no one could say for certain that the Neandertal bones were really old since no stone tools nor bones of extinct animals had accompanied the fossil, and no reliable methods of dating existed. Without proof of great age, it was thought best to err on the side of caution and presume a date not too remote from the present. It would not be fair to indict the cautious scientists of the day for inclining toward the safest position. Those who accepted the theories of Darwin were open-minded by any standard. It took a large measure of intellectual courage to surrender the accepted wisdom of centuries for Darwin's brave new world of evolution.

The Darwinists, to their great credit, were actively interested in discovering a primitive human ancestor from the moment that *On the Origin of Species* appeared. But they had no way of knowing where to look. Huxley, a bold and brilliant man, believed that there was little hope of finding fossils that would reveal human evolutionary history. Some of the evolutionists did not even think that it was necessary to peer into the past. They believed that the present offered examples of human beings who were intermediate between themselves and some primitive ancestral form. One presumed authority pointed to mental institutions: "I do not hesitate to uphold ... that microcephali and born idiots present as perfect a series from man to ape as may be wished for." Although such surmises received only slight approval, they do suggest one reason for the lack of understanding of the evolutionary significance of Neandertal man. Scientists evidently did not expect evolutionary intermediates to turn up in a cave and so they never really gave the evidence a fair chance.

As soon as Virchow had announced that the odd appearance of the bones from the Neander Valley was a result of disease rather than antiquity, the fossil ceased to disturb scientists. They simply forgot about it. Prehistorians, however, were still very interested in finding an ancient fossil ancestor of *Homo sapiens*—on condition. The fossil had to look like a modern human; anything that resembled an animal ancestor, an ape or monkey, was rejected almost automatically.

In 1886, additional primitive-looking fossils appeared. A cave near a town called Spy in Belgium (see page 290) yielded two skeletons. One skull, probably from a female, was reminiscent of the original fossil from the Neander Valley in Germany, although the cranium was higher and the forehead somewhat less slanted. The other skull was virtually identical to the German find (see Figure 14–1). Coincidence? Yes, said Rudolf Virchow, dismissing the Spy skeletons as further diseased specimens of modern humans. But this explanation began to sound hollow. Not only was such a coincidence of pathological deformity most unlikely, but these fossils were definitely very old, as indicated by primitive stone tools and remains of extinct animals found with them. Most scientists were obliged to admit that an archaic people, distinct from modern man, had indeed lived in Europe during some bygone era.

The fossil skeletons found at Spy lacked some parts, but they were complete enough to serve as models for a rough sketch of the Neandertal race. These people were short and thickset. Their heads were long and low, with large brow ridges. Their faces were massive and protruding, with a heavy jaw but a receding chin. Could these have been our ancestors? Nearly all scientists said no. They were willing to give Neandertal a place on the human family tree but not on a branch shared by modern humanity. Some authorities felt that the Neandertals might represent an offshoot from the main evolutionary line; if they were related to true humans at all, they were poor and distant relatives.

By this time the initial shocked reaction to Darwin's theory of evolution was over, and the disturbing idea that human beings had been around for tens or hundreds of thousands of years was becoming accepted. The fossils from Spy indicated that the Neandertals were ancient peoples, not modern ones deformed by disease. And Dubois' discovery of small-brained *Pithecanthropus* (Chapter 10) helped put the Neandertals in perspective. Although most experts were not yet willing to trace our lineage through a Neandertal stage of evolution, their belief that humankind could never have looked so primitive as a Neandertal was now recognized as perhaps a subjective feeling, and thus open to debate. But at this point, when the riddle of human ancestry seemed about to be solved, new evidence appeared that was to muddle the problem considerably.

In the first decade of the twentieth century, paleoanthropologists were at work in the Dordogne region of southwestern France. From the 1860s on, countless stone tools had been found in southwestern France, proof that the Dordogne had been a population center in ancient times. Beginning in the year 1908 a magnificent series of Neandertal fossils was also discovered. One of the first to turn up was the skeleton of an old man in a cave near the village of La Chapelle-aux-Saints. A nearby cave at Le Moustier, from which quantities of stone implements had been excavated earlier, yielded the skeleton of a Neandertal youth. A rock shelter at La Ferassie produced adult male and female Neandertals

Discoveries at Spy (1886)

Figure 14–1 The skull of Spy I, though incomplete, shows clearly the long head and brow ridges typical of Neandertals.

La Chapelle-aux-Saints and Other Finds (1908)

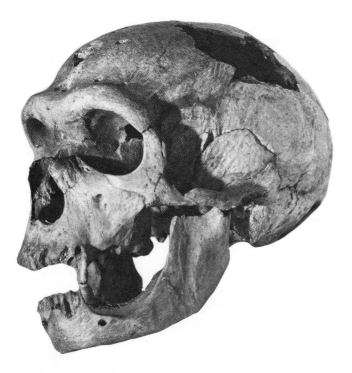

Figure 14–2   The skull of the old man of La Chapelle-aux-Saints shows he lost many teeth during life. He was less than 5 feet tall, bent by arthritis, but he had a large cranial capacity of about 1,600 cc (the average modern human capacity is 1,330 cc).

and later the remains of several children (see Figure 14–3). Another rock shelter at La Quina held parts of several Neandertal skeletons.

The great value of this material was its completeness. The bones from Spy had given a rough portrait of the Neandertal people, but as long as the fossil record remained essentially fragmentary, venturesome scholars could leap to extremes and see them as either *Homo sapiens* or gorillas. The wealth of skeletal material from southwestern France now seemed to promise enough data to set the vividest anthropological imagination to rest. Now scientists would be able to study the physical resemblances—or lack of them—between Neandertals and modern humans.

The man from La Chapelle-aux-Saints was selected for a detailed reconstruction of a typical Neandertal. The task of rebuilding the skeleton fell to a French paleontologist named Marcellin Boule, of the French National Museum of Natural History. On this project, Boule had an unusually fine set of bones to work with. The materials were well preserved, and although some of the bones were broken, almost everything of importance was available except some teeth and vertebrae. Yet Boule proceeded to commit an astonishing series of errors—and they were not corrected for decades. Boule misconstructed the bones to make Neandertal man appear much like an ape from head to toe (see Figure 14–4). He mistakenly arranged the foot bones so that the big toe diverged from the other toes like an opposable thumb; this feature presumably forced Neandertal man to walk on the outer part of his feet, like an ape. Boule's interpretation of the knee joint was equally incor-

Boule's Reconstruction (1911–1913)

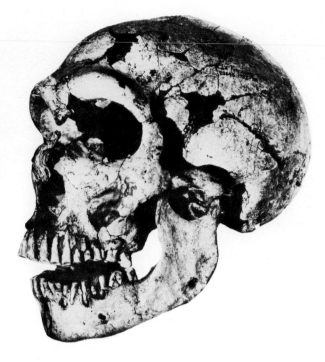

Figure 14–3 The male skeleton from La Ferrassie, buried with five others, had an even larger cranial capacity than La Chapelle—1,640 cc. His front teeth show a rare type of extreme wear that is found today among some Eskimo tribes and other hunting peoples. It may have been caused by chewing animal skins to soften them for clothing.

Figure 14–4 Marcellin Boule overlooked the effects of arthritis when he reconstructed the skeleton from La Chapelle-aux-Saints and so implied that all Neandertal people walked with stooping gait and bended knees.

rect: he declared that the Neandertal could not fully extend his leg, and this resulted in the bent-knee gait that observers could readily see the skeleton would adopt if it could walk. In every respect, the posture of Boule's reconstruction seemed nonhuman. The spine lacked the curves that allow modern people to stand upright. Atop this misshapen spine, the head thrust so far forward that Boule's Neandertal must have felt obliged now and then to use his arms in order not to fall on his face.

The most devastating conclusion of Boule's study focused on the intelligence of the man from La Chapelle-aux-Saints. Boule ignored the fossil's large cranial capacity. He looked only at the long, low skull— and perceived severe mental retardation. He cited the interior of the skull as support for this judgement; measuring the space behind the retreating forehead, the paleontologist determined to his satisfaction that there was not much room for the frontal portion of the brain, which was then thought (incorrectly) to be the center of higher intelligence. So Boule ranked the fossil man's brainpower somewhere between that of apes and modern humans, but closer to the apes.

Boule wrote disparagingly of the "brutish appearance of this muscular and clumsy body, and of the heavy-jawed skull that declares the predominance of a purely vegetative or bestial kind over the functions of the mind. . . . What a contrast with the men of the next period, the men who had a more elegant body, a finer head, an upright and spacious brow, and who were the first to merit the glorious title of *Homo sapiens!*" Boule was willing to grant the Neandertals the honor of the genus *Homo,* but he relegated them to a separate, aberrant species that had died out long ago.

Marcellin Boule was a man of excellent reputation and formidable diligence, virtues that made his errors all the more serious. Between 1911 and 1913, he published his conclusions in three exhaustive volumes. Packed with detail and ringing with confidence, these monographs had tremendous influence on scientists and the public alike. Although a small minority of prehistorians stuck to their view that Neandertals were respectable ancestors of modern humans, practically everyone now felt that such a lineage had been proved impossible.

The sheer force of Boule's work was not the only reason for its acceptance. Some circumstantial evidence pointed toward an evolutionary gap between the Neandertals and the later Cro-Magnons, those elegant "men of the next period" to whom Boule refers, who, as we saw in Chapter 4, by this time were acknowledged to be immediate ancestors of present-day humans. Even if the Neandertals were not quite so debased as Boule supposed, they definitely looked different from the Cro-Magnons, and no one had come across a fossil that indicated an evolutionary transition between the Neandertals and such a handsome, modern-looking human being as Cro-Magnon. Without an intermediate fossil, it was only prudent to assume that the Cro-Magnons derived from stock that had been occupying Europe or some other part of the world during or possibly before the era of the Neandertals.

Furthermore, archaeologists believed that there was no cultural connection between the Neandertal and Cro-Magnon peoples. The stone tools of the Cro-Magnons (to be discussed in Chapters 17 and 18) seemed markedly more sophisticated than the Neandertal implements. And when archaeologists dug down through successive layers in caves, they sometimes found sterile layers between the Neandertal deposits and the deposits left by Cro-Magnons, indicating that no one had occupied the cave for a time. These layers containing no sign of human occupation were interpreted as proof that the Neandertals had become extinct without having given rise to the Cro-Magnons.

Figure 14–5 The full reconstructions of Neandertal were even more misleading. The hunched shoulders and apelike posture are quite incorrect; worse still is the bovine expression, for the Neandertal people were of considerable intelligence.

During the decades after Boule's study, very little was said in support of the European Neandertals as human ancestors. His analysis not only won almost universal acceptance but also inspired some views even less flattering than his own. For example, the noted anatomist Elliot Smith wrote in the 1920s of the "uncouth and repellent Neandertal man" whose "nose is not sharply separated from the face, the two being merged in what in another animal would be called a snout." Smith further noted that Neandertal man was not only marred by a "coarse face" and a "peculiarly ungraceful form" but probably had "a shaggy covering of hair over most of the body." Despite the clearly human formation of the Neandertal hand, Smith claimed that it "lacked the delicacy and nicely balanced cooperation of thumb and fingers which is regarded as one of the most distinctive human characteristics."

Anthropology textbooks began to depict Neandertals with the slumped, bent-knee posture that Boule had presented. This stance put the creature's center of gravity in front of his center of support; by all

Other Views of the "Grisly Folk"

laws of physics he should have fallen flat on his face. Some textbook illustrators averted the danger by showing a Neandertal taking a long stride forward; presumably he had to keep walking to stay upright. Popular writers hardly exercised more restraint. In a short story entitled *The Grisly Folk and Their War with Men,* H. G. Wells offered this portrait of a Neandertal: "Hairy or grisly, with a big face like a mask, great brow ridges and no forehead, clutching an enormous flint and running like a baboon, with his head forward and not like a man with his head up, he must have been a fearsome creature for our forefathers to come upon." The Neandertal vocabulary, according to Wells, consisted mainly of the word "ugh." Predictably enough, the tale ended with the violent death of these brutes.

Boule had depicted Neandertals as creatures that might have had a hard time surviving, much less thriving, in the world. But if territorial range was any measure of success, these "grisly folk" seemed to have done quite well. As the years passed, Neandertal fossils were found all over Europe, from Rumania and the Crimea in the east to the western lands of Spain and the Channel island of Jersey. Still, as long as there was no evidence of them outside Europe, they could be written off as a localized evolutionary aberration. Prehistorians safely could claim that the main line of human evolution belonged elsewhere, in a still-unlocated Eden. (This problem-dodging tactic has been called the "over there" school of prehistory.)

But the grisly folk would not stay put. In 1921 some laborers who were mining lead and zinc ore in Northern Rhodesia (now Zambia), thousands of miles from Europe, uncovered a skull and other human bones that resembled Neandertals. The fossil fragments came from a cave in a knoll called Broken Hill (see page 290), which rose above plateau country just north of the Zambesi River. There were few clues to the actual date of the new find, but the presence of stone tools and extinct animal bones indicated considerable age.

This fossil man from Broken Hill had a heavy skull and receding forehead like the European Neandertals. The ridge of bone over the eyes was even more pronounced than any yet seen. But he also had a progressive trait: his limb bones were straighter and more slender than those of the European Neandertals were supposed to be.

The newly discovered fossil (shown in Figure 14–6) was named "Rhodesian man." Where did he fit into human evolution? Some scholars, echoing Virchow, proclaimed that he was a modern-day mortal deformed by disease. A British expert entrusted with the job of describing the bones for his fellow scientists went to the opposite extreme. Following Boule's example, he declared that the formation of the pelvis "leaves no doubt that the gait of Rhodesian Man was simian, and that he walked with a stoop." He considered the creature "nearer to the Chimpanzee and Gorilla than was Neandertal Man."

DISCOVERY OF NON-EUROPEAN NEANDERTALS

Rhodesian Man

Figure 14–6 People somewhat similar to the European Neandertal tribes flourished during the same period in Africa. This skull from Broken Hill, in Zambia, is exceptionally powerfully built. The hole in the temporal bone was probably caused during life by a small tumor.

Many scientists, however, believed that this man was an African version of the Neandertal type. They began to wonder if some other members of the breed had lived in Asia. A positive answer was soon forthcoming. During 1931–1932, fragments of eleven individuals were dug from the banks of the Solo River in Java, the Southeast Asian home of *Homo erectus.* The fossils, collectively named "Solo man," consisted of several skulls that were almost perfect but lacked their bases and faces, and other bones that were badly shattered. There were enough fragments to suggest a kinship with the Neandertals, although the thickness of the skulls suggested an even earlier evolutionary level.

The gap between Java and Europe was filled in by another find in the desolate Bajsun-Tau Mountains of south-central Russia, about seventy-eight miles south of the city of Samarkand. A cave in a cliff called Teshik-Tash (the Pitted Rock) yielded the fossilized remains of a boy who was clearly a Neandertal.

During the early 1930s a joint Anglo-American expedition was looking for fossils in what is now Israel, then called Palestine. The expedition had extraordinarily good luck in two caves on the slopes of Mount Carmel, overlooking the Mediterranean near Haifa. The first find, at Mugharet et-Tabūn (Cave of the Oven), was a female skeleton, definitely Neandertal but possessing a skull slightly higher than usual and a more vertical forehead (see Figure 14–7). A second Mount Carmel site, Mugharet es-Skhūl (Cave of the Kids), yielded remains of ten individuals. Some resembled Neandertals; others looked somewhat more advanced, and one approached the appearance of modern humans. This last individual displayed a trace of the thick Neandertal brow ridge, but the forehead was steeper, the jaw more delicate, the chin more pronounced, and the shape of the cranium distinctly modern. Today we have further important discoveries from Israel: a rather Neandertal-looking skeleton from Amud (north of the Sea of Galilee) and another thirteen more modern-looking skeletons from Kafzeh (south of Nazareth). Again the variation exhibited is striking. These

The Asian Fossils

Discoveries from Israel

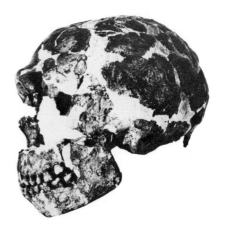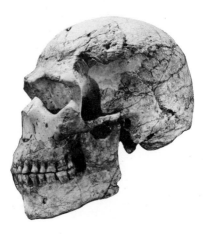

Figure 14–7 On the left is the skull of the woman from the cave of et-Tabūn on the slopes of Mount Carmel, who shares many of the features of the Western European Neandertal people. On the right is skull No. 5 from the neighboring cave of es-Skhūl. This male skull shows more modern features than the earlier one at et-Tabūn: the chin is more pronounced, the forehead steeper, and the brow ridges lighter.

and other similar fossil-bearing sites appear to span a period from about 70,000 B.P. to 40,000 B.P.

The total impression left by these people is that they occupied an evolutionary middle ground between the Neandertals and modern humans. But the assumption that all Neandertals belonged to a dead-end species was, by the 1930s, so deeply entrenched that most experts could not believe that the Mount Carmel specimens were direct ancestors of people living today. Some anthropologists concluded that the fossil people from Palestine were hybrids—products of interbreeding between true Neandertals and true modern-type people who lived somewhere in the same area. The children of such a union could be expected to show a blend of primitive and modern traits. Scientists who favored this view were quick to maintain that such interbreeding may have been rare and need not have affected the main course of human evolution; Louis Leakey suggested that any mating between Neandertals and modern-type people might well have produced sterile offspring, like a mule born of a horse–donkey mating.

SEARCH FOR THE ORIGINS OF MODERN HUMANS

All those who relegated Neandertals to a side branch of human evolution believed (and some still believe) that modern human beings existed somewhere on earth during the Neandertal era. A few scientists suggested that *Homo sapiens* existed millions of years ago. Most authorities, however, dated the origin of humans like ourselves to 200,000 or 300,000 years ago. They believed that early "true human beings" waited in the wings all through the heyday of the Neandertals, biding their time in an unknown land. Then, between 30,000 and 40,000 years ago, the true human supposedly leaped into the evolutionary spotlight, either killing off the Neandertals or allowing them to succumb to their own ineptitude.

If modern man existed so long ago, where was he hiding? Generations of scholars have devoted their careers to a search for a very ancient but modern-looking ancestor. Marcellin Boule, for one, presented two fossils as proof of the great antiquity of modern man. One, found in Italy, was called "Grimaldi man"; the other was "Piltdown man," from England. A recent analysis of the Grimaldi site has shown that the fossil is actually of rather recent vintage, postdating the Neandertals. The explanation for Piltdown man is simpler—and, as we have seen, considerably more embarrassing to those who had believed in him.

The Swanscombe and Steinheim Skulls (1933–1936)

The fossil that came closest to proving the early origin of modern man was a skull discovered in some gravel deposits in the Thames Valley, near the village of Swanscombe, England. Detailed geological knowledge about that part of England and the animal fossils found above and below the skull in a number of ancient terraces along the river enabled scientists to assign the Swanscombe fossil an approximate date of 200,000 to 300,000 years B.P. The skull consists of only three

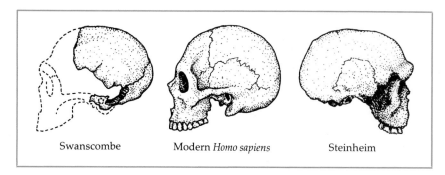

Swanscombe   Modern *Homo sapiens*   Steinheim

Figure 14–8 The Swanscombe and Steinheim skulls compared with the skull of a modern human being. The form of the back of the skull is quite comparable; the differences lie in the face.

bones from the roof and the back of the head. These appeared to fall within the range of variation of modern *Homo sapiens:* their size, their proportions, and particularly their curves are much the same as a modern human's (see Figure 14–8), and they definitely are not those of *Homo erectus* nor those of Neandertal man.

Inasmuch as science for many years regarded Neandertal man as much more primitive than ourselves, the modern-looking yet ancient Swanscombe fragments were obviously a gift for those who saw all the Neandertal fossils as representing a separate branch of hominid evolution. A fascinating alternative solution begins to suggest itself if we now turn to another skull, which had been discovered at Steinheim, in Germany, in 1933. This, too, has been dated with great care, and its age appears to be approximately the same as Swanscombe man's. The shape of the back of its head is also similar. What Steinheim man adds to the picture is a face, for the front of his skull has been preserved. It is not modern. It has quite heavy brow ridges and a low forehead that are neither quite primitive enough to fall within the range of variation of *Homo erectus* nor advanced enough to fall within the range of variation of modern *Homo sapiens.* Clearly it is an intermediate type. If the skulls were related, as they seemed to be, the Swanscombe fossil could be considered not a modern type of human but in fact a very early Neandertal.

The debate wavered back and forth until 1964, when two British scientists enlisted the help of a computer to ascertain the status of the Swanscombe skull. They took seventeen different measurements of the Swanscombe and Steinheim skulls; then, for purposes of comparison, they measured various Neandertal skulls as well as a large population of modern skulls to give some indication of the variability that can be expected in a natural population. The computer was programmed to work out "distance functions"—numerical statements of morphological resemblance. Its opinion was added to the debate: the Swanscombe fossil was no more modern than the Steinheim skull. Instead of being precociously sapient, both skulls were about as primitive as one would expect from their ancient date. Thus, what seemed to be evidence for the presence of a modern type of human being far back in time was discounted again.

The Evaluation of Swanscombe (1964)

The examination by computer of the Swanscombe fossil is one of many helpful new approaches to prehistory. During the nineteenth century and much of the twentieth, scientists had the unenviable task of making sense out of a mere handful of fossils. Dates were uncertain or sometimes impossible even to guess at. A lack of information about human variability often caused experts to make too much of one trait or another from a single find. It is easy to go wrong about fossils, exaggerating, for example, the significance of a particular curve at the back of a skull or incorrectly reconstructing features when parts are missing. Today these errors and inadequacies are being corrected. Statistical mathematics is used to reduce subjectivity in analyses of fossils or artifacts, and the invention of various sorts of radiometric techniques has enabled archaeologists to establish ancient dates far more accurately than used to be possible. Anthropologists and archaeologists no doubt still make mistakes, but let us hope they are fewer than ever before.

In 1971 a new discovery was made of fossil humans from approximately the period of the Swanscombe and Steinheim fossils. Henry and Marie-Antoinette de Lumley excavated a cave at Arago near Tautavel in the Pyrenees. Along with stone implements, the de Lumleys found the partial skull of a man about twenty years old (see Figure 14–9) and two

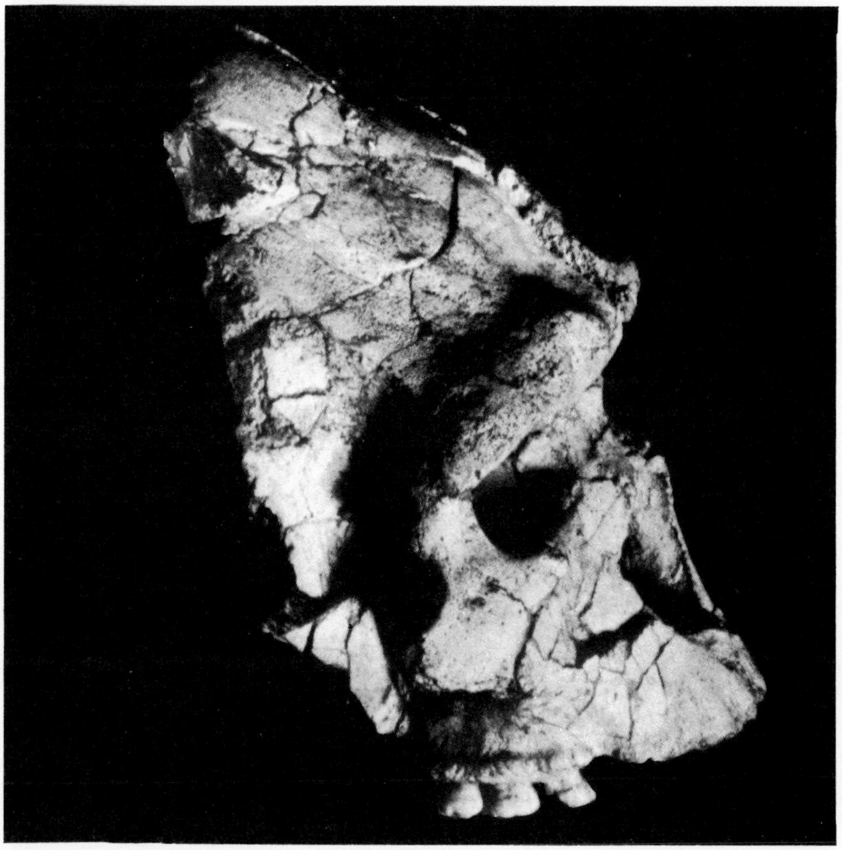

The Arago Discovery (1971)

Figure 14–9 The skull from Arago is much more robust than those from Swanscombe and Steinheim. It demonstrates the variability in early *Homo sapiens* populations in Europe, which date from the beginning of the Riss glacial period.

partial jaws of other individuals. The man had a forward-jutting face, heavy brow ridges, a slanting forehead, and a braincase somewhat smaller than the modern average. The two jaws were massive and somewhat resembled the Mauer jaw of much greater antiquity (see page 210); they seemed well suited to chewing coarse food. Altogether the fragments appear to be more archaic in form—that is, closer to *Homo erectus* —than Swanscombe and Steinheim.

In fact we see in the Swanscombe, Steinheim, and Arago specimens a sample of early *Homo sapiens* that shows considerable variability in form. A further jaw fragment from another cave in the Arago region near the village of Montmaurin is of the same age; it also fits this general type. Together these specimens give us an idea of hominids intermediate between *Homo erectus* and the later European Neandertals.

REASSESSMENT OF NEANDERTAL

Improvements in techniques have proved particularly fruitful for the study of the later Neandertals. New fossils have now been identified in many parts of the world—China, central and northern Africa, Iraq, Czechoslovakia, Hungary, Greece, and elsewhere—bringing the total number of Neandertal individuals today to more than a hundred. With the discovery of new and better evidence has come a drastic change in the appraisal of Neandertal.

The old prejudices began to evaporate in 1955, when several scientists suggested that Boule may have been in error in describing the posture of the Neandertal from La Chapelle-aux-Saints as slumped. Even young children learning to walk, it was pointed out, or apes standing on their hind legs, have a fully upright trunk. The major turnabout came in 1957, when two anatomists, William Strauss and A. J. E. Cave, took a second, closer look at the fossil from La Chapelle-aux-Saints. The fossil was supposed to be typical. Strauss and Cave, however, detected a deformation of its bone joints indicating that this particular Neandertal had suffered from a severe case of arthritis, which affected the formation of the vertebrae and the jaw. Strauss and Cave spotted many other mistakes in Boule's reconstructions. The Neandertal foot, for example, was definitely not a "prehensile organ," as Boule had said. The neck vertebrae did not resemble those of a chimpanzee, nor was the pelvis apelike in structure. All in all, Strauss and Cave found Neandertal man to be quite modern in shape. They wrote: "If he could be reincarnated and placed in a New York subway—provided that he were bathed, shaved and dressed in modern clothing—it is doubtful whether he would attract any more attention than some of its other denizens."

By removing the taint of apishness that had been associated with Neandertals for so long, the Strauss–Cave study effectively revived the Neandertals' candidacy as possible ancestors of modern man. It is still true, of course, that the fossil from La Chapelle-aux-Saints does not look much like Cro-Magnon or most humans of today, and many anthropologists continue to deny an ancestral relationship. However, the Neandertals uncovered at Mount Carmel definitely cannot be dismissed

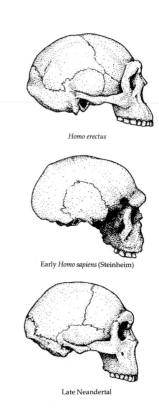

Homo erectus

Early *Homo sapiens* (Steinheim)

Late Neandertal

Figure 14–10 *Homo erectus,* **early** *Homo sapiens,* **and Neandertal form a series of variable populations that succeeded each other in many parts of the Old World. Here they are represented by typical skulls.**

from human lineage on the basis of looks. These Middle Eastern fossils therefore serve to establish a solid evolutionary link between some of the more extreme Neandertals and modern human beings.

In other words, the ranges of variation of Neandertal and modern humans overlap. Indeed, the more we learn about Neandertal, the greater the overlap appears to be. This eventually forces a critical question: Is Neandertal actually a different kind of human from *Homo sapiens*? Fifty years ago anybody rash enough to raise such a question would have been laughed out of the room. Today, with the overthrow of prejudices of the sort Boule displayed, and the clarified status of the Swanscombe fossil, most anthropologists agree that the Neandertals were sufficiently human in mind and body to have been members of our species, *Homo sapiens*. On the end of this title is tacked the sub-species name *neanderthalensis* (or *rhodesiensis* or *soloensis*), denoting some difference from fully modern people. But *sapiens* places the Neandertals squarely in the human fold.

This does not mean that there are not differences between the subspecies; there are plenty. To understand and evaluate both the differences and similarities, it will be necessary to reconsider for a moment some of the most modern ideas about how speciation takes place and what makes a species.

The classic definition of a species is, as we have seen: one or more groups of individual organisms, the members of which interbreed with one another in nature or are enough alike in structure and behavior that they could interbreed and produce fertile offspring if they had access to one another. This concept goes on to recognize that not all breeding populations within a species are always in contact with one another. If separation goes on for a long time, the different populations may become so changed through evolution that if they should come together again they might no longer interbreed. Then it would be correct to say that the original single species had been split into two species.

This is an extremely simplified statement of what is actually a very complex and subtle process. For one thing, separation is often behavioral: if one animal acts in a way that makes it impossible for it to breed with another, the separation between the two is as real as if they were kept apart by a mountain range. Consider, for example, the races of song sparrows that inhabit North America. There are song sparrows that habitually migrate north to Alaska every year, and there are others that go only as far north as the Gulf Coast during the breeding season. Theoretically both populations could interbreed, but their habits as migrants do not give them a chance to. What tends to hold them together as a single species is the existence of a large number of sparrows that summer in between the extreme northern and extreme southern breeding areas. Through these intermediary birds, the individuals on the northern and southern fringes keep in genetic touch. Their genes are distributed inward from the edges of an enormous pool of genes that represents all the traits of the species; at the same time,

Species and Speciation

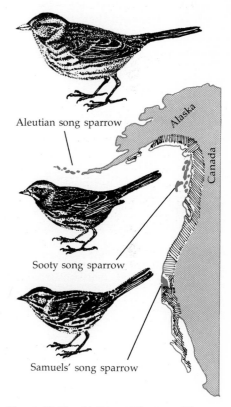

Aleutian song sparrow

Sooty song sparrow

Samuels' song sparrow

Figure 14–11   At present there are 29 subspecies of the song sparrow in North America; three are shown here. Their approximate breeding ranges and those of 14 other subspecies along the West Coast are also indicated (from the West Coast to the Midwest of the U.S. are the breeding ranges of 5 other subspecies). The subspecies vary greatly in color and size, but if we look at representatives of all 29, we find a continuous, gradual series.

they keep receiving genes that are passed out toward them from the center of the pool. This reduces any tendency toward extreme differentiation along the edges. In other words, genetic contact with the main body of birds tends to ensure that the outlying members of the species will continue to look and act pretty much like all the others as long as the contact is maintained. Two opposing influences determine the course of speciation in any group of organisms: one is environmental and selective, tending to create differences; the other is genetic and connective, tending to distribute the same traits through a population.

If we were collecting sparrow fossils and had only a couple of Alaskan specimens and half a dozen from the Gulf Coast to study, how would we relate them, particularly if we had no knowledge of any sparrows living anywhere else? Would we recognize the obvious differences between them and assign them to different species, or would we still consider them the same kind of bird? It is that problem that continually confronts the paleoanthropologist. His sample of human specimens is often so small that it is next to impossible for him to learn enough about the distribution of the people he is studying to tell whether his samples are from opposite fringes of a single, rather varied population or whether they are truly separate and different species.

Current species theory emphasizes whole populations, not individuals. Its concern is with the entire gene pool. It recognizes that differences exist among individuals or groups of individuals and that such differences continue to have a chance, through interbreeding, to be reabsorbed into the gene pool as a whole and in this way continue to be able to express themselves as part of the species' genetic makeup. Older theory tended to look at an evolving species as a solid tree trunk with distinct limbs branching off it from time to time as new species were created. The newer theory, by contrast, visualizes a species as a tangle of interlocking strands that separate and join again in no orderly pattern. How they join is not so important as that they do join. These constant joinings represent the individual mating decisions of countless members of the species and the fate of numerous small populations. If one or more populations should drift away from the main body to a point that these rejoinings no longer took place, then it would become a separate gene pool and eventually, perhaps, a separate species.

This flexible model of a species fits what we know about *Homo erectus* rather neatly. It emphasizes the similarities that exist among the various known specimens; at the same time, it acknowledges their differences by assuming that a good deal of variety will inevitably manifest itself in any widely distributed species. Neandertal peoples present us with a problem of a different sort. Compared with *Homo erectus* fossils, Neandertal remains are very numerous. The difficulty, then, is not so much with rarity as it is with how to interpret a rather embarrassing and perplexing abundance.

The first Neandertal finds came from western Europe, as we have discussed. Most of the field work of the last century and the early part

Characteristics
of Western Neandertal

of this one was done by Europeans, and much of it was concentrated in their own countries. As discovery followed discovery, it became increasingly clear that Neandertal peoples were already well established in Europe about 75,000 years ago.

This western European Neandertal, now called the "classic" type, is not hard to recognize. Although the cranium is large and could accommodate a brain just as big as a modern human's, it is differently shaped. It has a lower, flatter crown, and the equal size of its interior space is due to the fact that the skull is longer and bulges more at the back and sides. There is a very characteristic swelling at the back to which the neck muscles are attached—the Neandertal "bun." The face has four distinctions: a definitely receding chin under large, projecting jaws; large teeth and palate; round orbits; and extremely prominent brow ridges curving over each eye and connected across the bridge of the nose. It is this continuous ridge of bone that gives the classic Neandertal his famous beetle-browed look.

The rest of the skeleton marks a rather short but powerfully built body. Neandertal man stood just over five feet. His chest was broad and rounded. The long bones of his limbs were robust and slightly curved, which may have given him a somewhat bandy-legged appearance. His hands were large but his fingers were short and stubby. That his feet, too, had stocky proportions is borne out not only by the bones themselves but by the astonishing preservation of actual Neandertal footprints. Footprints such as these and a few handprints are the only direct evidence known to exist about any soft part of any prehistoric human being. The Neandertal was heavily muscled and appears to have been very strong.

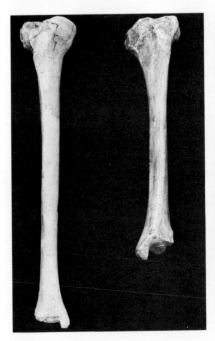

Figure 14–12 The short and strong tibia on the right is from Spy. It is noticeably different from the less robust, non-European Neandertal tibia on the left, which is from Skhūl. The plaster cast of a Neandertal footprint from an Italian cave suggests a broad, short foot.

Neandertal man continued to exist in western Europe right up to about 35,000 years ago, and then he disappeared. If we had only the evidence of Europe to go by, Neandertal man would certainly seem to follow the classic pattern of speciation. He was noticeably different from modern humans, and in addition to disappearing abruptly, the classic Neandertal in western Europe is replaced with equal abruptness by people like ourselves. There is no clear blending, little evidence of gradual shading from one type to the other. This certainly suggests two competitive species overlapping in time, with the more advanced one exterminating the more primitive one.

But of course, the classic European variety is not the only Neandertal to consider. As we have seen, other populations with different characteristics existed in a great many places besides western Europe: along the Mediterranean, in northern Africa, in eastern Europe, in Asia Minor, in Southeast Asia, in China, and in central Africa (see Figure 14–13). Significantly, some of the traits exhibited by the Neandertals in these latter places are not nearly so extreme as those of the western European classic type. These non-European peoples tend to be less massive,

Nonwestern Neandertal

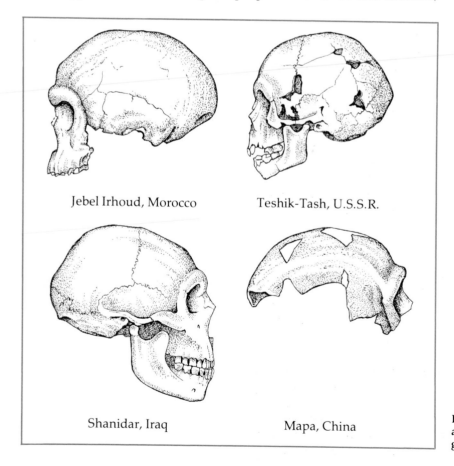

Jebel Irhoud, Morocco

Teshik-Tash, U.S.S.R.

Shanidar, Iraq

Mapa, China

Figure 14–13 The wide distribution and variability of Neandertal is suggested by these four examples.

taller, and more finely made. Their forearms and legs are not as robust and not as curved. Their skulls are a bit more lofty and their faces a trifle smaller, with bony features more like our own.

Perhaps a typical representative of this different Neandertal is a complete skeleton of a hunter, precisely dated by radiocarbon at 46,000 years of age, that was dug out of a cave at Shanidar in the mountains of northern Iraq in 1957. This man had been a victim of a hazard peculiar to cave dwellers in areas that were earthquake-prone: he had been crushed by a massive fall of rock from his own ceiling. At the time of his death he was about forty years old and had bad teeth. He was five feet three inches tall and, like his western cousins, barrel-chested; but, like the Tabūn woman's, his eyebrow ridge was less thick and heavy, giving the whole upper part of his face a more modern look. Further search in the Shanidar cave yielded five more adults; together with a baby previously found, they totaled seven almost complete skeletons, all showing this curious hint of modernity in the upper face, some of them with traces of other characteristics that hinted at a departure from the strict classic Neandertal model.

This provocative evidence from the Near and Middle East tells a story entirely different from that told in western Europe. It suggests an extremely varied gene pool capable of producing all kinds of individuals —some with this more primitive characteristic, others with that—but a gene pool that between 70,000 and 40,000 years B.P. was unmistakably moving in the general direction of modern man.

However, we cannot simply ignore those squat men from the icy caves of western Europe. Somehow we must fit them into our species model. Perhaps the best way to do this is to regard them as fringe dwellers like the Alaskan sparrows, representatives of a population living under drastically different environmental conditions and subject to different selection pressures than the main group of their kind, and probably even separated from them toward the end.

Isolated for periods of a good many thousands of years at a time, one or many localized inbreeding populations could have been created and could have evolved in what now appears to have been a primitive direction. Is the form of European Neandertal really primitive or is it simply adaptive? Some scientists believe that in a very cold climate the stockiest man with the shortest limbs will be the most efficient conserver of body heat. If this is true, he, and not the slender "more advanced" man, would have the survival advantage in this region.

Let us conclude, then, that the Neandertals were a widespread and widely varied group; not all of them exhibited the extreme characteristics of the classic type. Their gene pool evolved out of that bequeathed to them by *Homo erectus;* some Neandertals in turn bequeathed their gene pool to modern mankind. They did it gradually in the East and probably not at all in western Europe. Their disappearance in western

Neandertal and the Species Model

Neandertal's Present Status

Europe may or may not have been an actual extermination. If it was, it was a Cain and Abel affair: if they were killed, they were killed by members of their own species, by their distant cousins—not by a different kind of creature altogether.

Looking at human evolution in this way, we begin to get a picture of a world that may never have held more than one species of *Homo* at any one time. The vine stems may have been extremely tangled, and a few creepers may have strayed, like the classic Neandertal, far enough from the central cluster to have withered and died. If we wish to begin thinking about species, we would do well to examine the cluster vertically, not horizontally as many past students have done; we must take into account the element of time. When we do, the image of a vine becomes more compelling, with *Homo erectus* occupying one section of it and Neandertal man another section, higher up and later in time, as Figure 14–14 shows. To find out where one human line stops and the other starts, we will have to quite arbitrarily select a particular time and slice through the vine at that point to see what we get. Since evolution does not proceed in all places at the same rate or even in the same way, wherever we slice we will find some inconsistencies. If the slice is wide enough to include places like South Africa and Java, where other people lived contemporaneously with Neandertal man and shared some but not all of his traits, the inconsistencies become very plain. Nevertheless, the general indications of species relationships persist. They become more meaningful the more one thinks about the evolving gene pool as a whole, and not about individuals.

Neandertal man was the last of the archaic humans, not the first. Behind him stretched five million years of slow evolution, during which

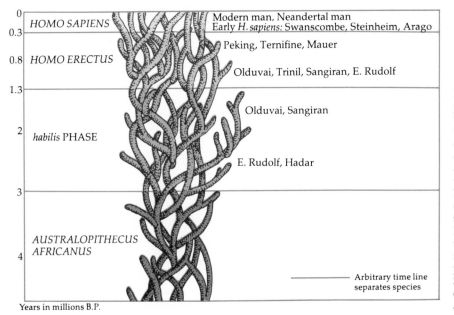

Years (millions B.P.)	
0	
0.3	HOMO SAPIENS — Modern man, Neandertal man; Early *H. sapiens*: Swanscombe, Steinheim, Arago
0.8	HOMO ERECTUS — Peking, Ternifine, Mauer
1.3	Olduvai, Trinil, Sangiran, E. Rudolf
2	*habilis* PHASE — Olduvai, Sangiran
3	E. Rudolf, Hadar
4	AUSTRALOPITHECUS AFRICANUS

Arbitrary time line separates species

Years in millions B.P.

Figure 14–14 The evolving gene pool of the hominid lineage contained many semi-isolated populations, some of which fused with each other, while some became extinct. This diagram symbolizes the complexity of this process, although we have no idea of the actual number of differing populations, varieties, and races involved. The fact that the more recent species of our lineage occupied a shorter time span than the earlier ones is due to the fact that the positive feedback loops portrayed in Figures 8–10, 20–2, 20–3, and 20–8 have accelerated the evolutionary process in this cultural animal.

Australopithecus became the first species of true human, *Homo erectus*, and *Homo erectus* evolved into the second species, *Homo sapiens.* The earliest *Homo sapiens* evolved into a long line of human varieties such as Neandertal and eventually into modern mankind.

		YEARS A.D.	NEANDERTAL DISCOVERIES	PUBLICATIONS

HOLOCENE

10,000

1971	At Arago
1965	At Hortus
1961	At Amud
1957	At Shanidar

1964 — Swanscombe report

1957 — La Chapelle reconsidered by Strauss and Cave

Peking man
Large-scale elephant hunts in Europe

500,000 —

PLEISTOCENE

Hearths at Escale;
  H. erectus expansion into Europe
Java man (Trinil, Sangiran)

1939	At Monte Circeo
1938	At Teshik-Tash
1935	First Swanscombe discoveries
1933	First Kafzeh discoveries; at Steinheim
1931	At Solo, Skhūl, and Tabūn

1 million —   *H. erectus* expansion into China

1926	Gibraltar child
1924	At Kiik-Koba
1921	At Broken Hill

A. robustus and *boisei* extinct

1914	At Ehringsdorf
1909	At La Ferrassie
1908	At La Chapelle, Le Moustier, and La Quina

1913 — Boule's monograph on La Chapelle man

Earliest Acheulian tools

1.5 million —

habilis at Olduvai

1886 — At Spy

Java man at Modjokerto

2 million

PLIOCENE

King creates species
  Homo neanderthalensis
1864 —
1863 — Huxley's report on the Neandertal skullcap
1859 — Darwin's *On the Origin of Species*

1856 — In Neander Valley

Earliest Oldowan tools

1848 — Gibraltar skull

DISCOVERY OF NEANDERTAL

The greatest period of Neandertal discoveries was between 1900 and 1940, and most finds came from Europe and the Near East. Finds from Africa and China are very rare. Today more research effort is being put into the earlier periods that preceded Neandertal man.

Chapter 15

Conquest of the North

The autumn always gets me badly as it breaks into colours. I want to go south, where there is no autumn, where the cold doesn't crouch over one like a snow-leopard waiting to pounce. The heart of the North is dead, and the fingers are corpse fingers.

D. H. LAWRENCE, 1885–1930.

Imagine one moment of perfect well-being, 250,000 years ago. A man is standing immobile in an upland meadow in the land we now call England, visibly pleased by the smell of warm meat in the air as his companions butcher a newborn fawn that they have killed. His task is to watch for predators or scavengers while the other men dismember the fawn with their heavy, sharp-edged stone tools. Even though the meadow appears empty, the man never relaxes his vigilance, for a lion could be crouching in the grass or a bear might be watching from the nearby woods.

Standing there in the sun, with a slender wooden spear in one hand, this man does not appear especially powerful, although he is five-and-a-half feet tall, well muscled, and clearly capable of speed on foot. His head might suggest meager intelligence, for the brow slants back from an out-thrust face and the skull looks low and pinched-in at the sides. But he has a larger brain than his ancestor, *Homo erectus,* who carried the torch of human evolution for a million years. He is a very early member of the modern human species, *Homo sapiens.*

The hunter belongs to a group of about thirty individuals. They inhabit a territory so large that a trip from border to border might take more than a day. Yet this expanse of land is just enough to keep them supplied with meat throughout the season; in a smaller territory they

THE GREAT INTERGLACIAL PERIOD

317

would have to hunt so intensively that the population of grazing animals would be depleted. At the edges of this range live other small bands of humans who speak a similar dialect and are closely related to the hunter's group through intermarriage. Beyond these immediate neighbors are other bands, less closely related, speaking alien languages. And beyond them are still others. The earth and mankind's role in it are greater than the hunter can possibly imagine.

Two hundred and fifty thousand years ago the human population was probably smaller than 3 million. But this unimpressive total is deceptive, for humankind occupied far more of the earth's surface than any other mammal species. The hunter in our scenario lived at the northwestern outpost of man's geographical range. To the east, beyond the horizon, similar small bands of a half-dozen or a dozen families were camped in a broad valley, which is today covered by the waters of the English Channel. Still farther east and south, hunter-gatherer groups were spread all across the face of Europe.

Range of Early *Homo sapiens*

Most of Europe was then woodland, frequently interrupted by lush meadows, with temperatures so warm that water buffalo thrived in central Germany and monkeys chattered in dense woodlands along the northern Mediterranean coast. Most of Asia was less hospitable, and human bands avoided the heartland of that continent because of the harsh winters and dry, blistering summers. But human groups scattered around the entire southern perimeter of Asia, from the Middle East to Java and northward into central China. In all probability the most densely populated continent was Africa. This sprawling land mass may have contained more people than the rest of the world put together.

The sorts of lands settled by these various peoples reveal much about their ability to deal with nature. They almost invariably lived in grassy or partially wooded country. There was a very good reason for this preference: these regions supported the herds of grazing animals that provided much of the meat in the human diet. Wherever animals were lacking, human beings also stayed away. The unoccupied areas included deserts, rain forests, and the dense evergreen woods of the north—a very substantial portion of the earth's surface. A few herbivorous animal species did exist in the forests of the north and south, but they tended to wander alone or in small groups, for the scantiness of forage and the difficulty of moving through the thick growth of a forest made herd life impractical. To find and kill solitary grazers was so difficult at this stage of human development that human groups simply could not prosper in these regions.

Another environment that resisted human invasion for a long time was the tundra of the far north. Here, obtaining meat was not the problem. Enormous herds of reindeer, bison, and other large, vulnerable animals found ready forage in the mosses, lichens, grasses, and shrubs of the nearly treeless tundra country. However, people could not yet cope with the extreme cold of the region. Early *Homo sapiens* consequently stuck to the same lands that had supported his *Homo erectus* ancestors: the savannas and open thorn woodlands of the tropics, and the grasslands and open deciduous woodlands found in the temperate latitudes.

It is remarkable that anthropologists have been able to learn as much as they have about the world of these early people, considering their distance in time and the scant evidence they left behind. Many materials that were essential to early humans are highly perishable. Foods, hides, sinews, wood, plant fibers, and even bone last no time at all except under the rarest conditions. The few scraps of organic materials such as these that have survived often seem more tantalizing than informative. Take, for example, a sharpened piece of yew wood, thought to be about 300,000 years old, found at Clacton-on-Sea in England (the wood was preserved because the site was waterlogged). This wooden point may have come from a spear, for having been dried over flames, it was hard enough to penetrate the hides of animals. However, it may have served some entirely different purpose, such as digging up edible roots.

Yet such seemingly ambiguous clues can be interpreted. In a case like that of the yew fragment, common sense helps. Human beings certainly were using both spears and digging sticks well before this artifact was made, but a person would probably be more likely to take the trouble to harden a spear point than a digging implement. Similarly, there is every reason to believe that people who lived in cool climates must have worn some sort of clothing many hundreds of thousands of years ago, even though their garments, undoubtedly of animal skins, have not endured. It also seems certain that shelters were regularly constructed; and, in fact, the impressions of postholes and sapling tips at Terra Amata on the coast of France prove that people knew how to make simple huts of branches (and probably animal hides) even back in *Homo erectus* times.

A posthole here, a piece of wood there, a bit of sharpened bone, an occasional hearth: these are whispered hints of human achievement in remote times. Some clues to the past speak more firmly. Geological deposits laid down during any given period can reveal a good deal about climate, including the temperature and the amount of precipitation. Pollen found in deposits can be identified under a microscope, indicating exactly what kinds of trees, grass, or other vegetation prevailed. But most important for the study of prehistory are, of course, stone tools.

In a sense, an archaeologist digging down through geological layers is in the position of a man on the moon listening to radio broadcasts from earth with a weak receiver: out of all the thousands of signals of music and talk that are being transmitted from stations around the globe, he picks up only one signal loud and clear—in this case, implements of stone. Yet much can be learned from a single station. First of all, wherever an archaeologist finds tools, he knows that human beings once lived there. A comparison of tools from one site with

Evidence of Adaptations

contemporaneous tools from another site may suggest cultural contacts between ancient populations; comparison of tools in successive layers can help trace the cultural progress and the skill of the early peoples who left them.

Stone tools reveal that although the human beings living 250,000 years ago were modern enough to deserve the title of *Homo sapiens,* as toolmakers they had a great deal in common with their less advanced *Homo erectus* forebears. They made their tools according to a style that had originally appeared hundreds of thousands of years earlier. This was the Acheulian tradition (Chapter 11), with its characteristic implement, the hand-axe. As we have seen, the Acheulian hand-axe would have been suitable for many purposes. It might have been wedged into a thick wooden club to form a compound implement like a modern hatchet or axe. More probably, it was always hand-held; perhaps a piece of animal hide was wrapped around the butt to protect the user's hand.

The double-edged hand-axe was supplemented by flakes of stone, which were sometimes notched or given a saw-toothed edge for finer work on carcasses or wood. Some people showed a preference for flakes instead of the larger of the hand-axes; others rounded out their tool kits with heavy cleavers. In general, though, at the time of early *Homo sapiens,* the basic outlines of the Acheulian tradition were still followed by people in all parts of the world except the Far East, where somewhat cruder single-edged implements were still used.

The lack of inventiveness indicated by the worldwide uniformity of stonecrafting gave way very slowly. Gradually, the hand-axe was improved, if only in small ways: the cutting edges became sharper and more regular. Other stone tools in the deposits left by early *Homo sapiens* people point to a greater willingness to experiment. Some particularly ingenious craftsmen initiated a major new technique for making flake tools. Instead of simply banging away at a large piece of flint to produce flakes, they developed a sophisticated and much less wasteful manufacturing process (see Figure 15–1). First, a flint nodule was chipped around the side and on the top. Then this prepared core was rapped at a particular point on its side. The blow resulted in a flake of predetermined size and shape, with long, sharp cutting edges. This *Levallois technique,* as it is called, represents a remarkable insight into the potential of stone, for no tool is visible until the very end of the process. In the making of a hand-axe, the tool gradually and reassuringly takes shape; but a Levallois flake springs full-blown out of a core of flint that in no way resembles a tool. The Levallois method seems to have originated about 200,000 years ago in Africa and to have spread outward from there, although it may have been discovered independently in several places.

When all the different kinds of evidence of early *Homo sapiens* are put together—tools, a few fossils, a bit of organic material, along with

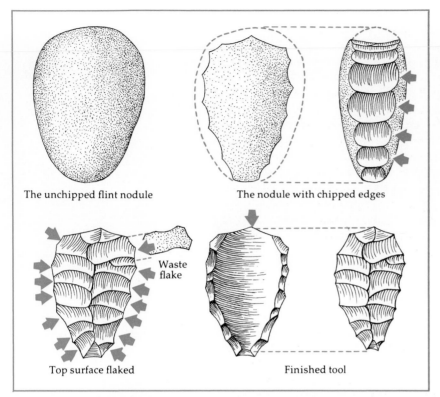

The unchipped flint nodule

The nodule with chipped edges

Waste flake

Top surface flaked

Finished tool

Figure 15–1 The Levallois flake has a distinctive predetermined shape. The toolmaker first prepares a nodule by trimming its sides (top right). Then he further refines this core by flaking small chips from both surfaces. A final brisk blow at one end removes the finished flake (bottom right), already sharp and in need of no further retouching.

pollen and various geological clues to climate—the people of that remote time start to come alive. They were sturdy folk, with quite modern bodies; they were master hunters who could cope with all but the harshest environments. Culturally, they clung to the traditions of the past, but they were slowly inventing their way toward a tighter, more secure hold over nature.

Theirs was a fairly hospitable world. But it was destined to change— abruptly in geological terms—to become in the regions we now call temperate as inhospitable an environment as the human race has ever known.

THE RISS GLACIATION

About 200,000 years ago, the weather in the northern hemisphere began to grow colder. Glades and meadows in the deciduous woodlands of Europe broadened at an imperceptible rate; the tangled lush woodlands along the Mediterranean began to wither; and the expanses of spruce and fir in eastern Europe slowly yielded to the expanding steppe, or grassy plain. Similar changes occurred in China. The increasing cold did not necessarily mean that the basic patterns of human life were about to change. Since *Homo sapiens'* way of life was nomadic to begin with, they had simply to follow wherever the herd animals led. But certainly the pressure to develop a different material culture was felt by groups that formerly had had no pressing need for fire, clothing, or artificial shelter. These groups now had to take a lesson in cold-weather survival techniques from more northern peoples, who had been practicing such arts ever since the days of *Homo erectus.*

Snow was falling in the mountain ranges of the world, more snow than could melt during the summer. Year by year it piled up, filling deep valleys and compacting itself into ice. The stupendous weight of the ice caused its lower layers to behave like very thick putty, sliding outward from the valleys as the ever-accumulating snow pressed down from above. Inching through the mountain ranges, the great fingers of ice plucked boulders from cliffsides and used them like a giant's scouring powder to grind the once-green land down to bedrock. In the summer, torrents of meltwater carried the debris of sand and rock dust out in front of the advancing ice, where it was later picked up by winds and blown across the continents in great yellowish-brown clouds. And still the snow continued to fall, until in some places the ice sheets grew more than a mile thick, burying the mountains and causing the very crust of the earth to sag under the load. At their fullest extent, the great sheets of ice called glaciers covered more than 30 percent of the world's land surface, compared to a mere 10 percent today. Europe was almost entirely ice-bound. The surrounding ocean and seas offered a limitless source of moisture for snow, which fed separate glaciers spreading outward from the Alps and the Scandinavian ranges to cover vast stretches of the continent.

This glacial age, known as the Riss, was one of the worst climatic traumata in the five-billion-year history of the earth. Although similar cold spasms had occurred before this glaciation (see Figure 15–2) during the days of *Homo erectus,* the Riss was the first to try the endurance of *Homo sapiens.* He was to survive 75,000 years of bitter cold, interspersed with mild spells, before this part of the earth warmed up again—for a time.

The impact of the climatic changes was enormous. During these cold periods, the wind system of the world was disrupted. Rainfall increased in some places and diminished in others. Patterns of vegetation were greatly altered. Many animals species died out or evolved new, cold-adapted forms, such as the cave bear and woolly rhinoceros.

During some particularly severe phases of the Riss glaciation, England, which has been so pleasant when the earliest *Homo sapiens* lived there, became so bitterly cold that midsummer temperatures were often below the freezing point. The temperate woodlands of central and western Europe were transformed into tundra or steppe. As far south as the shores of the Mediterranean, trees gradually died and were eventually replaced by grassland.

What happened in Africa is less clear. In some places, reduced temperatures apparently were accompanied by greater rainfall, allowing trees or grass to grow on formerly barren parts of the Sahara and Kalahari deserts. At the same time, changing wind patterns had a drying effect on the dense Congo rain forest, causing it to give way to open woodland or grassland. Thus, while Europe was becoming less habit-

Changes around the World

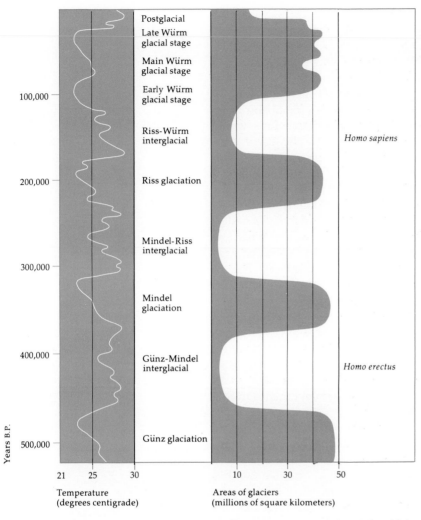

Figure 15–2 We know that mean annual temperatures in the North Atlantic have fluctuated widely over the past 500,000 years. These apparently random shifts can be interpreted as a series of ice ages, as indicated here. The absolute dates associated with ice ages are not clearly established, but the dates shown here are quite widely accepted. The species of *Homo* are indicated on the right side.

The names of glaciations used here were introduced to describe climatic changes in the region of the Alps. Though other terms are used in North America and elsewhere, the Alpine terms are most commonly used and here apply to the entire northern icecap.

able, Africa was becoming more so, favoring an expansion of people throughout much of that continent.

The land resources available to human groups during the Riss ice age also were increased by a worldwide lowering of sea levels. So much water became locked up in the huge ice sheets that the level of the oceans dropped by as much as 500 feet, exposing large areas of the continental shelves, those shallow submarine plains that reach outward from the continental margins, in some places for hundreds of miles, before dropping off steeply to the ocean floor far below. The baring of formerly submerged land gave hunters access to millions of square miles of new territory, and there is no doubt that they took advantage of this dividend of the ice age. Each year, bands and their game must have wandered farther out into newly drained land.

During the 75,000 years of the Riss glaciation, surviving inhabitants of northern latitudes suffered hardships that were unknown during the balmy period of the earliest *Homo sapiens* peoples. These hardships may

A Stimulus to Intelligence and Ingenuity

have had a stimulating influence on human intelligence. As we saw in Chapter 12, it seems likely that the great increase in cranial capacity that had already occurred during the era of *Homo erectus* was due to expansion out of the tropics and into cool regions where ingenuity and flexibility of behavior were more necessary for survival: *Homo erectus* pioneers had to learn to use fire, develop clothes and shelter, and adjust to complex seasonal schedules for the availability of animal and vegetable food. The Riss, with its widespread ecological disruptions, would have tested—and perhaps selected—intelligence in the same way.

Stone tools from a number of sites offer indirect proof that man was living in Europe as the ice advanced, but the most important evidence is the fossil skulls from Swanscombe, Steinheim, and Arago. The more northerly skulls, the Swanscombe and Steinheim, date from the very beginning of the Riss glaciation, from a time before the cold reached its most intense. The Arago people lived at a slightly later time when the north of Europe was probably quite uninhabitable and even the foothills of the Pyrenees were hardly a pleasant environment. The de Lumleys, who excavated the Arago site, reckon that at that time it took real hardihood to venture out into the freezing wind and endure the stinging dust and sand that blew across the plain. Far worse times must have followed quickly; the absence of tools in the layers above the human bones indicates that the Arago people were forced to leave for some better place. There is evidence that, for a time, the climate of southern Europe took on truly arctic bitterness.

Recently, at Lazaret in southern France, the de Lumleys made another spectacular find, remnants of shelters that had been constructed *inside* a cave. These simple shelters, dating to the latter part of the Riss, about 125,000 years ago, were tents, probably consisting of animal hides anchored by stones around the perimeter. Perhaps the hunters who occupied the cave from time to time set up the tents to give families some privacy or to keep off water that dripped from the ceiling. But the weather must have been a consideration, too. The entrances of the tents were oriented away from the cave mouth, suggesting that winds blew cold and hard even at this spot close to the Mediterranean.

Another remarkable clue to the growing complexity and subtlety of human behavior turned up at Lazaret. Just inside the portal of every tent, the de Lumleys found a wolf skull. The similar placement of each skull in each shelter makes clear that these remains were not bones tossed away as garbage. They undoubtedly signified something. Exactly what is still a mystery. One possibility is that whenever the hunters departed to pursue their nomadic activities elsewhere, they left the wolf heads behind as supernatural guardians of their homes.

The Riss-Würm Interglacial Period

Around 125,000 years ago, the long climatic agony of the Riss tapered off and another period of warmth began. It was to last about 40,000 years. Glaciers shrank back into their mountain fastnesses; the seas rose; and northern latitudes all across the world once again became an inviting place for humans. A few intriguing fossils dated to this period testify to continuing modernization of *Homo sapiens*. From a cave near the town of Fontéchevade in southwestern France come skull fragments, perhaps 110,000 years old, that seem more advanced than the Riss-age man from the Pyrenees.

By the time the warm period following the Riss glaciation reached its midpoint about 90,000 years ago, the occupants of Europe were the classic Neandertals, and the transitional period from the early *Homo sapiens* people was ended. These European Neandertals had evolved gradually, we presume, from people like the man from Arago and the later, more modern Fontéchevade *Homo sapiens*. The human jaw was still massive and chinless; the face was still out-thrust; and the skull was still low, with a sloping brow. But the volume of the braincase was now completely up to the present-day size. When anthropologists use the term Neandertal as a description of a certain evolutionary status, they are referring essentially to a type of man who had a modern-sized brain packaged in a relatively archaic-looking skull.

Cranial Capacity of Neandertal

It is difficult to evaluate this full-sized brain. Some theorists feel that it does not necessarily signal the attainment of the modern level of intelligence. Since brain size ordinarily increased with body weight, they suggest that Neandertals were not necessarily cleverer than their ancestors, just heavier. If Neandertals are rated on the basis of brain volumes as the equals of modern human beings in raw intelligence, then another problem arises. Why did the expansion of the brain cease about 100,000 years ago? Since intelligence is of such obvious value to humanity, why would the brain stop growing larger and presumably better?

Physical anthropologist C. Loring Brace has one interesting explanation. In his view, human culture in Neandertal times reached a point at which almost all members of a band had a fairly adequate chance of survival so long as they could master the traditions of their band. If language were sufficiently developed (a supposition disputed by some authorities) and if intelligence were sufficiently high that the least brainy members of a band could be taught the necessary survival techniques, then increased brain size would confer no further evolutionary advantage. Some individuals were especially innovative, of course, but their ideas would be communicated to everyone, and the whole band would benefit from any advance. Thus, according to Brace, the raw intelligence of humanity as a whole became stabilized, although people continued to increase their knowledge about the world.

This is certainly speculation, and most anthropologists prefer a more down-to-earth approach. They feel that the only fair way to assess the powers of the Neandertal brain is to find out how Neandertal peoples dealt with the world. These scientists tune in on stone technologies— that one loud, clear signal transmitted across the expanse of time—and detect evidence of quickening intelligence everywhere. As we have seen, the old Acheulian tradition of hand-axes still persisted, but it was becoming ever more varied. The double-edged hand-axes now came in

Evidence of Intelligence

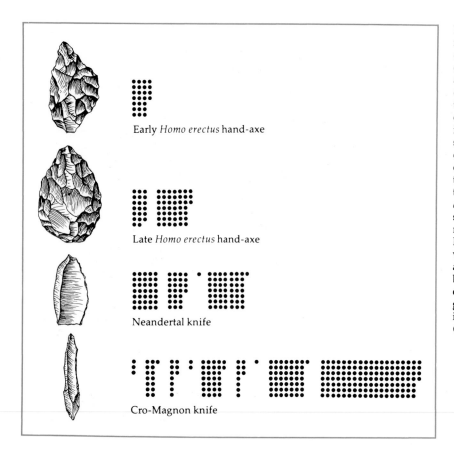

Early *Homo erectus* hand-axe

Late *Homo erectus* hand-axe

Neandertal knife

Cro-Magnon knife

Figure 15–3   Steady progress in the manufacture of tools is traced in this diagram, which shows how increasing numbers of blows (dots) and of different steps (clusters of dots) in toolmaking led to finer tools and more efficient utilization of the raw material. The most primitive tool required 25 blows and one step; the latest and most sophisticated took 251 blows and nine complex steps. The first and second tools shown represent the Acheulian toolmaking techniques of *Homo erectus*; they were rough-hewn from single pieces of flint. The third was made in Neandertal times by the Mousterian technique, which involved chipping a flake from a core and then modifying the flake. The bottom tool—a knife so sharp one edge had to be dulled to permit grasping—was shaped by the more intricate Aurignacian technique of Cro-Magnon.

many sizes and shapes, often so symmetrical and painstakingly trimmed that esthetic impulses seem to have guided their makers. When a man made a small hand-axe for roughing out spears or a notched flake to strip the bark off spear shafts, he made it just right, taking care to shape the implement for maximum efficiency at its intended work.

In toolmaking, Europe seems to have been a center of innovation. Since it is bounded by seas on three sides, the early *Homo sapiens* bands living there had had no easy avenue of escape to warmer regions during the Riss glaciation, and even the Neandertals were isolated occasionally for certain periods, when cold spells occurred during the warm era following the Riss. Disruptive environmental changes in Europe would have been a sharper spur to experimentation than the more even climates of Africa or Asia.

THE WÜRM GLACIAL PERIOD

About 75,000 years ago, that spur was applied to Neandertal man with renewed force as, once again, glaciers began to grow (see Figure 15–4). This most recent glacial age, known as the Würm, was not severe at first. The Würm initially brought snowy winters and cool, rainy summers. Nevertheless, open grassland spread, and formerly wooded portions of Germany and northern France were transformed into tundra

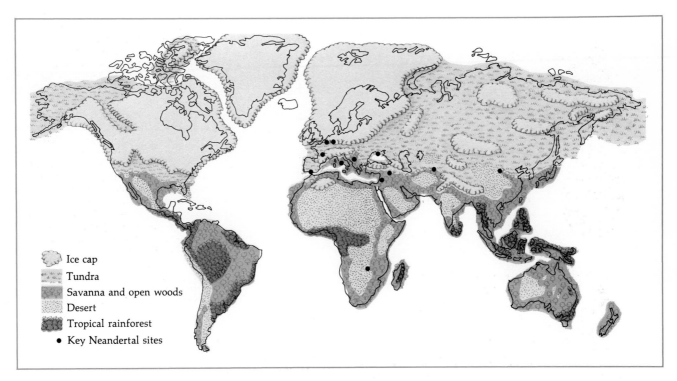

Ice cap
Tundra
Savanna and open woods
Desert
Tropical rainforest
• Key Neandertal sites

or a forest–tundra mixture where open areas of moss and lichens alternated with groups of trees.

During preceding ice ages, the early *Homo sapiens* bands generally had pulled back from such uncongenial lands. Now, in the summertime at least, the Neandertals stayed, subsisting off the herds of reindeer, woolly rhinoceros, and mammoth. They must have been first-rate hunters, for tundra country offered little vegetable food to tide them over lean days. Recent evidence from Russia shows that Neandertal settlements extended right up to the Arctic Ocean northwest of the Ural mountains. Here there are indications of huts built with mammoth tusks and skins, warmed by a series of small fires, together with remains of polar bears, which evidently were hunted. No doubt the death toll was high on the northernmost frontier, and bands remained small and probably not very healthy. Away from the frigid border of the ice sheets, populations were more dense.

To understand the extent to which these populations depended on cultural adaptations, we must remember that hominids, in a profound sense, are biologically adapted to a tropical climate. Hominids had evolved an efficient system of perspiration to prevent overheating in the tropics but had not previously needed to develop a counterbalancing system equally effective against overcooling. Such changes require a long time to evolve. Neandertal man did not need to wait for them to cope with the cold: he was intelligent enough to deal with the problem without depending on evolution. He generated extra heat with fire, put on hide clothes, and took shelter in caves.

Figure 15–4 This map gives an idea of the climate and vegetation of the world at the first peak of the Würm glaciation, about 60,000 years ago.

One physical change that apparently did come about in response to Neandertal's exploration of northern lands was associated less directly with cold than with the scarcity of sunlight during winter in the higher latitudes. Their skin probably got lighter. There is no certain evidence of this, but it seems likely that *Australopithecus* and early, tropical *Homo erectus*, as well, had been quite dark-skinned. In equatorial Africa, dark color is an advantage. Overexposure to the ultraviolet rays of the tropical sun is harmful to skin, and many experts feel that as the hominid skin became less hairy and more exposed, the *melanocytes* (the cells that produce the skin-darkening pigment melanin) compensated by producing extra pigment to block the ultraviolet rays.

But the presence of a screen of pigment inhibits the photosynthesis of vitamin D in the skin. This decrease of vitamin production is not a serious problem in the tropics, where there is so much sun that enough of the essential vitamin is made anyway. When people settled permanently in regions with less sunlight, however, they did not get enough vitamin D; pigment was no longer a protection but a drawback. This problem was exacerbated by the onset of cold. The well-fitted hides worn against the cold decreased the amount of sunlight that could fall upon the skin. This meant that if the human of the north was to get enough of the vitamin, any areas exposed would have to be able to absorb light and synthesize vitamin D extremely rapidly. In these conditions, a degree of pigmentation that could further the contribution of vitamin D to the body's chemistry was better for survival, and so lighter skin evolved. In this way we can account for the evolution of the blond northerner.

The significance of vitamin D in the lives of the early *Homo sapiens* populations was considerable. Today we know that man is unable to obtain the vitamin from any terrestrial foods, either vegetable or animal, but that fish oils contain vitamin D and fish can be eaten as a substitute for exposure to sunlight. Further, we have learned that a deficiency of the vitamin causes the bone-bending disease named rickets. It is not surprising, therefore, that we find many skeletons of Neandertals, especially children, showing direct evidence of a deficiency of the vitamin. And it is equally unsurprising that among the Cro-Magnon people who succeeded Neandertals in these icy regions, and whom we know to have had fishing tackle, the incidence of the disease is greatly reduced. The importance of sunlight to the survival of early *Homo sapiens* in northern lands, and the limitations that it placed on his further expansion, cannot be exaggerated.

The tenacity of the Neandertals in the north and the thriving state of those in milder areas must have been due, at least in part, to further cultural advances. During the early Würm, the Neandertals invented another new stoneworking method that brought about a permanent ascendancy of the versatile tools made from flakes over those made by shaping a heavy core. Fine flake tools had now been made for a long

Sunlight and Skin Color

Disk-Core Technique:
The Mousterian Industry

Figure 15–5   The disk above is all that remains of what started as a much larger core. Refinements in the initial shaping of the core, and in the way it was struck, permitted the toolmaker to flake the core until it was almost all used up. Such technical mastery could then turn the flakes into tools like the double-edged scraper (at top right) and the thin-bladed point (bottom), both shown in full view and profile.

time by the Levallois technique, but the new method was far more productive. Stone tool remains indicate that many Neandertals now
trimmed a nodule of stone around the edges to make a disk-shaped
core; then, aiming hammer blows toward the center of the disk, they repeatedly rapped at its edges, knocking off flake after flake until the core

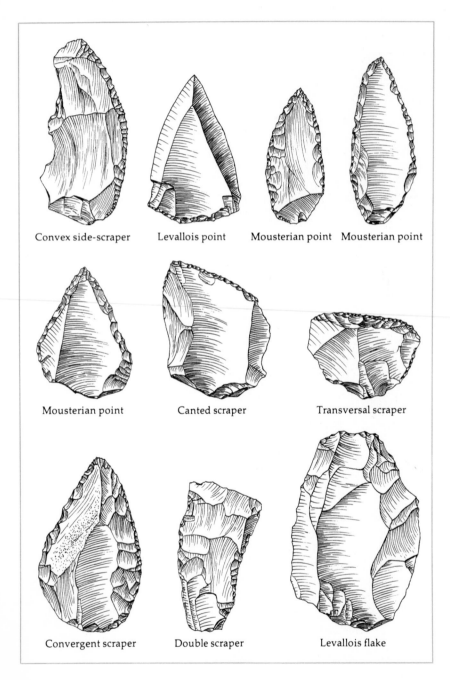

Convex side-scraper   Levallois point   Mousterian point   Mousterian point

Mousterian point   Canted scraper   Transversal scraper

Convergent scraper   Double scraper   Levallois flake

Figure 15–6   Flint tools of the
typical Mousterian.

was almost entirely used up. Finally, the unfinished flakes were further trimmed to give them the edges needed for work on wood, carcasses, or hides.

The great virtue of this new *disk-core* method was twofold. It permitted the production of large numbers of usable flakes with little effort. And since flakes can be retouched easily to give them a particular shape or edge, the new technique ushered in an era of specialization in tools. Neandertal tool kits were far more versatile than those of earlier peoples. François Bordes, a French archaeologist who is the world's foremost expert on Neandertal stonecrafting, lists more than sixty distinct types of cutting, scraping, piercing, and gouging tools. No single band of Neandertals used all these implements, but the kit of a given band nonetheless contained a great many special-purpose tools such as saw-toothed implements and stone knives with one blunt edge that enabled the user to apply pressure more firmly. Different tool kits were probably prepared for different needs. Possibly some pointed flakes were attached to the ends of spears by being wedged into the wood or tied on with thongs. With such an arsenal of tools, human beings could exploit the world of nature as never before.

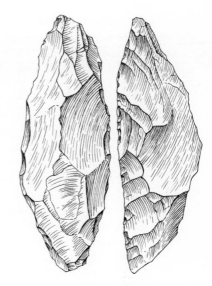

Figure 15–7 A Sangoan pick.

The Fauresmith and Sangoan Industries

Everywhere north of the Sahara and eastward as far as China, these retouched flakes became the preeminent tools. The tools made within this broad area are collectively called *Mousterian* (see Figure 15–6), after the French site of Le Moustier, where flake tools were first found in the 1860s. South of the Sahara, two distinct new styles appeared. One, called the *Fauresmith* tradition, was really a highly evolved version of the Acheulian, including small hand-axes, a variety of scraping tools, and narrow flake knives. The Fauresmith kit was used by people living in the same type of grassy landscape favored by earlier Acheulian hunters. The other new style, called *Sangoan*, was characterized by a type of long, narrow, heavy tool (see Figure 15–7), which may have served as a combination machete and stabbing weapon, as well as some hand-axes and small scrapers. This style, like the Mousterian, represented a major departure from the Acheulian tradition. Although the tools seem crude in appearance, they were well suited to cutting and shaping wood.

Expansion and Adaptations

From 75,000 to about 35,000 years ago, the Neandertals conquered a whole series of habitats that had repulsed their ancestors. The European Neandertals accepted the challenge of tundra country and won. Some of their African relatives, equipped with Sangoan tools, penetrated the forests of the Congo basin and hacked paths through the dense vegetation that replaced much of the grassland during rainy times. Other Neandertals were spreading across the vast plains of the western U.S.S.R., and still others ventured into the rugged mountain chains of southern Asia and out the other side, thereby opening up the Asian heartland to human existence. Moving along routes where waterholes were not too far apart, some Neandertals entered regions that were almost as arid as true desert. No band was suicidal enough to pack up its scanty possessions and walk a hundred miles into an area that its members knew nothing about. These conquests were achieved not by dramatic migrations, but by the process of gradual expansion known as budding.

Specialization was the order of the day. The northern Mousterians must have been the supreme clothesmakers of the world, as indicated by their numerous scraping tools, which could be used in preparing hides. The Sangoans may have been the most skilled woodcrafters. Perhaps they learned to construct traps to catch forest creatures that, wandering singly through the woods, were much more elusive than herds grazing on a savanna. People also were beginning to focus on the hunting of certain kinds of animals, a remarkable shift from the catch-as-catch-can approach that had characterized hunting since earliest times. The proof of the specialization among hunters can be seen in one particular European tool kit, known as *Denticulate Mousterian* because it emphasizes flakes with toothed or notched edges (Latin *dens*, tooth), such as those shown in Figure 15–8. Denticulate Mousterian tools are almost always found in association with the bones of wild horses. Apparently, the people who made these tools had so thoroughly mastered the knack of killing horses that they ignored all the other grazing animals around them and spent their days in quest of the kind of meat they liked best.

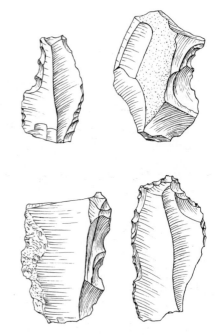

Figure 15–8   Four examples of typical Denticulate Mousterian tools.

Where certain key resources were lacking, the Neandertals undoubtedly tried to overcome the difficulty. On the treeless plains of central Europe, they began to experiment with bone tools that could take the place of wood. Water was another resource in short supply over large parts of the earth's surface, and humans always had been forced to stay within walking distance of streams, rivers, lakes, or springs. But the Neandertals invaded some very dry lands by utilizing water vessels. Recently, in the sun-baked Negev region of Israel, the shells of ostrich eggs were unearthed along with Mousterian tools. These large eggshells would have held enough water to enable a band to survive a journey across the parched hills from one waterhole to another.

The sheer abundance of Mousterian tools is in itself enough to affirm that the Neandertals outstripped their predecessors in their ability to gather a living from nature. There is no doubt that they considerably enlarged the dominion of mankind. The conquests of new territories that occurred during the time of the Neandertals represent the greatest expansion of humankind since *Homo erectus* had wandered out of the tropics and into cool latitudes hundreds of thousands of years earlier.

Unexplored Territories

Yet the failures of the Neandertals also are revealing. As far as we now know, these people never reached the heart of the tropical rain forests, and they probably did not make much of a dent on the thick coniferous forests of the far north. Colonization of these regions called for more sophisticated survival techniques than they could devise.

What about the New World? Access to the riches of the Americas was theoretically possible during the early part of the Würm ice age. As glaciers again began to lock up moisture and lower the sea level, a broad, flat land bridge emerged between Siberia and Alaska. This was inviting tundra country, with a wealth of big game. From Alaska south to the rest of the Americas, the road was closed at times by the glaciers of western Canada and the Rocky Mountains, but during some millennia passage was possible. However, the difficulties of getting to the land bridge were formidable—too formidable, as it turned out.

Eastern Siberia is a hilly region sectioned by mountain chains. Even today, its climate is almost intolerable, with some of the lowest temperatures ever recorded. During the Würm, conditions must have been still worse. A few hardy Neandertal bands seem to have established a foothold in the southern part of Siberia, which then consisted of grassland and partially wooded tundra, instead of the dense, unbroken forest that now mantles the region. Gazing north and east, they would have

Figure 15–9 Armed with clubs, Neandertal men interrupt their hunt for big game to pursue hares for the Stone Age equivalent of a light lunch. Although snow dusts the tundra landscape, the low-growing foliage is the green of late spring and the hares have begun to acquire their brownish summer coats. Such small game was a regular item of the Neandertal diet.

seen endless hills reaching into the unknown. Plentiful supplies of meat beckoned—horses and bison, and woolly mammoths with great curved tusks that could scrape at the crust of snow to get at the forage beneath. The temptation to follow the herds must have been great. But the Neandertals did not reach America. Until human beings developed better clothing, more efficient weapons, and warmer shelters, the New World would remain empty of humankind.

Although so successful, the Neandertals never really grasped the potential of bone as a material for tools; we believe that they did not know about the art of sewing, which would require bone needles; they did not know how to weave baskets or make pottery; their stone tools were inferior to those of the people who lived after them. But the Neandertals could be regarded from another viewpoint. If, by some miracle, the early *Homo sapiens* hunter who lived in a balmy England 250,000 years ago could have been transported to a Neandertal camp in glacier-gripped Europe during the Würm glaciation, he surely would have been overcome with amazement and admiration for what his species had accomplished. He would have seen men and women making a good living in an environment that would have overwhelmed him.

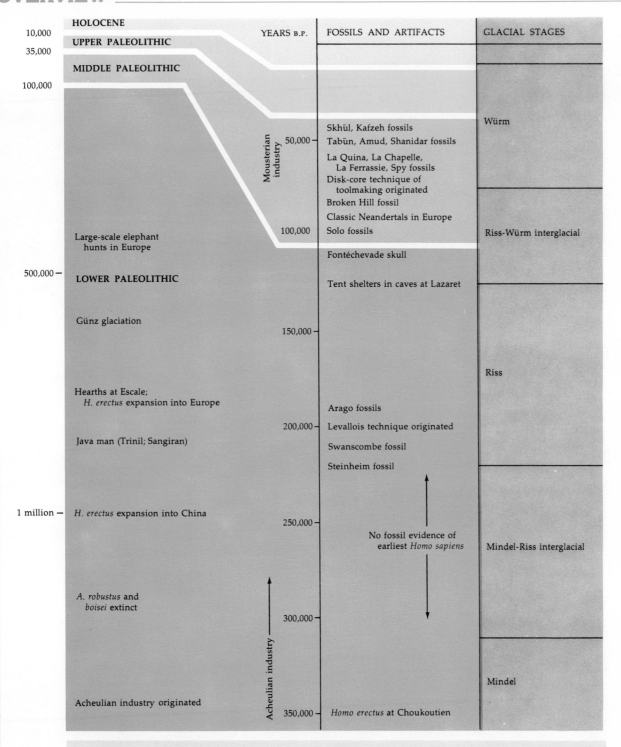

	YEARS B.P.	FOSSILS AND ARTIFACTS	GLACIAL STAGES
HOLOCENE 10,000			
UPPER PALEOLITHIC 35,000			
MIDDLE PALEOLITHIC 100,000			Würm
	50,000	Skhūl, Kafzeh fossils	
		Tabūn, Amud, Shanidar fossils	
		La Quina, La Chapelle, La Ferrassie, Spy fossils	
		Disk-core technique of toolmaking originated	
		Broken Hill fossil	
		Classic Neandertals in Europe	Riss-Würm interglacial
	100,000	Solo fossils	
Large-scale elephant hunts in Europe		Fontéchevade skull	
LOWER PALEOLITHIC 500,000		Tent shelters in caves at Lazaret	
Günz glaciation	150,000		Riss
Hearths at Escale; *H. erectus* expansion into Europe		Arago fossils	
	200,000	Levallois technique originated	
Java man (Trinil; Sangiran)		Swanscombe fossil	
		Steinheim fossil	
H. erectus expansion into China 1 million	250,000	No fossil evidence of earliest *Homo sapiens*	Mindel-Riss interglacial
A. robustus and *boisei* extinct	300,000		
			Mindel
Acheulian industry originated	350,000	*Homo erectus* at Choukoutien	

(side labels: Mousterian industry; Acheulian industry)

CONQUEST OF THE NORTH

The age of many of these specimens is still in doubt but the order of antiquity shown here is probably correct and the absolute age is fairly accurate for the more recent finds.

Chapter 16

Rituals of Life and Death

Man is no more than a reed, the weakest in nature. But he is a thinking reed.

> BLAISE PASCAL, 1623-1662.
> PENSÉES, VI, 347.

The scene is Germany; the year, 60,000 B.C. Winter reigns here in the forest belt south of the open tundra. Foxes creep through the underbrush, competing for meat with the bigger, stronger lynxes. Herds of reindeer, bison, and shaggy horses are scattered across the land. They forage in wind-swept meadows, or they scrape away the soft snow among the trees to get at the withered stems of grass beneath. These animals are constantly vigilant, for packs of wolves prowl the forest and tundra. And two-legged creatures, as terrifying as any wolves, hunt here too.

Every species of animal seems to avoid one particular locale, where a spring-fed stream slices between two hills. Up the slope of one of the hills a wall of animal hides is stretched over a framework of branches. From an opening above this wall, smoke curls into the air. Behind the skins is a cave, its entrance facing south, away from the direction of the arctic winds. A single fire is burning within, and the air is damp and tainted by the smells of excrement and unwashed bodies. This is the winter home of a Neandertal band.

A morning meal is about to begin. One of the women kneels by the fire and brushes the coals aside to expose a hearth of flat stones beneath. These stones are now extremely hot and will serve as a griddle. She selects several hunks of meat from a nearby pile and tosses them on the

LIFE DURING THE EARLY WÜRM

Neandertal Scenario: Winter

stones. Snatching up a piece of seared meat and gripping one end of it between his teeth and the fingers of one hand, a hunter cuts it in two with a sharp stone flake. Then he gobbles both pieces down, clinging ashes and all. The band of twenty-three needs almost 500 pounds of lean meat each week to stay in good health. Seldom is there enough meat to fill the communal storage pit that has been dug in the ground outside the cave. It is lined with stones and covered with a heavy stone slab to keep bears, wolves, and foxes out.

The men, after warming their hands above the fire, grasp their wooden spears and clubs and plunge into the cold. One of the five grown women of the band is preparing a hide for clothing. With a stone flake, she scrapes away the decaying tissue on the inner side of the pelt. After it has been fully cleaned, the hide will be dried slowly near the fire and then smoked to render it partially waterproof and resistant to shrinkage. Another woman takes some nuts from a pile in the back of the cave, cracks them open, and begins to pound them into an edible powder.

At times like this, when meat is running short, all the band but especially the children will have to rely heavily on stockpiles of nuts, bulbs, roots, and seeds that were gathered during the months before the snows came. Some of these gathered foods are strictly starvation fare, but there are delicacies too: one storage pit outdoors holds a supply of frozen berries.

After their meal, the children leave the cave to play outdoors. The game played by the two oldest boys is not frivolous. For hours at a time, they practice throwing spears and rocks at inanimate targets, perfecting their aim. Occasionally they charge towards a tree they have identified as an animal and beat it to death with their clubs. The women concentrate on their own chores: gathering firewood and digging up some precious meat from the outdoor storage pit. The hard life tells on them. A modern observer would say that the oldest looks 60, although she is only 45—and that is elderly by Neandertal standards.

Far from home, the men search the forest–tundra. To cover the maximum territory, they separate into pairs and set off in different directions. No man hunts alone; a partner is needed to summon help in case his fellow suffers injury. One of these teams of hunters, having travelled northward for more than an hour, halts for the first time. The oldest man pulls a few hairs from his clothing and tosses them into the air to test the direction of the wind. It is essential to travel into the wind, because almost every creature in this land has an acute nose for the scent of man. When the men have taken their bearings, they set off again, keeping about a hundred yards apart in order to sweep the broad area. As they traverse the low hills, the hunters find tiny clues to the presence of game: there are traces of hares, a lynx, a fox, elk, and reindeer.

Without warning, the silence of the hunt is broken by the sound of two stones struck together, a signal from one hunter to his partner. The two men meet silently and look out over a frozen lake where a herd of reindeer is resting. The reindeer prefer the safety of open spaces where wolves and other predators can be detected at a distance. Later in the afternoon, they will wander along the wooded shore, searching for food, but the hunters need not wait until then. In the woods or out in the open, the reindeer are swift creatures, capable of running at a speed that would carry them thirty miles in an hour. Since the chase will be difficult no matter when or where it takes place, it might as well begin.

The men move stealthily down the hill and along the shore to get as close as they can without being observed. Then they burst into the

Figure 16–1 Breaking from cover, a hunter hurls his spear into a reindeer. To catch such quick and alert animals, Neandertal man had to ambush them, stampede them into bogs, or, following the strategy of wolves, watch for signs of weakness in one of the herd, cut it out from the group, tire it, and then close in.

open. In a flash, the reindeer are up and gone, galloping across the snow-covered ice and into the trees on the far shore. But one big-antlered buck is a little slower in getting to his feet than the others. Both hunters spot that hesitation and see the slight hitch in the buck's stride, indicating an infected hoof or an injured leg. They immediately realize that if they have a chance to catch any of the reindeer, the injured buck will be the one.

The chase lasts half an hour. Although the hunters run steadily, they lag far behind their prey most of the way. When the hunters are only a mile from home, they sight their target again. The buck is struggling through a snowdrift, and the men close in and thrust their spears. With a last frenzied effort, the reindeer lunges out of the drift, with two spears protruding from its flanks.

The second stage of the chase ends quickly. Following the track of blood and hoofprints into a clump of trees, the hunters find the reindeer down on its knees. The lead runner goes up to the dying creature, lifts his club, and brings it down on the reindeer's head with such crushing force that the animal is dead almost as soon as the blow is struck.

Immediately, his partner heads for the cave to get butchering tools and bring the women back to help carry the meat. If the kill had taken place far from home, the hunters would have had to fashion tools from whatever rocks could be found nearby; and they might have been forced to spend the night there, huddled in the snow, protecting the carcass from scavengers. But no such wait is necessary this time.

Just before dark the triumphant Neandertal men and women reach home, carrying armloads of meat. The liver and fat are prized most of all, but the brain, kidney, heart, and lungs will be eaten too. Bones will be split open to get at the marrow, and the soft head of the leg joints will be chewed. Even the vegetable contents of the reindeer's two stomachs may be consumed, with blood added to the foul-smelling mixture to make it more palatable.

Later, after the meal is over, the entire band huddles around the fire. A baby sleeps in his mother's arms; a man begins to nod. The people have survived another day.

Neandertal Scenario: Spring and Summer

A year in the life of a Neandertal band contains many days like this one, although the fortunes of hunting vary greatly. During a two-week period later in the winter when a hard crust of snow covers the ground and seals off most forage, the hunters kill dozens of animals that have been weakened by starvation and disease. On other occasions, the men are away from the cave for days at a time, huddling under rock shelters at night, and still, despite their cunning, they return home empty-handed.

Spring approaches slowly. But the snow shrinks visibly, and soon the growing season is in full swing again. To escape swarming insects, many of the grazing animals move from the forests toward the open tundra. This is a fine time for hunting, because the reindeer trot along predictable routes and are ambushed easily. More animals than can possibly be eaten are driven into bogs or pools and dispatched with clubs.

One day in May the Neandertal band leaves the cave and heads north. All but a few stone tools are left behind, for it is easy to make new ones. Carrying babies, weapons, supplies of meat, and animal hides that will serve for tents, the men and women trudge along a river valley. At sunset each day they stop, rig up simple shelters, and light fires with smoldering embers that have been brought along in a cup formed from a blob of soft clay.

As the Neandertals journey onward, the trees begin to thin out. After a week of travel, the band reaches its summer domain, the open tundra. In spring the tundra landscape is covered lushly with grasses, low-lying shrubs, and mats of mosses and lichens, and spotted with streams, ponds, and lakes. During the sumptuous spring on the tundra, the band is fed better than at any other time of the year. The grazing animals are giving birth now, and the hunters take a number of calves. Huge flocks of geese, ducks, and swans have flown in from the south, and many of them fall victim to well-aimed stones as they feed in the lakes and ponds. Each day, the women and children find downy baby birds in nests on the ground. Occasional fish are taken in weirs of branches set up to form shallow pools. As the weeks pass the Neandertals grow noticeably fatter.

Even at the height of summer, the weather remains rather cool, averaging about 50°F. The band lives in a hut made of animal hides stretched over a framework of branches and large animal bones. From time to time, the camp is moved to a new location, but each site is occupied long enough for split bones and unwanted food scraps to litter the area.

Toward the end of summer, a tragedy occurs. A hunter, misjudging the strength left in a wounded bison, is badly gored while trying to deliver the killing blow. Poultices of herbs and clay have no effect against the deep chest wound and within a few hours the hunter is dead. Early the next morning the dead man is buried, along with his club, spear, and enough food for the journey into the world beyond the grave. When the burial is finished, the band leaves the camp. The dead man's woman moves to the bed of the bachelor hunter.

Summer on the tundra passes quickly. In September, the period of growth is over, and the reindeer show signs of restlessness. One morning, after a light rain, the band wakes to discover that the tent is encrusted with ice. They must head south. En route, they find more good hunting. Another band is met on the way and the two groups join forces. With every able-bodied man, woman, and child taking part, the two bands succeed in stampeding an entire herd of horses over a cliff. This is the high point of the year, a time for relaxation and impromptu contests, and a time when young men and women might find mates from the other band.

Days of intensive hunting lie ahead, but the animals eventually will grow wary. The storms of winter will drive the Neandertals back to their smoky cave. There will be sickness, perhaps death. But the band will

Figure 16–2 Horses, driven to the brink of a cliff by hunters waving torches, plunge to their doom. This successful kill needed the cooperation of many Neandertals—some to head the horses toward the cliff, others below to finish off the fallen animals with clubs and spears. The horses were smaller than those of today.

still be there next spring and the spring after, holding onto this difficult northern land with a fierce and indomitable grip.

The picture of Neandertal life given in this imagined journey backward in time may seem fanciful, but it is not fictional. Although the portrayal involves a certain amount of dramatic license, it is based on a good deal of factual evidence. It does not pretend to cover all people who lived in the world 60,000 years ago. It refers to a very special region: the open tundra and *taiga*—forest–tundra along the northernmost frontier of human settlement. What makes this region important is that the tundra country tested to the utmost the resourcefulness of the Neandertals. Their success in coping with the difficulties imposed by the region marks an important milestone in mankind's efforts to conquer nature.

It should be remembered, of course, that most of the world's population in those days lived in less hostile environments, and their modes of survival were very different in many respects from life in the cold north. For example, the life of a band in the African savanna revolved around seasonal shifts of dry and rainy weather; the women collected a completely different array of grass seeds, fruits, insects, caterpillars, and perhaps honey or the edible gum of certain trees; the men killed antelope and zebras instead of reindeer, woolly rhinoceros, and mammoths (Figure 16–3). Nevertheless, their hunter-gatherer life style displayed many of the same basic features that characterized the life of the Neandertals in Germany.

How scientists come by the evidence that allows reconstruction of Neandertal life is itself a fascinating story. One source is the study of life styles of the few hunter-gatherer societies that still survive in the world today. For example, certain hunter-gatherers of Siberia, known as the Yukaghir, kill reindeer mainly by chasing them on foot for many miles across the snowy terrain and then summon their women to carry the carcasses home. It is at least plausible to assume that the Neandertal hunters of Germany did the same. The Yukaghir like to eat frozen berries, and it is reasonable to believe that Neandertals shared this taste.

The model of contemporary hunter-gatherer societies is not the only source of suppositions about the prehistory of mankind. Some of the key ingredients in our description of life in a Neandertal band rest on solid documentary evidence. The presence of Mousterian tools in geological deposits in Germany proves beyond doubt that Neandertals did live there during the Würm glacial period. One especially well-excavated site near the town of Lebenstedt has supplied a wealth of information about the weather and vegetation at the edge of the northern tundra. No human fossils were discovered at the site, but numerous fossilized animal bones were found, indicating that the Neandertals hunted mostly reindeer but also went after mammoths, bison, horses, and woolly rhinoceros. A few remains of waterfowl, fish, and molluscs were also discovered.

Figure 16–3 The eight-ton, twelve-foot-tall woolly mammoth was ideally suited to the rigors of ice-age Europe. Shaggy hair and a layer of fat insulated it from the cold, and its ears were small to reduce heat loss. The woolly mammoth disappeared about 10,000 years ago, possibly unable to adapt to the increasingly temperate climate of its last home, the grazing grounds in Siberia and North America.

Tundra Adaptations

Figure 16–4 A crude Neandertal shelter made from saplings covered with animal skins. This reconstruction is based on the evidence of postholes and stones in the floor of a cave in southern France. The skins are lashed to the framework with leather thongs and anchored with stones.

That the Neandertals built artificial shelters when caves were unavailable is also known. Although no shelters have been found in Germany, clear evidence of a man-made shelter in open terrain was discovered at a Neandertal site a thousand miles to the east, in Molodova, in the Soviet Union. Other examples, of a different construction, are known in southern France (see Figure 16–4). Of course, no one can say for sure that all northern Neandertal bands constructed such huts; but it is much harder to conceive of their remaining ignorant of such an important adaptation to cold environments.

Careful study of the Lebenstedt site has indicated that the open tundra was occupied only during the warmer months, rather than all year round. It reveals that Neandertals lived there for a few weeks at a time during several summers. In winter, with few trees to fend off the freezing winds, conditions would have been unendurable; and in springtime the site was flooded by meltwaters. The German band almost certainly retreated into the forest during the winter.

For reconstructing some areas of Neandertal life common sense is a guide. A good example is the assertion by some authorities that the women of the band used birchbark containers when they gathered vegetable foods. All of the bark from that period has, of course, long since decayed. But almost all experts are agreed that mankind must have been using some sort of container from very earliest times, because the gatherers would hardly be so inefficient as to carry grain, nuts, or berries back to their camp handful by handful. Birch bark was available in the forest–tundra, and it would have made fine containers for a band living there. Other materials may have been used; animal skins or even the bladders or stomachs of animals would have been satisfactory.

In time much more hard evidence about the Neandertals' life—tools, fossils, and other remains—should turn up to fill in missing details in the picture. In the meantime, scientists have found ways to make the old evidence reveal new things. Even the most unlikely evidence occasionally turns out to be important. For instance, reindeer teeth have been used to show that some Neandertals in southern France occupied caves throughout the year. Reindeer are always born in the spring, and development of their teeth gives an accurate measure of their age. Cave excavations have produced teeth from reindeer of all different ages, which proves that the animals were killed during spring, summer, autumn, and winter. This is no trivial finding. The evidence that Neandertals could get enough food without having to move about in a large territory testifies to a high level of hunting ability. Probably only the inhabitants of the very richest lands could afford to lead a sedentary existence. In most places, camps had to be shifted from time to time as the game supply became depleted or when the weather became intolerable—or even because of the accumulation of garbage.

Some of the most intriguing information about the Neandertals is the least obvious. In the 1950s, F. E. Koby studied some Neandertal front teeth under a microscope and spotted hundreds of parallel scratches in the enamel. These scratches seem certainly to be a result of eating habits. The Neandertals, like modern-day Eskimos and other hunter-gatherers, must have stuffed meat into their mouths, clamped it between their teeth, and sawed off the excess with stone knives. The knives produced diagonal scratches, running from upper left to lower right. Since it can be assumed that the Neandertals would use their more adept hand to wield the stone knife and the other hand to hold the end of the meat, the direction of the scratches is one of the indications that these Neandertals were right-handed.

A natural reaction to this discovery might be: "So what?" Actually, the indication of hand preference among Neandertals may represent an important clue to human history. In the entire animal kingdom, only human beings favor one hand regularly over the other. Some scientists are beginning to suspect that the development of handedness is intimately related to the development of speech. The suspicion is based on complicated neurological studies, but if these scientists are indeed right in their assumption, those little scratches on some old front teeth may well be an oblique reference to something of great portent: the Neandertals' command of language.

One of the most provocative and controversial of recent studies of Neandertals examined this facet of Neandertal culture from a completely different angle—and produced completely different results. We have seen in Chapter 13 how Lieberman and Crelin attempted to bring those long-ago voices within hearing distance. Their investigation of the linguistic capabilities of the Neandertals suggested that European Neandertal man lacked a modern kind of pharynx and, as a result, would have been unable to utter the vowel sounds heard in the words *bar, boo, beep,* and *bought;* nor could he have formed the consonants *g*

Evidence for Handedness and Language

and *k*. His repertoire of sounds was quite limited compared to that of modern humans: it consisted of fewer consonants and a relatively narrow range of vowel sounds, those heard by us in such English words as *bit, bet, bat,* and *but.*

These findings have been disputed vigorously and no one is yet certain exactly what they mean. Most probably Neandertal man could communicate quite well with his own kind of speech and a more limited range of vowels and consonants. Interestingly enough, Neandertals outside of western Europe may have possessed a more efficient speaking apparatus. Lieberman and Crelin have determined that Rhodesian man in Africa had a slightly more modern pharynx, and the fossil skulls from Skhūl had a nearly modern vocal tract. If Lieberman and Crelin are right and the voices of a long-vanished people can indeed be summoned from their bones, who knows what else we may someday know about the Neandertals?

NEANDERTAL RITUALS AND ART

Discovery after discovery has shown that the Neandertals very probably started some of the activities and beliefs that are considered most characteristic of mankind. These ancient people conceived of a life after death. They attempted to control their own destiny through magical rites. They may even have taken the first hesitant steps into the realm of art. And they cared for aged and handicapped individuals. In fact, it seems they were the first human beings to display the complete spectrum of behavior that can be considered to constitute human nature.

Hunting Rites and Magic

It seems very probable that Neandertal man, like modern hunter-gatherers, had rites related to that most vital activity, hunting. The outcome of the hunt affected every individual. It was a matter of great importance that the supply of animals remain plentiful and that the men of the band enjoy good luck and personal safety in the hunt. But nothing in their world was guaranteed. Hunters could be injured. A long spell of bad weather could cut down on the catch. Animal herds might be destroyed by disease, changes in the predator population, or a host of other ecological factors. Mysterious forces operating beyond the horizon could interfere with animal migrations, causing herds to disappear.

Prior to the Neandertal era, these various liabilities probably were regarded as being largely beyond human control. But the Neandertals apparently attempted to manipulate the hidden forces of their universe that controlled success and failure in the hunt: they seem to have practiced hunting magic. One clue to their efforts comes from the so-called Cave of Witches, Grotto della Basua, west of Genoa, Italy. In the depths of the cave, almost 1,500 feet from the entrance, Neandertal hunters threw pellets of clay at a stalagmite that to this day has a vaguely animal shape. The inconvenient location of the stalagmite rules out the possibility that this was merely a game or a kind of target practice. The fact that the hunters went so far back into the cave to throw the pellets suggests that the activity had magical meaning of some kind.

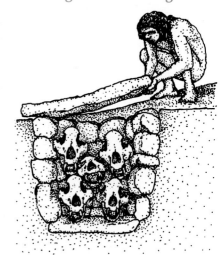

Figure 16–5 Discovery of bear skulls stacked in a pit supports the idea that the cave bear was the center of a Neandertal cult. Such skulls may have been man's first hunting trophies.

In 1970, Ralph Solecki discovered evidence of a deer ceremony at a cave in Lebanon. Here, about 50,000 years ago, some Neandertals dismembered a fallow deer, placed the meat on a bed of stones, and sprinkled it with red ocher. The natural pigment was almost certainly intended as a symbol of blood—the blood of the earth, in a sense. The rite seems to represent a ritualistic or magical attempt to control life and death in the deer kingdom.

The Bear Cult

The most famous example of Neandertal hunting magic is the bear cult. It came to light when a German archaeologist, Emil Bächler, excavated the cave of Drachenloch between 1917 and 1923. Located 8,000 feet up in the Swiss Alps, this "lair of the dragons" tunnels deep into a mountainside. The front part of the cave, Bächler's work made clear, served as an occasional dwelling place for Neandertals. Farther back, Bächler found a cubical chest made of stones and measuring approximately three and a quarter feet on a side. The top of the chest was covered by a single massive slab of stone. Inside were seven bear skulls, all arranged with their muzzles facing the cave entrance. Still deeper in the cave were six bear skulls, set in niches along the walls. Beside some of the skulls lay bear limb bones, not necessarily from the same animal as had provided the skull. A leg bone had been thrust through the arch of the cheekbone of one of the skulls, an arrangement that must have been made by humans. The Drachenloch find is not unique. At the site of Regourdou in southern France, a rectangular pit, covered by a flat stone slab weighing nearly a ton, held the bones of more than twenty bears.

The object of these rites was an extinct species, *Ursus spelaeus,* now known as the cave bear. This barrel-chested brute outweighed the grizzly and measured nine feet from nose to tail. Swift, powerful, and less predictable than any herd animal, it occupied a difficult environment, wintering in caves and ranging throughout the rugged, densely wooded sections of the European mountains during the milder seasons of the year.

The Neandertals' stone chests of bear bones were not simply trophies, like stuffed animal heads hanging in the dens of modern game hunters. If contemporary examples of hunting magic are any guide, the Neandertals were up to something much more serious. Rites involving bears are still performed—or at least were performed until quite recently—by a number of northerly hunting peoples, living in the wild lands that stretch from Lapland across Siberia and into the arctic regions of the New World. Certain Siberian tribes worship the bear as the mythical first man, and they make profound apologies to the animal before killing it. In other cases, the bears are considered to be intermediaries between human beings and the reigning spirits of the land. The Ainu of northern Japan capture a cub and treat it as an honored guest through most of the year (sometimes the women even nurse the cub); then, in the winter, the bear is sacrificed at the conclusion of a long ceremony, and the Ainu men drink its blood while the presiding shaman prays to

Figure 16–6 Although a formidable animal to hunt, the cave bear was probably fairly easy to kill during its hibernation. Neandertals often must have had to remove the bears from caves needed for living quarters. No doubt the size and danger of cave bears were the main reasons why their skulls were treated as sacred objects.

the Creator. These people believe that the spirit of the sacrificed bear will return to the forest and report the hospitality it received. Supposedly, a favorable report will persuade the forest gods to arrange for good hunting the following year.

The Neandertals' motives for killing cave bears and preserving the skulls in stone chests can be only guessed at, but it seems likely that beliefs about the functioning of the universe were involved. Possibly these beliefs were less intricate than those of modern hunter-gatherers. It is safe to say of the Neandertals' hunting magic, and any of their other rites as well, that they did not spring full-blown from the brow of some primordial genius. The beliefs underlying these rites must have begun with tiny, simple-minded speculations and gradually gained momentum over a period of tens of thousands of years.

Logic suggests that art, another remarkable product of the human imagination, started this way, too. That the beginnings of art may have occurred during Neandertal times is also a logical deduction, for the Cro-Magnons who lived about 25,000 B.P. were already accomplished artists who created engravings, statuary, and magnificent cave paintings. The only prehistoric arts for which there can be any surviving evidence are the visual kind. If music was played during Neandertal times, it is lost forever. The Neandertals may have been excellent singers and perhaps even imaginative dancers; dancing is an important form of expression among all known hunting peoples. But what little is known about the visual art of the Neandertals would indicate a low level of accomplishment.

The Neandertals occasionally made use of such natural pigments as red or yellow ocher and black manganese. These occur at Neandertal sites in powder form and sometimes in pencil-shaped pieces that show signs of being rubbed on a soft surface, such as human skin or animal hides. Neandertal men may have painted themselves before setting out on a hunt or a war mission; possibly they created visual patterns that were thought to have some supernatural power to strike fear into the enemy, bewitch animals, or otherwise augment their chances of success. No picture or pattern drawn with these pigments survives, if indeed any ever existed.

As for other possible art forms, there is no sign of a representational engraving or statue from the era of the Neandertals. Nor have their deposits yielded a single perforated tooth that might have been used in a necklace, a very common personal ornament among hunters, including the later Cro-Magnons. However, there are a few tantalizing indications that the Neandertals were beginning to sense the visual possibilities of the materials around them. A cave at Tata in Hungary has yielded a piece of ivory that had been trimmed into an oval shape, polished, and then coated with ocher. At the cave of Pech de l'Azé in southern France, a Neandertal bored a hole in an animal bone; the bone may have been an amulet of sorts. From another French cave at Arcy-sur-Cure come a pair of oddities—two fossils of marine animals. These

Beginnings of Art

are very humble art objects indeed, perhaps mere curiosities, but they have no obvious utilitarian function.

Equally cryptic are a few hints of the symbolic notation that would someday blossom into writing. A few pebbles from the Neandertal cave at Tata have grooves that may be symbolic. Some enigmatically engraved bones are known from several Neandertal cave sites in northern Spain. An ox rib from Pech de l'Azé bears a series of scratches on one side; these appear in groups of two, and they do not look at all like the marks that would have been left if someone were merely cutting meat off the bone. Perhaps these scratches are doodles, lacking in meaning. But symbolic notation had to start somewhere, and it definitely existed by 30,000 years ago, when the Cro-Magnons were making crude calendars.

All of what might be examples of visual expression by the Neandertals are very rudimentary and tentative, but the first step in any endeavor is the hardest. As far as is known now, the Neandertals had no tradition in the arts or in written symbolism to build on and no means of sensing the magnificent future of such expression. Yet they made a beginning. This beginning, like those in religion and magic, indicates an awakening, wondering mind. During Neandertal times, human nature was still in the making, but its outlines had become visible.

Of all the various indications of the humanlike behavior of the Neandertals, their practice of burying the dead is the best documented and easiest to interpret. Death is life's bitterest fact, the inescapable defeat at the end of a long struggle to survive and prosper, and man is not the only creature saddened by it. Many animals seem momentarily distraught when death claims one of their number; elephants, for instance, have been observed trying to revive a dying member of the herd, even attempting to get it back on its feet by lifting it with their tusks. But only people anticipate the event far in advance, acknowledging that inevitably it will occur, dreading it, refusing to accept it as conclusive, and taking some solace in a belief in an afterlife. One mark of this belief is burial of the dead.

The Neandertals were not credited with deliberately meaningful burial of their dead until more than a half-century after their discovery. The original Neandertal man taken from the cave in the Neander Valley of Germany may have been buried by his survivors, although no one suspected so when his bones were found in 1856. The two fossils discovered at Spy in Belgium in 1885 also had been buried; apparently fires had been lighted over the bodies, perhaps in an effort to counteract the chill of death. But once again no one guessed in 1885 that Spy had been the scene of an ancient burial. Then, in 1908, the cave of La Chapelle-aux-Saints in France almost shouted its evidence of a

Symbolic Notation?

Figure 16–7 **This small stone from a Mousterian site at Tata in Hungary, dated 50,000 years B.P. carries an engraved cross. We do not know its significance, but the stone is the earliest known example of artistic or symbolic decoration.**

DEATH AND BURIAL

Evidence of Burial Customs

Neandertal funeral rite. The excavators found an ancient hunter who had been laid out carefully in a shallow trench. A bison leg was placed on his chest, and the trench was filled with broken animal bones and flint tools. These various articles might have been seen as provisions for the world beyond the grave, since it was well known that many primitive peoples bury their dead with food, weapons, and other goods. And yet even then most experts failed to make the connection that now seems obvious.

The evidence continued to turn up. In 1912, two more Neandertal graves were found at the site of La Ferrassie, not far from the cave at La Chapelle. The diggers who carried out the excavation wrote:

La Ferrassie (1912–1934)

> We have been able to recognize, at the base of the Mousterian layer, the existence of two small trenches measuring 70 centimeters wide by 30 centimeters in depth, very precisely cut in half-sphere form in the underlying red-yellowish loamy gravel, filled with a mixture of nearly equal parts of the black earth of the Mousterian fireplace above and of the underlying gravel. The existence of artificially dug graves was absolutely obvious . . . . This is, then, in the clearest way, proof of a funeral rite.

The excavation of the Ferrassie site took many years, and the complete results were not published until 1934. This rock shelter appears to have served as a family cemetery. Six Neandertal fossils were eventually exhumed: a man, a woman, two children about five years old, and two infants (see Figure 16–8). Also found were several trenches that seemed to have been prepared as graves but lay empty, perhaps because the bones had somehow decomposed or the bodies had been dug up by a scavenging animal such as a cave hyena. Flint flakes and bone splinters had been put in the grave of the adult male, and a flat stone slab had been placed over his shoulders and head (to protect him? to restrain him from coming back to life?). The woman was buried in an exaggerated fetal position, with her legs tightly bent at the knees and pulled up against her chest. It looked as if thongs had been used to bind her legs before her corpse stiffened. This *flexing*, as the folding of legs is called, occurs in many Neandertal burials. Religious beliefs may account for the practice; many primitive peoples tie up the dead

Figure 16–8 The care that Neandertals lavished on their dead is made clear at La Ferrassie, France. Here anthropologists have discovered what may be a 60,000-year-old family cemetery containing the skeletons of two adults and four children. The presumed parents were buried head to head (at sites 1 and 2 in the drawing); two skeletons (3 and 4), possibly of their children, each about five years old, were neatly interred near their father's feet. The significance of the nine small mounds is not clear, but one contained the bones of a newborn infant and three beautiful flint tools (5). The triangular stone (6) covered the grave of a six-year-old child.

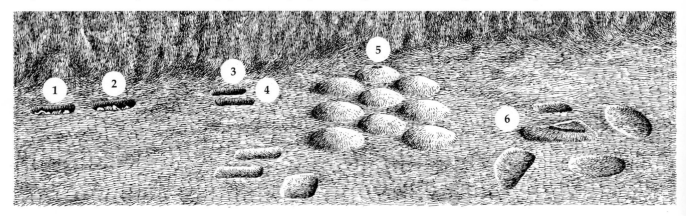

in order to prevent them from coming back to bother the living. However, some experts believe the flexing was merely a way of saving labor in the arduous work of hacking a trench in rocky ground with stone or wooden tools. A grave could be considerably smaller if the dead person were flexed instead of stretched out full length.

The most perplexing grave at La Ferrassie was located in the rear of the shelter. Here, in a gently sloping trench, the lower skeleton and skull of a child were interred, separated by a distance of about three feet. The skull was covered by a triangular limestone slab whose underside displayed a number of cup-shaped impressions, possibly symbolic markings of some sort. Why were the head and the rest of the body separated? One authority, the Abbé Bouyssonnie, a French prehistorian, has suggested that the child was killed and beheaded by a wild animal; later, the head was intentionally buried upslope from the body so that, in the afterlife, it might somehow find its way down the slope and rejoin the trunk. This is a pure guess, but there must be some reason for the odd arrangement.

As more and more Neandertal graves were found over the years, a larger puzzle emerged. It relates not to the meaning of specific funeral rites but to the identity of the people who performed them. Almost every Neandertal burial in western Europe is associated with a certain toolmaking tradition known as *Quina-Ferrassie* (see Figure 16–9). Yet this tradition is only one of four main styles that François Bordes believes were used in western Europe. In addition to the Quina-Ferrassie style (containing a high proportion of flake tools used for scraping), there are the Denticulate Mousterian (containing many notched or toothed flakes), the *Typical Mousterian* (highly developed pointed tools), and the *Mousterian of Acheulian Tradition,* or MAT in archaeological shorthand (a very diverse tool kit that includes numerous hand-axes). In Bordes' opinion, these four basic sorts of tool kits represent distinct cultures—different peoples occupying the same general area but having little contact with one another. No bones have been found associated with Denticulate tools, nor have human fossils been found in association with tools of the Mousterian of Acheulian Tradition. Did only the Quina-Ferrassie people, then, believe in a life after death? Not necessarily. In the first place, burial is not the only ritual way of entering the afterworld; Bordes speculates that the people of the other tool styles may have exposed corpses to the elements on platforms outside their caves or placed them in trees, as some modern tribesmen still do. Or they could have practiced cremation, a practical solution to the problem of frozen ground. But there is an alternative explanation: the different tool styles may prove to be different tool kits developed for different purposes by the same people. The different kits may have a functional rather than a racial significance.

This European puzzle remains unanswered. But from other parts of the world we have certain evidence that many other Neandertals did

Traditions of the Mousterian Industry

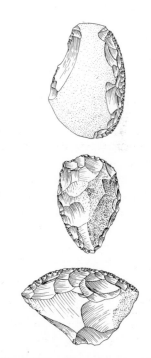

Figure 16–9 Three scrapers from the Quina-Ferrassie Mousterian tool industry.

Non-European Burials

bury their dead. Far to the east, on the Crimean peninsula that juts into the Black Sea, the graves of two individuals were found at a cave at Kiik-Koba in 1924. One trench held the remains of a year-old child resting on his side with his legs bent. This skeleton was in poor condition because later inhabitants of the cave had dug a pit for their fire directly over the grave and inadvertently disturbed the bones. Three feet away from the child was the grave of a man, also lying on his side with his legs tucked up. The body was oriented east–west—as were the Spy fossils and five out of six of the Ferrassie fossils. Possibly the orientation signified something about the rising or setting sun.

The early 1930s saw the discovery of the magnificent set of Neandertal fossils at Mount Carmel above Haifa in Israel (see page 290). On the terrace at the mouth of the Skhūl cave, five men, two women, and three children had been placed in shallow graves. The legs of all of the bodies were pulled up so tightly that the feet touched the buttocks. There is little other suggestion of ritual—with a single startling exception. One 45-year-old man held in his arms the jawbones of a huge boar. Did the boar cause his death? Or do the jaws represent a hunting trophy, proclaiming the man's prowess to whatever spirits might meet him in the afterlife?

The ambiguity surrounding this burial is echoed at another site farther to the east, in the mountains of Uzbek in central Asia. Here, in 1938, the cave of Teshik-Tash surrendered the body of a Neandertal boy. Although the grave had been damaged by an animal, a few mysterious signs of a funeral rite survived. Six pairs of goat horns, still attached to their skulls, were found pushed into the cave floor in a roughly circular arrangement around the grave. Some interpreters maintain that the horns were merely digging tools, but their placement in a rough circle makes a ritualistic significance seem plausible. Whatever the circle of horns means, it is a tribute to the hunting skills of the Neandertals. Catching the elusive, agile goats must have been quite a feat even for these experienced hunters.

The most amazing Neandertal burial of all was that in the Shanidar cave (see Figure 16–10). There Ralph Solecki dug down through compressed deposits to uncover a total of nine Neandertals. At the back of the cave, in a layer estimated to be 60,000 years old, he found the grave of a hunter with a badly crushed skull. As a routine procedure, Solecki collected samples of the soil in and around the grave (shown in Figure 16–11) and sent them to a laboratory at the Musée de l'Homme in France. There his colleague Arlette Leroi-Gourhan checked the pollen count, hoping it would provide useful information on the climate and vegetation prevailing during Neandertal times.

What she found was completely unexpected. Pollen was present in the grave in unprecedented abundance. Even more astonishing, some of it appeared in clusters, and a few clusters had been preserved along with the parts of the flowers that had supported them. No birds or animals or wind could possibly have deposited such material in the recess of the cave. Clearly, masses of flowers had been placed in the

Figure 16–10   Kurdish shepherds, helping with the excavations at Shanidar, still use the cave to shelter themselves and their animals during the cold winters, much as Neandertals did thousands of years ago.

grave by the companions of the dead man. Leroi-Gourhan believes that the Neandertal hunter was laid to rest on a woven bedding of pine boughs and flowers; more blossoms may very well have been strewn over his body.

Microscopic examination of the pollen indicated that it came from numerous species of bright-colored flowers, related to the grape hyacinth, bachelor's button, hollyhock, and groundsel. Some of these plants are used in poultices and herbal remedies by contemporary peoples in Iraq. Perhaps the Neandertals, too, felt that the blossoms possessed medicinal properties and added them to the grave in an effort to restore health to the fallen hunter in the afterlife. On the other hand, the flowers may have been put there in the same spirit that moves modern people to place flowers on graves and gravestones.

The Neandertals must have sensed the precious quality of life more keenly than any creatures before them, because funeral rites, at the most fundamental level, represent a commitment to human conservation. Funerals declare that some essential quality of human life, call it spirit or soul, cannot be destroyed but continues to exist after death, somewhere else, in some other form.

This growing sense of the value of life is reflected not only in death rites but also in the Neandertals' treatment of old or handicapped individuals. The man of La Chapelle-aux-Saints, for instance, was long past his prime when he died. His skeleton reveals that he had been bent

The Old and the Handicapped

Figure 16–11 The Neandertal skeleton known as Shanidar 4, which pollen tests show was buried with bunches of wild flowers, including hyacinths, daisies, and hollyhocks. The age is circa 60,000 B.P.

over by arthritis and could not possibly have taken part in a hunt. Even the act of eating must have been difficult for him, since he had lost all but two teeth. Had he lived at some earlier time, he might well have been abandoned to starve after his economic usefulness to the group was over. But the Neandertals evidently were not ruled by such stern logic. This man's companions unselfishly provided food, and they probably even softened it for him by partially chewing it.

The Neandertals' concern for the handicapped is suggested also by remains at Shanidar. Some of the Neandertal bones found there belonged to a 40-year-old man who probably was killed by a rockfall. Study of his skeleton revealed that before his accidental death he had had the use of only one arm; his right arm and shoulder were poorly developed, probably from a birth defect. Despite the major disability, he lived to a ripe age for a Neandertal. His front teeth are unusually worn, suggesting that he spent much of his time chewing animal hides to soften them for use as clothes or used his teeth in lieu of his arm in order to hold objects.

Evidence of Violence

The fact that the Neandertals could find a place in their society for aged or handicapped individuals does not necessarily mean that they were always kind and full of love for their fellow man. At Neandertal sites there is plentiful evidence for the darker side of human nature. For example, a fossil of a man found at Skhūl bears the traces of a fatal spear wound. The point of a wooden spear, long since decayed, had passed through the top of the man's thighbone and the socket of the hipbone, ending up inside the pelvic cavity.

Another ancient act of violence is recorded in the Shanidar deposits. One of the ribs of the fossil of a Neandertal hunter from the Iraq cave was deeply grooved by the point of a weapon, probably a wooden spear. The tip had penetrated the man's chest and perhaps punctured a lung, but this hunter somehow had survived the wound, for the bone shows signs of healing. The original Neandertal from Germany also had survived a grievous injury, although his recovery was incomplete: his left elbow bones were so misshapen that he could not have raised his hand to his mouth. Whether the damage was done by man or beast will never be known. There may be a hint in an interesting correspondence noted by T. Dale Stewart, who points out that the injuries of the men from Skhūl, Shanidar, and the Neander Valley involved in all three cases the left side of the body. This is the side that would tend to be most easily injured in combat between right-handed opponents.

That Neandertals sometimes killed one another should surprise no one. Perhaps more surprising is the ample evidence that they also ate one another. In 1899 the mutilated remains of about twenty Neandertals—men, women, and children—were found at the site of Krapina in Yugoslavia. Skulls had been smashed into fragments; limb bones had been split lengthwise, presumably for their marrow; and there were traces of charring to hint that the human meat had been cooked. In 1965 another collection of charred and shattered human bones, again involving at least twenty individuals, was found at the cave of Hortus in France. The remains were mixed with other animal bones and food refuse, as if some ancient inhabitants of the cave had drawn no distinction between human meat and that of a bison or reindeer.

Some anthropologists feel that the cannibalism at Krapina and Hortus was motivated by nothing more than hunger. They suggest that a band of Neandertals, having run short of other game, simply decided that the neighbors would make a nice meal. This idea does not get much support from a study by physical anthropologists Stanley M. Garn and Walter D. Block, who looked at the problem of cannibalism from the viewpoint of practical dietetics. According to the arithmetic of the two anthropologists, the edible muscle mass of a 110-pound man skillfully butchered would yield about 10 pounds of useful protein—not very much food, compared to the meat of a mammoth or a bison. Furthermore, contemporary peoples who practice cannibalism are not driven simply by hunger or blind ferocity. Members of some societies believe that they can acquire strength and courage by eating the flesh of an enemy. There are also documented cases of murderers eating the flesh of their victims in order to prevent the ghost of the dead from haunting them; or the relatives of a murdered person may eat his flesh, in the belief that it will aid them in their quest for revenge. However, the slaughters at Krapina and Hortus seem to have been more savage and less selective than any cannibalistic rite of today.

Cannibalism and Ritual

Ritualistic motives appear more likely at another ancient feast on human flesh. The evidence is in the group of skulls excavated on the banks of the Solo River in Java. Though eleven skulls were dug up, no other skeletal parts were found except for two shin bones. The facial bones had been smashed off every skull, and not a single jaw or tooth was left. The bodiless isolation of the skulls is enough to hint at some ritual intent. Even more suggestive is the treatment of the opening at the base of the skull. The foramen magnum is normally about an inch and a half in diameter. In all but two of the Solo skulls, it had been widened considerably by hacking with stone or wooden tools. Similar mutilation of skulls has been observed among cannibals of the present day, who widen the opening so they can reach into the skulls to scoop out the brains.

Not all authorities accept a direct connection between cannibalism and the widening of the foramen magnum. Certain contemporary peoples keep skulls as trophies or as cherished mementos of departed relatives. They clean the skulls by opening up the base and removing the brain. However, it is doubtful that any of the skulls from Java were cherished, because, in every case, the face had been knocked off, and at least one of the men had been killed by a crushing blow to the back of the head.

Bodiless skulls of Neandertals have been found in Europe as well as Asia, prompting speculation about a worldwide Neandertal skull cult. One skull, belonging to a five- or six-year-old child, turned up in a cave on the Rock of Gibraltar. The discoverer, struck by the absence of any other human bones, suggested that the solitary skull had been placed there as a trophy or sacred relic. A similar find occurred at Ehringsdorf, Germany. Here, the jaw of an adult, the remains of a ten-year-old child, and the cranium of a woman were unearthed. The woman had been clubbed repeatedly on the forehead; her head was severed from her body; and, as at Solo, the foramen magnum had been enlarged. Although some experts believe these skulls could have been brought to their strange state by natural causes—hyenas, the pressure of falling rock, and so on—another skull, from Monte Circeo in Italy, would seem to resolve such doubts.

Monte Circeo is a limestone hill on a peninsula about 55 miles south of Rome. During Roman times, Monte Circeo was a popular coastal resort, and the ruins of ancient villas can still be seen amid the flowering shrubs on its slopes. The twentieth-century tourist trade was responsible for the discovery of a Neandertal sanctuary hidden far beneath these slopes.

In 1939 the owner of a seaside inn decided to expand his premises to accommodate his steadily increasing trade. When workmen dug into the limestone to make room for a bigger terrace, they bared the entrance of a cave, about 15 feet above sea level. Apparently the cave had been sealed off by a landslide long ago, transforming it into a pristine time vault such as archaeologists dream of. The proprietor of the inn

A Cult of Skulls?

Figure 16–12 Monte Circeo man was a classic Neandertal found in an Italian cave sealed for some 60,000 years. He was about forty years old and had been murdered. His right temple was smashed, and a hole was cut in the base of his skull, probably for picking out the brain. He seems to have been a victim of ritual cannibalism: his skull had been carefully centered in a ring of stones.

and several of his friends crept on their hands and knees along a narrow corridor leading into the hillside. The corridor opened onto a chamber where no human being had set foot for perhaps 60,000 years. By lantern light the explorers could see that in this eerie sanctuary a shallow trench had been scooped out of the ground near the farthest wall. A single skull rested there, surrounded by an oval ring of stones.

Subsequent examination of the skull showed that it had belonged to a Neandertal man who had been killed by a blow to the temple. And once again, the foramen magnum had been enlarged. This mutilation, plus the presence of the ring of stones, provided plain evidence that a ceremony had been staged in the cave.

The stone-encircled skull at Monte Circeo could signify almost anything. Consider a rite of some contemporary head-hunting tribes in New Guinea. When a child is born into a tribe, the tribesmen kill a man from another tribe; the father or a near relative of the infant beheads the victim and opens the foramen magnum to extract the brain, which is baked with sago (a starch made from the pith of a palm) and then eaten. All this is done in the belief that the newborn child cannot be assigned a name without the ritual treatment of the brain of a man whose name is known; an anonymous corpse would not do. This violent rite is so alien to Western culture that its explanation seems incredible, despite the testimony of eyewitnesses. The practice could not possibly be guessed at if there were only a mutilated skull and some sago to go by. Although it does no harm to speculate about the rite at Monte Circeo, our chances of being correct are not much better than those of a New Guinean hunter trying to guess why peoples of the Western world traditionally launch a ship by breaking a bottle of champagne across the bow.

Neandertal man's rites of burial and cannibalism may be only the visible tip of an iceberg of hidden ceremonies. Practically all known primitive peoples have special beliefs and practices pertaining to key steps in the human life cycle, and it is at least reasonable to assume that the Neandertals did too. Birth, for instance, may have been treated as more than a purely biological event. Perhaps the Neandertals had ritualistic ways of ensuring the safety of the mother, welcoming the child into the world, giving it a name, and aiding its chances of good fortune later in life. Other likely occasions for ceremonies were the attainment of puberty, the initiation of hunters, marriage, or the choice of a leader. Serious illness, too, might have called for a special attempt to enlist help from extrahuman sources or to drive malevolent spirits from the body of the afflicted person. And death, of course, stirred the ritual impulse most deeply of all.

The story of the Neandertals should rightly end about 35,000 years ago. Imagine a man of the time. Give him an intermediate head, with a fairly high cranium, a jaw that would look only mildly outsized on a man of today, and a bit of brow ridge. Endow him with an intelligence just about equivalent to the modern level, even though his verbal communication may be less efficient than that of modern mankind.

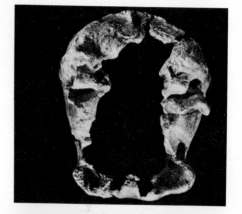

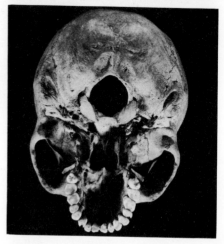

Figure 16–13 This cast of a skull from Ngandong (top) shows the face and base of the skull broken away. Below it for comparison is a basal view of an unmutilated skull from North America.

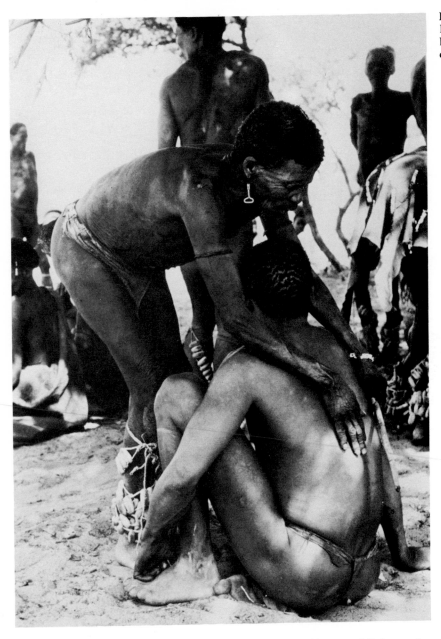

Figure 16–14 Neandertals may have had rituals like these !Kung Bushmen's laying on of hands to cure disease.

His technology marks the end of a very ancient tradition of flake tools, and his hunting-gathering way of life is not much different in kind from that of people who lived hundreds of thousands of years earlier. But he is no shambling ape-man, as nearly everyone thought until fairly recently. He is a true human in every sense, and our ancestor. We should regard him with respect, because almost everything that we are springs directly from him.

OVERVIEW

		YEARS A.D.	DISCOVERIES OF EVIDENCE OF NEANDERTAL RITUALS

HOLOCENE

10,000

UPPER PALEOLITHIC

35,000

Skhūl fossils

MIDDLE PALEOLITHIC
Würm glaciation
Classic Neandertals

100,000

Riss-Würm
  interglacial

200,000

Arago, Swans-
  combe, and
  Steinheim fossils;
  Riss glaciation

**LOWER
PALEOLITHIC**

300,000

Mindel-Riss
  interglacial

Peking man

Mindel glaciation
Large-scale elephant
  hunts in Europe

400,000

Günz-Mindel
  interglacial

500,000

600,000 Günz glaciation

700,000

Hearths at Escale;
  H. erectus expansion
  into Europe

800,000

1970 — Evidence of deer ceremony in Lebanese cave

1965 — Smashed and charred skulls at Hortus

1960 — Crushed skull and burial with flowers at Shanidar

1939 — Mutilated skull at Monte Circeo
1938 — Skull surrounded by goat horns at Teshik-Tash

1931 — Skulls at Solo with foramen magnum enlarged
1930 — Mount Carmel burial with jaw bones of bear

1925 — Skull at Ehringsdorf with foramen magnum enlarged
1924 — Kiik-Koba burials

1917 — Ceremonial arrangement and stone chests of bear skulls at Drachenloch

1912 — "Family cemetery" at La Ferrassie

1908 — La Chapelle burial with artifacts

1899 — Smashed and charred skulls at Krapina

RITUALS OF LIFE AND DEATH

Evidence of the burial rituals of Neandertal man has taught us a great deal about these people; they prove to have been more like ourselves than had ever been supposed.

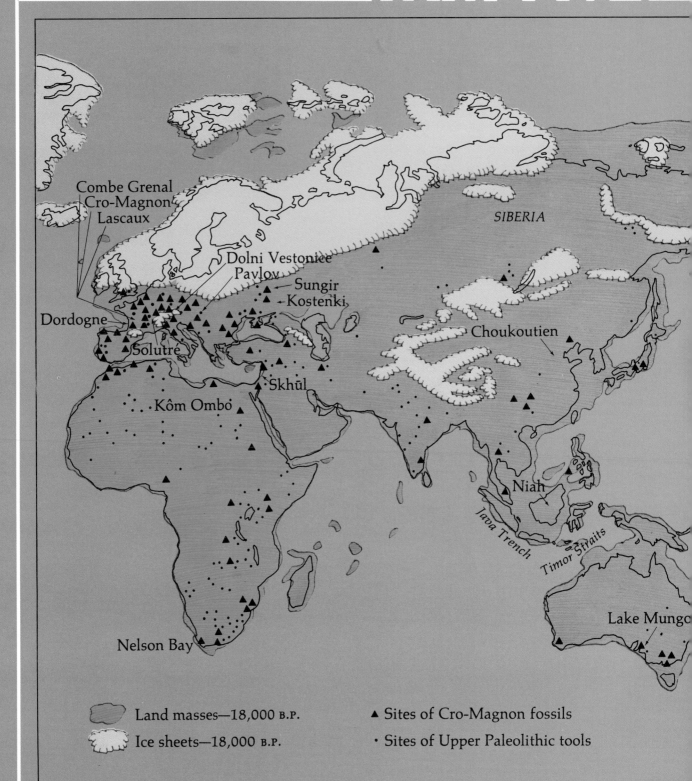

PART FIVE

Combe Grenal
Cro-Magnon
Lascaux

SIBERIA

Dordogne

Dolni Vestonice
Pavlov
Sungir
Kostenki

Choukoutien

Solutré

Skhūl

Kôm Ombó

Niah

Java Trench

Timor Straits

Lake Mungo

Nelson Bay

Land masses—18,000 B.P.   ▲ Sites of Cro-Magnon fossils

Ice sheets—18,000 B.P.   · Sites of Upper Paleolithic tools

MODERN HUMANITY

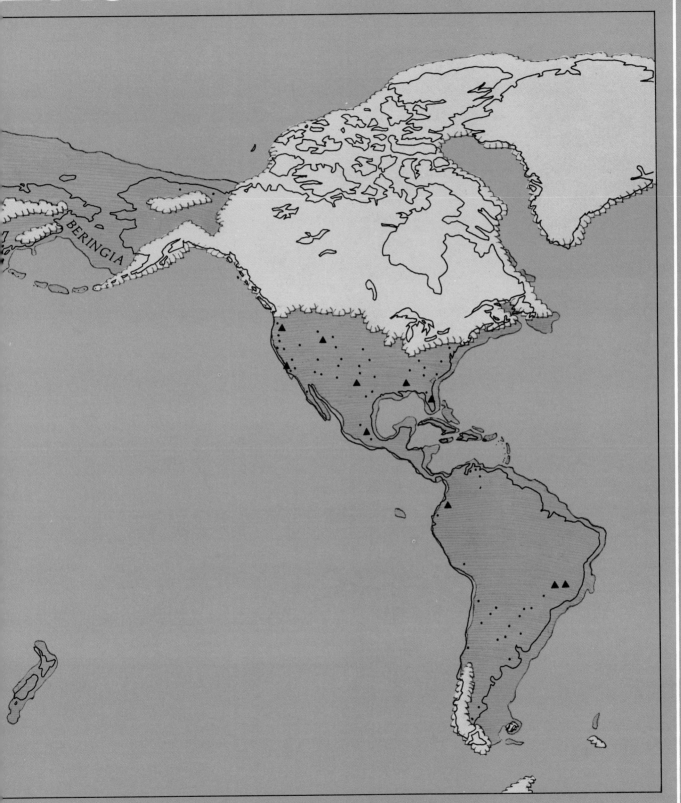

BERINGIA

Chapter 17

Enter Cro-Magnon

The troubles of our proud and angry dust
Are from eternity, and shall not fail.
Bear them, we can, and if we can we must.
      A. E. HOUSMAN, 1859-1936.
      LAST POEMS, ix.

THE FIRST MODERN PEOPLE

In recent years prehistorians have begun to seek the origins of modern man in diverse parts of the globe—in Africa, the Orient, Australia, and the Americas. But the story of the first modern people properly begins in the Dordogne region of France, where four generations of archaeologists from many countries have excavated and analyzed and argued since the first Cro-Magnon site was laid bare by the railroad builders of Les Eyzies in 1868.

Discovery in the Dordogne

The limestone cliffs in this region seem peculiarly adapted for human abodes. These masses of rock were formed more than a hundred million years ago by the accumulation of tiny lime-containing animals on the floor of the shallow ocean that once covered most of Europe. Untold trillions of such creatures, little cement mixers, helped produce a building material that was to be useful to the future race of man. Strong but water-soluble, the exposed lime of the Dordogne cliffs was honeycombed and tunneled by rivers and waterfalls, scooped into shelters and caves, leveled off into ledges, porches, and overhangs.

The portal to one cave, Font-de-Gaume, halfway up a cliff that juts out into a little valley, effectively commanded the approach of animals, friends, or enemies. Surely, over tens of thousands of years these cliffs had a positive effect on the formation of human character in this region. In a sense, they provided a stage setting that enabled man to see himself as a dominant creature in his local environment. During the times when he lived here more or less permanently, the cliff dwellings must have enhanced his sense of identity and contributed to early stirrings of community pride. Here were his burial pits and the secret shrines where rituals of the hunt were performed. Here were the scenes of his mating and the birthplace of his children. The special beauty of the area around Les Eyzies must have aroused particularly strong attachments to home and earth, and hunters returning after long trips in pursuit of big game could hardly have failed to welcome the sight of these lush valleys and protective cliffs with pride and satisfaction.

The Cro-Magnons were not the first human beings to occupy this beautiful place. Many of its caves and shelters had once been used by Neandertals and even more ancient people, whose tools and fossils have been found buried in the lower strata of cave floors. At Combe Grenal, for example, a cave about fourteen miles from Les Eyzies, many thousands of tools probably made by Neandertal toolmakers have been unearthed. Had Cro-Magnon people any awareness, conveyed by ritual or special art objects, of these former tenants of their home ground? It is impossible to say. But it is not far-fetched to think that they did associate with these places a dim sense of ancient presence that gave their homes an additional and powerful appeal.

A more concrete advantage of the Dordogne region was the extraordinary natural riches it offered its prehistoric inhabitants. The Massif Central, a mountainous plateau that covers most of central France, begins about fifty miles east of Les Eyzies. Its high plains would have been a fruitful summer hunting ground that provided reindeer, horses, and bison in abundance. West of Les Eyzies, the coastal plain stretching toward the Atlantic was also good grazing ground. The Vézère River ran then in much the same course as it does now, providing water and, to the later Cro-Magnons who learned to take advantage of it, a ready supply of fish. Many of the caves and shelters face south, offering maximum warmth and protection from the cold winds of winter. Although many peoples around the world 30,000 to 20,000 years ago were nomadic, following game through seasonal migrations, it seems likely that the hunters who dwelled in this fortunate region were able to stay in residence for the greater part of the year.

In the years since the discovery of the Cro-Magnon fossils in France (see Figure 17–1) the ancient skeletal remains of modern people, that for convenience we may broadly call Cro-Magnon, have been turning up all over the world: in Hungary, in the USSR, in the Middle East and North Africa, as well as in South Africa, China and Southeast Asia, and even Australia and North America. Not all of the fossils are complete, of course, and some are no more than fragments, but everywhere they are what scientists call anatomically modern.

**Characteristics
of Cro-Magnon**

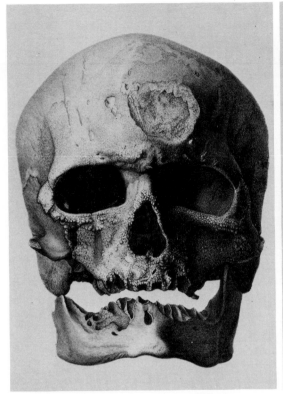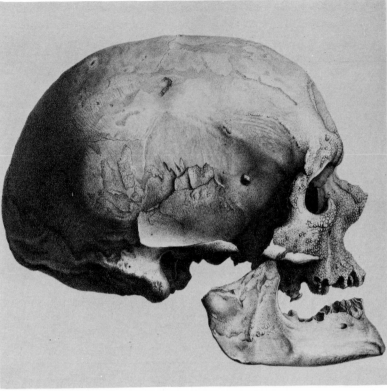

The bones of these fossils are frequently lighter than those of their predecessors. Further, the Cro-Magnon skull is uniformly like the skulls of people living today: it has a definite chin; a high forehead; small, even teeth; and a cranial capacity equal to that of modern humans. We also believe that Cro-Magnon people had, for the first time, the necessary physical equipment for constructing complex and elaborate patterns of speech such as we ourselves use. Possibly, the range of vocalizations available to them was also just as great as what we hear today. According to Lieberman and Crelin, the arrangement of Cro-Magnon man's oral and nasal cavities, his longer pharynx, and the flexibility of his tongue enabled him to shape and project sounds over a much wider range, and much more rapidly, than earlier humans could. (His superior vocalizing powers were gained at one big expense, however: modern man is the only creature who can choke to death on food caught in his windpipe, because his longer pharynx must do double duty as the route to his alimentary canal.)

Figure 17–1 A nineteenth-century drawing of the fossilized modern skull of *Homo sapiens* from Cro-Magnon, France, which was the first specimen of Cro-Magnon man to be found.

But what became of those Neandertal men and women who struggled so hard against the world around them to sustain their developing humanity? As we have seen (Chapter 14), some anthropologists believe that many but not by any means all Neandertals evolved into modern

THE FATE OF NEANDERTAL

human beings. Others make no exceptions and feel that all Neandertals evolved into modern humans. Still others, a minority nowadays, insist that all Neandertals became extinct and were replaced by modern people who had evolved from an unknown genetic stock in an unlocated Eden. One scientist likens the problem of trying to determine the genetic relationship between Neandertals and Cro-Magnon to trying to trace the connection between buggies and automobiles on the basis of hubcaps and broken wheels. Actually, our most abundant evidence, stone tools, is even less direct than that, although it is highly suggestive.

Only a few years ago, textbooks used to cite the sequence of tool-bearing layers in caves and rock shelters as absolute proof that all Neandertals became extinct. It was thought that the tools made by Neandertals declined in number and quality as the end of their period neared; then no tools were made at all, resulting in sterile layers with no sign of human habitation; then brand-new styles of tools abruptly began. What could such a sequence mean?

The Sequence of Tools

Although an off-and-on sequence of tool-bearing strata—Neandertal layers fading to sterile layers that are followed by Cro-Magnon layers—is indeed found at some Neandertal sites, archaeologists have begun to discover many exceptions to the old rule. At some sites, successive layers show that toolmaking proficiency rose, rather than declined. Also, sterile layers do not always appear between layers containing Neandertal and Cro-Magnon tools; more often, there is no break, indicating that occupation of the site was virtually continuous. Finally, the difference between Neandertal and Cro-Magnon tools does not necessarily indicate that one culture disappeared to be replaced by an unrelated one. This last fact may hold the key to the Neandertal mystery. Closer study of the differences between tools could show how Neandertals, far from being replaced by Cro-Magnons, actually evolved into them.

The tools associated with Neandertal peoples all over the world are categorized as *Middle Paleolithic,* a word derived from the Greek *palai* (long ago) and *lithos* (stone); the term is a broad one that covers Mousterian tools as well as other types in eastern Asia, Africa, and elsewhere. The comparable term for tools associated with the Cro-Magnon phase of evolution is *Upper Paleolithic* ("upper" because these tools appear in layers lying on top of the earlier tools). Most Middle Paleolithic tools consist of flat flakes of fine-grained rock shaped and retouched to provide the desired working edge. Upper Paleolithic toolmakers produced flakes, too, but they specialized in a kind known as *blades,* defined as flakes that are at least two times as long as they are wide. This shift in the fundamental unit of the tool kit is marked enough that many collections of Middle and Upper Paleolithic tools can be distinguished at a glance.

Flakes and Blades

Blades are more economical to make than flakes, because they yield more than five times as much cutting edge per pound of stone. Progress is also apparent in craftsmanship. Tools of the Upper Paleolithic are more finely made, requiring extremely precise chipping to produce the desired point, notch, or cutting edge. And there are many more kinds of special-purpose tools. Upper Paleolithic kits often include a high percentage of *burins*—chisel-like tools useful, as we shall see, for cutting bone, antler, and ivory. Neandertals made fewer burins and presumably were not as well equipped as Cro-Magnon tool users to exploit this wider range of materials.

Without a doubt, then, Upper Paleolithic tools are superior to those made by the Neandertals. It seems equally clear that the changeover in tool styles occurred very quickly. Earlier generations of anthropologists, working under the assumption that the Neandertals belonged to a separate species of mankind almost unrelated to Cro-Magnon, naturally saw the changes in stone tools as proof that the Cro-Magnons moved in and took over. But now that the Neandertals are seen as genetically closer to the Cro-Magnons, scientists are beginning to wonder if the shift can be explained by a rapid evolution of tools rather than by the arrival of a new culture. If Upper Paleolithic implements developed out of Middle Paleolithic styles of stoneworking, the transition should be indicated by some tools that display characteristics of both types. Now, after years of speculation, evidence of a transition has indeed appeared.

In southwest France, the two earliest Upper Paleolithic tool types are called *Perigordian* and *Aurignacian.* The Aurignacian (shown in Figure 17–2) is so completely unlike any typical Middle Paleolithic style that it almost certainly was imported to western Europe. Tools resembling the Aurignacian have been unearthed from an earlier level in eastern Europe, suggesting that immigrants brought their new tool style from there.

The Perigordian style (Figure 17–3) of Upper Paleolithic tools is another story. Despite some claims that it is an import from the East, more

The Perigordian Industry

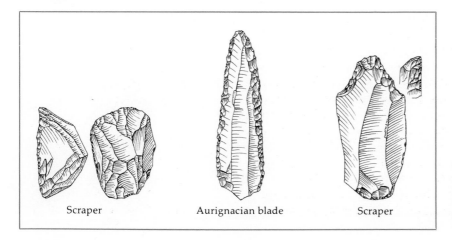

Scraper   Aurignacian blade   Scraper

Figure 17–2 Typical Aurignacian tools of the Upper Paleolithic. Although some similarities with the Quina-Ferrassie tradition can be recognized, the Aurignacian appears to have developed to the East.

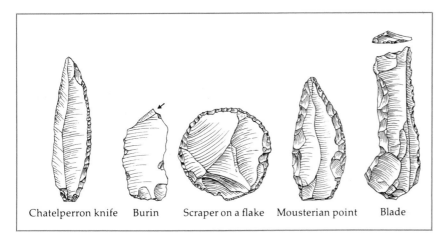

Chatelperron knife   Burin   Scraper on a flake   Mousterian point   Blade

Figure 17–3 Typical Perigordian tools of the Upper Paleolithic. This tradition began with strongly marked Mousterian features; later, Perigordian tool kits contained a high proportion of burins and points.

and more evidence supports a local origin. The Perigordian now can be seen to have grown directly out of the Mousterian of Acheulian tradition, that most complex and ingenious of all Middle Paleolithic Mousterian types (see Figure 17–4). At a number of sites in Europe, successive Mousterian layers dated near the end of the Neandertals' time show a steady increase in the ratio of blades to flakes. The frequency of certain favorite Upper Paleolithic tools, such as burins, also rises. The shift is gradual, and there is no discontinuity that indicates one culture or people came to an end and were abruptly replaced.

Evidence for indigenous evolution of the Upper Paleolithic out of the Middle Paleolithic has also been found at some sites in eastern Europe, Asia, and Africa, but most archaeologists are steering clear of generalizations until the evidence has been analyzed more thoroughly. The truth is that no one really knows how toolmaking traditions change. Are innovations spread by migrations, barter, conquests, or word of mouth, or as a result of exchange of individuals between neighboring bands? Are changes spurred by rising intelligence, increasing linguistic capability, or some other factor not even guessed at?

The Fossil Record

Fossils might provide a more direct line of inquiry than tools into the fate of the Neandertals, provided enough could be found. If there were a complete series of fossils from all over the world dated from about 50,000 to 30,000 years ago, any amateur could study the remains and tell what happened to the Neandertals. Regrettably, the trail of humanity through this period is not at all well marked by bones.

No Neandertal fossil has been given a reliable date more recent than 40,000 years B.P. (though Mousterian cultures survived in southern France after 35,000 B.P.). The oldest securely dated modern peoples from Europe are from near the town of Pavlov in Czechoslovakia; they lived about 26,000 years ago. The earliest Upper Paleolithic cultures in western Europe date from 34,000 B.P., while in Poland and Hungary they appear to have been present since 40,000 B.P. From elsewhere, we have few well-dated sites: a skull from Niah in Sarawak carries an astonishingly early date of 40,000 B.P., and another from Florisbad in South

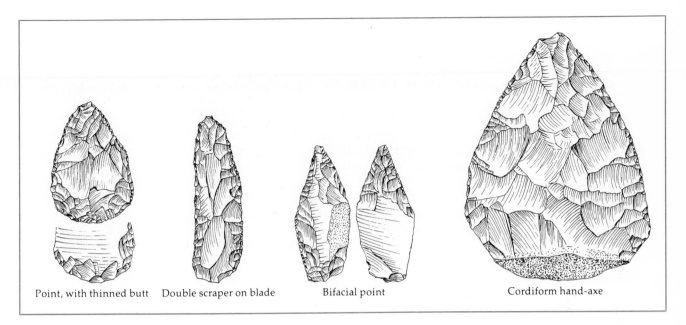

Point, with thinned butt   Double scraper on blade   Bifacial point   Cordiform hand-axe

Africa is dated 35,000 B.P. Whereas the Florisbad skull carries a mixture of Neandertal and modern features, the earlier Niah skull is completely modern in form. These two remote finds serve only to make the transition from Neandertal to modern more mysterious. If further finds prove the early date of Niah to be reliable (neither carbon 14 nor potassium–argon dates can be relied on without question, especially if determined only once) then we will have evidence of a Southeast Asian population of modern appearance that predates the European populations. The same may prove to be the case in South Africa, when new dates of other modern skulls have been checked and confirmed. There is indeed some indication that Europe was backward at this time in the evolution of modern mankind, and this may well be attributable to the barriers of ice of the Würm glaciation.

The world was certainly fully populated throughout the period between 50,000 and 30,000 B.P. But populated by whom? On one side of the gap in the fossil evidence were the Neandertals, still somewhat backward in technological skills. On the other side are the Cro-Magnons, modern from head to toe, talented as artists, initiators of the idea of writing. Are the striking differences between Neandertals and Cro-Magnons simply a result of their separation in time? If so, how did human evolution cross the gap so fast, and where, and when, and why?

The first step in attempting to trace human evolution through this fascinating 20,000-year period is to measure the physical difference between Neandertals and Cro-Magnons, a procedure that is not as easy as it sounds. When two extreme fossil types—for example, the man from La Chapelle-aux-Saints and the original Cro-Magnon man—are viewed side by side, the difference seems tremendous. The classic Neandertal has a long, low cranium, bulging at the sides, with a pro-

Figure 17–4   Typical tools of the Mousterian of Acheulian tradition, which appeared during the Middle Paleolithic. The presence of up to 40 percent hand-axes characterizes this variety of Mousterian industry.

Anatomical Comparison: Neandertal and Cro-Magnon

truding bun at the rear, a slanting forehead, and a heavy brow ridge. The Cro-Magnon has a high cranium, rounded at the rear and vertical at the sides, with a vertical forehead and no brow ridge to speak of. The faces are quite dissimilar, too. The Neandertal has an out-thrust face, a broad nose, and a large, chinless jaw. By contrast, the face of the Cro-Magnon, with its regular features, was entirely modern.

But these are the extremes. Some other Neandertals have definite chins, smaller jaws, rather high-vaulted craniums, little sign of a bun at the back of the skull, fairly steep foreheads, and only a moderate brow ridge. And some Cro-Magnons have a rather pronounced brow ridge, sloping foreheads, and large jaws.

Visual comparison of fossils is such a fallible approach that anthropologists have been resorting more and more to statistical comparisons of tooth size, cranial height, brow formation, and so on. These efforts have gone a long way toward dispelling old impressions. Many scientists once believed, for example, that Neandertals had strayed far from the mainstream of human evolution. As we have seen in Chapter 14, the range of variability of Neandertal features has been shown to overlap with the modern range of variability more than once was thought. This means that occasionally you might see Neandertal features just by strolling through the nearest crowd, although no individual will have a complete array of Neandertal characteristics. Similarly, in the past, most authorities believed that the Neandertals, especially those of western Europe, were remarkably homogeneous. Their alleged lack of variety was interpreted to mean that they had somehow lost evolutionary flexibility, become specialized, and come to a dead end. Now, statistical analyses have indicated that the range of variability within Neandertal populations was as great as the variability among *Homo sapiens* today.

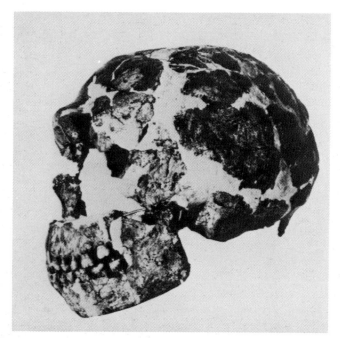
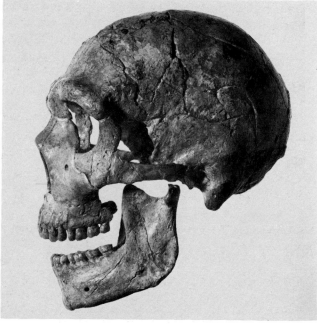

It helps to know that Neandertals came in many shapes and sizes, and that these are sometimes matched by the various conformations of the first modern human beings. There is no doubt that somewhere the evolutionary gap was crossed by a steady progression of changes, each so small as to be imperceptible yet adding up to the differences between Neandertals and Cro-Magnons. Here is a brief, region-by-region summary of the skeletal material supporting the belief that through long series of small changes the features of most Neandertal populations in the world become those of modern peoples.

In the Middle East, an ancestral relationship between the local Neandertals and the local Cro-Magnons seems probable. This is the only locality where a whole series of candidates for an intermediate type of man have appeared. The fossils from Skhūl and Kafzeh in Israel seem to belong between the Neandertal and Cro-Magnon camps. The skulls display a fairly even blend of archaic and modern traits.

In eastern Europe, an ancestral relationship seems entirely possible, since the most recent Neandertals appear to have been rather advanced and the oldest Cro-Magnons, such as those from Předmost in Czechoslovakia, rather robust. In addition, an intermediate-looking upper jaw has been found at Sipka in Czechoslovakia.

In Southeast Asia, an ancestral relationship also seems possible, because new fossils from Australia hint at an evolutionary link between Solo man, that early Neandertal from Java, and the most ancient fossils of Australian Aborigines, who were full-fledged modern *Homo sapiens*.

In Africa, apart from the Florisbad skull, which has some Neandertal characteristics, transitional specimens are lacking. However, a number of rugged-looking modern skulls have turned up in eastern and southern Africa. These modern fossils could be more than 40,000 years old, al-

Regional Survey

Figure 17–5 This sequence of skulls from Israel shows some of the changes that occurred in the evolution of Neandertals to modern human beings. From left to right, they are from Tabūn, Amud, Skhūl, and an Upper Paleolithic Natufian site in Israel.

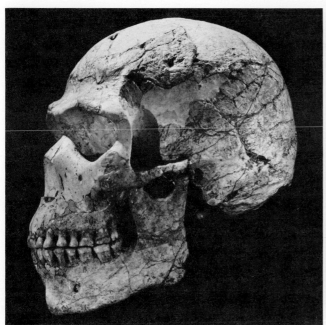
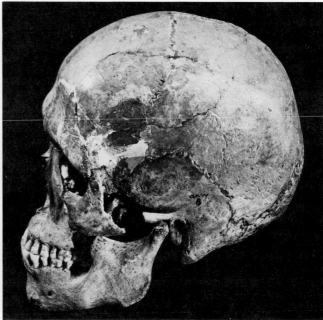

though their dates—and those for the Neandertals like Rhodesian man —are still imprecise. An ancestral relationship between the two types is considered possible, and some anthropologists feel that the African Neandertals were the first to have crossed the threshold to modernity.

One area has been left off this list of places where the evolution of Neandertals into modern human beings is generally regarded as possible or probable. Western Europe is known as one of the richest fossil fields in all the world, and it has been scoured carefully for more than a century. Yet no true fossil intermediate between the local Neandertals and Cro-Magnons ever has been found there. Since no fossil comes close to fitting into the middle ground, many scientists are inclined to shut the western European Neandertals out of the direct line leading to modern man.

The Problem of
Western Europe

Agreement is far from universal. C. Loring Brace, among others, believes there is no justification for treating western European Neandertals differently. Brace feels they showed definite signs of evolving in a Cro-Magnon direction. He further suggests they may be older than is believed. In his opinion, the fact that their progressive tendencies look muted could be because of this hitherto unsupposed antiquity. It is true that no well-preserved fossil from the region can be reliably dated, since most were dug up earlier in this century when excavation and dating techniques were crude. Some recent studies suggest that the fossils from La Ferrassie, La Chapelle-aux-Saints, Monte Circeo, and elsewhere are at least 60,000 years old—an age that would lend support to Brace's point that the local Neandertals had plenty of time in which to evolve a modern appearance.

However, a good case can be made for the opposite viewpoint: that western European Neandertals missed the turn toward modernity and later died out. Geological factors may have influenced their fate. During certain severe cold phases of the Würm glaciation, the Scandinavian and Alpine ice sheets pushed toward each other and came within 300 miles of meeting in Germany. Neandertals trapped behind the glaciers might have been more or less isolated from the evolutionary advances occurring elsewhere in the world. Although the isolation would have been neither total nor permanent, such geographic features could have operated as a fine-mesh genetic screen, severely limiting east–west contacts. In this way, the people of western Europe might have periodically pursued an independent evolutionary course.

If these people were indeed an evolutionary dead end, what accounts for their demise? The usual answer is that invading Cro-Magnons from the east exterminated the western Neandertals. Some anthropologists speculate that the classic Neandertals were in no condition to resist when and if the invaders arrived. As a case in point, we have seen that the fossil evidence indicates that many western European Neandertals suffered from rickets, caused by a lack of vitamin D. But vitamin deficiency alone could not account for the death of hundreds of thousands of people. Certain experts have conjured up the specter of ecological catastrophe, proposing that the local Neandertals were so inflexibly adapted to cold that they could not handle the warm spell that began around 39,000 years ago and lasted for 2,000 years. This notion makes little sense, however, because Neandertals had thrived during earlier warm spells and it is hard to imagine a warm spell being stressful, let alone fatal.

A more persuasive explanation for the disappearance of the western European Neandertals at the hands of invading Cro-Magnons involves linguistic ability. If the local Neandertals could not communicate so well as an invading people, they would have been at a tremendous competitive disadvantage—one that would drastically reduce their chances of survival. The analysis of the reconstructed vocal tract of the fossil from La Chapelle-aux-Saints by Lieberman and Crelin provides experimental support for this idea (see Chapter 13). African Neandertals had a somewhat more highly evolved pharynx and the advanced-looking Neandertals of the Middle East had an almost completely modern vocal tract.

The Lieberman–Crelin hypothesis of linguistic deficiency, though widely challenged, begins to offer a more credible explanation for the doom of western European Neandertals. Yet in modern times, the overwhelming of one race by another, as the American Indians were overwhelmed by the invading Europeans, always turns on cultural and especially technological advantage, and ultimately on the relative abilities of each competing population to extract resources from the environment. This was surely also the case in the transition from Neandertal to Cro-Magnon: aspects of culture and technology quite probably not represented in the fossil record were almost certainly a critical factor in that competitive situation (if such it was), as they always are today. Language ability was probably just one factor in the development of a broadly superior culture.

The debate is bound to continue for years, since the evidence of stone tools suggests at least some indigenous cultural linkage between Neandertals and Cro-Magnons in western Europe. And in any case, even if the local people were overwhelmed by invaders, some intermarriage must have taken place. It is not likely, therefore, that the genes of the western European Neandertals disappeared entirely from humankind.

This supposition is based on our understanding of what has been called *genetic swamping*, which is a common occurrence when a large population overruns and absorbs a smaller one. The genes of the smaller population are preserved but make little contribution to the physical characteristics of the successor population. In the instance of the succession of Cro-Magnon, we can also postulate a similar *cultural swamping*. We see this phenomenon within historical times, in instances where, for example, ancient languages or religions (such as those of the American Indians) have died out and been replaced to a great extent by the culture of more numerous invaders, even though the people who carried the ancient culture have survived as a genetic minority.

A fundamental question remains. If most of the Neandertals evolved into Cro-Magnons, as seems likely, why did such a change take place? What evolutionary forces could explain the remodeling of the human skull from the form that had characterized human beings since *Homo erectus* times, a quarter of a million years or so before? Until that question is firmly answered, the transformation of the Neandertals into modern peoples will remain enigmatic.

One hypothesis directed to this problem focuses on the Neandertal face. Anyone seeing a Neandertal skull for the first time is struck by the appearance of the face. What conceivable purpose could that long and decidedly out-thrust facial structure serve? Many authors believe that Neandertal teeth suggest an answer to this question. They view the large face with projecting jaws as a supporting structure for the very large teeth. According to Loring Brace, the size of the front teeth in particular was a sort of "technological" adaptation. Brace thinks that Neandertals regularly used their front teeth as a built-in tool, serving as pliers to hold one end of some material such as wood or hide so that one hand would be free to cut, scrape, or pierce the material with a stone implement. Wear patterns on the incisors of some fossils suggest that the Neandertals softened animal hides by chewing them; workers also may have twisted plant fibers or straightened wooden shafts with the aid of their teeth.

To provide room for the big, strong front teeth that all work of this sort would favor, the face had to extend well out. Furthermore, the jaw had to be large and thick in order to withstand the stresses generated when the teeth were used as gripping, tearing, or hide-softening tools. Other skull features may have been affected too. Probably the heavy brow ridge of the Neandertals functioned as a structural support to take up chewing stresses. Probably the shape of the back of the skull was dictated by the massive tooth-bearing structures up front. The bunlike extension of the rear of many Neandertal skulls may have acted to balance the out-thrust face, distributing the weight of the head evenly above its supporting point at the top of the spine. More important, the neck muscles, which balance the head upon the vertebral column, would be more effective in supporting the heavy face and jaws given the longer lever arm provided by the extended bun. Another conceivable reason for the elongated skull concerns rotary motion. The head is swiveled from side to side partly by means of the neck muscles. Extension of the back of the head again gives the muscles a longer lever arm to work with, lightening the task of moving the heavy, forward-jutting face.

Why would the skull evolve into its modern form? Brace feels that improvements in stone implements caused the Neandertals to rely less and less on their front teeth as a built-in tool. This decreased re-

FROM NEANDERTAL TO CRO-MAGNON

Brace's Hypothesis

liance led to a gradual reduction in tooth size, which in turn permitted a reduction in the jaw, face, and other features, giving rise to people with heads like ours.

Many scientists feel that Brace's hypothesis cannot account adequately for the transformation of the Neandertals into people of modern appearance, and they offer alternatives. David Pilbeam proposed another sort of evolutionary mechanism that might have brought about the changes in the human skull. Expanding on the Lieberman–Crelin hypothesis, Pilbeam suggests that with the possible exception of western European Neandertals, the Neandertal head gradually became more modern in form because of the evolution of the upper part of the throat into a pharynx capable of producing the full range of modern vocalizations. As Crelin and Lieberman pointed out, the development of a pharynx in man can be traced by studying new-born human infants, who lack complete pharynges. When this essential part of the vocal tract starts to take on its final shape at the age of three months, the larynx (or voice box), as we saw in Chapter 13, moves down in the throat, and the base of the skull, which is rather flat at birth, takes on a concave arch. The pharyngeal space is thus formed in front of the topmost vertebrae, and the arch in the base of the human skull serves as a roof.

Pilbeam believes that the evolution of the pharynx's arched roof may have affected the overall structure of the human skull. As the arch formed, the base of the skull shortened (just as the ends of a piece of cloth that is lifted slightly in the middle pull together). If the starting point for this process were a long, low Neandertal skull, the shortening of the skull base might have caused the facial region to pull inward from its formerly out-thrust position. With the face thus pulled in, the whole braincase would have had to become higher in order to contain the same amount of brain tissue. And as this happened, the brow and the sides of the skull would have become more vertical. Thus, the Neandertal skull could have been transformed into a modern *Homo sapiens* skull. Neandertal and modern-type skulls are, in effect, just different ways of packing the same quantity of brain tissue. The overall shape of the package is dictated by only one of its dimensions—the length of the base of the skull—which is in turn related to the presence of a modern pharynx.

Pilbeam's logical chain of events does explain the fast rate of the evolutionary changes that turned Neandertals into Cro-Magnons. The development of a pharynx could have occurred very rapidly, since speech was now becoming an extremely valuable adaptation. Natural selection would have worked at maximum efficiency to weed out the slow talkers and foster better speaking ability. It is almost impossible today, tens of thousands of years later, to sense the powerful and urgent evolutionary pressures that would have been launched when this new element was introduced into the vocal tract. The development of a modern pharynx, with its huge potential for communication, could very well explain an enormous leap in physical and cultural evolution.

Changes in teeth or noses probably would not have gone forward at the same rapid pace.

The most probable answer to our question of why the modern head form evolved is that all the factors that have been mentioned were at work: the pharynx almost certainly did increase in length, and the jaws, teeth, and associated bony structures were indeed reduced in size. The changes at the back of the skull were most probably no more than a product of the important new developments taking place at the front.

Much has been learned of the period of transition between Neandertal and Cro-Magnon times, and much remains to be learned. Hardly any relevant fossil evidence is available from some crucial areas of the world: Arabia, located at the crossroads of two continents; the endless reaches of central Asia; and the subcontinent of India, rich in game and characterized by the sort of warm climate that early man favored for millions of years. Nor can anthropologists say when the transformation of the Neandertals started. Perhaps some modern-looking individuals began to appear in Neandertal populations 60,000 or even 100,000 years ago.

Whenever and wherever it began, the evolutionary transition probably affected most of humankind. From the savannas of Africa to the hills of Czechoslovakia and eastward to China, human beings were joined in a single enormous gene pool—a great mixing vat in which traits of appearance or behavior could be exchanged by interbreeding among neighboring bands of hunter-gatherers. Because the tradition of exogamy was probably long established by this time, an evolutionary surge in one place eventually made itself felt everywhere else in the common gene pool; humankind climbed toward modernity as a single unit. By about 30,000 years ago the changes were largely complete, and the world was populated with people that looked like ourselves. Human beings were living in larger bands than they ever had before. Cultures were branching and rebranching along countless idiosyncratic paths, like a plant that has lived long in the shade and is suddenly offered the full strength of the sun. Successful initiatives in technology or art or symbolmaking brought on more initiatives, and cultural change steadily accelerated.

Completion of the Transition

OVERVIEW

	YEARS B.P.	EMERGENCE OF MODERN HUMANS	TYPES OF *HOMO SAPIENS*

HOLOCENE — 10,000

UPPER PALEOLITHIC — 35,000

MIDDLE PALEOLITHIC
Neandertal in Europe, Asia, Africa — 100,000

Arago, Swanscombe, and Steinheim; Levallois technique

Peking man

Large-scale elephant hunts in Europe

500,000 — Günz glaciation

Hearths at Escale; *H. erectus* expansion into Europe

1 million — *H. erectus* expansion into China

A. robustus and *A. boisei* extinct

LOWER PALEOLITHIC

Acheulian industry

1.5 million —

habilis at Olduvai

2 million — Oldowan industry

Left timeline scale (years):
- 10,000 — HOLOCENE
- 35,000 — UPPER PALEOLITHIC
- 100,000 — MIDDLE PALEOLITHIC
- 500,000
- 1 million
- 1.5 million
- 2 million

Right scale (YEARS B.P.):

Iron Age
Bronze Age: pottery
Copper Age

First agriculture: domestication of plants and animals
New Stone Age (Neolithic)

PRESENT-DAY HUMANS

10,000

20,000 — Cro-Magnon, Dordogne: first modern skull found

Pavlov: oldest dated European modern skull; Předmost: robust modern skulls

CRO-MAGNON

30,000

Florisbad: modern and Neandertal features; most recent Mousterian tools

La Quina, La Chapelle, La Ferrassie, and Spy: Neandertal fossils; oldest Upper Paleolithic tools found; Niah: modern skull

40,000

Skhūl and Kafzeh: blend of archaic and modern features

Sipka jaw fragment: blend of archaic and modern features

50,000 — Tabūn, Amud, Shanidar: advanced Neandertal; very few modern features

TRANSITIONAL: NEANDERTAL, NEANDERTALOID, AND MODERN

60,000 — Monte Circeo: classic Neandertal

70,000

Mousterian industry appears; disk-core technique used

80,000

NEANDERTAL

Broken Hill: very robust skull, large palate, more modern limbs

90,000 — Earliest evidence of classic Neandertal in Europe

ENTER CRO-MAGNON

This chart shows the approximate chronology of the Middle to Upper Paleolithic sequence. No dates are entirely reliable, and many are not based on carbon 14 dating but on more indirect dating methods.

Chapter 18.

Adaptation and Survival

Human life is everywhere a state in which much is to be endured and little to be enjoyed.

SAMUEL JOHNSON, 1709-1784.
RASSELAS, CH. 7.

A NEW BREED

Variability of Cro-Magnon

Although consistently modern in anatomy, the Cro-Magnon peoples were by no means everywhere the same. Bones unearthed in the Soviet Union are different from bones found in France or Africa or China, and skeletal types might be different from one site to another within a single region. Some anthropologists think that Cro-Magnon man may have come in more different varieties than his modern descendants. Because his population was less mobile, it was less homogeneous; groups tended to preserve their special traits.

At the outset, this degree of variation among peoples of Cro-Magnon times misled scientists. Although bones are no clue to the color of skin or the texture of hair, the temptation to flesh out the skeletons, so to speak, was irresistible. Some strange ideas sprang up. Until well into the twentieth century, for instance, many experts believed that they had found the immediate ancestors of modern Africans and Eskimos living side by side in southern Europe. The Grimaldi "Negroid" fossils, found in a cave on the Italian Riviera, were so identified mainly because their lower faces—their upper and lower jaws—projected like those of some modern Negroes. The projection was later found to be a distortion caused by the way the fossils had been buried. The single "Eskimo" man, found near Chancelade, France, was classified on the basis of his wide cheekbones and heavy lower jaw. But by the 1930s anthropologists realized that these characteristics are also typical of many other peoples.

379

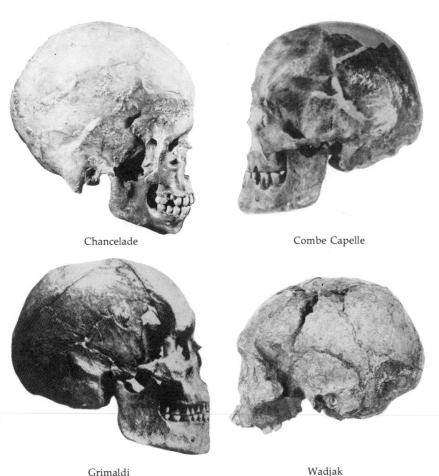

Chancelade   Combe Capelle

Grimaldi   Wadjak

Figure 18–1   Three European Cro-Magnon skulls show some of the variation we would expect to find in a population the size of that which occupied western Europe. These three are from Chancelade and Combe Capelle in France and from Grimaldi in Italy, near the border with France on the Mediterranean coast. The Wadjak skull is from Java. All are dated at about 20,000 B.P.

Knowledge of anatomy simply had become far more sophisticated than it once was; according to one report, the person who reassembled the Chancelade skeleton was discovered to have put the nasal bones in the wrong way round. Until the mistake in labeling was discovered, however, modern Eskimos were believed by some people to have originated in southern France and to have followed the retreating glaciers northward and eastward across Europe into Siberia and ultimately across the Bering Strait into frigid regions of North America—surely one of the longest treks of all time.

Though the Italian Negroes and French Eskimos turned out to be mistakes, the fact remains that Cro-Magnon looked rather different in different places. Like human beings living today, he developed characteristic physical types from region to region, and even from site to site within a single region. The nature of his environment, its climate and food supply, account for some of these variations. Such physical characteristics as tallness and shortness, dark skin and light skin, straight hair and curly hair, had formed and would continue to evolve during the millennia when the human body had to accommodate itself to heat and cold and to the variations of sunlight in different latitudes. The relatively short, thick body of the Eskimo, for instance, conserves heat better than the tall, thin bodies of some African Negroes, which present a much greater area of skin to be cooled by the air. Similarly, thick, straight hair, in the opinion of some scholars, might help to maintain the temperature of the brain in cold climates, whereas tightly curled hair seems an adaptation guarding against hot tropical sunshine; it is a noticeable characteristic of genetically unrelated peoples in Africa and the islands of Southeast Asia and the South Pacific.

Advantages of the Large Gene Pool

By Cro-Magnon times many of the physical changes wrought by the environment had largely reached their present state. The fact that Cro-Magnon peoples varied in physical type from one location to another may be related as much to demography as to geography, for there was a great increase in numbers of people and a continued division of human populations into many fairly isolated groups. The gene pool grew with the expanding total population, but it remained divided into small breeding populations that still partially inhibited gene flow.

When the total population of a species is relatively small, the genetic material available to it is relatively limited in scope, and the variant physical types may be few. But as the population increases it also begins to vary more, simply because greater numbers provide more opportunities for variations to appear. When gene flow within a large population is limited, as it was in Cro-Magnon times, the variations may become specialized, adapting to local environments according to the dictates of natural selection and perhaps the chance consequences of the founder effect (page 52). Since no newly limited or newly founded breeding population possesses the full genetic complement of its parent group, its hereditary traits are immediately slightly different from those of that group. After scores of generations under the effect of mutation and natural selection, members of the split-off group may bear little or no resemblance to the people who were their distant ancestors. The reverse process is also in constant operation. Separate groups unite or, more commonly, foreign mates are brought into a group. Either way, gene flow is enhanced and new genes are introduced into the breeding population. Through such constant selection and partial gene flow, Cro-Magnon man gradually developed all the variant physical traits that exist among people today.

NEW LANDS AND ADAPTATIONS

Of course, we cannot tell for sure if Cro-Magnon man had straight or curly hair or thick or thin lips, since these are fleshy attributes, not bony ones. We can guess that there were superficial anatomical resemblances that might lead us to say that such-and-such a Cro-Magnon type resembled such-and-such a modern type. But more important than such resemblances was an inner similarity to present-day humans. The brain capacity of the Cro-Magnons was as large as the average for modern Europeans. What the Cro-Magnons did with their large brains was remarkable. They produced a culture that, in variety and elegance, far outstripped anything that Neandertal man in his most daring moments could have aspired to. As we shall see in this and the following chapter, their progress here is easier to trace than the frustratingly elusive cultural record left behind by Neandertal.

The basis for the cultural record of Cro-Magnon is in his travels. Neandertal man was well rooted in many parts of the world before he evolved into Cro-Magnon. He had already moved out of the easy life of the tropics into the brisker climate of the temperate zone. But there were still plenty of places in the world where humans had not set foot—Siberia, most of the present Arctic, the continent of Australia, the whole length and breadth of the New World. Cro-Magnon man moved into all. Largely through his own capacity to change and adapt culturally as well as biologically, and partly with the help of climatic changes, he took over every part of the globe that it is possible for human beings to inhabit.

Cro-Magnon lived during the second half of the last ice age, known as the Würm glaciation in Europe and the Wisconsin in North America. Warm periods and cold ones followed one another in close succession—close at least by geological time—and with each cold climatic interlude the glaciers advanced and withdrew. Islands rose and fell like steppingstones, and natural causeways and corridors appeared, making new traffic routes for the comings and goings of man. Along one of these ancient routes Cro-Magnon man may have moved northward from what is now China into the chilly reaches of Siberia. Along another one he apparently migrated from Siberia, across the wide land bridge of Beringia, now covered by the Bering Sea, into the continent of North America (see page 361). Australia, however, remained an island; and climatic alterations seem to have played only a small part in the migration of Cro-Magnon to that continent.

Although the vast ice caps of the most recent glaciation locked up enough of the world's water to drop sea levels as much as 400 feet, adding great expanses of dry land to the continents, such extensions never joined Australia to the mainland of Southeast Asia. The subsidence of waters from the comparatively shallow Sunda Shelf united Borneo, Java, and Sumatra and probably exposed enough small islands to make island-hopping feasible. But between Australia and the shelf at the edge of the Asian mainland there still remained the 26,000-foot-deep waters of the Java Trench—sixty miles of open sea. How did people living as far back as Cro-Magnon times manage to get across it?

It was long assumed that humans did not reach this major island continent until the ancestors of the modern Aborigines migrated there by boat, probably from Southeast Asia, some 8,000 to 10,000 years ago. Then in the 1930s, finds indicated an earlier human arrival, and in 1968 archaeologists digging near Lake Mungo in New South Wales discovered a 25,000-year-old skeleton of a woman, unmistakably modern in her anatomy, and artifacts dating back as far as 32,000 years B.P.

The millennia around the year 30,000 B.P. represent a period of time long before any archaeological evidence of the existence of boats. Yet the evidence from southern Australia clearly indicates that people

New Territories Occupied

living more than 30,000 years ago somewhere in Southeast Asia already must have invented some sort of watercraft. Was it simply a raft
of bundled bamboo and reeds, meant for offshore fishing? Or was it
perhaps a primitive version of the dugout canoe used today by modern
Melanesians? Even more intriguing is the question of how the voyagers
happened to journey to Australia. Were they carried there inadvertently
by a wayward current or, according to one far-out speculation, by a
massive tidal wave like the one that rolled out from the island of Kraka-
toa during a volcanic eruption there in the nineteenth century? Did they
go to Australia on purpose, and if so, what drew them?

No one believes that exploration per se was Cro-Magnon man's
forte, nor was it his main cultural accomplishment. Like the migrations
of all the hunter-gatherer peoples who had gone before him, his movements were concerned with getting food. In the means he used to
achieve this end—in his implements, his techniques, his social organization, his choice of habitation—he went far beyond what anyone
had done before. His diet included almost every sort of food the earth
provided, and he became enormously adept at acquiring it. Indeed, in
terms of living off the land, and living well, Cro-Magnon man may
have been far more successful than anyone before his time or since.

When the first human groups developed their skills as hunters, they
tapped a source of food energy unavailable to vegetarian predecessors.
When they began to hunt migratory grazing animals and an occasional
predatory animal whose territory extended beyond their own, their
intake of food energy began to draw upon a still wider range of resources. Thus, when territorial expansion took man into the temperate
zone, where grazing herd animals sometimes migrate between winter
and summer feeding grounds, his food intake tapped nutritional
energy from distant sources that sometimes were extremely different
from the resources supplied by his own immediate environment.
Neandertal man, harvesting the reindeer of the Dordogne region, was
benefiting from the nutrients of the northern pastures and coastal
plains where the reindeer herds did some of their grazing but where he
himself seldom, if ever, ventured. Scientists call this kind of long-
distance food collection "living on *unearned resources.*" Of all the ways
in which organisms had adapted to and drawn sustenance from their
environment short of actually controlling it, this was the most sophisticated. Not until agriculture was developed did man's exploitation of
nature become more effective.

By the time Cro-Magnon man arrived on the earth, men were already
using the unearned resources of migratory animals to supplement a diet
of plant foods; Cro-Magnon man did it far more efficiently. With his
quicker wits and his better weapons, he harvested animals in such
abundance that it became possible for him to survive in the Arctic,
where plant foods are so scarce that almost all human food resources
are unearned. All across Siberia, from the valley of the Yenisei River
in the west to the Kamchatka Peninsula in the far east, Soviet archae-

Diet and Hunting

The Siberians

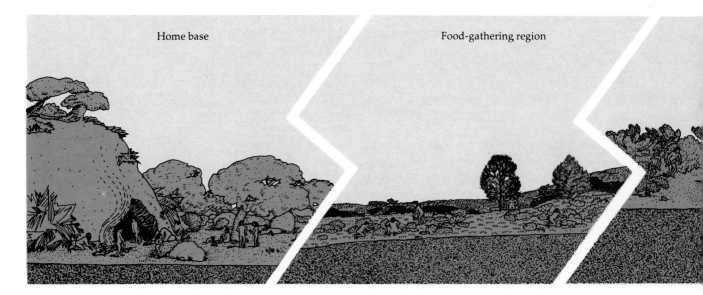

Home base   Food-gathering region

ologists are uncovering in more than a dozen sites the evidence of
human habitation going back perhaps 30,000 years. Siberian winters
were even longer and colder then than they are now, and there were
few trees to break the fierce winds that drove across the miles and miles
of open steppes. Three feet down, the ground was permanently frozen,
discouraging any sort of deep-rooted vegetation. But the top layer of
soil supported the sturdy grasses and low-growing shrubs that make
perfect grazing for herd animals.

Siberia, in fact, was a frosty paradise for hunters, and Cro-Magnon
man prospered in it, despite the cold. The refuse heaps outside his
Siberian habitation sites are thick with the bones of reindeer, wild
horse, antelope, mammoth, and bison, and on rare occasions he apparently hunted even bear and lion with success. There are also the
bones of fox and wolf, which may have been eaten but more likely were
treasured for their thick, warm pelts, which the Siberians tailored into
clothing. And finally, at several of these Siberian sites the refuse heaps
contain evidence of two new food sources that other Cro-Magnon peoples also were occasionally tapping: birds and fish.

In so rigorous a land, where the winters were long and cruel, the
Siberians must have led a far more carefully planned existence than the
easy life of their tropical contemporaries. When the weather was at its
worst, they settled into snug houses of skin with stone foundations
sunk as much as thirty inches into the earth. In an almost equally rigorous environment in the Ukraine, similarly constituted houses were
large enough to accommodate as many as fifteen or twenty people.
Tucked into frigid storage vaults behind the stone foundations was
enough meat to last many days. Some of it was frozen; some had been
dried in the sun or smoke-dried.

While these northernmost ancestors of modern man were learning
to cope with a rugged climate, another group of Cro-Magnon peoples

The Nelson Bay People

Winter grazing and hunting grounds   Summer feeding grounds

Figure 18–2   "Unearned resources" refers to migratory herds that live for part of the year outside the home range of the hunting bands. Herds that feed in the mountains during the summer may come down to the valleys during the winter where they are hunted. Thus the valley hunters are drawing on food resources of the entire region, without actually travelling through it.

in an equable environment halfway around the world were adapting to a radical change in ecology. Nelson Bay Cave lies about 300 miles east of Cape Town, South Africa, along the Indian Ocean. It is carved into a 200-foot-high sandstone bluff about 65 feet up from the present beach. As Richard Klein has shown, it was inhabited continuously during Cro-Magnon times by a succession of peoples, beginning about 18,000 years ago. A spring rises near the back of the cave and has done so for more than 35,000 years, so there was always a convenient supply of fresh water. As a dwelling place the cave offered so many natural advantages that there is no reason to wonder at its continuous occupation by four hundred generations of hunters and gatherers— even when the food available to them outside altered drastically.

For its first 6,000 years as a home for modern man, the cave overlooked an open grassland studded with low-growing trees, not unlike the modern African savanna. The sea lay as much as fifty miles away, and the Nelson Bay peoples rarely, if ever, went there; at this level the cave contains no fossil marine life of any kind. Instead, the early residents lived on what was close at hand. While the women perhaps collected seeds and berries and dug up roots and bulbs, the men no doubt hunted the game that roamed in abundance over the wide plain.

During this period the Nelson Bay Cave may have been occupied year round except for occasional hunting forays. To make the cave more homelike, its occupants added certain refinements. They encircled their hearths with stones and may have built a semicircular windbreak between the hearths and the mouth of the cave; the postholes for a somewhat later windbreak are still there. The covering could have been animal skins or brushwood or a palisade of saplings. In winter, and especially at night, this windbreak would have been comforting, for the climate of South Africa was cooler then than now, and moist. Outside the cave there might have been frost, and even a light dusting of snow.

Beginning around 12,000 years ago this life style changed, suddenly and dramatically in terms of geological time. The world's climate, which had gradually been warming for 4,000 to 5,000 years, had melted enough of the glacier ice to raise the sea level above the shelf that marked the end of the fifty-mile-long Nelson Bay plain. Almost like a river in flood that overflows its banks and spreads quickly over the low-lying countryside, the sea moved relatively rapidly up the shallow slope of the plain and was soon breaking just a few miles away from the base of the cliff where the cave was situated. With their former grazing land now underwater, the animals naturally moved inland, and it would have been just as natural for the Nelson Bay peoples to do the same, reestablishing themselves elsewhere.

But they did not. The cave continued to be a base of operations, though not one that was lived in throughout the year. In summer the inhabitants went off on extended hunting trips, tracking and killing the game and collecting the bulbs, berries, and seeds that had formed their traditional food supply in centuries past. In winter, however, they returned to the Nelson Bay Cave to harvest another source of energy: food taken from the sea.

Instead of gathering seeds and digging up roots, they now scavenged for limpets and abalone in the wake of receding tides, prying them from the surfaces of rocks in tidal pools and deeper waters. To aid them in this task they had a nine-inch flat bone knife and probably some sort of container, a basket or leather pouch, into which they dropped their catches. So dexterous did they become at this new form of food collecting that archaeologists have found piles of discarded marine shells as much as 20 feet deep. The fishy residue of this midden must have smelled to high heaven and given reason enough for these later Nelson Bay peoples to leave home periodically, as some present-day aborigines do when their kitchen refuse gets out of hand. In the cave dwellers' seasonal absence, rodents, sea birds, and the scouring sea winds would have cleaned up the stinking mess.

While the women harvested shellfish, the men of Nelson Bay went fishing or walked several miles up the beach to a rocky outcropping that had become a breeding ground for Cape fur seals. It takes no great skill to kill a seal in a rookery where the animals congregate by the thousands. The Nelson Bay hunters probably used the same tactics as twentieth-century seal hunters, wading among the furry hordes and hitting the animals over the head with heavy clubs. Seals added still another unearned food resource to the Cro-Magnon diet: in the summer months the Cape fur seal feeds on small fish and squid several hundred miles offshore.

Possibly the seal hunters were acquiring more than a new source of food. Eskimos, whose economy depends to a large extent on seals, use the fat of the animals for lamp oil, their sinews for thread and bindings, and their waterproof skins for clothing, storage bags, and even boats— the Eskimo kayak is made of sealskin stretched over a wood or bone frame. The Nelson Bay peoples may not have explored all these potentials. They would not, for instance, have needed the Eskimos' tailored sealskin clothing; and though they lived along the sea, they were probably not tempted to venture onto it in any sort of boat for the surf near Nelson Bay was high and rough then as it is now. (Today it is known to surfers the world over for its big waves.) But seal oil burning in stone lamps could very well have supplemented firelight in the Nelson Bay Cave as a source of illumination. And among the many uses that could have been found for the seal's tough sinews, very possibly one was fishing line.

The Kôm Ombo People

For the Nelson Bay peoples, life settled into a routine of food-gathering that took them at regular intervals from one environment to another, from the coast to the interior, and from a diet composed primarily of seafoods to one that combined the traditional inland meat and plant foods. But 4,500 miles away, along the Nile, lived another community of Cro-Magnon peoples who could enjoy a similar variety of food without leaving home.

Beginning around 17,000 years ago and for a period of about 5,000 years, until some climatic change, perhaps a drought, altered their life style, groups of people with at least five different tool kits settled down in the wide Kôm Ombo plain, 28 miles downriver from the present Aswân Dam, and took the steps that a few thousand years later would lead to farming. They became intensive foragers, gathering enough of a few types of plants and animals so that they could settle in one place and live year round on their specialized foods. They harvested the seeds of wild grasses systematically and efficiently.

Then as now, the Kôm Ombo plain stretched inland from the east bank of the Nile, and it was crisscrossed with channels of the Nile that ran from August through October, swelled by the monsoon rains that fell on East Africa and fed the river's headwaters. From March to August the plain had a dry spell, though probably it was not as dry as now, for the North African climate 17,000 years ago was generally cooler and wetter than it is today.

These seasonal changes brought into the plain a constantly changing succession of wildlife. Wild cattle, which like to be near water, grazed over the area when the streams were full and the grasses young and succulent. Gazelles and hartebeests moved in during the dry season when the vegetation was more like that of their regular savanna habitat. When the river and streams were high, there were catfish, perch, soft-shelled Nile turtle, and hippopotamus to be caught. And all through the year there were water birds of many kinds, some of them local, some of them annual migrants from the cold European winter. In support of this concentration of varied wildlife, large portions of the plain were covered with thick stands of cereal grasses that may have been related to such grains as sorghum and barley.

Not surprisingly, Kôm Ombo's varied food supply, its streams, and its spacious meadowlands attracted many people to the area. Archaeologists think that the plain may have supported as many as 150 to 200 people at a time. At nearly one person per square mile, that would have amounted in Stone Age terms to crowding. This concentration of a human population seems to have produced some interesting results. Clustered in enclaves along the banks of the many streams, each group of people, numbering perhaps about 25 or 30, developed its own distinctive style of living. A communal trademark might be, for example, a particular technique for food-gathering. Competition in a world suddenly grown populous may be what drove the groups into some of these forms of specialization.

Some of the most fascinating of these group specializations were practiced by peoples who were more interested in grains than any of their predecessors on the plain had been. They harvested and processed the wild grains with such intensity that a good part of their nutritional needs may have been met by grain alone. Archaeologists think that the task of grinding may have been a group activity and that the grain harvest probably was, too. As the ears of the grasses ripened, the band would hand-strip the seeds or cut the stalks with stone sickles, and carry the grain to the site of the grinding stones for threshing—possibly underfoot—and milling.

Except for the sickles and grinding stones, none of the artifacts of the entire harvesting process remain. We are left with many questions. Did the Kôm Ombo peoples thresh the grain with bundles of sticks, as primitive farmers still do today? Did they free it of what little chaff it may have had by tossing it in the air on a windy day? And what sort of container did they use to transport the grain to the mill? Drawing upon the Nile's abundant supply of reeds and grasses, the successors to these Stone Age peoples became skillful basketmakers. Did the earlier Nile people try their hand at weaving and construct a kind of mat or tray on which to pile the grain?

Even more intriguing, what did they do with the product? Presumably, they used it for porridge and for thickening meat stews. But

Figure 18–5 The ten-pound grindstone and crude pestle at top attest to the adaptability of hunting societies in North Africa's Kôm Ombo areas toward the end of the ice age. Abundant wild grains, milled with tools like these, became an important part of their diet. Stone sickles were used to cut the stalks of the grain. The sickle below, made from antler with flint teeth, is from Mt. Carmel, dating from about 7,000 B.P.

the fact that they ground the grain into meal suggests that they also made some form of bread, perhaps an unleavened mixture of meal water-baked on a hot stone, such as many present-day peoples make. Some scholars have even suggested that the grain harvesters of Kôm Ombo may have made beer from some of the grain.

AN END TO WANDERING

In the fertile valleys of Egypt, on the frigid plains of Siberia, along the seacoast of Africa, Cro-Magnon man was demonstrating that he not only could stay alive but could actually prosper under conditions of extraordinary diversity. Cold was no barrier to his existence; when meat was scarce his food became fish; and, at least in one area, with foresight and planning he harvested natural grains in one concerted operation. After centuries of nomadism, of moving from place to place in pursuit of game or of fresh supplies of plant food, he was finally able to stay in one place and systematically exploit the seasonal resources of one locality. He was, in short, becoming the master of the world he inhabited.

A New Life Style

This change in subsistence inevitably produced profound changes in his physical well-being and mode of living. For one thing, Cro-Magnon man was probably healthier than his predecessors. With a sufficiency of food and a more rounded diet, he must have been stronger and more alert, better able to outrun and outmaneuver many of the animals he hunted. Possibly, he also lived a bit longer, and the extra time on earth allowed him not only to accumulate more knowledge but to pass on more of his knowledge to his children and grandchildren.

Along with better health, Cro-Magnon's efficiency as a food producer gave him certain other advantages. Since he was often able to lead a more sedentary life, he could acquire more material goods, objects that would have been impractical to own as long as he was on the move. The inhabitants of several late Cro-Magnon sites in central Europe, for instance, were shaping objects from clay and, as we shall see, even firing them in dome-shaped kilns. Even more important than material wealth was the evolution of social behavior, which became a base for the full development of language, art, and religion, and the complex forms of social and political organization that are the hallmark of all developed human cultures.

Someday in the distant future, when the gasoline engine is a quaint relic of the past and steel is obsolete, archaeologists may look back on the twentieth century and marvel that human beings with such a limited technology managed to get on so well. In the same way, if people today think of their Cro-Magnon ancestors (those brutish creatures who battered at mammoth carcasses with chunks of rock), they might wonder that such ill-equipped people could cope with their harsh ice-age environment. Perhaps we could learn a lesson or two from Cro-Magnon if we were to compare his form of adaptation to the world with ours; but to get a sense of the sheer force of his achievement we might do better to compare his cultural record not with ours but with that of his predecessors.

During the 30,000 or so years of their tenure, Cro-Magnon peoples made more technological progress, and in the process gained more control over their environment, than had been made or gained in all the million years of human experience that preceded them. They were the master stoneworkers of all time, improving old techniques to produce stone tools of greater effectiveness and variety. The Cro-Magnons also exploited other materials—bone, antler, and ivory—that had been little used earlier, selecting and working each to best advantage in fashioning not only new weapons and new tools but domestic inventions and decorative objects as well. They learned to build better fires more easily and to use them for new purposes. Some Cro-Magnon shelters were but a step away from real houses; they were more durable than earlier ones and afforded more protection against the elements. And when the climate changed, the Cro-Magnon peoples invented ways to deal with it. Technological innovation and cultural adaptation almost replaced physical evolution, and man's links to his animal past were now beginning to lie more and more behind him. These people still depended on nature, but nature no longer ruled them.

Mastery of Fire

For example, the Cro-Magnons added new dimensions to the use of fire by man. For one thing, they were the first to leave proof of their ability to strike a fire quickly whenever they needed one. A cave site in Belgium yielded a beautifully rounded piece of iron pyrite (Figure 18–6). This substance is one of the few natural materials from which flint will strike sparks that will set dry tinder on fire; sparks struck from two flints or two ordinary rocks are not hot enough to do so. What is more, the Belgian pyrite has a groove showing where it had been struck again and again with pieces of flint. Since iron pyrite is not easy to find lying about on the ground, each such firestone was undoubtedly a cherished item that would have been carried wherever a band roamed.

A more dramatic example of Cro-Magnon man's growing mastery of fire, evidence of which has turned up in sites in the Soviet Union and France, seems prosaic at first glance: a series of shallow grooves dug into the bottom of a hearth, and a channel curving away from the hearth like a tail. So simple an innovation may well have been overlooked many times in earlier archaeological excavations, but in fact it was the first small step toward the blast furnaces of modern steel mills. The grooves and channels in those prehistoric fireplaces allowed more air to reach the fuel, and the fires in them could thus burn hotter.

The ancient Russians who built these special hearths needed them because of the type of fuel they used. In an area where wood was scarce, they had to turn for fuel to a material that normally does not burn well: bone. Although bone is hard to ignite and burns inefficiently, being only about 25 percent combustible material, it gives off adequate heat. That the Russians did burn it is proved by the lack of charred wood and the considerable quantities of bone ash found in their specially vented hearths.

The hearth was home, and Cro-Magnon man, who changed so much else, also changed the concept of home. Where he lived in the caves

Figure 18–6 The oldest known firestone, this iron pyrite—shown enlarged one and one-half times—is from a Belgian cave. The Cro-Magnons were apparently the first to discover that flint and iron pyrite used in combination yielded sparks hot enough to ignite tinder.

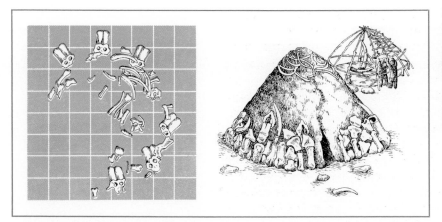

Figure 18–7 Careful mapping of an upper Paleolithic site in the Ukraine shows mammoth bones lying in a semicircle, suggesting that they were part of a round structure. The original dwelling was probably dome-shaped, covered with hides, and weighted down with other bones, as depicted in the reconstruction.

and rock shelters that had protected his predecessors, he seems, in some places at least, to have kept cleaner house than those earlier tenants had; litter was thrown outside instead of being allowed to pile up inside.

It was in regions that offered no ready-made habitations that Cro-Magnon man's home improvements were most noticeable. Particularly in central and eastern Europe and Siberia, remnants of many sturdily built shelters have been found in open country (see Figure 18–7).

Solutrean Laurel Leaves

Improvement in his stone tools was crucial to Cro-Magnon man's new technical mastery. It is ironic that despite all efforts at deciphering his cultural remains no one really knows what purpose was served by the most beautiful examples of this new skill. Anyone who has ever held in his hands and examined a European *Solutrean* tool such as the magnificent eleven-inch-long "laurel-leaf" blade (see page 393) must eventually have wondered how this implement could have been used. Too delicate for a knife, too big and fragile for a spearhead, so beautifully crafted a piece of flint seems to be a showpiece. Clearly, to produce an object of such daring proportions required craftsmanship bordering on art, and many archaeologists think this masterpiece and others like it may have been just that—works of art that served an esthetic or ritual function rather than a utilitarian one and that may even have been passed from one person or group to another as highly prized items.

If the large laurel-leaf blades were made for no useful purpose, they were clearly, then, an instance of technology transcending itself. The smaller, everyday implements on which such showpieces were modeled had strictly practical functions. They are known in the thousands and come in various styles from sites all over the world. Stone points in various sizes have been found in excavations in Solutrean cultural levels in western and central Europe (that is, implements fitting into the cultural style typified by finds from Solutré, in southern France), and there is no doubt that many of these could have served most effectively as spear points or knives with razor-sharp edges. They were significant items in the armory of a people who depended for their existence less and less on the simple strength of their biceps and more and more on their brain power and the efficacy of their weapons.

The smaller stone blades of Cro-Magnon man were unquestionably sharp and efficient. Modern experiments have shown that well-made flint projectile points are sharper than iron points of a similar type and penetrate more deeply into an animal's body. Flint knives are equal, if not superior, to steel knives in their cutting power. The only drawback of flint is that, because of its brittleness, it breaks more easily than metal and has to be replaced more often.

The importance of such blades in the lives of European Cro-Magnon hunters lends authority to the theory that the large, non-utilitarian examples, of which at least several dozen have been found, might have been ritualistic objects representing the quintessential spear point. They might, too, have been used as a primitive currency for trade. On the other hand, it has also been suggested that a magnificent laurel leaf might have been simply a tour de force tossed off by a virtuoso tool-maker to demonstrate his talent. If this is the case, any admiration or praise his work received was well deserved. The laurel leaf is without doubt a splendid creation, and there are fewer than a handful of people in the world today who are skilled enough in the ancient craft to produce one.

Tool Specialization

However individualistic the Cro-Magnon tool industries may have been in style, in utility they had much in common. Cro-Magnon groups everywhere produced tools more specialized than any that earlier human groups had used. Archaeologists identify sixty or seventy types of tools in the tool kits of some Neandertals—scrapers meant to be held horizontally, knives with blunted backs, others with double edges, and so on. But they count over a hundred types in the tool kits of the Cro-Magnons—knives for cutting meat, knives for whittling wood, scrapers for bone, scrapers for skin, perforators, stone saws, chisels, pounding slabs, and countless others. Among the innovations of Cro-Magnon man are two-part tools. He is believed to have taken to putting bone and antler handles on many of his stone tools, such as axes and knives. By providing him with a firmer grasp and enabling him to use to a much greater extent the muscle power of his arm and shoulder, the handles increased the power he could put into a blow with a tool by as much as two to three times.

One of the most important tools that Cro-Magnon man developed was the cutter called a *burin* (see Figure 18–8). It is tempting to say he invented the burin, but it had existed in a few tool kits of Neandertal man and even *Homo erectus*. In the hands of the first modern people, however, the burin was gradually improved and became more important and much more numerous. A burin was a kind of chisel. Today the name is given to a fine steel cutting tool used by engravers in preparing copper plates. In the Stone Age it was a tool with a strong, sharply beveled edge or point used to cut, incise, and shape other materials, such as bone, antler, wood, and sometimes stone. It differed from most other stone tools of prehistory in that it was not used by itself to kill

Figure 18–8 This Upper Paleo-lithic burin is the first chisel—a new and important technological development. Its main use was perhaps to make other tools of wood or bone.

animals, cut meat, clean hides, or chop down saplings for tent poles. Rather, like the machine tools of the modern age, it had as a chief function the manufacture of other tools and implements. With a tool that made other tools, Cro-Magnon man's technology could expand many times faster than ever before.

The burin probably helped produce many wooden implements, but only fragments of these have survived. So the best record of the object's effectiveness is found in the surviving tools it shaped, superb tools that, like the burin itself, stand out as a mark of Cro-Magnon sophistication.

Three organic raw materials, bone, antler, and ivory, helped supply the needs of Cro-Magnon man's ever-expanding economy, and the burin made possible their widespread exploitation. *Homo erectus* and Neandertal man had used bone to some extent for scraping or piercing or digging, but not nearly so much as the Cro-Magnons did. In a typical Neandertal site perhaps twenty-five out of a thousand tools turn out to be made of bone; the rest are stone. In some Cro-Magnon encampments the mix may be as much as half and half or even greater.

Bone and antler and ivory were the wonder materials of Cro-Magnon times, much the way plastics are today. Less brittle and therefore more workable than flint, much stronger and more durable than wood, they could be cut, grooved, chiseled, scraped, sharpened, shaped. They could be finely worked into tiny implements like needles, or used for heavy work. A deer antler makes an excellent pick, a mammoth leg bone cracked lengthwise needs only minor modifications and a handle to become an efficient shovel. Ivory could be steamed and bent, adding yet another dimension to toolmaking.

Best of all, the very animals that Cro-Magnon man hunted and depended on for food provided these materials in abundance. All animals have bone, of course, and many of the large animals—red deer, reindeer, mammoth—had antlers or tusks as well. Antlers seemed almost to be nature's gift to man because he did not have to kill an animal to obtain them: every year the deer shed their old ones, which lay on the ground for the picking up. Since reindeer and red deer were at one time or another perhaps the most abundant game animals in western Europe, antler was used there more than bone or ivory. In parts of eastern Europe and Siberia, where wood was relatively scarce, skeletons from giant mammoths that had died a natural death or had been trapped by hunters were a source of tools. One mammoth tusk might measure over nine feet and weigh more than a hundred pounds; there were a lot of implements to be made from that much ivory.

The only problem with bone, antler, and ivory was that in order to work them a special kind of tool was required. We have seen what that tool was. With its strong chisel point, the burin could easily scratch or dig into bone without breaking. To cut up a bone, the toolmaker could incise a deep groove around the bone and then, with a sharp blow, break it cleanly at the cut, just as a glazier today cuts a groove in a glass pane before breaking it. To get slivers for needles, points, and awls, it was necessary only to draw a burin repeatedly lengthwise down a bone to score two parallel grooves deep enough to hit the soft center. Then

Figure 18–9 A laurel leaf blade is so delicate it could have served no practical purpose. The blade—eleven inches long but only four-tenths of an inch thick—may have been a ceremonial object or even the proud emblem of a master toolmaker. These finely chipped blades are part of the Solutrean tool industry.

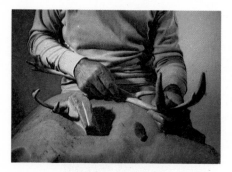

1. Preparing to make a needle, the toolmaker holds an antler in his hands. On his lap are a burin and a piece of grooved sandstone, which was cut with a burin.

2. Having scratched the outline of a triangle on the antler with a burin, the toolmaker finishes carving the triangle. He must cut deeply to completely separate it from the antler.

3. By pressing his finger on one end, the toolmaker has lifted the triangle from the antler and now rubs its wide end against sandstone to thin the triangle so that it can be pierced.

4. To make the needle's eye, the toolmaker holds the triangle and gently begins to bore a hole in it. He will turn the triangle over and work on the other side to refine the eye.

5. The eye—only one-sixteenth of an inch in diameter—is finished, and the toolmaker uses a burin to shape the triangle into a rounded needle.

6. To finish the needle, the toolmaker sharpens the point by rubbing it back and forth in a groove in a piece of sandstone. The finished needle is pointed enough to penetrate leather or skins easily.

the piece of hard material between the grooves was pried out and ground to shape. Other pieces of bone could be turned into spatulas, scrapers, beads, bracelets, digging tools, and more.

In addition to domestic utensils, bone and antler provided spear points, lances, and barbed harpoon tips, with which Cro-Magnon could take advantage of bountiful supplies of game. Probably at no time since have there been so many grazing animals roaming the face of the earth: in Europe and Asia there were mammoth, horses, red deer, pigs, reindeer, and bison; in Africa lived all the animals that are known there today, as well as a great many others that are now extinct—enormous relatives of buffalo, hartebeest, and zebra.

The scene was set for man the hunter and gatherer to reach the peak of successful adaptation. This full exploitation of these rich resources not only gave mankind an extraordinary amount of control over his environment, but was to form the stable basis of still further cultural developments.

Figure 18–10 Making a needle out of antler.

	YEARS B.P.	FOSSIL AND ARCHAEOLOGICAL RECORD	MAJOR TOOL INDUSTRIES OF WESTERN EUROPE

HOLOCENE
10,000
UPPER PALEOLITHIC
35,000
MIDDLE PALEOLITHIC
Neandertal in Europe, Asia, Africa
100,000

Arago, Swanscombe, and Steinheim; Levallois technique

Peking man

Large-scale elephant hunts in Europe

500,000

Günz glaciation

Hearths at Escale; *H. erectus* expansion into Europe

1 million — *H. erectus* expansion into China

A. robustus and *A. boisei* extinct

Acheulian industry

1.5 million —

LOWER PALEOLITHIC

habilis at Olduvai

2 million — Oldowan industry

Würm glaciation
20,000
30,000

Riss-Würm interglacial
60,000
80,000

Riss glaciation
100,000
120,000

Shellfish harvested at Nelson Bay Cave
Iron pyrite in Belgium
Seeds of wild grasses harvested at Kôm Ombo

Oldest dated European moderns: Pavlov
Lake Mungo, Australia, fossils
Transition to Cro-Magnon complete; Siberia and North America inhabited

Florisbad skull

La Quina, La Chapelle, and La Ferrassie fossils; modern skull at Niah

Skhūl and Kafzeh fossils

Tabūn, Amud, and Shanidar fossils

Monte Circeo fossils

Disk-core technique used

Broken Hill fossil

Solo and Ehringsdorf fossils

Fontéchevade fossils

MESOLITHIC CULTURES

MAGDALENIAN   **SOLUTREAN**

PERIGORDIAN   **AURIGNACIAN**

MOUSTERIAN

ACHEULIAN

ADAPTATION AND SURVIVAL

Many of the dates given to finds are based on indirect evidence and are estimates; the dates given to cultural phases are approximations.

Chapter 19

Hunting, Magic, and Art

There we see what made his world and preoccupied him. The cave
paintings fix forever the universal base of his culture . . . the hunter's
knowledge of the animal that he lived by and stalked.

J. BRONOWSKI, 1908–1974.
THE ASCENT OF MAN.

Two dazzling examples of Cro-Magnon hunting success have been unearthed by archaeologists in Europe. Near the town of Pavlov, in modern Czechoslovakia, excavations have revealed the remains of over 100
mammoths in one giant bone heap; near Solutré, in France, an even
more staggering bone pile contains the fossils of an estimated 10,000
wild horses lying in a tangled heap at the bottom of a high cliff. The
mammoth bones are apparently the leavings of hunters who trapped
the giant beasts in pitfalls; the horses had perhaps been stampeded off
the cliff over a period of many years, even generations, by intelligent
hunters who were familiar down to the last detail with the terrain of the
region and the behavior of their victims.

It is likely that the people of this period—including the ancestors of
the tribes who would in time be ranging the plains of North America—
understood as much about hunting large herd animals as any other
human groups in history. They undoubtedly knew just what plants the
animals preferred to eat; they knew when seasonal migrations began
and how fast the animals travelled; they knew what panicked them and
what soothed them. They knew how to drive them into pit traps, how to
snare them with baited thong nooses, how to guide them into natural
or man-made corrals, either by stampeding them or herding them
quietly from a discreet distance. Once trapped, the animals could be
dispatched with spears or knives and butchered on the spot. The meat

CRO-MAGNON: HUNTER PAR EXCELLENCE

was then taken back to camp, perhaps in processed form, possibly cut up in strips and smoked or sun-dried.

There can also be little doubt that these hunters knew a great deal about the anatomy of their victims and the virtue of eating certain of their organs. Today the inland Alaskan Eskimos save the adrenal glands of slaughtered caribou to give to young children and pregnant women. Chemical analysis of the gland reveals an astonishingly high content of vitamin C, an essential element but hard to come by in the standard diet of the Eskimo. Without overestimating the Cro-Magnon hunter's knowledge in these matters, it can be assumed that he, too, knew exactly which parts of the animals he hunted were good, and also which parts were good for him.

Cro-Magnon's profound understanding of his prey, combined with significant technical advances in his hunting equipment, paid off in increased food supplies. Hunters had long had wooden spears with fire-hardened tips or sharp stone heads to thrust or throw at their prey, but the effectiveness of a thrown spear against even a young deer, to say nothing of a thick-skinned giant auroch, must have been marginal, especially if the animal was in full retreat. The Cro-Magnon hunters made the spear an effective weapon for killing their prey at a greater distance by inventing the spear thrower.

The oldest tangible evidence of this rodlike device dates from about 14,000 years B.P. It comes from the cave of La Placard in France. Here several fragments of spear throwers were discovered, including a length of bone with a hooked end that looks like nothing so much as an oversized crochet needle. All told, more than seventy reindeer-antler spear throwers have turned up in southwestern France and near Lake Constance along the northeastern border of Switzerland. There is a curious dearth of them elsewhere in the Old World, perhaps because they may also have been made of perishable wood and rotted away. By about 10,000 years ago, the wooden spear thrower was being used by the Indians of North and South America; the Aztecs called it the *atlatl*. The Eskimos employed it until recently, and Australian Aborigines still use it today and call it a *womera*.

The spear thrower is, in the simplest terms, an extension of the arm. It is a foot to two feet long, with a handle at one end and a point or hook at the other to engage the butt end of the spear. The hunter holds the thrower behind his shoulder, hook up, and lays the spear along it so that the spear points forward and slightly upward. During the throw he keeps hold of the thrower, which may have a thong tied to its end to go around his wrist. When throwing, he swings his arm forward and snaps his wrist, launching the spear with great velocity from the end of the thrower at the top of its arc, in this way taking advantage of the centrifugal force generated. The spear travels faster than if hand-thrown because the extension of the throwing arm provides more leverage; its front end moves faster than the hand holding it.

Modern experiments have demonstrated the great advantage a spear thrower gives. A seven-foot spear can be thrown no more than 60 or 70

Spear Throwers and Points

Figure 19–1 The method of throwing a spear has not changed since spear throwers were introduced in Magdalenian times, about 10,000 to 20,000 years ago. Here an Australian is shown poised to throw his stone-tipped spear. The womera can be clearly seen.

yards when launched directly from a hunter's hand, but it can be projected up to 150 yards with a spear thrower, and it can kill a deer at 30
yards. This increase in range gave the ancient hunter a tremendous
advantage. No longer having to get within a short distance of his prey,
he could more often get a throw at the animals before they ran away.
Now he could, when the occasion arose, hunt alone instead of in a
group, because it was no longer necessary to surround an animal in
order to spear it. And, of course, the spear thrower made hunting safer,
for hunters did not have to get so close to dangerous teeth, antlers, and
hooves. The benefits are obvious: hunters who killed more often and
got hurt less lived better and longer lives.

The first spear throwers were undoubtedly of wood as the Australian
womeras are today, but soon they were also being made from antler. A
group of late Cro-Magnon people known as the *Magdalenians* embel-
lished many of their throwers with carved figures and designs and may
even have painted them. One ancient Magdalenian thrower bears
traces of red ocher in its hollows, and some have black painted into the
eyes. Other throwers display exquisite renderings of animals, including
horses, deer, ibex, bison, birds, and fish. At least three show an ibex
defecating, held by the art of the engraving in the moment when the
animal will slow down or be still, when a kill may be made. These
carvings on weaponry represent a combination of esthetics and utility
that is echoed in many aspects of Cro-Magnon's life.

Other functional advances were in the spear itself. By this time,
hunters had realized that a barbed point does more damage than a
smooth one. Harpoon-style points, fashioned from bone or antler, often
had several barbs on one or both sides. Another development stemmed
from the difficulty of killing an animal outright by one spear wound
alone; the hunters would have to follow their wounded prey for a while
until loss of blood made it weak enough for them to kill. To speed this
process, some hunters developed bone spearheads with grooves along
each side—runnels apparently designed to increase the flow of blood
from the wound.

Figure 19–2 This barbed Magdalenian harpoon is beautifully made.
It forms part of a highly evolved
collection of fishing tackle which
these people developed.

Bow and Arrow?

An interesting puzzle concerns Cro-Magnon's use of the bow and
arrow. There is no clear-cut archaeological evidence that he used such a
weapon until, at the earliest, the very end of his period of dominance.
Since bows are normally made of wood and sinew or gut, it would be a
lucky accident indeed if any had survived the last ice age. A couple of
bows have been uncovered in Denmark that date back approximately
8,000 years, and a larger number of stone-tipped wooden arrow shafts,
perhaps 10,000 years old, have been found in campsites of ancient
reindeer hunters in northern Germany. In a cave in La Colombière, in
France, there have been found small stones, possibly over 20,000 years
old, with pictures scratched on them that may represent feathered projectiles; whether these were arrows or dartlike spears, however, is
uncertain.

It is clear, though, that Cro-Magnon man had the wit and ingenuity
to invent the bow. He must have known that saplings bend under

tension and spring back when released; he had leather thongs and almost certainly knew that dried animal gut and sinew make a strong and flexible cord. Believing this, many archaeologists today are convinced that some Cro-Magnon hunters did indeed use the bow before 10,000 B.C., despite the lack of physical proof.

Certainly the bow would have given Cro-Magnon man an enormous advantage when hunting. The spear thrower, no matter how valuable an aid, required him to break cover and stand out in the open where he could be spotted by his prey; an unsuccessful launch would have scared off the target. But with the bow, he could remain hidden. If he missed with his first arrow, he might have time to shoot again. Moreover, the arrow was swifter than the spear and its striking power was greater over a longer distance. It could be shot at a variety of animals big and small, standing, running, or on the wing, with a better chance of hitting them.

Fishing Gear

Perhaps even more significant than the invention of the spear thrower or bow in helping Cro-Magnon man to expand his food supply and make a living in varied environments was his development of fishing gear. Human groups had earlier availed themselves of the bounty offered by streams, rivers, and the sea; but for some Cro-Magnon peoples, fishing became almost a way of life. The record left by the hunter-gatherers who lived in Nelson Bay Cave in South Africa (discussed in Chapter 18), for example, shows that here again an improved technology was vital to success.

One ingenious development was a device called the *leister:* a trident-like spear with a point and two curving prongs of bone that held the fish securely after it had been lanced. Another was the *fish gorge,* a small sliver of bone or wood, perhaps two inches long, with a leather or sinew line tied around its middle. A fisherman dropped his baited line into the water; the gorge, once swallowed by a fish, cocked sideways in its throat in such a way as not to come out easily; and the fisherman hauled in his catch.

From a slightly later date, we have evidence suggesting that in South Africa and perhaps in Europe, people began catching fish in much greater numbers than ever before. Small, grooved, cylindrical stones found in South Africa may have been weights on nets made of thongs or plant fibers. With a net, two or three fishermen could catch a whole school of fish in one sweep.

The *weir,* a stone corral for trapping fish that is still employed by primitive peoples, was probably also used by Cro-Magnons. This would have been especially effective on rivers such as the Dordogne and Vézère in France, where spawning salmon swarm upstream in great numbers. It seems likely that at the spawning season, parties went to the fishing grounds to lay in a supply of salmon for the whole band, which may have had its home base miles away. The fish may have been cleaned and perhaps sun-dried or even smoked at the place where they were caught, and then carried to camp. At Solvieux, in France, a large rectangular area carefully paved with small stones has been excavated.

Figure 19–3 The leister is a three-pronged fishing spear. The middle prong (not visible here) is shorter than the other two. Here an Australian employs the implement, which has been in use for at least 10,000 years.

Its placement and design strongly hint that it was used as a fish-drying platform.

As human groups learned to use the potential of rivers and seas, climatic changes complemented their improving technologies. The rising sea level that was associated with the retreat of the ice submerged the Atlantic continental shelf and so increased the area of warm, shallow sea in which many species of fish could breed. The systematic exploitation on a worldwide basis of the waters' abundant protein resources—which included great quantities of shellfish as well as fish—was highly significant, not only because it broadened the base of the human diet but because it led human beings toward the next great step in cultural evolution: settled living. With fish and shellfish as a dependable supplement to their regular meat and plant foods, the Cro-Magnon people did not have to move around so much in quest of sustenance. With nets they could gather more nourishment with less effort than they could as nomadic hunter-gatherers, and thus one place could support a greater number of people. The approach to a sedentary way of life was a crucial development, and one closely related to what became a rapidly expanding population.

Improving their tools and food-gathering techniques was a major preoccupation of the last ice-age peoples, but this was not their only concern. As they learned to help themselves more prodigally from nature's bounty, they also found ways to protect themselves more effectively from nature's rigors. The fabrication of carefully sewn, fitted clothing was part of what enabled them to conquer the far north and eventually to penetrate the vast continent of North America.

The hide clothing of these people was probably much like that of the Eskimos of recent times. A tunic or pullover with tightly sewn seams to keep heat from escaping, pants, easily tucked into boots, and some sort of sock, perhaps of fur, would have been warm enough in all but the coldest weather. For frigid days, outer clothing consisting of a hooded parka, mittens, and high boots would have served to keep a person from freezing. What is our evidence for clothing of this sort? Female figurines from Stone Age Russia look as if they are clothed in fur. Furthermore, even in more moderate climates, good sewn clothing seems to have been an advantage; the earliest eyed needles to be discovered were fashioned by the same expert Solutrean craftsmen of Europe who produced the laurel-leaf blades.

Up until now, our discussion of Cro-Magnon man has centered on his improvements in working stone and particularly bone, and on the cultural developments furthered by these technological improvements. Notable as these changes are, it has to be his intellectual and spiritual achievements that make Cro-Magnon man so impressive to us today. This is particularly true of his astounding artistic ability, a talent that seems to have sprung full-blown out of nowhere. There are dozens of sites of Cro-Magnon cave art in France alone. These date from approx-

Sedentary Life and Sewn Clothing

ART AND RITUAL OF CRO-MAGNON

Cave Art

imately 28,000 to 10,000 B.C. Cro-Magnon peoples were close observers of the animals they hunted as well as magnificent artists. More than that, the record they left behind shows that they had a sufficiently sophisticated way of life to be able to appreciate and encourage their own talents and to work them into their dreams and rituals.

From all indications, the prodigious output of paintings and carvings of Cro-Magnon peoples is closely associated with their spiritual life. One strong indication of this is seen in the places they chose to put wall paintings. There are basically two kinds of caves in the Dordogne. There are the rock overhangs, more or less open and facing out over the valleys. These can be made livable by the addition of barriers of brushwood or animal skins to keep out the wind and snow, and they are the rock shelters that Cro-Magnon peoples lived in. They are full of the signs of many generations of occupancy; tools lie in all strata in their floors together with buried skeletons. Hearths abound, tending to become bigger the more recent they are.

Some fragments of wall decoration have been found in these open shelters; perhaps originally there was more that has since been destroyed by exposure to the elements. But the most spectacular Cro-Magnon wall art is confined to true caves: deep underground fissures with long galleries and passages. These caves have their own subterranean pools and rivers, their festoons of stalactites and stalagmites. They are dark and mysterious; they could be entered only by people holding stone lamps or torches. Certainly these dark caverns were inappropriate as dwelling places, and they contain little or no evidence of having been

Figure 19–4 Seen from a cliffside ledge north of Les Eyzies, the Vézère Valley presents a peaceful panorama little changed since Cro-Magnons surveyed the scene. At left, the ledge leads past a shallow rock shelter, one of hundreds of prehistoric dwellings that are still unexcavated.

lived in. By their very nature removed from day-to-day life, these caves quite probably were used by Cro-Magnon man as shrines.

Some attention has been given by archaeologists to the theory that Cro-Magnon man used these underground passages for certain rites. The fears inspired by low, damp corridors and total darkness might have been similar to those provoked in other ways by some modern-day puberty initiation rites. Cro-Magnon people were human enough and probably socially developed enough to have elaborated rites of this sort, and the evidence from the cave called Le Tuc d'Ardoubert suggests such a practice. Another interesting point about cave art has been brought out by the late Abbé Henri Breuil, the French priest who devoted his life to the study of prehistory, and by Johannes Maringer, who has also studied this art intensively. It seems that the paintings or engravings were often made in the least convenient places for viewing: in narrow niches, behind protrusions of rock, sometimes in areas that must have been not only difficult but actually dangerous for the artist to work in. "It is simply impossible," says Maringer, "that this art should have been invented, in these locations, to give pleasure to the eye of the beholder; the intention must always have been to veil it in mysterious secrecy."

Painting and Hunting Magic

Figure 19–5 Protected by jutting walls and a 100-foot overhang, the broad floor outside a limestone cave in the Gorge d'Enfer made an ideal living space for ancient families. The 12-foot-high cave entrance (at the center) leads to a small chamber. Many deep caves, hollowed out by circulating water, were used for wall paintings, for burials, and possibly for ritual ceremonies.

Figure 19–6 Two 24-inch-long clay bison lean against a limestone block in a remote chamber of Le Tuc d'Audoubert Cave near Ariège, France.

What was its purpose then? According to Maringer and numerous other experts, cave art was a vehicle for magic—more specifically, a vehicle for a form known as *sympathetic* hunting magic. Cro-Magnon was strong and intelligent, and he was well equipped with all kinds of weapons from spears and knives to slings. He knew how to make traps for small animals and pitfalls for large ones. He could ambush and stampede. And, as we have seen, he has left impressive records of his prowess behind him. Nevertheless, despite his formidable powers, he walked always in the shadow of unpredictable and incomprehensible events, which he may have understood as malign forces. Doubtless he felt it necessary to try to forestall misfortune, injury, and sometimes death, for some of the animals he came up against were extremely dangerous. Doubtless, too, he believed, like so many people living today, that magic could help him not only dodge misfortune but also gain control over the animal he wished to kill. By painting its picture he became in effect the animal's master and strengthened his chances of dealing it a mortal wound during the hunt. Even today many isolated peoples believe that creating the likeness of a person or thing gives the creator some supernatural power over his subject.

This interpretation of the paintings as hunting magic has a variety of evidence to support it. First, and most direct, is the large number of animals painted with spears lodged in them or marked with the blows

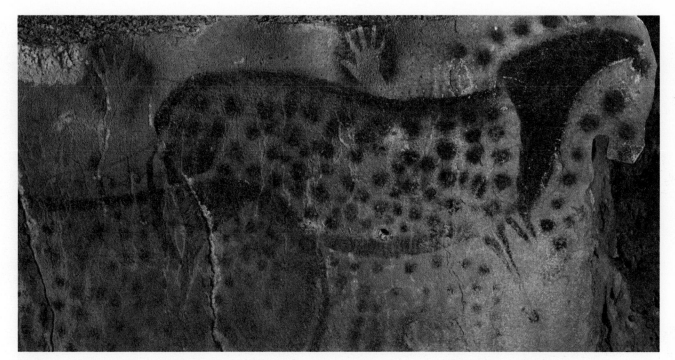

Figure 19–7   Pelted with dots, a painting of two horses in the Pech Merle Cave (Dordogne) combines two kinds of symbols for what could be simple decoration or signs of hunting magic. The dots could represent projectiles; the handprints surrounding the horses, a person's power over his prey. Taken together, the dots and hands would then be an invocation to the supernatural, intended to assure the hunters of a successful kill.

of clubs, as though the artist intended to illustrate what he hoped would be the outcome of the chase. Less obvious are the drawings of rectangular enclosures with animals seemingly trapped in them. The most frequently seen example of these is in a cave at Font-de-Gaume near Les Eyzies, where a magnificent painted mammoth seems to be caught in a pitfall even though his enormous tusks thrust beyond the snare.

There is also a hint of hunting magic in the practice of superimposing one picture over another. This phenomenon has been observed over and over again in the caves. In one spot at Lascaux in France, the paintings are four layers deep, even though there is plenty of empty wall space nearby. If the painter's intention had been simply to express himself or give pleasure to others, he would likely have started with a clean wall surface for each animal depicted. The concentration of paintings in one spot, atop one another, suggests that the placement of the painting was somehow important and that the overpainting was done for a purpose. Certain areas of the cave were favored for some reason, and it would be logical to suppose that paintings that had previously brought hunters good luck might in themselves come to be regarded as good hunting magic. Since all ritual depends on duplicating as closely as possible a procedure that has proved successful in the past, certain spots in the cave would come to be regarded as lucky.

In some instances entire caves seem to be imbued with an aura of good fortune. In Les Combarelles in southwestern France nearly three hundred animals crowd onto the cave walls. Perhaps it is this crowding that produced still another phenomenon of Cro-Magnon wall art: the tendency to overpaint one animal's head on another's body. Where space was at a premium, it would have been more provident to use the magic already available than start afresh. Or perhaps the artist was simply looking for a less arduous way of working magic, for many of the cave paintings obviously took time and effort to execute. It is not difficult to imagine a wishful hunter contemplating a beautifully painted bison and deciding to take a magical shortcut by substituting a deer's head for the bison's.

Hunting magic could also explain the occasional man–beast figures that are found in some caves, strange-looking creatures with human bodies and animal or bird heads, often appearing to be engaged in some kind of dance. These shaman or sorcerer figures may be straightforward pictures of hunters disguised as animals and may have been intended to guarantee successful stalking. On the other hand, they may be more symbolic. Perhaps they were projections of the hunter's feeling that a painting showing a ritual dance by a magician or shaman would work more potent magic on the game that would be pursued. The man–beast figures may even have been attempts to represent a superhuman being, such as a spirit of the hunt or the deity of the animals.

Although hunting magic logically explains a great deal of Cro-Magnon cave art, that same art is open to other interpretations. For some authorities these animals and cryptic geometrical signs are sexual in nature, and the paintings are fertility magic. Pairs of animals were often shown together, sometimes in the act of mating. Horses, does, and cows were painted with swollen bellies (as in Figure 19–8), which have been interpreted as a sign of advanced pregnancy. In other paintings, the udders were enlarged, as if to emphasize the rich supply of milk that the mother would be capable of giving to any offspring that might be born.

Art and Fertility

Fertility of the game hunted was a natural concern for the hunters. Scarcity of food must have been a periodic problem in many regions. During the colder episodes of the last glacial period the Cro-Magnon hunter took mammoths, woolly rhinoceros, ibex, steppe horses, and particularly reindeer, which flourished in large numbers in the tundra environment. When the climate warmed from time to time, he undoubtedly hunted the deer, bison, and wild cattle that replaced the cold-adapted species. But the need to feed increasing numbers, and the beginnings of a tendency toward a settled life hinted at by cave occupancy, may well have led Cro-Magnon man to encourage the natural productiveness of his game through the use of fertility magic.

Other authorities think that Cro-Magnon cave art, though sexual in content, is far less utilitarian in its purpose. Instead of fertility magic, they see it as an attempt to express in visual symbols the dual forces in human nature—male and female. The most notable spokesman for this post-Freudian point of view is French anthropologist André Leroi-Gourhan, who has made an extensive study of Cro-Magnon cave art. Leroi-Gourhan has charted the frequency of occurrence of the various kinds of animals and signs, along with their locations in the caves and their positions in relation to each other. He thinks that most of the paintings and drawings have specific sexual connotations—that deer

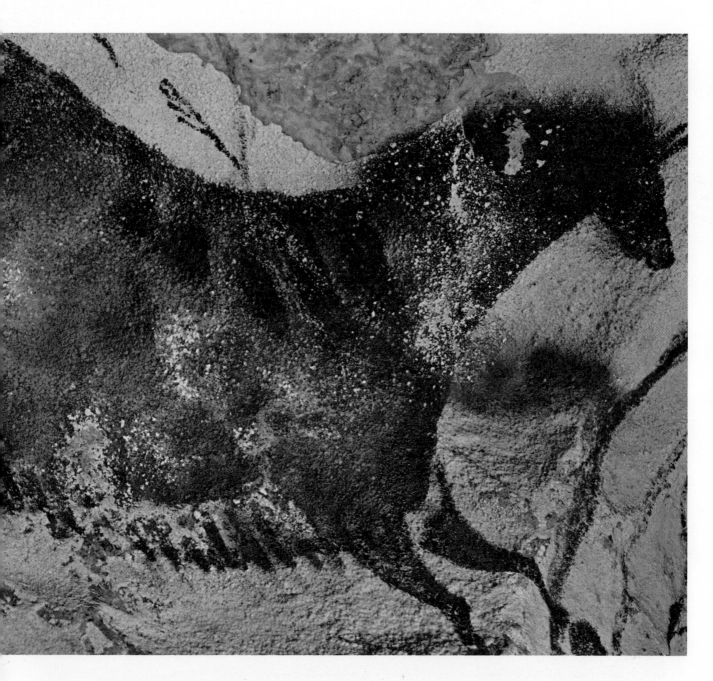

and bear are masculine for instance, along with such signs as spears and clubs, whereas cattle and bison, as well as the enclosed figures that other authorities identify as traps in support of the theory of hunting magic are feminine.

Whatever the pictures' meaning, the skill of the artists and the beauty of their work is astonishing. Every animal is an individual portrait, drawn from life, by a painter in complete control of his medium. His

Figure 19–8 A pregnant horse gallops across the limestone ceiling of Lascaux. The slash marks above its shoulders may indicate spears.

The Craft of the Painter

outlines were sure and bold. He painted in various tones of black, red, yellow, and brown obtained from natural clays and mineral oxides. Sometimes he mixed his colors with charcoal and animal fat to make a thick pigment, which he used like a crayon or daubed on with moss, frayed twigs, or even a primitive paintbrush made of hair. At other times, he seems to have blown his dry colors directly onto the wall in powder form, possibly through a hollow bird bone.

Once applied to a wall, these colors were slowly absorbed by the limestone. This begins to explain their phenomenal durability. Thanks to the constant humidity and temperature of the caves, much of Cro-Magnon art in western Europe has retained its original brilliance for 10,000 to 20,000 years, some of it for even longer. An ominous exception is the great cave at Lascaux. After its discovery in 1940, nothing was done with it until the end of World War II, at which time the French government stepped in and declared the cave a historical monument. It was fitted with doors, electric lights, and an air-conditioning system, and became one of the great tourist attractions of France. By the early 1950s those who knew the cave best were beginning to wonder if its paintings were not fading a little. By the 1960s this was no longer a wonder but a certainty. Furthermore, green algae were beginning to creep over the walls, defacing some of the finest animal portraits. Some experts blamed the air conditioning for making the cave drier than it had been. Others thought the humidity had risen excessively as a result of the breathing of the many visitors, and still others blamed the chemical toxicity of human breath. The problem was studied by a team of experts, two of whom finally identified as the culprit an alga name *Parmellococcus*. It had been thriving on light, moisture, carbon dioxide, and other substances that had been brought into the ancient cave by modern scientists and tourists. Once it had been identified, the alga was checked with antibiotics and then removed with a bath of detergent and formaldehyde. But the danger of recontamination remains, and for this reason, only special visitors are now admitted to this and some other caves.

In addition to painting, Cro-Magnon man showed considerable proficiency as a sculptor and engraver. In early examples of his skill, he incised the outlines of animals on cave walls. Later artists went on to develop the more advanced technique of carving subjects in high relief, often utilizing the contours of the walls. Le Cap Blanc, near Les Eyzies, has a marvelous set of horses done in this way. The entire frieze is about forty feet long; the largest horse is seven feet long. As the bulging sides of the horses' bodies reveal, the artist incorporated the natural curves of the rock into his work with great skill. Apparently, more than one artist was guided by the formation of the rock in carving this single frieze, for the animal figures appear to have been worked on at various times.

Cro-Magnon artists also made complete statues in the round. In doing so, they left us a means of gaining further insights into Stone Age

Figure 19–9 (Opposite page) Painted inside the main hall at Lascaux, an animal cavalcade proceeds toward the cave's entrance, now free of algae.

Sculpture and Ceramics

life and thought. The statues are normally of stone, bone, or ivory, although some were carved out of a mixture of clay and ground bone that had been fired to make it hard. The first evidence of firing comes from the site of Dolni Vestonice in Czechoslovakia. At a settlement dated about 27,000 B.P. there is a kiln where the bone and clay mixture was fired into a new, rock-hard material. This is the first example in technological history of what was to become a ubiquitous process eventually leading to glass, bronze, steel, nylon, and most of the other materials of everyday life—that is, the combination and treatment of two or more dissimilar substances to make a useful product unlike either starting substance. It would be another 15,000 years or so before other peoples, living in what is now Japan, learned to turn clay into pots; yet, as the evidence from Dolni Vestonice attests, ceramics had already been invented.

When the kiln hut was first investigated in 1951, its sooty floor was littered with fragments of ceramic figurines. There were animal heads—bears, foxes, lions. In one particularly beautiful lion head was a hole simulating a wound, perhaps intended to help some hunter inflict a similar wound on a real lion. The floor was also cluttered with hundreds of clay pellets bearing the fingerprints of the prehistoric artisan; he probably pinched them off his lump of unbaked clay when he first began to knead and shape it to his desire. And there were limbs broken from little animal and human figures. They may have cracked off in the baking, or when the ancient ceramist tossed aside a work that failed to please him.

More intriguing than any waste fragments or even clay animal figures on the hut floor are the human statuettes found there, particularly the female figures. Unlike the animals, these are not naturalistic but almost surreal. They have a very wide distribution in Stone Age sites over much of Europe and eastward as far as western Siberia. Although they vary a good deal in appearance, they have some significant things in common. The most obvious of these is that the sculptor's interest was focused on the torso. Arms and legs are extremely small in proportion to the trunk, and in some cases they are merely suggested (see Figure 19–10). Heads are also small and typically show little attempt to portray features, although the famous Venus of Willendorf, a four-inch figurine made of limestone, does have a wavy hairdo executed with considerable care. All the emphasis is on the bodies, with their female characteristics—breasts, belly, and buttocks—greatly exaggerated in size. They look like tiny earth goddesses or fertility figures, and a good deal of informed speculation suggests that this is what they were.

There is some evidence for this idea, mostly based on where these statuettes are found and when they are believed to have been made. The majority of them come from the period of the Upper Perigordian, a late Paleolithic culture of western Europe that existed between 20,000 and 25,000 years ago. During this period, the weather ranged from cool to very cold. In the cold periods it was bitter in the extreme, especially

Female Figurines

Figure 19–10 This Czech clay figure shows the Venuses' typical traits: huge breasts and belly and shapeless arms. This figure's legs are now broken, but they probably had no feet.

Figure 19–11 The Venus of Abri Patuad, the armless body of a woman incised in a small piece of rock, is one of the few art objects found at the excavation. It was made some 20,000 years ago.

on the eastern European plains; nevertheless, many peoples continued to live there. Some made their homes in shallow pits they dug in the ground and then roofed over with hides or other material. The vague outlines of the walls of many of these sunken huts may still be seen. The interesting thing about the female figurines is that some of their most abundant occurrences are in sites like these, where they are often found lying right next to the walls or buried near hearths. The figurines themselves often taper to a point at the bottom, as if they had been designed to be stuck into the earth or into a base of some sort.

On this evidence it is fairly clear that the figurines were closely associated with the daily life of the peoples who made them and have a significance utterly unlike that of the wall art that was created in secret, deep in underground caves. Speculating on their purpose, various authorities have proposed various theories. To Johannes Maringer the figurines seem to point to a change in the status of women. Maringer thinks that a combination of climatic conditions and a relatively sedentary way of life account for that change. When people settle down in one place for considerable periods of time, the home becomes important; and homemaking is usually regarded as the woman's prerogative. In the cold of the windswept eastern steppe, it was the women who had the job of planning, rationing, utilizing, and storing supplies so that the group could get through the winter. Storage pits were found in many sites, some with animal remains. Probably, women would also have been responsible for making the fur clothing that the people are thought to have dressed in. They perfected the eyed needle, and by sewing carefully they could make warm clothing that fitted the body well, particularly around the arms and legs.

But the role of woman could also have become important because of her procreative function. The mysteries of fertility and birth made woman the guardian not only of hearth and home but of life itself. In the minds of some experts the female figurines are cult objects. They represent the tribal ancestresses from whom the group is descended, assuring them of continuity as a group and increasing their population and

Figure 19–12 The skeleton of a Cro-Magnon man lies just as the body was buried 23,000 years ago in an ocher-sprinkled grave at Sungir, 130 miles northeast of Moscow. The man was ceremoniously laid to rest, laden with beads, bracelets, a headband of carved mammoth ivory, and the teeth of arctic foxes, in what appears to have been a burial ground—suggesting that the hunter-gatherers of Sungir lived at least part of the year in a settled community where they developed complex customs.

the population of the animals they hunted. Whether the little figures were worshipped as goddesses or simply venerated as good-luck charms is not known.

Death as well as life concerned Cro-Magnon peoples, and their treatment of their dead was careful and thoughtful. The bodies were often placed in graves dug in the ashes of previously occupied living sites, and in many places it was a common practice to sprinkle the deceased with red ocher, perhaps in an effort to bring back the flush of life to pallid skin. The practice of including grave offerings, begun in Neandertal times, was expanded by some Cro-Magnon peoples of Eurasia to extraordinary heights of funerary luxury. An example is the grave of two young boys (shown in Figure 19–13) that was excavated during the 1960s in a Paleolithic settlement about 130 miles northeast of Moscow, at Sungir. The grave suggests either that the boys were very important or that the settlers who lived at Sungir 23,000 years ago had some fairly elaborate ideas about an afterlife. The boys—one about 7 to 9 years old, the other 12 or 13—were laid out in a line, skull to skull. Both had been dressed from head to toe in clothing decorated with ivory beads carved from mammoth tusks, and they wore bracelets and rings of the same material. On the older boy's chest lay a disk of mammoth tusk carved into the shape of a horse, and both boys were equipped with an assortment of ivory weapons such as lances, spears, and daggers. The lances had been formed from a split mammoth bone that had been warmed over a fire in order to be straightened, a technique that requires considerable sophistication.

Not all the human skeletons from the late Stone Age bear witness to such concern with ritual burial. Large numbers of human bones are

Burial Customs and Rites

Figure 19–13 The skeletons of two boys who died 23,000 years ago lie head to head in a grave at Sungir in Russia. The elaborateness of their grave suggests that the boys were laid to rest amid solemn ritual, perhaps with a view to an afterlife.

found scattered at random. In some instances, leg bones have been cracked apart, as if somebody had been after the marrow in them; in other cases, someone has smashed the skulls from behind, perhaps to get at the brain. This raises the possibility of cannibalism, which we have seen to be strongly suggested also by the remains of Peking man and Neandertal man. However, any use that Cro-Magnon man or his predecessors may have made of human bones seems again to have been largely of a ritualistic nature. Some societies today keep skulls, and others preserve the ashes of their ancestors in urns. Australian Aborigines expose and dry some of the bones of their dead, and later carry them around in long packages. There are tantalizing bits of evidence that Cro-Magnon man, too, made a practice of keeping human bones for a reason. One cave in France has yielded three human skulls placed with obvious forethought on a slab of rock. Another contained the skull of a woman with a number of shell ornaments carefully arranged around it. Possibly, these represent ritual observances of some kind. Elsewhere in this same cave were pieces of skulls arranged with equal care. Detailed examination of these skullcaps by Abbé Breuil and by the German anthropologist Hugo Obermaier suggests that they were once used as shallow cups. Their position in the cave, arranged in a row and lying open side up at the end of a small tunnel, was suggestive to begin with. When the fragments were examined, they showed signs of having been worked. Each one bore marks on its surface indicating that the muscles and flesh that originally covered it had been hacked or scraped away with some kind of stone implement and that the lower parts of the skull had then been chopped off and the rough edges smoothed all around, leaving a skullcap that made a shallow cup.

Whether the skullcaps were those of relatives or ancestors and used out of affection and pride, or whether they were the skulls of enemies and used in triumph, cannot be determined. History is crowded with instances of both usages up through medieval times, when the skulls of Christian saints were still employed as ceremonial drinking cups. Prior to that, many peoples like the Teutons and Scythians drank from the skulls of their fallen enemies, and set particular store by those of the bravest men.

The more we learn about Paleolithic peoples from the evidence of their living sites, the narrower the gap will become between the Old Stone Age and ourselves. But it will never be entirely closed. The intimate details of social life, the games children played, the gestures and courtesies that give a society its flavor—all these have necessarily vanished. We have no knowledge of how one Cro-Magnon addressed another, or what words they used. And we never will know.

Some details have enlightened us, however, and some generalizations can be made. As these first modern people stretched their powers, they came to dominate nature in ways their ancestors could not have dreamed of. Their ability to exploit a variety of environments led to a great growth in their numbers, and populations increased as much

Conclusions

as ten times in some parts of the world. By the end of their time, some 10,000 years ago, Cro-Magnon peoples had set the stage for the last steps in the emergence of humankind: agriculture, domestication of animals, metalworking, complex forms of social and political life, writing, and perhaps even war.

OVERVIEW

	YEARS B.P.	HUNTING, RITUAL, AND ART

HOLOCENE

10,000

UPPER PALEOLITHIC
Cro-Magnon

35,000

MIDDLE PALEOLITHIC
Neandertal

100,000

Tents in caves at Lazaret

10,000 — Arrows used in northern Germany; wooden
spearthrowers used in the Americas

Levallois technique
Arago, Swanscombe,
Steinheim fossils

250,000

15,000 — Clay pots made in Japan

Spearthrower at La Placard, France

Peking man

20,000

Elaborate burials at Sungir

25,000 — Female figurines

Mammoth bones at Pavlov; kiln at Dolni Vestonice

500,000 — Mauer jaw

Early cave art

30,000 — Crude calendars made by Cro-Magnon

40,000 — Bear skulls at Drachenloch

Hearths at Escale;
H. erectus expansion into Europe

750,000

60,000 — Burial with flowers at Shanidar;
stone-encircled, mutilated skull at Monte Circeo

Java man (Trinil; Sangiran)

Family cemetery at La Ferrassie;
burial with artifacts at La Chapelle

80,000

1 million

LOWER PALEOLITHIC

Mutilated skulls at Solo

1.25 million

Sharpened wood point at Clacton-on-Sea
Charred skulls at Choukoutien
Large-scale elephant hunts in Europe

500,000

Acheulian industry

1.5 million

1 million

1.75 million — *habilis* at Olduvai

1.5 million

Bolas at Olduvai

Butchering sites on Olduvai living floors

Chapter 20

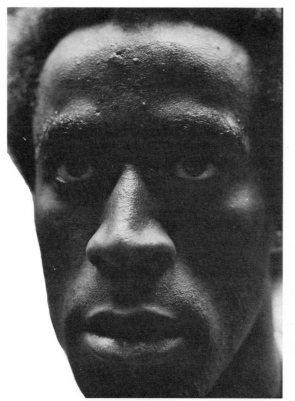

The Human Condition

But man, proud man,
Drest in a little brief authority,
Most ignorant of what he's most assured,
His glassy essence, like an angry ape,
Plays such fantastic tricks before high heaven
As make the angels weep.

WILLIAM SHAKESPEARE, 1564-1616.
MEASURE FOR MEASURE, II, ii.

It is hard to realize that the story we have recounted in these nineteen chapters took some 50 million years in its enactment. The development of technology alone has taken at least 3 million years. During this incredibly long period of emergence, the animal that became *Homo sapiens* has been shaped by its environment and its social experience— both its body and its culture changing in adaptation.

Evolutionary biology, of which paleoanthropology is a division, makes this much clear to us: each species is a product of genes and environment. That is, each characteristic of every species is a product of mutation and natural selection and in a very immediate way *fits* its environment. Fishes have fins, horses have hooves, primates have hands. Each characteristic of the human body is a direct product of the interaction between genes and environment. This is not to say that natural selection is directed or moves toward any goal; nor that the characteristics that *have* been selected by the environment are the only ones that might have been. Nature shows us that there is more than one solution to any problem. If in the long run we do not understand the genesis of every human characteristic, we know at least that we can never understand either its genesis or its function without considering the environment in which it evolved.

THE STORY OF
MANKIND

419

Australopithecus africanus

Homo erectus

The story of man's environment is relatively clear. The tropical rain forest was the womb from which human ancestors emerged into the world. As our ancestors evolved, they moved out from the shelter of the trees to occupy the tropical savannas throughout the Old World. As they expanded north into temperate zones, they came to occupy an increasing number of different *biomes* or ecological zones. To grassland and woodland alike they adapted, and eventually to the cool taiga and icy tundra. They moved in and out of the northern coniferous forests and followed game to alpine pastures. They evolved the flexibility to live in all these different biomes and became the first organism to do so.

This flexibility mankind owed, of course, to the second strand of our story: to the evolution of his remarkable and extraordinarily adaptable body and of his astounding brain. We have seen how the suggestive teeth and jawbones of *Ramapithecus* qualify it as a probable ancestor of the more fully known *Australopithecus* and how this latter creature was certainly a bipedal savanna-living hominid with very human teeth. *Australopithecus africanus* was well adapted to the new life style of the savanna dweller—flexible in behavior, omnivorous, and highly social. The species seems to have been a constant part of the savanna faunas for at least 5 million years. From it there sprang bigger-brained forms, who went on to invade the temperate zones: these were the first true humans, *Homo erectus*. Expansion northward continued until the Neandertals entered the arctic regions, equipped with highly developed technology. These people were already biologically modern, members of our own species, *Homo sapiens*. Following these phases, we find modern people who were indistinguishable physically from ourselves settling throughout the Old World and entering the New World and Australia. This was the start of modern times.

The human organism, miraculous though it may seem in its com-

Environmental History and Adaptations

Neandertal

Cro-Magnon

plexity, was still a product of natural selection: the human brain was no more than what was needed for survival in all these different environments. From an average of perhaps 400 cubic centimeters some 5 million years ago, human cranial capacity has risen to vary between 1,000 and 2,000 cubic centimeters. This increase in size has been exceedingly rapid in evolutionary terms, and has produced a brain of unprecedented complexity. Though whale and elephant have far bigger brains than ours, their brains are less complex and they do not have the brain power nor the behavioral adaptability of hominids.

This unique adaptability had led to a second human characteristic that was also a response to the environment: culture. Man's social culture consists of those behaviors and ideas that are the property of the society and that are maintained by mutual learning and teaching among its members. In human evolution, symbolic language became a new means of transmitting and remembering culture. Language was a unique and revolutionary organic adaptation. It opened up whole new possibilities of existence and paved the way for the second aspect of human culture: technology.

The first developments of technology came at an unimaginably slow rate. Any idea of progress would have been entirely foreign to early people; only the very simplest ideas would have been entering their heads. From using naturally occurring flakes as knives, people went on to learn to prepare their own simple choppers. Slowly, over millions of years, they improved the cutting edge and varied the form of tools for their different purposes. The large hand-axe appeared, the knifelike blade; manual skill became essential to the development of technology. In the cave dwellings of the northern hemisphere the priceless and virtually irreplaceable fire began to be kept alive in the hearth. The rate of change quickened and cultural developments came more rapidly;

Figure 20–1 From bipedal *Australopithecus* on the savanna to Cro-Magnons in the Dordogne, from Oldowan choppers to Solutrean eyed needles, human development has been the result of the interaction of environment, body, and culture.

Cultural History

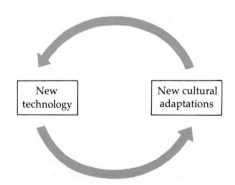

New technology

New cultural adaptations

Figure 20–2 Positive feedback loops can be constructive and creative, or destructive: in either case they tend to accelerate change in their components. This loop brings about very rapid cultural and technological changes.

particularly in the cold winters a relatively complex technology was crucial for human survival. Although we have little direct evidence, we can safely assume that clothing, wood and bone tools, and containers of all kinds became an essential part of our ancestors' survival kit. People learned from each other, and from time to time an invention was made, but what today we see as a progressive journey was for these early people simply the way things were; the life style they had was the only life style.

Eventually, human beings learned to change their environment in a more fundamental way. They began to follow wild game and protect it from other predators so as to reserve it for themselves. They learned to select and breed animals: they domesticated sheep and cattle. They planted seeds and harvested cereals, becoming farmers. Not long after, they discovered how to heat ores in a fire and smelt copper and zinc. The age of metals began to open up immense new possibilities. By this time, all these things were happening in relatively quick succession. The developing technology accelerated the growth and complexity of culture.

Environment, body, culture: these three are the threads of the human story we have told. During humankind's emergence each acted on the others in mutual feedback; any change in one necessitated adjustment in the others. This was something new in evolution, for learning to change the environment was something no animal had ever been through before, beyond building a nest or preparing a small arena for courtship. Human beings were to change their environment drastically—and as we can now see, this has perhaps been overdone. But this was humanity's unique achievement, and it constitutes the story of human prehistory. Human work and human nature are indeed one. All are now directly and systematically related to each other.

Within this dynamic system that is unique to humankind, both human culture and the human body show much variability. In this, humanity is not alone. Variability in behavior and appearance is characteristic of all living organisms, and it is probably no greater in human beings than in other forms. Among humans everyone (except identical twins) carries different genetic material; differences due to age and sex also exist. Beyond this, we find variability that has evolved in response to local (and equally variable) environmental conditions. This is especially noticeable as we pass between continents and cross seas and mountain ranges, and observe populations that have adapted to different environmental conditions. These are the geographical races of man, the major units into which *Homo sapiens* can conveniently be subdivided. Since the distinctions among the races are not clear-cut, there are many ways of classifying them. The classification offered in the discussion that follows is based on the main geographical races as they usually are recognized (see Figure 20–4).

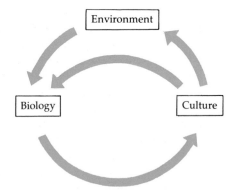

Figure 20–3   This feedback loop shows the increasing influence of culture on our biology—our heredity. The biological rate of change always lags behind the cultural rate of change, a lag that implies failure in adaptation.

HUMAN VARIABILITY

Africans

The group known as Africans includes people whose homeland is south of the Sahara Desert. Through Sudan, Ethiopia, and Egypt, they blend with the lighter-skinned Caucasians to the north, and many Caucasian features are found among essentially African peoples as far south as Tanzania. In the southern part of Africa, we find remnants of the Khoisan peoples—the small group of short, yellow-skinned people we call the Bushmen. These people are believed to have once occupied a far greater area of southern Africa, possibly as far north as Tanzania, but they have been squeezed into the Kalahari Desert between the waves of black Africans coming south and white Caucasians who spread north from the Cape. The colored people of the Cape are a cross between the Khoisan peoples and colonizing Europeans.

Like the other main racial groups, the Africans vary enormously at a local level, and many local races have been described and named. However, all these people have a number of features in common, such as their tightly curled hair and yellow or black skins, and they can conveniently be linked in a single geographical race. The physical characteristics of Africans are broadly related to high mean temperatures and high levels of sunlight (*insolation*).

Amerindians

The aboriginal peoples of the Americas include an even greater variety of local races, from the Eskimo in the north to the rain forest tribes of Brazil. Since their arrival in the New World by approximately 30,000 years ago, they have evolved independently in a wide variety of habitats, and the main thing they have in common is a common ancestry from Asiatic peoples in northeast Siberia. As a group they obviously cannot be associated with any particular biome since they span them all and, being relatively recent arrivals in America, have not yet adapted to the different climates as much as other races.

Australians

The aboriginal people of Australia have a peculiar combination of characteristics that separates them rather clearly from the Asiatic peoples who live to the north. Their dark skins, wavy hair, and rather Caucasian features suggest that they may have derived from an archaic Caucasian stock that occupied eastern Asia before the appearance of the true Asiatics. Other aboriginal peoples possibly related to them are found in southern India and Sri Lanka (Veddahs), the Malay Peninsula, and some islands of Southeast Asia. A few of these groups have tightly curled hair reminiscent of the hair of Africans, but they probably evolved this feature independently. The physical characteristics of Australians suggest adaptation to high levels of sunlight and medium to low humidity.

Asiatics

The Asiatic, or Mongolian, people are rather easily recognized by their small stature, straight black hair, rather fair skin, and slanting eyes. They occupy a large area of eastern Asia from Tibet and parts of central Siberia to the northwest, across to Malaysia and Indonesia in the southeast. They blend with Caucasians to the west (in parts of the USSR) and with Amerindians (the Eskimos) to the northeast. In the southeast they have recently extended their range and mingled with aboriginal peoples in some of the islands. Their physical adaptations seem to imply cold mean temperatures and very low humidity. They probably originated in Siberia.

The Caucasian peoples include the so-called white races from northern Europe and northwestern Asia, the Arabs of the Middle East and Africa north of the Sahara, the Indians of the Indian subcontinent, and many other local races. Thus their homeland ranges east from Europe to meet the Asiatics' homeland in western Siberia and Burma. They have been minutely subdivided by anthropologists but generally have much in common. Their adaptations are broadly to temperate zones with lower insolation and some humidity. Skin color varies a good deal but is never black; its variations seem to reflect the level of insolation and mean temperature.

Caucasians

The Oceanics are even less homogeneous than the other racial groups; they are sometimes divided into three separate races, the Polynesians, Melanesians, and Micronesians. Some—such as Melanesians, Papuans, and New Guineans—seem to be closely related to Australians. Others, such as Polynesians, seem to bear a distant relationship with Asiatics. All peoples that may be classified as Oceanics have, however, been island dwellers long enough to have become distinct from their parent groups. It is not possible to summarize the biological adaptations of such a far-ranging and variable group of peoples.

Oceanics

It must be obvious that these units into which the human species may be classified are not clearly distinct. Contact between them has never been broken for long (if at all), and at the present time no racial groups are isolated. Indeed the fact that interracial marriages are common and fertile only proves that the differences between the races are superficial. This is literally true: the surface of the body (skin and hair), which forms the barrier between organism and environment, is the first characteristic to respond to environmental peculiarities. The most obvious differences we see between the races are little more than skin deep and are an evolutionary response to the environments in which the various racial groups have lived and evolved. Furthermore, they are of recent origin: present-day racial differences are all far less than the differences between modern man and his Neandertal forebears. This is not to say that racial diversity as such is something new, for it is not. It is the normal state of affairs in any widely dispersed animal species. But while there have always been races, they have not necessarily always had the form and distribution that we see in today's peoples. Modern races were probably hardly recognizable more than 30,000 years ago.

Racial Differences

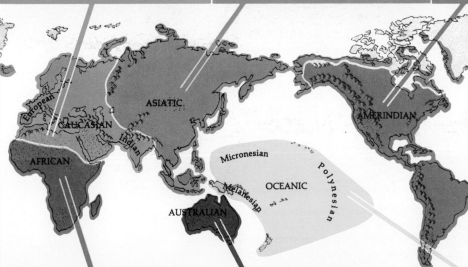

EUROPEAN

CAUCASIAN

Indian

AFRICAN

ASIATIC

Micronesian

OCEANIC

Polynesian

Melanesian

AUSTRALIAN

AMERINDIAN

Figure 20–4 There are no hard lines at racial boundaries and intermediates of all kinds exist. There are also no typical facial types. This map gives an idea of the pre-Columbian distribution of the major human racial groups; the photographs have been selected to show some of the characteristics of the different races. There is great variability within each race, and many individuals cannot be easily categorized.

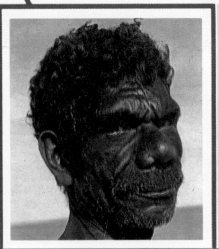

One of the reasons why racial differences introduce so many problems into our lives is that they are naturally (but not necessarily nor invariably) accompanied by cultural differences. Cultures, like characteristics of the body, consist in part of adaptations to environmental variables such as the form of food resources and the climate, and they vary accordingly. In a very real sense, the so-called advanced civilizations developed in temperate rather than tropical zones simply because adaptations to temperate climates are necessarily more complex than adaptations to tropical ones. For example, fire seems to have been used in Eurasia long before it was used in the tropics: it simply was not necessary in the equatorial regions. Just as humans evolved the optimum physical characteristics they needed in response to environmental stress, so they also developed the optimum necessary culture. The function of culture and technology is not only to protect against environmental stress (such as cold) but, more important, to make the best use of available resources. A trip to the moon is in essence a by-product of resource utilization technology.

Since these cultural variations are added in many instances to the minor biological variations between races, they seem, like language, to emphasize racial differences. One day in the future, we may all share a common culture and language. This would surely aid international understanding, but it would mean a sad loss of cultural variability, which makes travel so fascinating and human culture so rich. Similarly, extensive racial crossing would eventually lower racial tensions, but our species would ultimately lose in racial variability—an essential prerequisite for further evolution.

Racism and IQ

Racism, the belief in the superiority of one or more races over others, is, in the light of even this short review, a meaningless concept. *Superior* is a word that says nothing until we know what quality it refers to: it could mean a thousand things, biological or cultural. If we are discussing athletics, we can reasonably expect to find the superior runners among the tallest, slimmest peoples; on the other hand, we might expect the pygmy peoples to do much better as gymnasts in the Olympic games. If we are thinking of ability to survive in arctic conditions, then it seems that the Eskimo people are superior to other groups, just as black-skinned people are superior in their adaptations to sunny humid lands, in the absence of cultural protection. If we consider the ability to write and communicate mechanically, then we refer to certain cultural developments, and the racial groups probably could be ranked differently in this respect.

But we are not really concerned with these things. By superiority, it seems that those who use this term usually mean superior *intelligence*—that intellectual quality that human groups in the West have elevated to an extraordinary height. There are a number of things to be said here. First, those who are concerned with these things do not agree in their definition of the characteristic they are attempting to measure. Second, all tests of so-called intelligence operate through linguistic and other cultural modes that are not shared between races. No intelligence test devised is culture-free, and therefore none can be used cross-culturally. Third, it is now known that I.Q. (intelligence quotient) scores are altered by malnutrition of the mother, both prenatal and postnatal, and by malnutrition of the growing child. (About one third of all peoples in the world today suffer from some malnutrition.) I.Q. scores are also altered by psychological traumata during growth. In fact, almost any kind of stress can be shown to alter them. All this suggests that when we compare the I.Q. of two different races—or even two individuals—we are not learning anything of importance about the nature of our subjects beyond their individual ability to do I.Q. tests.

There are surely many kinds of intelligence and many varieties of aptitude, and it is neither useful nor possible to measure them under a single entity. As we have said before, variety is the essential biological characteristic of living species. Cultures should encourage and enhance these differences, rather than try to modify and classify them into meaningless hierarchies. Any system of values imposed on variables reflects only ignorance and prejudice. If the white man has an aptitude for technology, he also has an aptitude for self-destruction. His present behavior is maladaptive and in that sense it seems to show a very low level of general adaptive intelligence.

There is nothing unusual, from the zoological viewpoint, about human races; it would be strange if none existed. But this kind of understanding can be derived in one way only: from taking an evolutionary viewpoint, and allowing our knowledge of genetics and evolutionary development to inform us in our day-to-day dealings with our fellow men.

David Hamburg once remarked that one of the best relics we have of early man is modern man. It is because we still have populations with relatively simple technologies that we are able to make so many deductions about the behavior of early humans. What these living populations have in common with each other and with Paleolithic societies is that they all are broadly based on hunting and gathering as a way of life, and not on agriculture. That kind of an existence imposes strict limitations on the size of social units, since large numbers of people cannot practice it in a small area and survive. Bands of Aborigines seldom exceed fifty individuals and are often limited to the members of a single family group. That is not to say that they do not know and mingle occasionally with other tiny groups like their own. They do, sometimes walking for many miles to attend large song-and-dance festivals. Their society is loosely organized into larger groups according to complex blood relationships. These larger groupings have clearly defined areas of land within which the small family bands operate. Nevertheless, each band tends to stay within a smaller range of its own, and the basic unit is the family.

It is impossible not to speculate, as we have done, for example, in Chapter 9, that prehistoric hunting societies lived in similar small

MODERN MAN: A RELIC OF EARLY MAN

groups. As long as the emphasis was on gathering, a band of hominids probably acted much like a band of apes, moving slowly about, eating what it could find in the way of vegetables, berries, fruits, and nuts, along with occasional young and small injured animals. There was probably a minimum of food sharing, since all members of the band were more or less equally skilled at food-gathering from the time they were weaned. However, as a shift of emphasis from gathering to hunting took place, getting meat became more and more the responsibility of the males. As we have seen, it became less and less adaptive for females and young to expose themselves to the dangers of the hunt, and also probably impossible for them to keep up if the hunt was a long and arduous one. For females and infants, then, hunting undoubtedly came to mean waiting at some safe spot for the hunters to return with food. From this we may speculate that hunting, food sharing, homemaking, and the family group all developed more or less together.

But Hamburg's statement has more profound implications. The fact that he is a psychiatrist illustrates once again the eclecticism of modern anthropology, for it pulls together the fossil expert and the psychologist, each turning to the other to help bridge the gap that lies between their disciplines. Psychologists and physiologists are currently trying to learn more about the problems of stress and aggression in modern life and how these forces affect the physical and emotional health of people today. In their search for causes they quickly find themselves talking to paleoanthropologists, sharing ideas and data in an effort to lay bare the origins of emotional patterns that are assumed to have arisen millions of years ago.

Stress

It has long been suspected that emotional states are associated with bodily changes, but the exact nature of some of these changes—how and why they take place and what use they are to us—has not been clearly documented until this century. In the 1920s a great American physiologist, Walter Cannon, made a classic study of a set of physiological changes that took place in cats and dogs during periods of excitement. He worked with the hormone adrenalin and investigated its affects on the nervous system. Cannon discovered that adrenalin acts like a shot in the arm at times of stress, calling forth carbohydrates from storage in the liver and pouring them into the bloodstream in the form of sugar for quick conversion to energy. He also found that it increases the flow of blood to the heart, lungs, central nervous system, and limbs, while decreasing the flow to the abdominal organs. These changes, as Cannon showed, help to mobilize the muscular and nervous reserves of the individual; they enable him to withstand fatigue, move more speedily, and endure longer.

Obviously adrenalin has great survival value for the individual in a "fight-or-flight" situation. But how is it released into the system? Cannon demonstrated that it is released during periods of intense emotion, whether or not they are followed by activity. A human being has only to feel a rush of fright or anger and his system's emergency reaction will prepare him for what he has to do next. Fear does not always paralyze him; on the contrary, it usually keys him up and improves his chances of reacting in a crisis.

This is confirmed by observation of present-day hunter-gatherers. Anthropologist Irven DeVore and his associate, Richard Lee, made a study of Bushmen in Botswana in southern Africa. Bushmen in their daily lives are constantly confronted by situations that are greatly eased by adrenalin. The anticipation of the chase, the excitement of seeing and stalking an animal, trigger off the hormonal response that will be needed to attack and kill it in a sudden burst of exertion. The interesting thing about Bushman activities is that these bursts of exertion are only part of their hunting activity. Bushmen hunters often follow an animal's tracks for many miles before coming upon the animal. Then, tired as they may be, they must still summon the energy to sprint forward in the hope of planting a poisoned arrow before the animal runs out of range. If it is a large animal, the poison will take

The Bushman and Stress

Figure 20–5 The Bushman hunter with bow, poison arrows, and digging stick knows how to make the best use of every resource in his environment. This includes storing water in buried ostrich egg shells.

effect slowly and the Bushmen may have to follow it doggedly for many more miles, and sometimes for several days, before they are able to close in and kill it. During this lengthy chase they may eat only a handful of food from time to time to sustain them as they run. Nevertheless, they have had the all-important stimulus at the crucial moment, and with the flow of adrenalin that has resulted, they can call on their bodies' resources to help them in this prolonged effort. Other materials such as cholesterol and fatty acids also have built up in the bloodstream, to be worked off during the long tracking that is a constant part of a hunter-gatherer's life.

Cholesterol and Life Style

This discussion of adrenalin may appear to have taken us rather far from the behavior of ancient and modern humans, but that word *cholesterol* brings us back to Hamburg's studies in the field of what might be called *stress biology*, the study of the effects of reactions to stress situations on the human body. Although readers of this book may no longer live a hunting life, they are still physically hunter-gatherers. The human body is still an efficient machine for facing daily perils, surviving long periods of deprivation while tracking prey, and mustering built-in energy reserves for sudden and unforeseen action. Our glands react as they have been reacting for hundreds of thousands of years. Unfortunately, most present-day humans do not have the chance to burn off the materials that once aided their ancestors; instead, most of us live sedentarily, in an environment in which the stresses come one after another, their side effects building up in our bodies and apparently doing us harm. Many modern physiologists have addressed themselves to this problem. Noting that we are biologically equipped for one kind of life but live another, they then go on to ask: is there any connection between the primitive hunter-gatherer's emotional reaction under stress and the killing ailments of modern society, like heart disease?

Logically, there could be a connection. For example, modern medicine is extremely suspicious of the role cholesterol may play in heart disease. If strong emotions mobilize cholesterol, if a person's way of life no longer provides an opportunity of disposing of built-up cholesterol, and if its buildup is bad for him, then the point is clear: modern human beings are not equipped for modern life but are still back in the Stone Age emotionally and physiologically—and the strain is killing us.

Consider the plight of the businessman on his way from his home to an important conference. Success or failure for him may ride on how well he aggressively takes charge of the meeting, beats down the arguments of others, rallies support to his own point of view. Although no physical energy will be expended, this promises to be a real battle nonetheless, and in preparation for it his system has been churning out hormones ever since breakfast. Thoroughly aroused by a challenging situation, and repeatedly rearoused as further crises in the meeting itself trigger off still higher levels of cholesterol and fatty acids in his blood, he leaves the meeting at the end of the morning and sits down to a heavy lunch preceded by a couple of cocktails. Then the meetings continue in the afternoon. If he does not succeed in his purpose, the high hormone level and resulting tension may remain through the evening and far into the night.

His glandular system cannot be blamed. It has responded loyally and with great efficiency to the demands made on it. But if our businessman is not able to behave appropriately himself and engage in the kind of vigorous physical activity needed to burn up the accumulations in his bloodstream, then he is in serious trouble. He cannot change the activities of his glands or his nervous system; a stressful situation will make him feel angry whether he shows it or not. If he cannot express his anger, the only alternative is to change his way of life.

Odd as it may seem, there may be real practical value in learning as much as we can about the ways of hunter-gatherers. If we can find out what our systems were actually designed for, we may perhaps behave more like these primitive forebears and lead healthier lives. The solution cannot be as simple as taking a walk after a tension-building situation, but that might help. Many heart specialists have advocated walking and cycling as beneficial exercise, arriving at their recommendation through observations of many patients. The paleoanthropologist might have come to the same conclusion, but from an entirely different direction. He would have noted that *Homo sapiens* is a creature whose evolutionary history has been one of adaptation to efficient upright striding and whose way of life as a hunter-gatherer required a great deal of steady walking and running. To ignore this way of life, he would conclude, may well be dangerous—just as dangerous as keeping a hunting dog cooped up in a city apartment or trying to adapt a lowland marsh plant to life on a mountaintop. Neither dog nor flower would do very well in its alien environment. The surprising thing about people is that we do as well as we do.

This is not to say that the human body is not changing in response to its new environment; the principles of natural selection certainly are still working for us as they always have. Therefore, if our environment were to stay as it is for a long enough time, we could assume that the hormonal responses we have inherited from our ancestors would ultimately prove so inappropriate and so damaging to us that they would be eliminated, through heart attacks and other natural ailments, as a result of selection against those of us who still carry the traits for the ancient hormonal reactions. If medical science comes to protect every individual from these particular ailments until his child-rearing days are over, we may well avoid this effect of natural selection, but it will probably strike in another way. There is no doubt that stress damages our mental health, and the medical problems here are much more complex. Certainly the modern world would be a healthier and safer place to live in if its human inhabitants were gentler and more patient than

Adaptations to Modern Life

they are. We might even make a long guess that the present very high rate of death from heart disease among men in the United States may be natural selection working in a part of the population that is well adapted to short-term success but poorly adapted to survival in our society.

The problem is that there is not enough time; the modern world does not stand still. What characterizes human culture is the increasingly rapid rate of its development. It leaves biological man far behind, tied to the ponderous machinery of natural selection, which, as we have seen, requires periods of time on the order of hundreds of thousands of years before it can produce significant differences in the human species. As René Dubos has said: "Even when man has become an urbane city dweller, the paleolithic bull which survives in his inner self still paws the earth whenever a threatening gesture is made on the social scene." Given emotionally archaic people such as we are and the fearsome power that modern technology has put in our hands, the situation may well become self-correcting, with archaic emotions bringing about the destruction of our culture. Then, should we find ourselves running exhaustedly after our food once again, at least we can console ourselves that we are again doing what our bodies were designed for. We are not doing it now.

All of this may convey the impression that there is something necessarily damaging about culture, if all it can do is produce more heart attacks and worse wars. Nothing could be further from the truth. Evolutionary success, as has already been explained, is measured not by the fates of individual members of a species but by the record of the species as a whole. As a species, *Homo sapiens* has to date been overwhelmingly successful. Our sheer numbers prove it. Edward S. Deevey has estimated that the hominid population of the earth two million years ago was little over 100,000 individuals. Three hundred thousand years ago, toward the end of *Homo erectus'* known tenancy, the human population had climbed to a million; and 25,000 years ago, during the time of the Cro-Magnon peoples, it had jumped to perhaps more than

SUCCESS OR FAILURE?

Population and Evolutionary Success

Year	2,000,000 B.C.	300,000 B.C.	25,000 B.C.	6000 B.C.
Population	125,000	1,000,000	3,340,000	86,500,000
Persons per square mile	.01	.03	.1	2.6

three million. It has risen at an increasingly steep pace since then. Deevey brings home the extraordinarily rapid mushrooming of today's human population when he shows that about 3 percent of all human beings who have ever lived are alive today.

The increase in population, according to Deevey, has not gone in a steady curve. Rather, it has had a series of surges, reflecting the great cultural innovations associated with human evolution. The first, of course, was the development of stone tools. This allowed for population increase in two different ways. It enabled hominids to venture out into a vast number of different environments that people without such tools could not have survived in; it also made populations more efficient, enabling them to exploit various environments more intensively. The population density of Africa in the days of the crude Oldowan chopping-tool industry has been estimated at only one per hundred square miles. By the end of the Paleolithic, humans had spread throughout Europe and Asia as well as Africa, and their density had risen tenfold, to one per ten square miles (see Figure 20–6).

The second innovation was the double discovery of how to grow crops and how to domesticate animals. This came about 10,000 years ago. It enabled people to settle permanently for the first time, and for the first time to live together in large numbers. Even nomadic herdsmen could exist in far greater concentrations on a given area of land than hunters could. The effect on world population was extraordinary. In 4,000 years it jumped from an estimated 5 million to 86 million.

The third innovation was the industrial age. It had its beginnings about 300 years ago when the human population of the world was in the neighborhood of 550 million. World population has been ballooning ever since and today is some 4 billion. If it continued at its present rate of increase it would double within fifty years.

While these figures are impressive, even more impressive is the acceleration of the rate of population growth. It took a million years to get through the first phase; the second took only ten thousand years; and the third has been going on for only a few hundred. How long it will continue or what the human population of the earth ultimately will be is anybody's guess. But we can be sure that since the surface

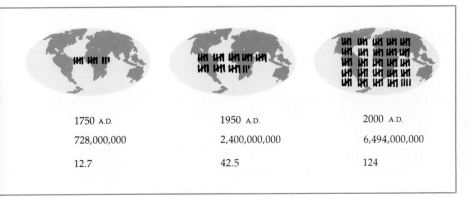

1750 A.D.	1950 A.D.	2000 A.D.
728,000,000	2,400,000,000	6,494,000,000
12.7	42.5	124

Figure 20–6   Until about 25,000 B.P. mankind was a stable part of the equilibrium among animals and plants. With better hunting technology, animal domestication, and agriculture, mankind began to increase dramatically and to destroy the wilderness of which we had been a part. The figures given for the population of the past are of course estimates and that for 2000 A.D. a projection.

of the earth is finite, as are its resources, present rates of increase will bring us to the limit very soon.

It seems clear that the increase in our population is primarily due to making greater and greater use of available resources. When a forest is cleared and crops are grown in its place, all the sunlight in that area is contributing to the synthesis of food for human beings. When wild animals grazing in meadows and savanna grasslands are killed and replaced by cattle, sheep, and goats, the conversion of plant energy into animal protein is turned to man's benefit. In these cases we can see that the ultimate limitation is the amount of energy that can be delivered by the sun to the earth's surface and turned into carbohydrates by photosynthesis in green plants. Every green plant needs a place in the sun. Other limiting factors are the other requirements of plants: water, minerals, and an appropriate soil. Lack of water in particular has long been a problem for farmers, though they have occasionally overcome it with irrigation. But the ultimate limits are firm both on land and in the oceans. Eventually, as Malthus predicted, these factors will indeed operate to halt human population growth, if we do not bring about stabilization voluntarily.

In some parts of the world, famine is already becoming a normal condition, and malnutrition is almost worldwide. People are dying of hunger by the tens of thousands. This is partly because the increase in population is due not merely to increased resources but also to advances in medicine. These have brought about an increased life expectancy. *Australopithecus* may have had an average life expectancy of some 15 to 20 years; *Homo erectus* lived for some 20 to 30 years; today, a citizen of the United States can expect to live to 70 years. A doubling of life expectancy has brought a doubling of population without a corresponding increase in our efficiency at utilizing resources. Thus in

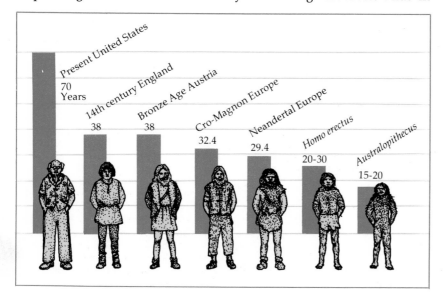

Figure 20–7 Since the time of the Cro-Magnons life expectancies have doubled in countries with modern medicine and technology. We probably live three to four times as long as *Australopithecus* did. The increased lifespan has made possible a rapid increase in cultural complexity, skill, and knowledge.

many cases the countries now suffering famines are those that have some of the benefits of medical progress without the advances of modern agricultural technology.

Large segments of human society have certainly come a long way: in lifespan, efficiency at extracting resources, in population density, in technological complexity, and in increased physical comfort. Whether we are really better off as a species, and whether our progress will continue, remains to be seen. Population size is certainly a measure of evolutionary success, but another measure that may be more significant is evolutionary longevity. A million years is nothing in terms of universal and geologic time, and a million species have evolved and gone extinct in the process of earth history. Compared with most mammals, we are infants of evolution. From this point of view our apparent present-day success can continue only if we can achieve some sort of stability in our relationship with the earth's resources. Otherwise we shall surely perish.

Humanity is still evolving. Invisible and immeasurable changes are slowly taking place in the general and average characteristics of *Homo sapiens*. Evolution never stops but continues blindly, as our environment continues to select the fittest and destroy the unfit. Whereas in the past the selective agents were perhaps the rigors of climate and disease, today they may well be atmospheric nitric oxide or emotional stress.

Humanity, however, is undergoing evolution with a new twist. Among many animal species, those individuals that survive and breed are the stock selected by nature to continue the species. But *Homo sapiens* is a social and cultural species. Just as the infertile worker bees make an essential contribution to the survival of the bee colony, so in our own society, all members contribute to the species' survival even if they bear no children. This is all the more true as our skills and roles in society become increasingly specialized (like the bees'). In the present state of human overpopulation, it is surely clear that those who do not reproduce are making a greater contribution to the species as a whole than those who do, because the stress of overdense populations is the greatest single threat to our survival.

For a species like ours, whose survival depends on culture (which is based on knowledge), it is essential to use all available knowledge and understanding toward achieving a better adaptation to a changing environment. This is perhaps our most difficult problem: that each new cultural adaptation we make alters the environment to which we are adapting. New adaptations increase population; greater population densities require further adaptation; new adaptations deplete world resources; resource depletion requires further adaptation. And so it goes on. We find ourselves in a vicious circle of ever-increasing instability. What is surely vital now is an all-out attempt to break that positive feedback loop and bring about a new stability in population size, in technological investment, in consumption.

Survival

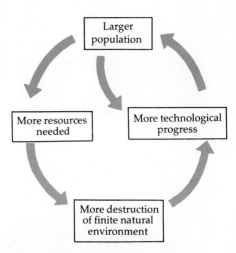

Figure 20–8 This positive feedback loop is the most dangerous to us, since it is accelerating very rapidly and involves environmental destruction. With the resource base of our livelihood seriously depleted, survival in our present numbers is threatened.

How humanity will handle this critical problem is impossible to predict. The present—and projected—enormous number of people, together with the poverty and political instability that accompany them in many parts of the world, are of great concern to economists and sociologists everywhere. It is all very well to talk about the success of the species as a whole, but if species success can be accomplished only with uncontrolled crowding and almost world-wide misery, then there is something wrong. *Homo sapiens* is not just another species of animal. We are the first in the history of the world to understand something of our place in it and the laws that govern our activities here. This makes us unique in having within our grasp the possibility of doing something sensible about the crushing problem of our numbers. But the mere fact that we have access to this kind of knowledge is no guarantee that we will use it. We have not always done so in the past; we do not seem to be doing so now. Not only do we damage ourselves individually with jolts of things like cholesterol. We are doing even worse things to each other on a world scale by our inability and unwillingness to control many of our actions.

For all the surface glitter of our culture, the one thing of true value that humanity has achieved is a rather impressive amount of knowledge and understanding of ourselves and the world. Much of this knowledge is not yet widely available; sadly, it is rejected by many who do have access to it. Nevertheless it is there. The principles of evolution we have discussed in this book are true, and their truth can be demonstrated to any open-minded person. We ignore them at our peril. They have a vital bearing on our understanding of ourselves and thus they affect the future of all of us, since it is surely only a matter of time before we will have it in our power to direct the course of our own evolution. Here, and not in moon shots, lies humanity's greatest challenge. For the first time in the 3.5-billion-year history of life will come a chance to try to combine the good of the species with the good of the individual. This dilemma has not been resolved very well in the past and, judging by our recurring lack of vision and understanding, is not being resolved very well by the human species today.

Prospect of Failure

Figure 20–9 The combination of transport needs and the population explosion resulted in the development of the internal combustion engine; the effect on the environment is shown vividly in these pictures. Technological development and the high density of our population have profoundly altered the quality of the earth's surface and the air we breathe, thus bringing about the need for additional new technology, and for cultural and biological adaptations. (Opposite page)

BIBLIOGRAPHY

PART I THE STUDY OF MAN

General References for Further Reading

Campbell, Bernard, *Human Evolution* (2nd ed.). Aldine, 1974.
Dobzhansky, Theodosius, *Evolution, Genetics and Man*. Chapman & Hall, 1955.
_____, *Genetics and the Origin of Species*. Columbia University Press, 1969.
_____, *Heredity and the Nature of Man*. The New American Library, 1964.
_____, *Mankind Evolving*. Yale University Press, 1962.
Le Gros Clark, Wilfred E., *The Antecedents of Man* (3rd ed.). Quadrangle Books, 1971.
Mayr, Ernst, *Populations, Species and Evolution*. Belknap Press of Harvard University Press, 1970.
Sinnott, Edmund W., L. C. Dunn, and Theodosius Dobzhansky, *Principles of Genetics* (5th ed.). McGraw-Hill, 1958.
Stern, Curt, *Principles of Human Genetics* (2nd ed.). W. H. Freeman, 1960.
Wallace, Bruce, and Theodosius Dobzhansky, *Radiation, Genes and Man*. Methuen, 1960.

Sources

Boule, Marcellin, and Henri V. Vallois, *Fossil Men*. Dryden Press, 1957.
Brothwell, Don, and Eric Higgs, eds., *Science in Archeology* (2nd ed.). Praeger, 1970.
Butzer, Karl W., *Environment and Archeology: An Ecological Approach to Prehistory*. Aldine-Atherton, 1971.
Darwin, Charles, *On the Origin of Species* (facsimile of First Edition). Harvard University Press, 1966.
Darwin, Charles, and Alfred R. Wallace, *Evolution by Natural Selection*. Cambridge University Press, 1958.
Darwin, Francis, ed., *The Life and Letters of Charles Darwin* (2 vols.). Basic Books, 1959.
Darwin, Francis, and A. C. Seward, eds., *More Letters of Charles Darwin* (2 vols.). John Murray, 1903.
De Vries, Hugo, *The Mutation Theory* (Vols. I and II). Open Court Publishing Company (Chicago), 1909–10.
_____, *Species and Varieties*. Open Court Publishing Company (Chicago), 1905.
Eiseley, Loren, *Darwin's Century: Evolution and the Men Who Discovered It*. Doubleday, 1958.
Fisher, Sir Ronald Aylmer, *The Genetical Theory of Natural Selection*. Clarendon Press, 1930.
Haldane, J. B. S., *The Causes of Evolution*. Longmans, Green, 1932.
Huxley, Sir Julian, *Evolution in Action*. Chatto & Windus, 1953.
_____, *Evolution—The Modern Synthesis*. Allen & Unwin, 1942.
Huxley, Thomas Henry, *Man's Place in Nature*. University of Michigan Press, 1959.
Irvine, William, *Apes, Angels, and Victorians*. Weidenfeld & Nicolson, 1955.
Leakey, L. S. B., and Vanne Morris Goodall, *Unveiling Man's Origins*. Schenkman, 1969.
Leakey, L. S. B., and J. and S. Prost, *Adam or Ape*. Schenkman, 1971.
Libby, Willard F., *Radiocarbon Dating* (2nd ed.). University of Chicago Press, 1955.
Moore, Ruth, *Charles Darwin: A Great Life in Brief*. Hutchinson, 1957.
_____, *The Coil of Life*. Alfred A. Knopf, 1961.
Morgan, Thomas Hunt, *Evolution and Adaptation*. Macmillan, 1903.
_____, *The Mechanism of Mendelian Heredity*. Constable, 1915.
_____, *The Physical Basis of Heredity*. J. B. Lippincott, 1919.
Muller, Hermann J., *Genetics, Medicine and Men*. Cornell University Press: Oxford University Press, 1947.
Romer, Alfred S., *Man and the Vertebrates* (2 vols.). Penguin Books, 1954.
Schultz, Adolph H., *The Life of Primates*. Universe Books, 1969.
Simons, Elwyn L., *Primate Evolution*. Macmillan, 1972.
Simpson, George Gaylord, *The Major Features of Evolution*. Simon and Schuster, 1953.
_____, *The Meaning of Evolution*. Oxford University Press, 1950.
Tuttle, Russell, ed., *The Functional and Evolutionary Biology of Primates*. Aldine-Atherton, 1972.
Wallace, Alfred Russel, *My Life: A Record of Events and Opinions* (2 vols.). Chapman & Hall, 1905.
Wendt, Herbert, *In Search of Adam*. Houghton Mifflin, 1956.

PART II *AUSTRALOPITHECUS*

General References for Further Reading

Day, Michael, *Guide to Fossil Man.* Meridian Books, 1965.
Le Gros Clark, Wilfrid E., *Man-Apes or Ape-Men?* Holt, Rinehart and Winston, 1967.
Pilbeam, David, *The Ascent of Man.* Macmillan, 1972.
van Lawick-Goodall, Jane, *In the Shadow of Man.* Houghton Mifflin, 1971.

Sources

Broom, Robert, *Finding the Missing Link.* Watts, 1950.
Butzer, Karl W., *Environment and Archeology: An Ecological Approach to Prehistory.* Aldine-Atherton, 1971.
Campbell, Bernard, "Conceptual Progress in Physical Anthropology: Fossil Man." *Annual Review of Anthropology*, Vol. 1, 1972.
_____, *Human Evolution* (2nd ed.). Aldine, 1974.
Clark, J. Desmond, *The Prehistory of Africa.* Praeger, 1970.
Dart, Raymond, *Adventures with the Missing Link.* Viking Press, 1959.
DeVore, Irven, ed., *Primate Behavior.* Holt, Rinehart and Winston, 1965.
Howells, William W., ed., *Ideas on Human Evolution.* Atheneum, 1967.
Jay, Phyllis C., *Primates.* Holt, Rinehart and Winston, 1968.
Jolly, Alison, *The Evolution of Primate Behavior.* Macmillan, 1972.
Jolly, Clifford, "The Seed-eaters." *Man*, Vol. 5, No. 1, March 1970.
Kummer, Hans, *Social Organization of Hamadryas Baboons.* University of Chicago Press, 1968.
Leakey, Mary D., *Olduvai Gorge* (Vol. 3). Cambridge University Press, 1971.
Napier, John, and P. H. Napier, *Handbook of Living Primates.* Academic Press, 1967.
Oakley, Kenneth, and Bernard G. Campbell, and Theya I. Mollison, eds., *Catalogue of Fossil Hominids—Part I* (2nd ed.). Trustees of the British Museum (Natural History), 1976.
Schaller, George B., *Year of the Gorilla.* University of Chicago Press, 1964.
Schaller, George B., and Gordon Lowther, "The Relevance of Carnivore Behavior to the Study of Early Hominids." *Southwestern Journal of Anthropology*, Vol. 25, No. 4 (University of New Mexico Press).
Tobias, Phillip V., *The Brain in Hominid Evolution.* Columbia University Press, 1971.
Washburn, Sherwood L., *Social Life of Early Man.* Aldine, 1961.
Washburn, Sherwood L., and Phyllis Dolhinow, eds., *Perspectives on Human Evolution* (4 vols.). Holt, Rinehart and Winston, 1968–76.

PART III *HOMO ERECTUS*

General References for Further Reading

Howells, William W., "Homo Erectus." *Scientific American*, Vol. 215, No. 5, 1966.
_____, *Mankind in the Making.* Doubleday, 1967.
Pilbeam, David, *The Ascent of Man.* Macmillan, 1972.

Sources

Butzer, Karl W., "Acheulian Occupation Sites at Torralba and Ambrona, Spain: Their Geology." *Science*, Vol. 150, No. 3704, 1965.
_____, *Environment and Archeology: An Introduction to Pleistocene Geography.* Aldine, 1964.
Campbell, Bernard G., "Conceptual Progress in Physical Anthropology: Fossil Man." *Annual Review of Anthropology*, Vol. 1, 1972.
_____, "The Physical Basis of Language Use in Primates." In *Frontiers of Anthropology*, edited by M. J. Leaf. Van Nostrand, 1974.
_____, ed., *Sexual Selection and the Descent of Man, 1871–1971.* Aldine, 1972.
Chang, Kwang-chih, *The Archaeology of Ancient China.* Yale University Press, 1968.
Count, Earl W., "The Biological Basis of Human Sociality." *American Anthropologist*, Vol. 60, No. 6, 1958.
de Lumley, Henry, "A Paleolithic Camp at Nice." *Scientific American*, Vol. 220, No. 5, 1969.
DeVore, Irven, ed., *Primate Behavior.* Holt, Rinehart and Winston, 1965.

Gardner, R. Allen, and Beatrice T. Gardner, "Teaching Sign Language to a Chimpanzee." *Science*, Vol. 165, No. 3894, 1969.

Geschwind, Norman, "The Neural Basis of Language." In *Research in Verbal Behavior and Some Neurophysiological Implications*, edited by K. and S. Salzinger. Academic Press, 1967.

Hockett, Charles F., "The Origin of Speech." *Scientific American*, Vol. 203, No. 3, 1960.

Hood, Dora, *Davidson Black: a Biography*. University of Toronto Press, 1971.

Howell, F. Clark, "Observations on the Earlier Phases of the European Lower Paleolithic." *American Anthropologist*, Vol. 68, No. 2, 1966.

Isaac, Glynn L., "The Diet of Early Man: Aspects of Archaeological Evidence from Lower and Middle Pleistocene Sites in Africa." *World Archaeology*, Vol. 2, No. 3, 1971.

_____,"Studies of Early Culture in East Africa." *World Archaeology*, Vol. 1, No. 1, 1969.

Ju-kang, Woo, "The Skull of Lantian Man." *Current Anthropology*, Vol. 7, No. 1, 1966.

Krantz, Grover S., "Brain Size and Hunting Ability in Earliest Man." *Current Anthropology*, Vol. 9, No. 5, 1966.

Kurtén, Björn, *Pleistocene Mammals of Europe*. Aldine, 1968.

Lancaster, Jane B., "Primate Communication Systems and the Emergence of Human Language." In *Primates: Studies in Adaptation and Variability*, edited by Phyllis C. Jay. Holt, Rinehart and Winston, 1968.

Lieberman, Philip, Edmund S. Crelin, and Dennis H. Klatt, "Phonetic Ability and Related Anatomy of the Newborn and Adult Human, Neanderthal Man, and the Chimpanzee." *American Anthropologist*, Vol. 74, No. 3, 1972.

Napier, John, "The Evolution of the Hand." *Scientific American*, Vol. 207, No. 6, 1962.

Noback, Charles R., *The Human Nervous System: Basic Principles of Neurobiology*. McGraw-Hill, 1975.

Oakley, Kenneth P., *Frameworks for Dating Fossil Man* (revised ed.). Aldine, 1968.

_____, *Man the Tool-Maker* (6th ed.). Trustees of the British Museum (Natural History), 1972.

Semenov, S. A., *Prehistoric Technology*. Cory, Adams and Mackay, 1964.

Shapiro, Harry L , "The Strange Unfinished Saga of Peking Man." *Natural History*, Vol. LXXX, No. 9, 1971.

Struhsaker, Thomas T., "Auditory Communication among Vervet Monkeys (*Cercopithecus aethiops*)." In *Social Communication among Primates*, edited by Stuart A. Altmann. University of Chicago Press, 1967.

Tobias, Phillip V., *The Brain in Hominid Evolution*. Columbia University Press, 1971.

van Lawick-Goodall, Jane, *In the Shadow of Man*. Houghton Mifflin, 1971.

von Koenigswald, G. H. R., *Meeting Prehistoric Man*. Harper and Brothers, 1956.

Washburn, Sherwood L., *Social Life of Early Man*. Aldine, 1961.

_____, "Tools and Human Evolution." *Scientific American*, Vol. 203, No. 3, 1960.

Washburn, Sherwood L., and Phyllis Dolhinow, eds., *Perspectives on Human Evolution* (4 vols.). Holt, Rinehart and Winston, 1968–76.

Weidenreich, Franz, *Apes, Giants and Man*. University of Chicago Press, 1946.

PART IV EARLY *HOMO SAPIENS*

General References for Further Reading

Bordes, François, *The Old Stone Age*. McGraw-Hill, 1968.

Howells, William W., *Mankind in the Making*. Doubleday, 1967.

Sources

Bordes, François, *A Tale of Two Caves*. Harper & Row, 1972.

Brace, C. Loring, "The Fate of the 'Classic' Neanderthals: A Consideration of Hominid Catastrophism." *Current Anthropology*, Vol. 5, No. 1, February 1964.

_____, "Ridiculed, Rejected, but Still Our Ancestor, Neanderthal." *Natural History*, May 1968.

Brose, David S., and Milford H. Wolpoff, "Early Upper Paleolithic Man and Late Middle Paleolithic Tools." *American Anthropologist*, Vol. 73, October 1971.

Chapman, Frank M., *Handbook of Birds of Eastern North America*. Dover, 1966.

Clark, J. Desmond, *The Prehistory of Africa*. Praeger, 1970.

Eiseley, Loren, "Neanderthal Man and the Dawn of Human Paleontology." *The Quarterly Review of Biology*, Vol. 32, No. 4, December 1957.

Flint, Richard Foster, *Glacial and Quaternary Geology*. John Wiley & Sons, 1971.

Howell, F. Clark, "European and Northwest African Middle Pleistocene Hominids," *Current Anthropology*, Vol. 1, 1960.

———, "Recent Advances in Human Evolutionary Studies," *Quarterly Review of Biology*, Vol. 42, 1967.

Kurtén, Björn, *Pleistocene Mammals of Europe*. Aldine, 1968.

Leakey, L. S. B., and Vanne Morris Goodall, *Unveiling Man's Origins*. Schenkman, 1969.

Lieberman, Philip, and Edmund S. Crelin, "On the Speech of Neanderthal Man." *Linguistic Inquiry*, Vol. II, No. 2, Spring 1971.

Oakley, Kenneth P., *Frameworks for Dating Fossil Man* (revised ed.). Aldine, 1968.

———, *Man the Tool-Maker* (6th ed.). The University of Chicago Press, 1972.

Oakley, Kenneth P., Bernard G. Campbell, and Theya I. Mollison, *Catalogue of Fossil Hominids* (3 vols.). Trustees of the British Museum (Natural History), 1967–75.

Ovey, C. D., "The Swanscombe Skull." *Occasional Papers of the Royal Anthropological Institute 20,* London, 1964.

Semenov, S. A., *Prehistoric Technology*. Cory, Adams and Mackay, 1964.

Smith, G. Elliot, "Neanderthal Man Not Our Ancestor." *Scientific American*, August 1928.

Solecki, Ralph S., *Shanidar, The First Flower People*. Alfred A. Knopf, 1971.

Weckler, J. E., "Neanderthal Man." *Scientific American*, Vol. 197, No. 6, December 1957.

PART V   MODERN HUMANITY

General References for Further Reading

Garn, Stanley M., *Human Races*. Charles C. Thomas, 1961.

———, ed., *Readings on Race*. Charles C. Thomas, 1960.

Howells, William W., *Mankind in the Making*. Doubleday, 1967.

Service, Elman R., *The Hunters*. Prentice-Hall, 1966.

Sources

Breuil, Abbé H., *Four Hundred Centuries of Cave Art*. Centre d'Études et de Documentation Préhistoriques, 1952.

Campbell, Joseph, *The Masks of God: Primitive Mythology*. The Viking Press, 1959.

Clark, J. Grahame D., *Aspects of Prehistory*. University of California Press, 1970.

Clark, J. Desmond, *The Prehistory of Africa*. Praeger, 1970.

Clark, J. Grahame D., *Prehistoric Europe, the Economic Basis*. Philosophical Library, 1952.

Cole, Sonia, *The Prehistory of East Africa*. The New American Library, 1965.

Coon, Carleton S., *The Hunting Peoples*. Little, Brown, 1971.

———, *The Origin of Races*. Alfred A. Knopf, 1962.

———, *The Story of Man*. Alfred A. Knopf, 1970.

Daniel, Glyn A., *A Hundred Years of Archaeology*. Gerald Duckworth and Co., 1950.

Klein, Richard G., *Man and Culture in the Late Pleistocene*. Chandler Publishing Company, 1969.

Kranzberg, Melvin, and Carroll W. Pursell, Jr., eds., *Technology in Western Civilization* (Vol. 1). Oxford University Press, 1967.

Kurtén Björn, *The Ice Age*. G. P. Putnam's Sons, 1972.

———, *Pleistocene Mammals of Europe*. Aldine, 1968.

Laming, Annette, *Lascaux*. Penguin Books, 1959.

Lee, Richard B., and Irven DeVore, eds., *Man the Hunter*. Aldine, 1968.

Leroi-Gourhan, André, *Treasures of Prehistoric Art*. Harry N. Abrams, 1967.

Maringer, Johannes, *The Gods of Prehistoric Man*. Alfred A. Knopf, 1960.

Maringer, Johannes, and Hans-Georg Bandi, *Art in the Ice Age*. Praeger, 1953.

Marshack, Alexander, *The Roots of Civilization*. McGraw-Hill, 1972.

Mulvaney, D. J., and J. Gordon, *Aboriginal Man and Environment in Australia*. Australian National University Press, 1971.

Oakley, Kenneth P., *Frameworks for Dating Fossil Man* (revised ed.). Aldine, 1968.

Oakley, Kenneth P., Bernard G. Campbell, and Theya I. Mollison, *Catalogue of Fossil Hominids* (3 vols.). Trustees of the British Museum (Natural History), 1967–75.

Turnbull, Colin M., *The Forest People*. Simon and Schuster, 1962.

Ucko, Peter J., and Andrée Rosenfeld, *Palaeolithic Cave Art*. McGraw-Hill, 1967.

Van Doren Stern, Philip, *Prehistoric Europe*. W. W. Norton & Company, 1969.

GLOSSARY

Acheulian industry: a method of making stone tools that first appeared about 1.4 million years ago. This style of toolmaking, which was used by *Homo erectus* and spread over Africa, Europe, and Asia, is distinguished from those preceding it by use of the bifacial technique (see *biface*).

Adaptation: a change resulting from natural selection that better suits a population to its environment, thus improving its chances for survival; a characteristic resulting from such a change.

Aegyptopithecus: apelike fossil of the *Oligocene* epoch, found in Egypt in 1966. Although its skull was shaped like a monkey's, its jaws and teeth were apelike. Most primitive ape yet discovered.

Ainu: aboriginal Caucasian people who until recently lived by hunting in Japan's northernmost islands.

Angular gyrus: part of the human brain's *cerebral cortex* allowing information received from different senses to be associated (e.g., the *sight* of a cup to be associated with the *feel* of a cup and the sound "cup").

Anthropoid: relating to humans, apes, and monkeys.

Anthropology: the science of mankind; systematic study of human evolution, human variability, and both past and present behavior.

Ape: large, tailless, semierect mammal of the family Pongidae and the primate order. Living species are the chimpanzee, gorilla, gibbon, and orangutan.

Aphasia: loss or distortion of speech.

Arboreal: adapted for living in or around trees, like the monkeys and some apes.

Archaeology: systematic study of the human past; finding and interpreting the cultural products of prehistoric people.

Arcuate fasciculus: bundle of nerve fibers in the human brain transmitting signals from *Wernicke's area* to *Broca's area*, making possible vocal repetition of a heard and memorized word.

Artifact: purposefully formed object.

Aurignacian industry: *Upper Paleolithic* tool culture of early *Cro-Magnon* peoples in Europe that appeared from about 43,000 to 19,000 years ago. Characterized by extensive use of bone in addition to stone tools, especially bone points, it is completely unlike earlier styles found in Europe and seems to have originated elsewhere. Aurignacian culture included art and ritual.

Australopithecus: extinct hominid that walked erect and had humanlike teeth but whose skull, jaw, and brain size were apelike. Evidence of three species—*africanus, robustus,* and *boisei*—has been found in Africa, where *Australopithecus* is believed to have lived from about 6 to 1 million years ago (see also *habilis*).

Baboon: large monkey of the primate order. Baboons have long, doglike muzzles; most have short tails and live on the ground in troops. They live close to the trees in East and Central Africa and in rocky desert land in Ethiopia (see also *gelada* and *hamadryas*).

Band: a small, economically independent group.

Biface: tool made by chipping flakes off both sides of a core to make a flat tool with an edge straighter and sharper than earlier types, which were chipped on one edge only (see also *Acheulian industry*).

Biome: an area characterized by a broadly uniform type of climate and vegetation and consisting of a distinctive combination of plants and animals.

Bipedalism: walking erect on the hind limbs only, which frees the hands for other uses.

Blade tools: *flake tools* at least two times as long as they are wide, which were common in *Upper Paleolithic* tool kits.

Bola: two or more stones connected by thongs or a cord for use as a weapon in hunting.

Brachiation: locomotion in the trees by means of the arms.

Bramapithecus: name given to a fossil lower jaw later found to be identical with *Ramapithecus*.

Branching: splitting of a family tree into separate evolutionary lines, as the monkeys, apes, and living prosimians diverged from a common prosimian ancestor and the hominid line diverged from the apes.

Breccia: fragments of rock consolidated and cemented in a fine matrix of soils, sand, or clay.

Broca's area: part of the human *cerebral cortex* that sends codified signals to the part of the brain controlling the muscles that produce speech.

Brow ridge: continuous ridge of bone in the skull, curving over each eye and connected across the bridge of the nose. An extremely prominent brow ridge is characteristic of the classic *Neandertal* people.

Budding: gradual expansion into new areas by a group of individuals splitting off from a prospering *population* to set up an autonomous band in an unexploited area nearby.

Burin: chisellike *Upper Paleolithic* tool used to cut, incise, and shape other materials, such as bone, antler, wood, and stone. A tool for making other tools, it is found frequently at *Cro-Magnon* sites and, less frequently, at *Neandertal* sites.

Canines: pointed teeth in the front of the mouth between the incisors and premolars. In monkeys and apes, canines are usually large, projecting beyond the other teeth, and are used for tearing up vegetation and for threats and fights. Hominid canines are much smaller.

Carbon 14 (C^{14}): a radioactive element present in the atmosphere as CO_2 that disintegrates at a predictable rate. The amount of carbon 14 remaining in fossils therefore indicates their age.

Catastrophism: theory proposed by Georges Cuvier stating that vast floods wiped out ancient forms of life again and again, clearing the stage for new creations.

Cenozoic: geologic era that began about 65 million years ago.

Cerebral cortex: gray, wrinkled outer layer of the brain. The largest part of the primate brain, it generates much of human reasoned behavior and abstract thought. It is the site of memory.

Chain of Being: pre-Darwinian belief in a hierarchy for all living things, lowest to highest, with humankind at the top; it was thought to have been fixed forever at the Creation, which meant that no species could change into other forms.

Chimpanzee: a social primate, least specialized of the great apes and thought to be the most like the ancestor from which apes and humans are descended. Lives in the trees of equatorial Africa. In the trees it climbs and *brachiates*; while on the ground it usually moves by *knuckle walking*.

Chopper: crude stone tool chipped from a pebble core to give a rough but serviceable cutting edge. Characteristic of the *Oldowan industry*.

Chromosomes: threadlike structures bearing the genes in every living plant and animal cell (see also *meiosis* and *mitosis*).

Class: a taxonomic rank in biology. Humans belong to the class Mammalia.

Cleaver: *Acheulian* stone implement with a straight cutting edge at one end. It looked like a modern axehead and probably was used for heavy chopping or hacking.

Cobble: stone worn smooth by sand and water in running streams or on a rocky seashore. Often used as a core for making a stone tool.

Coccyx: bones at the end of the human and ape spine, which have been reduced by selection from an ancestral tail.

Condyle: the part of a bone that fits into another bone, forming a movable, hingelike joint, like the part of the lower jaw which attaches to the skull.

Core tool: implement made by hitting a piece of stone with another to remove chips; the stone that remains becomes the tool. (Compare with *flake tool*.)

Cranium: the skull without the jaw.

Cro-Magnon: broadly, refers to the first modern human beings, who lived between about 40,000 to 10,000 years ago. (In strict usage, *Cro-Magnon* refers only to people living in southwestern France during that period.)

Cultural evolution: changes in human *culture* resulting from the accumulated experience of mankind. Cultural evolution can produce more rapid adaptations to the environment than organic evolution.

Culture: system of learned behaviors, symbols, customs, beliefs, institutions, artifacts, and technology characteristic of a group and transmitted by its members to their offspring.

Demography: study of the size, density, distribution, and other vital statistics of populations.

Denticulate tools: *Mousterian* implements made with toothed or notched edges.

Disk-core method: toolmaking technique developed by the *Neandertals* in which a stone is trimmed to a disk-shape, numerous flakes are chipped off until the core is almost used up, and the flakes are then trimmed for use as tools.

Diurnal: active mostly during the day, as apes, monkeys, and human beings are.

DNA (deoxyribonucleic acid): the chemical substance that forms the chromosomes, reproduces itself, and carries the genetic code. It is found in every cell.

Dryopithecus: extinct primitive anthropoid of the *Miocene* period found in Europe, China, India, and Africa; may have been ancestral to the living great apes and mankind.

Ecotone: line along which two ecological zones meet, such as the edge of a forest that borders a savanna.

Endogamy: selecting a mate from inside one's own group.

Eoanthropus dawsoni: see *Piltdown man*.

Estrus: phase of the approximately four-week cycle in female mammals around ovulation when the female is receptive to males and encourages copulation; it is also called "heat." (The cycle is called the estrous cycle; the heat phase does not occur in humans.)

Ethology: scientific study of animal behavior.

Evolution: cumulative changes in the mean or average characteristics of *populations* or organisms occurring over the course of many generations (see also *natural selection*).

Family: in biology, a taxonomic rank. Humans belong to the family Hominidae.

Fauresmith industry: highly evolved version of the *Acheulian industry* found south of the Sahara, mostly in steppelike areas, from about 60,000 to 40,000 years ago. It included small hand-axes, scraping tools, and narrow flake knives.

Feedback: process by which a change in one component in a system affects other components, which in turn bring about change in the first component.

Femur: the thighbone.

Flake tool: stone implement made by striking a chip or flake from a stone; the flake becomes the tool. (Compare with *core tool*.)

Foramen magnum: large opening at the base of the skull through which the spinal cord passes to the brain.

Founder effect: the genetic difference that exists between a newly founded *population* and its parent group, because the *gene pool* of the new population is only a segment of the old one.

Frontal bone: part of the primate skull that constitutes the forehead and comes down around the eye sockets (orbits).

Gelada: a species of terrestrial monkey related to the baboon, found in the mountains of Ethiopia.

Gene: distinct unit of the *chromosomes* in cell nuclei controlling the coding and transmission of physical traits.

Gene flow: the exchange of genes from one *population* to another, thus increasing the variety of genes available to each and creating or maintaining similarities in the genetic makeup of the populations.

Gene pool: all the genes of a *population* at a given time.

Genetic drift: random changes in a population's *gene pool* due to such factors as differential reproduction rates, not to *mutations* or *natural selection* or *gene flow*. Not significant except in small, isolated populations.

Genetic load: harmful recessive genes that are expressed only in the rare *homozygous* condition.

Genetic swamping: overrunning and absorption of a small population by a larger one in which the genes of the minority are preserved but contribute little to their successors' physical characteristics.

Genotype: the genetic makeup of a plant or animal; all characteristics contained in the organism's genes. (Compare with *phenotype*.)

Genus: taxonomic category composed of a group of species that have more in common with each other than with other groups.

Geology: study of the earth's physical formation, its nature, and its continuing development.

Gibbon: small, long-armed, tree-dwelling, brachiating ape of Southeast Asia. Smaller than other apes and least like human beings.

Gorilla: largest ape, a social, terrestrial, knuckle-walking vegetarian living in the rain forests and mountain forests of equatorial Africa.

Günz: first major period of glaciation in the Alps during the *Pleistocene*, occurring from about 600,000 to 450,000 years ago.

Habilis: a gracile or delicate-boned toolmaker that probably lived from about 3 to 1.3 million years ago. First discovered by Louis Leakey. Some claim *habilis* is a species of *Australopithecus;* others that it is a member of the genus *Homo.*

Hamadryas: a species of baboon adapted to dry desert regions of Ethiopia.

Hand-axe: typical stone implement of the *Acheulian industry.*

Handedness: human preference for using the right hand or the left, possibly connected with changes in the brain associated with the development of language.

Heidelberg man: a lower jaw (also called the Mauer jaw) about 500,000 years old, eventually identified as a fossil of *Homo erectus*.

Heterozygous: controlled by nonidentical genes. (Compare with *homozygous*.)

Hominid: primate of the family Hominidae, which includes ourselves, earlier human subspecies, *Australopithecus,* and *Ramapithecus*.

Hominoid: primate of the superfamily Hominoidea, including the gibbons, great apes, and humans.

Homo erectus: extinct human species that probably lived from 1.3 million to 300,000 years ago; the first true human being.

Homo sapiens: most recent species of the human family believed to have first appeared about 300,000 years ago. A bipedal, social, omnivorous primate.

Homozygous: controlled by identical genes. (Compare with *heterozygous.*)

Hybrid: offspring of parents of different species or of different inbred lines.

Ilium: the hipbone, which forms part of the pelvis.

Inbreeding: mating within a closed *population;* in a small population, sometimes causes *homozygous* pairing of harmful recessive genes, increasing disease and mortality.

Incest: copulation between closely related individuals. How closely related individuals must be for their mating to be considered incestuous differs from culture to culture.

Interglacial: period when glaciers retreat and the climate warms. In the *Pleistocene* epoch there were three major interglacial periods.

Iron pyrite: one of the few natural materials that, when struck with flint, makes sparks that will light a fire.

Java man: fossil *Homo erectus* skulls found in Java by Dubois and von Koenigswald.

Kenyapithecus: fossil hominid found in Kenya, East Africa, by Leakey; later classified as *Ramapithecus.*

Knuckle walking: quadrupedal walking on the knuckles of the hands and soles of the feet; a way of locomotion used by chimpanzees and gorillas on the ground, which some consider a halfway step between quadrupedalism and bipedalism.

Langur: slender, long-tailed Asian monkey.

Larynx: voice box; organ found in the throat containing vocal cords, important in human speech production.

Laurel-leaf blade: *Cro-Magnon* stone artifact so finely worked it may have had an esthetic or ritual function. Associated with *Solutrean* tool kits.

Leister: three-pronged spear for fishing.

Levallois technique: a toolmaking method in which a core stone is first shaped and then a flake of predetermined size and shape is knocked off. Used by early *Neandertal,* this method is believed to have originated about 200,000 years ago in Southern Africa. Its use is characteristic of many *Mousterian* cultures.

Limbic system: emotional brain; a group of structures in the brain important in regulating such behavior as eating, drinking, aggression, sexual activity, and the expression of emotion. Proportionately smaller in humans than in other primates, it operates below the level of consciousness.

Loris: a prosimian of India, Southeast Asia, and Africa that is small, solitary, quadrupedal, and slow-moving, with thick fur and a vestigial tail.

Lothagam jaw: 5.5 million-year-old fossil jaw fragment of *Australopithecus.*

Lower Paleolithic: earliest part of the stage in human culture called the Old Stone Age, lasting from about 2 million to 100,000 years ago.

Magdalenian industry: *Upper Paleolithic* style of toolmaking used by *Cro-Magnon* people of Western Europe from about 20,000 to 10,000 years ago. It is distinguished by the prevalence of *blades* and the appearance of prototype harpoons.

Meiosis: process resulting in the formation of sex cells, each of which will have half the number of chromosomes present in the original cell.

Melanocyte: special cell in the skin that produces pigment and gives skin color.

Midden: refuse heap or dunghill at an archaeological site in which artifacts may be preserved.

Middle Paleolithic: part of the Old Stone Age from 100,000 to 35,000 years ago (see also *Mousterian, Sangoan,* and *Fauresmith* industries).

Mindel: second major European glaciation of the *Pleistocene,* occurring about 350,000 years ago.

Miocene: geological period 25 million to 5 million years ago.

Mitosis: process in which a cell reproduces itself, resulting in two cells that each have a full and identical set of chromosomes.

Monkey: usually small or medium-sized, long-tailed, arboreal, quadrupedal, vegetarian primate. There are two groups: New World monkeys and Old World monkeys.

Morphological pattern: the distinctive form of a species; those features that are common to members of a species and that as a group distinguish them from other animals.

Mosaic evolution: evolution of different parts of the body at different rates over long periods of time.

Mousterian of Acheulian Tradition (MAT): tool style that included very diverse tools, including numerous hand-axes; used by *Neandertals* in western Europe during the *Middle Paleolithic* period.

Mousterian industry: *Middle Paleolithic* style of toolmaking used by *Neandertals* of Europe, Asia, and Africa in which both the *Levallois* and the *disk-core* techniques were used, producing a number of *flake tools* from one core. Varieties of the Mousterian include *Mousterian of Acheulian Tradition, Denticulate Mousterian,* and *Quina-Ferrassie.*

Mutation: relatively permanent change in a gene. The accumulation of such changes may lead to the evolution of new species of animals and plants.

Natural selection: principal mechanism of evolutionary change, by which the individuals best adapted to the environment contribute more offspring to succeeding generations than the remainder. As more of the characteristics of such individuals are incorporated into the *gene pool,* the characteristics of the *population* change.

Neandertal: *Homo sapiens neanderthalensis,* a subspecies of modern human beings living in Europe, Africa, and Asia from about 100,000 to 35,000 years ago.

Neuron: nerve cell; the basic unit of the nervous system. A cell that transmits messages in the form of electrical impulses.

Niche: the precise environmental and resource base of a species or race.

Oldowan tool industry: the earliest method of stone toolmaking, it was employed by *habilis* as long as 2.6 million years ago. The products were very crude stone tools (see also *chopper*).

Oligocene: geologic period lasting from about 35 to 25 million years ago, in which monkeys and most other modern mammals first appeared and evolved rapidly.

Omnivore: an animal that eats both meat and vegetation.

Opposable thumb: the primate's ability to hold thumb and finger together for grasping, giving hominids the *precision grip* that enables them to use tools.

Orangutan: tree-dwelling ape of Borneo and Sumatra. Has four prehensile hands for seizing and grasping; limbs articulated for reaching in any direction, and very long arms. Climbs in trees and rarely is quadrupedal on the ground.

Order: a taxonomic rank. Humans belong to the primate order.

Palate: bony plate separating the mouth from the nasal cavity, which is arched in humans and flat in apes. The arched palate of *Australopithecus* distinguishes it from the apes.

Paleoanthropology: study of the fossil remains and other evidence of the ancient forms of hominid life.

Paleocene: first epoch of the *Cenozoic* era, from about 65 to 58 million years ago.

Paleolithic: see *Stone Age*.

Paleontology: study of the fossil remains and nature of organisms that lived in the past.

Paranthropus robustus: fossil now classified as *Australopithecus robustus*.

Particulate inheritance: transmission of hereditary characteristics by discrete units of genetic material; first proposed by Gregor Mendel (see also *genes*).

Peking man: fossils now classified as *Homo erectus*, formerly called *Sinanthropus* and *Pithecanthropus pekinensis*, first found by Davidson Black in China.

Pelvis: bony structure forming a basinlike ring of bone with which the legs articulate at the base or posterior end of the vertebral column.

Perigordian tradition: *Upper Paleolithic* culture of early *Cro-Magnon* people in western Europe, largely contemporary with the *Aurignacian* culture. It seems to have grown out of the *Mousterian of Acheulian Tradition*.

Pharynx: the throat, above the *larynx*.

Phenotype: observable characteristics of a plant or an animal. (Compare with *genotype*.)

Phylogeny: the evolutionary lineage of organisms; their evolutionary history.

Phylum: a taxonomic rank.

Piltdown man: doctored modern human skull and ape jaw "discovered" in 1911 that was supposed to represent a very primitive human, *Eoanthropus dawsoni*, but was exposed as a hoax in 1953.

Pithecanthropus: see *Java man*.

Pleistocene: geological period that lasted from about 2 million to 10,000 years ago.

Pliocene: geological period lasting from about 5 million to 2 million years ago.

Polymorphism: the appearance of a genetic characteristic in more than one form among individuals of a population.

Population: a local or breeding group; a group in which any two individuals have an equal probability of mating with each other.

Positive feedback: process in which a positive change in one variable component of a system brings about positive changes in other variables in that system, which in turn bring about further positive changes in the first component.

Power grip: a grip involving all fingers of the hand equally, as a branch is gripped in climbing a tree.

Precision grip: holding by opposing the tip of the thumb with the tips of other fingers, which allows firm and precise control of an object. Characteristic of the human hand. (Compare with *power grip*.)

Primates: placental mammals, most of them arboreal, with two suborders: the anthropoids and the prosimians.

Proconsul: apelike fossil of East Africa that closely resembled the chimpanzee but had some monkeylike characteristics; 15 to 20 million years old.

Propliopithecus: a fossil from the *Oligocene* epoch in Egypt believed to be an ancestor of the apes and of humankind.

Prosimians: the "premonkeys," Old World arboreal mammals, include the small lemurs, lorises, and tarsiers. Less closely related to us than the other primates, they have survived little changed for possibly more than 100 million years. The descendants of extinct prosimians developed into today's monkeys and apes.

Quadrupedal: locomotion on four feet.

Quina-Ferrassie: *Middle Paleolithic* toolmaking tradition associated with almost every *Neandertal* burial in western Europe. It is characterized by a high proportion of *flake tools* used for scraping.

Race: a group of *populations* of a species that is distinct from other groups of the same species in at least a few characteristics.

Ramapithecus: apelike creature that is believed to have lived from 14 to 6 million years ago and to be a human ancestor and is classified as a hominid. Fossils found in Europe, Asia, and Africa suggest that, compared with apes, it had shorter wider jaws with slightly curved sets of teeth and smaller canines.

Rhodesian man: *Neandertal* skeleton 50,000 to 90,000 years old found at Broken Hill, Zambia (formerly Northern Rhodesia) in southern Africa.

Riss: third major glaciation of the *Pleistocene* covering 30 percent of the earth's surface, lasting from about 200,000 to 125,000 years ago.

RNA (ribonucleic acid): found with *DNA* in the chromosomes of every living cell and similar chemically to DNA, RNA transmits from DNA the genetic code that directs the formation of proteins.

Sangoan: tool tradition found south of the Sahara in African forests from about 45,000 to 35,000 years ago that specialized in long, narrow, heavy stone tools (which may have served as combined machete and stabbing weapons), hand-axes, and small scrapers.

Savanna: tropical or subtropical grassland, sometimes with scattered trees (woodland savanna).

Scraper: stone or bone tool for preparing hides and leather, used to scrape the fat and other tissues from the inner surface of the skin.

Selection: see *natural selection*.

Selective pressure: influence exerted by the environment promoting the maintenance of those traits that help a *population* to survive in that environment and the elimination of other, nonadaptive traits; natural selection.

Sexual dimorphism: characteristic anatomical (and behavioral) differences between males and females of a species.

Sexual selection: effect of differences in sexual characteristics on rates of reproduction.

Sickle-cell anemia: a genetically caused disease, which can be fatal, in which the red blood corpuscles carry insufficient oxygen. Endemic in some parts of West and Central Africa.

Sinanthropus: see *Peking man*.

Solo man: *Neandertals* found in Java dated between 50,000 and 150,000 years ago.

Solutrean: *Upper Paleolithic* culture occurring in western Europe from about 19,000 to 15,000 years ago. Among the artifacts associated with this culture are the superb *laurel-leaf blades* and the first eyed needles.

Speciation: gradual separation of one interbreeding *population* into two or more groups that do not interbreed.

Species: a group of *populations* of organisms that are enough alike in structure and behavior that the individuals can interbreed and produce fertile offspring if they have access to one another. They are reproductively isolated from other species.

Steinheim man: early *Homo sapiens* skull of 150,000 to 250,000 years ago found in Germany.

Stone Age: earliest period in cultural evolution from about 2.5 million to 5,000 years ago. Recognizable periods within the Stone Age are the Paleolithic or Old Stone Age, the Mesolithic or Middle Stone Age, and the Neolithic or New Stone Age (see also *Lower Paleolithic*, *Middle Paleolithic*, and *Upper Paleolithic*).

Stratigraphy: the sequence of geologic strata or layers formed by materials dropped by water or wind; also, the study of this sequence.

Taiga: northern coniferous forest bordering the *tundra*.

Tarsier: small East Indian arboreal prosimian with large eyes and long tail.

Taxonomy: classification of plants or animals into groups according to their relationships and ordering these groups in hierarchies.

Terrestrial: adapted to living on the ground.

Territoriality: an animal's distinctive behavior toward and tendency to defend a recognizable area of land.

Tool kit: all the tools or implements used by a primitive culture; its technology. *Neandertals* had sixty or seventy kinds of tools but *Cro-Magnons* had more than a hundred.

Tufa: rocklike substance formed from volcanic ash.

Tundra: treeless arctic or subarctic plain, swampy in summer, with permanently frozen soil just beneath the surface and low vegetation.

Uniformitarianism: geological theory proposed by Charles Lyell in the 1830s stating that the forces now affecting the earth—wind and flowing water, frost, volcanism—acted in a similar or "uniform" way in the past.

Upper Paleolithic: most recent part of the Old Stone Age, from about 35,000 to 10,000 years ago. (See *Aurignacian, Perigordian, Solutrean, and Magdalenian,* which were major cultures of this period.)

Veld (or veldt): South Africa's open grassland, which has few bushes or trees.

Weir: a barrier or dam made of stones or sticks set out in a stream or river and used as a fish trap.

Wernicke's area: part of the human brain that is essential in the comprehension and production of meaningful speech.

Würm: last major glacial period of the *Pleistocene* epoch, beginning about 75,000 years ago.

Zinjanthropus boisei: Olduvai fossil hominid found by Louis and Mary Leakey; now usually termed *Australopithecus boisei*.

Acknowledgments (*continued*)

Figure 1–4 photograph by Hugo van Lawick. From *In the Shadow of Man* by Jane van Lawick-Goodall. Copyright © 1971 by Hugo and Jane van Lawick-Goodall. By permission of the publisher, Houghton Mifflin Company. *Figure 1–5* Paul W. Gately. *Figure 1–6* Joanne Verburg. *Figure 1–7* From left to right, photographs by Edna Bennett, Doug Fulton, Guy Gillette, Dick Hanley. Courtesy of Photo Researchers Inc. *Figure 1–8* courtesy Countway Library of Medicine. *Figure 1–9* Andy Bernhaut, Margot Granitsas; Photo Researchers, Inc.

Chapter 2 *Page 28* photograph by Frank Siteman.
Figure 2–1 Bettman Archives. *Figure 2–9* Brown Brothers.

Chapter 3 *Page 40* photograph by Frank Siteman.
Figure 3–1 courtesy The American Museum of Natural History. *Figure 3–2* courtesy Jerome P. Miksche, Brookhaven National Laboratory. *Figure 3–5* courtesy Dr. J. H. Tjio, National Institutes of Health. *Figure 3–7* courtesy Boston Sickle Cell Center.

Chapter 4 *Page 56* courtesy The American Museum of Natural History.
Figure 4–1 Bettman Archives. *Figure 4–2* The Granger Collection, New York. *Figure 4–3* The Rainbow Publishing Group, Ltd. *Figure 4–5* Rheinishes Landsmuseum, Bonn. *Figure 4–6* courtesy The Peabody Museum, Harvard University. *Figure 4–8* courtesy The American Museum of Natural History. *Figure 4–10* courtesy The American Museum of Natural History. *Figure 4–11* courtesy *The Star* and The Bernard Price Institute for Paleontological Research, Johannesburg, S.A. *Figure 4–15* Dr. Richard Klein.

Chapter 5 *Page 82* photo montage by Frank Siteman; Dürer etching courtesy Culver Pictures.
Figure 5–9 Irven DeVore/Anthro-Photo; Ralph Morse, courtesy of Animal Talent Scouts, Inc., and L. D'Essen and V. Phifer. *Figure 5–10* Fritz Goro. *Figure 5–11* Elwyn Simons. *Figure 5–12* courtesy of the Trustees of the British Museum (Natural History). *Figure 5–13* redrawn from *The Fossil History of Man* by M. H. Day. © Oxford University Press 1972. *Figure 5–14* courtesy of the Trustees of the British Museum (Natural History).

Chapter 6 *Page 106* Ernest Shirley.
Figure 6–1 Ernest Shirley. *Figure 6–2* Michael Irwin, courtesy Transvaal Museum. *Figure 6–3* William Terry. *Figure 6–4* redrawn and adapted by permission of the publisher from *Man-Apes or Ape-Men* by W. E. LeGros Clark. © 1967 Holt, Rinehart and Winston, Inc. *Figure 6–5* A. R. Hughes, University of Witwatersrand. *Figure 6–7* Transvaal Museum. *Figures 6–8 and 6–9* F. Clark Howell. *Figure 6–10* Kenneth MacLeish.

Chapter 7 *Page 122* John Reader. © Time Inc.
Figure 7–1 United Press International Inc. *Figure 7–2* Robert Campbell. © National Geographic Society. *Figure 7–3* Jen and Des Bartlett—Photo Researchers. *Figure 7–4* Des Bartlett—Photo Researchers. *Figure 7–7* redrawn and adapted by permission from B. Campbell, "Conceptual Progress in Physical Anthropology: Fossil Man," *Annual Review of Anthropology*, vol. 1, 1972. *Figure 7–8* F. Clark Howell. *Figure 7–9* John Reader. © Time Inc. *Figures 7–10 and 7–11* National Museums of Kenya. *Figure 7–12* Dr. Don C. Johanson. *Figure 7–14* Jay H. Matternes.

Chapter 8 *Page 148* Richard Wrangham/Anthro-Photo.
Figure 8–1 photograph by Hugo van Lawick. From *In the Shadow of Man* by Jane van Lawick-Goodall. Copyright © 1971 by Hugo and Jane van Lawick-Goodall. By permission of the publisher, Houghton Mifflin Company. *Figure 8–2* Dr. Geza Teleki. *Figure 8–3* Irven DeVore/Anthro-Photo. *Figures 8–5 and 8–6* Irven DeVore/Anthro-Photo. *Figure 8–7* redrawn by permission of the publisher from *The Fossil History of Man* by M. H. Day. © Oxford University Press 1972. *Figure 8–9* redrawn by permission from R. H. Tuttle, "Knuckle Walking and the Problem of Human Origins," *Science* 171:959. © 1969 *Science*. *Figure 8–11* redrawn by permission from *The Antecedents of Man* by LeGros Clark. Quadrangle/The New York Times Book Co., New York. © 1969 W. E. LeGros Clark. *Figure 8–12* National Museums of Kenya. *Figure 8–13* M. D. Leakey, 1971.

Chapter 9 *Page 172* Richard Wrangham/Anthro-Photo.
Figure 9–3 Joseph Popp/Anthro-Photo. *Figure 9–7* Irven DeVore/Anthro-Photo. *Figure 9–8* redrawn from Toldt, *Atlas of Human Anatomy,* vol. 1. Copyright 1948 The Macmillan Company. *Figure 9–9* Dr. Geza Teleki. *Figure 9–10* Alan Root. *Figure 9–11* painting by Burt Silberman; background photograph by Pete Turner. *Figure 9–13* George Schaller. *Figure 9–12* painting by Burt Silberman; background photograph by J. Alex Langley from D.P.I.

Part III map, page 198 part used by permission from *Atlas of Fossil Man* by Brace, Nelson, and Korn. © 1971 Holt, Rinehart and Winston, Inc.

Chapter 10 *Figure 10–1* courtesy Annette E. Carmean and Jean M. F. DuBois. *Figure 10–2* Culver Pictures. *Figure 10–3* courtesy of The American Museum of Natural History. *Figure 10–4* courtesy of Prof. J. S. Weiner and Dr. A. Hooijer. *Figures 10–5 and 10–6* courtesy Annette E. Carmean and Jean M. F. DuBois. *Figures 10–7 and 10–8* courtesy of The American Museum of Natural History. *Figure 10–9* United Press International. *Figure 10–11* courtesy of The Peabody Museum, Harvard University. *Figure 10–12* United Press International. *Figure 10–13* courtesy of The American Museum of Natural History.

Chapter 11 *Page 224* Nina Leen.
Figure 11–1 courtesy Henry de Lumley *Figure 11–2* redrawn by permission from "A Paleolithic Camp at Nice," by Henry de Lumley, *Scientific American* 220:5. © 1969 Scientific American, Inc. All rights reserved. *Figures 11–3 and 11–4* courtesy Henry de Lumley. *Figure 11–9* painting by David Leffel; background photograph by Robert Walch. *Figure 11–10* redrawn by permission from *The Old Stone Age* by François Bordes. © François Bordes 1968. Translation © George Weidenfeld and Nicolson Limited 1968. Courtesy McGraw-Hill Book Company. *Figures 11–11 and 11–12* Mark Riboud—Magnum. *Figures 11–13 and 11–14* Lee Boltin, courtesy Ralph S. Solecki, Columbia University.

Chapter 12 *Page 250* Irven DeVore/Anthro-Photo.
Figure 12–2 from P. Molloy, *The Cry of the Fish Eagle.* Michael Joseph, Ltd. *Figures 12–3 and 12–4* F. Clark Howell. *Figure 12–5* Nicholas Fasciano. *Figure 12–6* F. Clark Howell. *Figure 12–7* M. Shostak/Anthro-Photo. *Figure 12–8* Irven DeVore/Anthro-Photo.

Chapter 13 *Page 274* Irven DeVore/Anthro-Photo; Peter Southwick—Stock Boston.
Figures 13–1 and 13–2 photographs by Hugo van Lawick. From *In the Shadow of Man* by Jane van Lawick-Goodall. Copyright © 1971 by Hugo and Jane van Lawick-Goodall. By permission of the publisher, Houghton Mifflin Company. *Figure 13–3* Nina Leen. *Figure 13–6* redrawn from *Electrical Stimulation of the Brain* by D. C. Sheer. © 1961 University of Texas Press. *Figure 13–7* Irven DeVore/Anthro-Photo.

Part IV map, page 290 part used by permission from Sally R. Binford and Lewis R. Binford, "Stone Tools and Human Behavior," *Scientific American* (April 1969). Copyright © 1969 by Scientific American, Inc. All rights reserved.

Chapter 14 *Page 292* courtesy Musée de l'Homme.
Figure 14–1 courtesy of The American Museum of Natural History. *Figures 14–2 and 14–3* courtesy Musée de l'Homme. *Figure 14–4* courtesy of Masson et Cie, Paris. From M. Boule, "L'homme fossil de la Chapelle-aux-Saints," *Annales de Paleontologie,* 1913. *Figure 14–5* courtesy of the Field Museum of Natural History, Chicago. *Figure 14–6* courtesy of the Trustees of the British Museum (Natural History). *Figure 14–7* courtesy of the Trustees of the British Museum (Natural History); courtesy of The Peabody Museum, Harvard University. *Figure 14–8* redrawn from *Mankind in the Making* by William Howells. Copyright © 1959, 1967 by William Howells. By permission of the publisher, Doubleday & Co., Inc. *Figure 14–9* Sebastian Milito, courtesy Marie-Antoinette and Henry de Lumley. *Figure 14–12* courtesy Musée de l'Homme; courtesy The Peabody Museum, Harvard University. *Figure 14–13* redrawn from *Mankind in the Making* by William Howells. Copyright © 1959, 1967 by William Howells. By permission of the publisher, Doubleday & Company, Inc.

Chapter 15 *Page 316* De Wys, Inc.
Figure 15–2 adapted and redrawn by permission from *Human Evolution,* Second Edition, by Bernard G. Campbell (Chicago: Aldine Publishing Company, 1974). Copyright ©

1966, 1974 by Bernard G. Campbell. And from Sherwood L. Washburn, "Tools and Human Evolution," *Scientific American* (September 1960). © 1960 Scientific American, Inc. All rights reserved. *Figure 15–5* Lee Boltin; courtesy Ralph S. Solecki, Columbia University. *Figures 15–6, 15–7, and 15–8* redrawn from *The Old Stone Age* by François Bordes. © François Bordes 1968. Translation © George Weidenfeld and Nicolson Limited, 1968. Courtesy McGraw-Hill Book Company. *Figure 15–9* painting by Herb Steinberg; background photograph by Dean Brown.

Chapter 16   *Page 336* Stock Boston; De Wys, Inc.
Figure 16–1 painting by Herb Steinberg; background photograph by Dean Brown. *Figure 16–2* painting by Herb Steinberg, background photograph by Bernard Wolf. *Figures 16–5 and 16–6* redrawn with permission of the publisher from *Gods of Prehistoric Man* by Johannes Maringer. © 1960 by Alfred A. Knopf, Inc. *Figure 16–7* from *The Old Stone Age* by François Bordes. © François Bordes 1968. Translation © George Weidenfeld and Nicolson Limited 1968. Courtesy McGraw-Hill Book Company. *Figure 16–8* Otto van Eersel. *Figure 16–9* redrawn from *The Old Stone Age* by François Bordes. © François Bordes 1968. Translation © George Weidenfeld and Nicolson Limited 1968. Courtesy McGraw-Hill Book Company. *Figures 16–10 and 16–11* Ralph S. Solecki. *Figure 16–12* courtesy Musée de l'Homme. *Figure 16–13* courtesy The Peabody Museum, Harvard University. *Figure 16–14* Irven deVore/Anthro-Photo.

Chapter 17   *Page 362* courtesy of the French Cultural Services.
Figure 17–1 courtesy of the Trustees of the British Museum (Natural History). *Figures 17–2, 17–3, and 17–4* redrawn from *The Old Stone Age* by François Bordes. © Francois Bordes 1968. Translation © George Weidenfeld and Nicolson Limited 1968. Courtesy McGraw-Hill Book Company. *Figure 17–5* From left to right: courtesy of the Trustees of the British Museum (Natural History); courtesy of the Israel Department of Antiquities and Museums; courtesy of The Peabody Museum, Harvard University; courtesy of The Peabody Museum, Harvard University.

Chapter 18   *Page 378* Victor Englebert, DeWys, Inc.
Figure 18–1 Top: Musée de l'Homme. Bottom: courtesy of The Peabody Museum, Harvard University; courtesy of the Rijksmuseum van Natuurlijke Hisorie, Leiden. *Figures 18–3 and 18–4* Dr. Richard Klein. *Figure 18–5* Top: Jerry Pase, courtesy Dr. Philip E. Smith, University of Montreal. Bottom: redrawn from *Man the Toolmaker* by Kenneth Oakley. © 1961 Trustees of the British Museum (Natural History). *Figure 18–6* Patrimoine de l'Institut Royal des Sciences Naturelles de Belgique. *Figure 18–7* Otto van Eersel. *Figure 18–8* Richard Jeffery, courtesy J. Tixier. *Figure 18–9* Pierre Boulat, courtesy Musée des Antiquités Nationales Sainte-Germaine-en-Laye. *Figure 18–10* Pierre Boulat, courtesy J. Tixier.

Chapter 19   *Page 396* De Wys, Inc.
Figure 19–1 Axel Poignant, from *The Stone Age Hunters* by Grahame Clark. © 1967 Thames & Hudson. Used with permission of the publishers. *Figure 19–2* courtesy of The American Museum of Natural History. *Figure 19–3* Axel Poignant, from *The Stone Age Hunters* by Grahame Clark. © 1967 Thames & Hudson. Used with permission of McGraw-Hill Book Company. *Figures 19–4 and 19–5* Enrico Ferorelli. *Figure 19–6* Photo collection Bégouën; cliché Jean Vertut. *Figure 19–7* Jean Vertut. *Figure 19–8* Ralph Morse. *Figure 19–9* Courtesy French Government Tourist Office. *Figure 19–10* Bedrich Kocek, courtesy Brno Antropos Museum. *Figure 19–11* Gordon Tenney. *Figure 19–12* Novosti Press Agency. *Figure 19–13* Novosti Press Agency.

Chapter 20   *Page 418* Top: Alan Mercer, Ellis Herwig. Bottom: Owen Franken, George Bellerose. From Stock Boston.
Figure 20–4 Top: David Douglas Duncan; Howard Sochurek; Mark A. Binn. Bottom: Eliot Elisofon; Jane Goodale, Marshall Expedition, The Peabody Musuem, Harvard University; Eliot Elisofon. *Figure 20–5* Stanley Washburn. *Figure 20–9* Clockwise: Bettman Archives, Brown Brothers, Bettman Archives, Culver Pictures, Wide World Photos (last three).

INDEX

Abbevillian, 240
Abri Pataud, France, 65
Acheulian, 165–166, 240–241, 243–247, 320, 325–326, 331, 367
Adaptation, 11, 24–25
Adenine, 49
Adrenalin, 429–430
Aegyptopithecus, 91, 95–96, 100
Aeolopithecus, 99
African race, 423
Aggression, 269–271
Ainu, 347
Allison, A. C., 54
Ambrona, Spain, 198, 235, 257–264. *See also* Torralba
America, peopling of:
  by Cro-Magnon, 382–383
  and Neandertal, 332–334
American Sign Language, 280
Amerindians, 423
Amino acid, 50
Amphipithecus, 89
Amud, Israel, 290, 302
Andersson, John Gunnar, 211
Andrews, Roy Chapman, 212
Angular gyrus, 283–284
Apes. *See also* specific species
  brain of, 234–235
  characteristics of, 91–94
  communication among, 23, 156, 193, 277–278, 283–284
  dentition of, 94–95, 97–98, 111, 161, 163–165
  early, 91–101
  locomotion of, 93–94, 107, 109, 152–155, 157, 159–161
  skeleton of, 92
  vocal anatomy of, 282, 287
Aphasia, 283
Apidium, 89–91, 100
Arago, France, 290, 305–306, 312, 324–325
Arambourg, Camille, 134–135
Archaeological inference, 227–228, 319–320
Arcuate fasciculus, 283
Arcy-sur-Cure, France, 348
Ardrey, Robert, 269
Art:
  Cro-Magnon, 399, 401–413
  and fertility, 406–407
  and hunting, 403–406
  Neandertal, 346–349
  techniques used in, 407–408
Arthritis, 299, 306, 354
Asiatic race, 423–424
Athens, Greece, 99
Atlatl, 398
Aurignacian industry, 326, 367–368
Australia, peopling of, 382
Australian Aborigines, 371, 382, 398–399, 414, 423
Australopithecines, 10, 69–71, 79, 98, 104–120, 230, 313, 420–421
  anatomy of, 160
  behavior of, 141–144, 194–196

and bipedalism, 107, 109, 117, 144, 230
brain of, 233–234
dating of, 140
dentition of, 111, 161, 163–164, 232
diet of, 252–253
distribution of, 235
at East Rudolf, Kenya, 136–138
evolution and taxonomy of, 10, 114–119, 131–134, 138, 144–146, 220–221
and family, evolution of, 181, 264, 266
at Hadar, Ethiopia, 138–139
hunting by, 187, 189–191, 193–196
and language, 143, 192, 285–287
living floors of, 167–168
at Olduvai Gorge, Tanzania, 124
in Omo Valley, Ethiopia, 135–136
skin color of, 328
social organization of, 183–186
tools and tool use among, 119–120, 127–128, 140–141, 165–170, 186, 246
Australopithecus africanus:
  anatomy of, 128, 142, 231–232
  cranial capacity of, 130
  dating of, 115–116, 127
  evolution and taxonomy of, 69–70, 109–110, 114, 116–117, 119, 129, 132–134, 136–138, 143, 196, 312
  tools and tool use among, 119, 141
Australopithecus boisei:
  anatomy of, 126, 128
  cranial capacity of, 130
  dating of, 127–128
  discovery of, 125–127
  evolution and taxonomy of, 132–134, 136–138, 143, 196
  tools and tool use among, 140–141, 166
Australopithecus habilis. See Homo habilis
Australopithecus robustus:
  anatomy of, 128
  cranial capacity of, 130
  evolution and taxonomy of, 112–115, 119, 127, 132–134, 137
  tools and tool use among, 141
Aztecs, 398

Baboons, 150, 156, 159
  communication among, 277–279, 285
  dentition of, 161, 163–164
  dominance among, 175–176
  food sharing by, 183
  friendship among, 177
  hunting by, 190
  intelligence of, 182
  sexual dimorphism in, 175–176
  social organization of, 167, 173–174, 178–181
Bächler, Emil, 347
Balzac, Honoré de, 60
Bateson, William, 44
Bear cult, 346–348
Behavior, animal, 14–15, 149–150. *See also* species, or specific type of behavior

Behrensmeyer, Kay, 170
Biface, 243, 246
Biome, 420
Bipedalism:
  and *Australopithecus*, 107, 109, 117, 144, 230
  evolution of, 99, 162, 191, 195, 221
  and *Homo erectus*, 214, 230–231
  physical adaptations for, 159–160, 181–182
  and tool use, 158–159, 161, 181
Black, Davidson, 68, 210–215
Blades, 366–368, 391–393
Blending inheritance, 29–30
Block, Walter D., 355
Böhlin, Birgir, 212
Bolas, 257
Bordes, François, 243–244, 331
Boucher de Perthes, Jacques, 59
Boule, Marcellin, 298–301, 306
Bouyssonnie, Abbé, 351
Bow and arrow, 399–400
Brace, C. Loring, 132, 325, 372, 374–375
Brachiation 152–155, 157, 159–160
Brain:
  of apes, 234–235
  evolution of, 15–16, 93–94, 162, 217, 221
  and flexibility, 420–421
  of *Homo erectus*, 230, 232–234
  human, 234–235
  and hunting, 194–196, 254
  and language, 21–23, 282–284
  of Piltdown, 218
  and tool use, 140–141, 153, 158, 161
Brain, C. K., 119
Bramapithecus, 98
Breuil, Abbé Henri, 403, 414
Broca's area, 282–284
Broken Hill, Zambia, 290, 301
Brongniart, Alexandre, 60–61
Bronowski, J., 397
Broom, Robert, 110–119, 127, 132, 145
Buckland, William, 60
Burial:
  by Cro-Magnon, 413–414
  by Neandertal, 349–354
Burin, 367–368, 392–393
Bush baby, 85
Bushmen, 194, 265–266, 270, 358, 423, 429–430

Candr, Turkey, 99
Cannibalism, 270–271, 355–358, 414
Carbon 14 dating, 75, 77, 261, 311, 369, 387
Catastrophism, 61
Caucasian race, 423–424
Cave, A. J. E., 306
Cave of Witches, Italy, 346
Cell:
  egg, 44–45
  division of, 44–46
  sperm, 44–45

Ceramics, 409–410
Cerebral cortex, 282
Cerralbo, Marqués de, 259
Chain of Being, 295
Chancelade, France, 379–380
Chellean industry, 240
Chimpanzees:
    anatomy of, 19, 88, 114, 154–155, 160, 218–219, 301
    behavior of, 13, 149–151
    communication among, 23, 156, 193, 277–281
    cranial capacity of, 130
    dentition of, 97, 161, 163
    development of, 185
    dominance among, 175–176
    evolution of, 62, 96, 100
    and family, 177–178, 181
    food sharing by, 183
    hunting by, 186–187, 189, 190, 194
    and incest, 267
    life expectancy of, 196
    locomotion of, 159–161
    sexual dimorphism in, 176
    social organization of, 173–174
    taxonomy of, 10
    tool use among, 152–158, 167
Cholesterol, 430–432
Chopper tool, 166–167, 239–240, 242–246, 421
Choukoutien, 199, 211–217, 221–222, 230, 235–238, 240, 263, 269–270
Chromosomes, 44–47
    and DNA, 48–49
    maps of, 46–47
    sex, 47
Clark, J. Desmond, 239
Cleaver, 246, 320
Clothing, 263, 319, 324, 332, 401, 422
Color vision, 18–19, 23, 255
Combe Capelle, France, 380
Combe Grenal, France, 290, 364
Communication:
    ape, 23, 156, 193, 276–281, 283–284
    baboon, 277–279, 285
    and language, 191–193 (see also Language)
    limbic, 278, 283–284, 288
    nonlimbic, 287–289
    nonverbal, 193, 279
Core tool, 242–243
Correns, Karl, 38
Cowper, William, 29
Cranial capacity:
    of apes, 214, 233
    of Australopithecus, 129–133, 233
    of Cro-Magnon, 381
    of Homo erectus, 209, 212, 214, 233
    of Homo sapiens, 130, 233
    and intelligence, 214
    and language, 287
    of Neandertal, 299, 325
Crelin, Edmund S., 286–287, 345–346, 365, 373, 375

Crick, F. H. C., 49
Cro-Magnon:
    art of, 348, 401–413
    burials by, 413–414
    characteristics of, 363–365, 379–381
    diet of, 383
    discovery of, 65–67
    environmental adaptation by, 381–390, 401
    evolution of, 80, 300, 306, 368–374
    and fire, 390–391
    fishing by, 400–401
    hunting by, 383, 397–400
    life expectancy of, 434
    skin color of, 328
    tools and tool use among, 326, 366–367, 392–394, 421
    writing by, 349
Crook, John H., 178, 181
Culture. See also Language; Religions; Social Organization; Technology
    and adaptation, 24–25, 421–426
    and population growth, 433
    and survival potential, 435
Cuvier, Georges, 60–61, 63
Cytosine, 49

Danaida tytia, 40–41
Danais plexippus, 42
Dart, Raymond, 69–70, 107–119, 145
Darwin, Charles, 2, 9–12, 29–30, 33, 36, 38, 50, 62–64, 67, 78, 107, 202–203, 213, 276, 295–296
Dating techniques, 73–76
    Carbon 14, 75, 77, 261, 311, 369, 387
    DNA, 12, 14, 75–76
    faunal, 145, 261
    geological, 73, 302
    potassium-argon, 74–75, 98, 127, 135, 145, 261, 269, 369
    protein, 48–49, 75
    stratigraphic, 73–74, 98
Dawson, Charles, 217–220
Deevey, Edward, 432–433
Dentition:
    of apes, 94–95, 97–98, 111, 161, 163–165
    Australopithecine, 111, 161, 163–164, 232
    evolution of, 163–164, 374–375
    of Homo sapiens, 94, 97–98, 110, 232
    of monkeys, 89–90, 94, 161, 163–164
    of Neandertal, 374–375
Dentition of Sinanthropus, 213–214
Deoxyribonucleic acid. See DNA
Descent of Man, 62–63, 107
DeVore, Irven, 269, 429
DeVries, Hugo, 36–37, 40
Diet:
    Australopithecine, 252–253
    of Cro-Magnon, 383
    of Homo erectus, 252–253
    of Neandertal, 383
Disk-core technique, 328–331

Division of labor, 264–267, 280
DNA, 14, 48–50, 75–76
Dobzhansky, Theodosius, 11
Dolni Vestonice, Czechoslovakia, 410
Dominant trait, 32
Dordogne, France, 65–67, 297–298, 363–364
Drachenloch, Switzerland, 347
Draftsman, 13
Dragon bones, 205, 210–211
Drosophila melanogaster, 46–47
Dryopithecus, 4–5, 95–97, 100
    africanus, 96–97
    major, 97
Dubois, Eugene, 67–69, 202–210, 215–216, 297
Dubos, René, 432

East Rudolf, Kenya:
    dating, 140
    hominids, gracile, 137–138, 144–145
    hominids, robust, 136–137, 144–145
    tools, 140, 170
Ecotone, 157, 163
Ehringsdorf, Germany, 356
Elephas antiquus, 258
Eoanthropus dawsoni, 218
Eocene, 89
ER 1470, 137, 139
Escale cave, France, 198, 236
Eskimo, 379–380, 398, 401, 423
Esper, Johann Friedrich, 59
An Essay on the Principle of Population, 10
Estrous cycle, 177–178, 267
Ethology. See Behavior, animal; and specific species
Evolution, 9–12, 38, 40, 43–44, 50, 52, 62–63. See also specific fossils
    development of theory of, 58–62
    hypotheses of human, 132–133
    modern human, 419–437
    mosaic, 220
Exogamy, 268
Extremity Bones of Sinanthropus, 213

Family:
    Australopithecine, 181, 264, 266
    evolution of, 177–181, 264–267
    Homo erectus, 264–266
    and hunting and gathering, 427
    and incest, 268
Fauresmith tradition, 290–291, 331
Fayum, Egypt, 89, 94–96
Feedback systems, 161–162
    in biological evolution, 312
    in cultural evolution, 421–422
    and hunting, 189
    and language, 286
    and seed-eating hypothesis, 163
    and survival of the human species, 435

Femur, 26
    comparison of, in hominoids, 160
    of *Homo erectus*, 207
Fertilization, 44
Fire:
    at Choukoutien, 236–238
    and Cro-Magnon, 390–391
    and cultural evolution, 421, 426
    at Escale Cave, France, 236
    and hunting, 258–259, 263
    and intelligence, 324
Fisher, Sir Ronald Aylmer, 40, 42–44, 48, 51
Flake, 167, 242–243, 320, 328–331, 366–368, 421
Florisbad, South Africa, 368–369, 371
Focke, W. O., 38
Font-de-Gaume, France, 363, 405
Fontéchevade, France, 290, 325
Foot:
    comparison of, in hominids, 160
    of *Homo erectus*, 213
Fort Ternan, Kenya, 98–99, 144
Fossey, Dian, 150–151
Fossils. *See also* specific fossils and sites
    dating of, 73
    discovery of, 63–71
    excavation of, 76
    scarcity of, 71–72
    sites of, 72–73
    study of human, 12–15
Founder effect, 52–53, 381
Franklin, Benjamin, 225
Freeman, L. G., 259
Frere, John, 59
Fuhlrott, J. K., 294

Galileo, 58
Garn, Stanley M., 355
Gelada baboons, 163–164, 179–180
Gene, 46, 55
    flow, 52–53, 381
    frequency, 52
    linkage, 46
    pool, 43, 51–52, 308, 311, 381
Genetical Theory of Natural Selection, 44
Genetic drift, 53
Genetic load, 53–55
Genetics:
    mathematical, 42–43
    Mendelian, 29–38, 40, 44, 46–48, 50
Genotype, 32–33, 51–53, 55
Genus, 9. *See also* specific genera
Geochemist, 13
Geologic time, 84
Geologist, 13, 230
Geology, as a dating technique, 73, 302
Gibbon, 10, 93, 96, 100, 150, 154, 159, 204
Gibraltar Neandertal, 64, 290, 295
Gombe Stream Reserve, 150–151, 156
Goodall, Jane, 150–151, 153, 155–156, 186, 189

Gorillas:
    characteristics of, 150, 154–155, 214, 301
    cranial capacity of, 130
    dentition of, 111, 161
    evolution of, 96, 100
    intelligence of, 156–157
    locomotion of, 160–161
    taxonomy of, 10
Grimaldi skull, 379–380
The Grisly Folk and Their War with Men, 301
Grooming, 177
Guanine, 49

Hadar, Ethiopia, 104, 138–140, 145, 312
Haeckel, Ernst Heinrich, 202–203, 207
Haldane, J. B. S., 16, 42–44
Hamadryas baboon, 149, 180
Hamburg, David, 174, 427, 430
Hand-axe, 240–241, 244–246, 320, 325–326, 331, 351, 421
Hands:
    evolution of, 87–88
    and human evolution, 152–154
    and language, 245–246
Heidelberg jaw. *See* Mauer jaw
Herder, Johann Gottfried, 276
Heredity. *See* Genetics
Heterozygous, 32
Hobbes, Thomas, 293
Holloway, Ralph, 131
Home base, 268–269
Hominidae, 9, 10. *See also* species
Hominoidea, 10. *See also* species
Homo, 10
    characteristics of, 129
    evolution of, 141
    taxonomy of, 9, 138
    tool use among, 167, 263
Homo erectus:
    aggression by, 270–271
    at Ambrona, Spain, 259–263
    and Arago, France, 290, 305–306, 312, 324–325
    and bipedalism, 214, 230–231
    brain of, 230, 232–234
    characteristics of, 230–232, 328
    cranial capacity of, 130, 214
    diet of, 252–253
    discovery of, 67–69
    distribution of, 198–199, 235, 237, 332
    evolution and taxonomy of, 9, 79, 132–133, 139, 196, 215–216, 220–222, 253–254, 308, 311–312, 319, 420
    family, origin of, 264, 266
    and fire, 236–238
    and glaciation, 322
    at Heidelberg, 68–69, 210, 220, 230
    and home base, 268–269
    hunting by, 251–252, 256–257
    and incest, 267–268
    intelligence of, 254–255, 324

Java man, 68–69, 78, 109, 205–209, 215–218, 220
    and language, 193, 276, 280, 282, 285–288
    life expectancy of, 434
    and Neandertal, relation to, 302, 308
    at Olduvai Gorge, Tanzania, 129
    Peking man, 68–69, 109, 210–217, 220, 230, 312, 414
    and Steinheim, relation to, 304
    and Swanscombe, relation to, 304
    at Terra Amata, France, 225–230
    tools and tool use among, 166, 239–240, 246–247, 320, 326, 392–393
    at Torralba, Spain, 259–263
Homo habilis:
    cranial capacity of, 130, 233
    discovery of, 128–129
    evolution and taxonomy of, 129–134, 138, 312
    and home base, 268
    hunting by, 253–255
    tool use among, 166–167, 246
Homo heidelbergensis, 68–69, 209, 220, 230
Homo neanderthalensis, 245–246. *See also* *Homo sapiens neanderthalensis*; Neandertal man
Homo sapiens:
    at Arago, France, 290, 305, 306, 312, 324–325
    characteristics of, 15–23, 231–232
    cranial capacity of, 130, 233
    Cro-Magnon, 65–67, 69, 80, 300, 306, 363–365, 368–374, 379–381, 434 (*see also* Cro-Magnon)
    early, 290–291, 303–304, 306, 318–322, 325–327
    dentition of, 94, 97–98, 110, 232
    development of, 184
    evolution and taxonomy of, 8, 9, 100, 132–133, 220–222, 312, 420
    and fire, 236–238
    and language, 282
    life expectancy of, 434
    locomotion of, 16–17 (*see also* Bipedalism)
    neanderthalensis, 9, 307–308 (*see also* *Homo neanderthalensis*; Neandertal man)
    at Olduvai Gorge, Tanzania, 166
    origins of, 57–62
    physiological adaptations of, 430–432
    population growth of, 435–436
    and race, 422–425
    rhodesiensis, 307
    at Steinheim, Germany, 303–304
    survival potential of, 435–436
    tools and tool use among, 240, 320

Inbreeding, 53
Incest, 267–268

Infant dependency, 182–183
Ingram, Vernon M., 50
Insectivores, 85, 100, 151
Intelligence:
    of apes, 156
    of baboons, 182
    and brain, 21, 152–154, 233
    and climate, 323–324
    and cranial capacity, 214
    and hunting, 87, 254–255, 262–263
    and I.Q., 427
    of Neandertal, 299
    and racism, 426
    and tool use, 325–326
In the Shadow of Man, 151
Isaac, Glynn, 170

James IV of Scotland, 215
Java man:
    discovery of, 68–69, 78, 205–209, 218
    evolution and taxonomy of, 109, 215–216, 220
    fate of, 216–217
Jebel Irhoud, Morocco, 310
Johannsen, Wilhelm, 46
Johanson, Don C., 138–139, 145
Johnson, Samuel, 379
Jolly, Clifford, 163–164

Kafzeh, Israel, 290, 302–303, 371
Kanapoi, Kenya, 104, 138, 140, 145
Kattwinkel, Wilhelm, 123
Keats, John, 201
Keith, Sir Arthur, 129–130
Kenyapithecus, 98
Khoisan, 423
Kiik Koba, U.S.S.R., 290, 351–352
King, William, 295–296
Klein, Richard, 385
Knuckle walking, 159–161
Koby, F. E., 345
Koenigswald, G. H. R. von, 69, 71, 215–216, 271
Kôm Ombo, Egypt, 387–388
Koobi Fora, Kenya, 170
Krantz, Grover S., 256–257, 287–288
Krapina, Yugoslavia, 355–356
Kromdraai, South Africa, 104, 112–115, 140, 145

La Chapelle-aux-Saints, France, 290, 297–299, 306, 349–350, 353, 369, 372–373
La Colombière, France, 399
La Ferrassie, France, 290, 297, 350–352, 372
Lake Mungo, Australia, 360, 382
Lake Rudolf, Kenya, 12, 104, 134–136, 138.
    See also East Rudolf, Kenya
Lancaster, Jane, 284
Land bridges, 233, 235, 382

Language, 279–280
    Australopithecine, 143, 192, 285–287
    and brain, 21–23, 282–284
    Cro-Magnon, 364–365, 373, 375–376
    and culture, 24, 421
    evolution of, 191–193, 275–288, 289
    and handedness, 245–246
    Homo erectus, 234
    and hunting, 255
    and intelligence, 325
Langurs, 150
Lantian, China, 199, 221, 235
La Placard, France, 398
La Quina, France, 290, 298
Larynx, 281–282, 287, 375
Lascaux, France, 405, 407, 409
Lawick, Hugo van, 151
Law of independent assortment, 34–35, 46
Law of segregation, 34–35, 46
Lawrence, D. H., 317
Lazaret Cave, France, 324
Leakey, Jonathan, 128–129
Leakey, Louis, 70–71, 98, 123–128, 130, 133, 144–145, 150, 165, 167, 221, 230, 239, 255, 257, 303
Leakey, Mary, 71, 98, 123, 125–128, 130, 145, 165–168, 170, 186, 221, 230, 239, 257
Leakey, Richard, 71, 135–140, 144–145, 170
Lebenstedt, Germany, 343–344
Le Cap Blanc, France, 409
Lee, Richard, 429
Le Gros Clark, Sir Wilfrid, 116, 130, 132, 216, 218–219
Le Moustier, France, 290, 297, 331
Lemur, 10, 85, 88, 130
Lemur catta, 85
Leroi-Gourhan, Andrè, 406–407
Leroi-Gourhan, Arlette, 352–353
Les Combarelles, France, 405
Les Eyzies, France, 65–66, 363–364, 402, 405, 409
Le Tuc d'Ardoubert, 403
Levallois technique, 320–321, 330
Lewis, G. E., 97–98
Lichtenberg, George C., 149
Lieberman, Philip, 286–288, 345–346, 365, 373, 375
Life expectancy, of hominids, 434–435
Limbic system, 278, 283–284, 288
Limenitis archippus, 42
Limnopithecus, 99
Linnaeus, Carolus, 9
Locomotion. See also Bipedalism; Brachiation; Knuckle walking
    evolution of, 157–159, 221
    hominid, 157–164
    of nonhuman primates, 149–157, 159–161
Longfellow, Henry Wadsworth, 173
Lorenz, Konrad, 270
Loris, 10, 85–86, 88, 151
Loris tardigradus, 86

Lothagam, Kenya, 12, 104, 138, 140
Lowther, Gordon, 193–194
"Lucy," 139
Lumley, Henry de, 225–228, 305, 324
Lumley, Marie-Antoinette de, 226, 305, 324
Lyell, Charles, 61–62, 78

Macaque, 88, 267
McCulloch, Warren, 22
McEnery, Father I., 60
Madagascar, 88
Magdalenian, 398–399
Magic:
    and art, 349
    and the bear cult, 347–348
    fertility, 406–407
    hunting, 346–347, 403–407
Makapansgat, South Africa, 104, 119, 140, 145
Malaria, 50, 54
Malthus, T. R., 10, 434
Mandari, 256
Mandibles of Sinanthropus, 213
Mann, Alan, 196
Mapa, China, 291, 310
Maringer, Johannes, 403–404, 412
Mason, Revil, 119
Matterness, Jay H., 142
Mauer jaw, 68–69, 198, 209–210, 235, 306, 312
Meiosis, 45
Melanesian, 424
Melanocytes, 328
Mendel, Gregor Johann, 44, 46–48, 50
    experiments by, using one characteristic, 30–33
    experiments by, using many characteristics, 33–34
    laws by, 34–35
    and multiple independent characteristics, 35–36
    rediscovered work of, 36–38, 41
Mettrie, Julien Offroy de la, 280
Microcephaly, 233
Micronesian, 424
Middle Paleolithic, 366–369. See also Mousterian
Middle Pleistocene, 198–199, 207, 218, 246
Miescher, Friedrich, 48
Mimicry, 40–42
Miocene, 96–97, 99–101, 107
Mitosis, 44–45
Modjokerto, Java, 199, 215
Molodova, U.S.S.R., 344
Mongolian race, 423
Monkeys, 88–92, 94, 96
    communication among, 278
    dentition of, 89–90, 94
    locomotion of, 93, 107, 109
    New World, 10, 89, 100, 150–151
    Old World, 10, 89, 100, 150
    skeleton of, 92
    vocal anatomy of, 282

Montagna, William, 354
Monte Circeo, Italy, 290, 356–357, 372
Morgan, Thomas Hunt, 46–48
Mosaic evolution, 220
Mount Carmel, Israel, 302–303, 306, 352, 388
Mousterian, 290–291, 326, 328–332, 343, 349–350, 366–369
    Acheulian Tradition, 351, 368–369
    Denticulate, 332
    Quina-Ferrassie, 351, 367
    Typical, 367
Muller, H. I., 47–49
Mutation, 36–37, 40–44, 46, 48

Napier, John, 17, 19, 133
Natural selection, 11, 24, 29, 36, 40–44, 50, 52–55, 85–86, 158, 161, 381, 421, 431–432
Neandertal man:
    and Arago, France, 306
    art of, 346–349
    brain of, 325–326
    burials by, 349–354
    cannibalism among, 345–355, 414
    characteristics of, 66, 298–300, 308–311, 325, 369–372
    dating of, 303
    death of, 349–354
    diet of, 383
    discovery of, 63–65, 67, 109, 293–314
    distribution of, 331–332, 382
    at Dordogne, France, 364
    European, 308–311, 325
    evolution and taxonomy of, 80, 132–133, 145, 203–204, 306–308, 311, 365–369, 372–376, 420
    at Gibraltar, Spain, 64
    and glaciation, 326–327
    handedness of, 345–346, 355
    language of, 282, 286–287, 345–346
    life expectancy of, 434
    life style of, 337–345
    non-European, 301–303, 310–311
    religion and ritual of, 347–354, 356
    skin color of, 328
    at Spy, Belgium, 65, 297
    at Steinheim, Germany, 303–304
    at Swanscombe, England, 303–304
    tools and tool use among, 328, 366, 368, 392–393 (see also Mousterian)
    type skull of, 63–64, 290, 294–296, 349, 355
Negro race, 379–380
Nelson Bay Cave, South Africa, 384–387, 400
Neptis imitans, 42
Neurons, 22
Newton, Sir Isaac, 58
Ngandong, Java, 357
Ngorora, Kenya, 138, 143
Niah, Borneo, 368–369
Niche, 157

Nonlimbic communication, 278–279
Nuclear family, 177
Nucleic acid, 48
Nucleotides, 49

Obermaier, Hugo, 414
Oceanic race, 424
Ocher, 347–348, 407–409, 412–413
Oenothera, 40
    laevifolia, 37
    lamarckiana, 37
    rubrinervis, 37
Oldowan culture, 124, 165–167, 170, 239–240, 243–244, 246, 421
Olduvai Gorge, Tanzania, 71, 104, 145, 150, 198, 235, 312
    Australopithecus boisei at, 125–127, 136
    butchering sites at, 169–170, 257
    dating of, 127–128, 140
    discoveries at, 123–124
    Homo erectus at, 221, 230, 257
    Homo habilis at, 128–134, 138
    occupation floors at, 167–168
    shelters at, 168–170
    tools at, 140, 165–167, 242, 246 (see also Oldowan culture)
Oligocene, 89, 100, 152
Oligopithecus, 99
Olorgesailie, Kenya, 198, 251–252, 257
Omo Valley, Ethiopia, 104, 134–135, 259
    dating of, 140
    hominids in, 135–136, 138, 145
    tools in, 170
Orangutan, 10, 96, 100, 150, 154, 159, 204, 219–220
Orbital closure, 91
Oreopithecus, 99
On the Origin of Species, 9, 62, 295–296
Osborn, Henry Fairfield, 208
Outbreeding, 53
Ova Tjimba, 168
Oxnard, Charles, 160

Paleoanthropology, 12
Paleocene, 84–85
Paleoenvironment, 236, 318–319
Paleolithic, 226, 240
    Lower, 124, 165–166, 170, 239–241, 243–244, 246, 320, 325–326, 420
    Middle, 326, 328–332, 343, 349–350, 366–369
    Upper, 66, 326, 331, 367–368, 391–393, 410, 421
Paleontologist, 14
Palynology, 13, 227, 259, 319, 352–353
Papilio agestor, 42
Paranthropus robustus, 114. See also Australopithecus robustus
Parapithecus, 89–91, 100
Patterson, Bryan, 145
Pauling, Linus, 50
Pavlov, Czechoslovakia, 397

Peas, use in genetics, 44
Pebble tool, 165–166. See also Oldowan culture
Pech-de-l'Azé, France, 348–349
Pedologist, 13
Pei, W. C., 212
Peking man. See also Choukoutien, China; Homo erectus
    cannibalism by, 270–271, 414 (see also Cannibalism)
    culture of, 214–215
    discovery of, 68–69, 109, 210–213
    evolution and taxonomy of, 213–216, 220, 230, 312
    fate of the fossils of, 216–217
Pelvis, 26
    and bipedalism, 159, 213
    comparison of, in hominoids, 160
    sexual dimorphism of, 181–182
Perigordian, 367–368, 410
Petrologist, 13
Peyrère, Isaac de la, 58–59
Pharynx, 281–282, 287, 345–346, 365, 375
Phenotype, 32, 51, 55
Phonemes, 205
Phonetic code, 278
Photographer, 13,
Physical anthropologist, 14
Pilbeam, David, 191–192, 270, 375–376
Piltdown, England, 110, 198, 217–220
Pithecanthropus, 221, 297. See also Homo erectus; Java man
    erectus, 207–209, 216
    pekinensis, 216
    taxonomy, 215–216
Plesiadapis, 91
Pliny the Elder, 123, 251
Pliocene, 107, 158, 218
Pliopithecus, 99
Polymorphism, 53–55
Polynesian, 424
Pope, Alexander, 1
Population:
    breeding, 51–55, 307–308, 581
    growth of human, 10, 432–433
    importance of, to interpretation of fossils, 136–137
Potassium-argon dating, 74–75, 145
    of Australopithecus boisei, 127, 135
    at Omo Valley, Ethiopia, 135, 140
    of Ramapithecus, 98
Potto, 151
Power grip, 19–21
Precision grip, 19–21, 23
Predmost, Hungary, 371
Preparator, 14
Primates:
    apes, 89–99 (see also particular species)
    behavior, 14–15, 149–150 (see also particular types)
    brain, 233
    fossil, 89–97 (see also species)
    hominid (see species)
    locomotion, 149–157, 159–161 (see also

Primates: (*continued*)
Brachiation; Knuckle walking; Locomotion)
monkeys, 90–91 (*see also* Baboons; Monkeys)
prosimian, 84–91 (*see also* species)
social organization, 173–181, 183, 186–187, 189, 190, 194 (*see also* Social Organization; or species)
Principles of Geology, 62
Proconsul, 96. *See also Dryopithecus*
Propliopithecus, 94–96, 100
Prosimian. *See also* particular species
characteristics of, 86–89, 91
dentition of, 90
evolution of, 84–86, 100
locomotion of, 94, 151–152
taxonomy of, 10
Protein, 48–49
dating technique, 75
Punnett, R. C., 44
Pygmy, 256
Pyrite, 390

Quadrupedalism, 152–154, 160

Races:
classification of, 422
differences between, 424–426
geographical, 422–425
origin of, 379–381
Racism, 426–427
Radium-lead dating, 74
Ramapithecus, 4–5, 10
dentition of, 98–99, 143
discovery of, 97–98
evolution and taxonomy of, 98–101, 107, 143–145, 157, 170, 181, 420 (*see also Bramapithecus; Kenyapithecus;* Ngorora)
freybergi, 99
punjabicus, 99
wickeri, 99
Ray, John, 58–59
Recessive trait, 32, 53
Reck, Hans, 123
Regourdou, France, 347
Religion:
at Ambrona, Spain, 261
and art, 401–413
and bear cult, 347–348
burial as evidence for, 352, 413–414
and cannibalism, 270–271, 355–356
at Lazaret, France, 324
of Neandertal, 346–347
and skull cult, 356–358
Solutrean, 392
at Torralba, Spain, 261
Rhesus monkeys, 150
Rhodesian man, 301, 346, 372. *See also* Neandertal man

Ribonucleic acid. *See* RNA
Rickets, 328, 372
Rift Valley, Africa, 134
Riss glaciation, 321–322
effect of, on ecology, 322–323
as stimulant for intelligence and culture, 323–324, 326
Riss-Würm interglacial, 324–325
Ritual. *See* Religion
RNA, 48, 50
Robinson, John, 118–119
Roles, male and female, 264–267, 412. *See also* Division of labor
Rousseau, Jean-Jacques, 276

Sangiran, Java, 199, 215, 235, 312
Sangoan tools, 290–291, 331
Schaaffhausen, Hermann, 294–295
Schaller, George, 150–151, 187–188, 191, 193–195
Schlosser, Max, 211
Schmerling, P. C., 59
Schoetensack, Otto, 209
Sculpture, 409–413
Seed-eating hypothesis, 163–164
Semenov, S. A., 239
Serengeti Plain, 193–194
Sex cells, 44–45
Sex-linked traits, 46
Sexual
dimorphism, 175–176, 181–182
reproduction, advantages of, 52
selection, 53
Shakespeare, William, 7, 15, 419
Shaman, 347, 406
Shanidar, Iraq, 290, 310–311, 352–355
Shelley, Percy Bysshe, 275
Shungura formation, 134
Siamang, 10
Sickle-cell anemia, 50, 54–55
Simons, Elwyn, 98–99
Simopithecus, 251
Sinanthropus pekinensis, 212–216, 221. *See also* Choukoutien, China; *Homo erectus;* Peking man
Sipka, Czechoslovakia, 371
Siwalik Hills, India, 97, 99
Skeletons:
Australopithecus africanus, 128, 160, 220, 230
Australopithecus boisei, 128
Australopithecus robustus, 128
chimpanzee, 159, 160
gorilla, 92
Homo erectus, 220, 230
Homo sapiens, 26, 159, 160, 182, 220, 230
"Lucy," 139
Neandertal, 299
Skhūl, Israel, 290, 302, 309, 346, 352, 354–355, 371
Skin color, as a climatic adaptation, 253–254, 328

Skull of Sinanthropus, 213–214
Smith, G. Elliot, 206, 300
Smith, William, 61
Smith, Woodward A., 218, 220
Social carnivores, 187–189, 255
Social organization, 173–196. *See also* particular species
and age, 174
and communication, 177, 277
and dominance, 174–177
and family, evolution of, 177–181
and food sharing, 183, 190, 192
and friendship, 177
among hunters and gatherers, 427
and hunting, changes brought about by, 186–187, 263–264
and kinship, 174
and male-female role behavior, 174, 179, 181–189, 277
and mother-infant bond, 173–174, 192
and play, 174
Solecki, Ralph, 347, 352
Solo man, 290, 302, 356, 371
Solo River, Java, 205, 215, 302, 356
Solutré, France, 397
Solutrean tools, 391–393, 421
Solvieux, France, 400–401
Spear thrower, 398–399
Speciation, 51–53, 85–86, 157, 307–308, 310
Species, 10, 51–55, 307–308
Sperm cell, 44–45
Spheroids, 257
Spy, Belgium, 65, 290, 297–298, 309, 349, 352
Statistical analysis, 304–305
Steinheim, Germany, 290, 303–306, 312, 324
Stereoscopic vision, 17–19, 87, 158
Sterkfontein, South Africa, 104, 112, 114, 116–117, 119–120, 140, 144–145
Stewart, Dale T., 355
Stone tools. *See* Tools
Stratigraphy, 73–74, 98
Strauss, William, 306
Stress, human adaptation to, 428–432
Strum, Shirley, 279
Sungir, U.S.S.R., 412–414
Surveyor, 13
Survival potential, human, 435–436
Swamping, 373
Swanscombe, England, 290, 303–306, 312, 324
Swartkrans, South Africa, 104, 113–114, 140, 145
Sympathetic magic, 404

Tabūn, Israel, 290, 302, 311
Taieb, Maurice, 138, 145
Talleyrand, Charles Maurice de, 275
Tarahumara Indians, 256
Tarsiers, 10, 85, 151

Tasaday, 270
Tata Cave, Hungary, 348–349
Taung child, 70, 104, 107–111, 114, 140, 145. *See also Australopithecus africanus*
Taxonomy, 9–10. *See also* individual species
Technology, and cultural evolution, 421–423. *See also* Tools
Ternifine, Algeria, 198, 221, 235, 312
Terra Amata, France, 198, 225–230, 235, 258, 263, 268–269
Teshik-Tash, U.S.S.R., 290, 302, 310, 352
Theory of the Earth, 61
Thymine, 49
Tobias, Phillip V., 131–132
Tongue, 281–282, 365
Tool industries:
    Abbevillian, 240
    Acheulian, 165–166, 240–241, 320, 325–326
    Aurignacian, 326, 367–368
    Chellean, 240
    Fauresmith, 331
    Mousterian, 326, 328–332, 343, 349–350, 366–369
    Oldowan, 124, 165–167, 170, 239–240, 243–244, 246, 421
    Perigordian, 367–368, 410
    Sangoan, 331
    Solutrean, 391–393, 421
Tools, types of:
    atlatl, 398
    biface, 243, 246
    blades, 366–368, 391–393
    bolas, 257
    bow and arrow, 399–400
    burin, 367–368, 392–393
    chopper tool, 166–167, 239–240, 242–246, 421
    cleaver, 246, 320
    core tool, 242–243
    flake, 167, 242–243, 320, 328–331, 336–338, 421
    hand-axe, 240–241, 244–246, 320, 325–326, 331, 351, 421

pebble tool, 165–166
spear thrower, 398–399
spheroids, 257
Tool use and toolmaking:
    Australopithecine, 119–120, 127–128, 140–141, 165–170, 186, 246
    and bipedalism, 158–159, 161, 181
    by chimpanzees, 152–158, 167
    by Cro-Magnon, 326, 366–367, 392–394, 421
    by disk-core technique, 328–331
    feedback and evolution of, 162, 164
    and fire, 238
    first appearance of, 170–195
    by *Homo erectus,* 166, 239–240, 246–247, 320, 392–393
    and intelligence, 325–326
    and language, 285, 287–288
    by Levallois technique, 320
    by Neandertal, 290–291, 328, 366, 368, 392–393
    and specialization, 392–394
    techniques of, 166–167, 320, 328–331
Torralba, Spain, 198, 235, 257–264, 280
Transvaal Museum, Pretoria, South Africa, 112, 118
Tree shrew, 85, 87–88
Trinil, Java, 199, 205–207, 209, 235, 312
Tschermak, Eric, 38
Typical Mousterian, 351. *See also* Mousterian

Unearned resources, 383–385, 387
Uniformitarianism, 61
Upper Paleolithic, 66, 366–368, 391
Ursus spelaeus, 347
Ussher, Archbishop James, 58

Vallonet Cave, France, 259
Veddahs, 423
Venus figurines, 410–413
    Venus of Abri Patuad, 411
    Venus of Willendorf, 410

Vértesszöllös, Hungary, 198, 221–222, 235, 240
Vervet monkey, communication, 278
Virchow, Rudolf, 63–64, 296–297, 301
Virus, 48
Vision, 17–19
    color, 18–19, 23, 255
    evolution of, 87
    stereoscopic, 17–19, 87, 158
Vitamin D, 328, 372
Vocal anatomy, 281–283, 287

Wadjak, Java, 204–205, 208, 380
Wallace, Alfred Russel, 2, 9–11, 67, 204
Washburn, Sherwood, 157–158, 160–161, 164, 174, 181, 194, 269, 279
Watson, James D., 49
Weidenreich, Franz, 213–217
Weiner, J. S., 218–219
Well, H. G., 301
Wernicke's area, 283–284
Wild dogs, 188
Wisconsin glaciation, 382
Womera, 398–399
Wright, Sewall, 42, 48
Writing, 349
Würm glaciation, 326–328, 343, 369, 372, 382

X-rays, 47–48

Yerkes, Robert, 149
Yukaghir, 343

Zinjanthropus boisei, 126–127. *See also Australopithecus boisei*
Zoological Evidence as to Man's Place in Nature, 62
Zuckerman, Sir Solly, 149